PEARSON INVESTIGATING SCIENCE

*BIOLOGY*SOURCE

11

Senior Program Consultant

Lionel Sandner
Science Education Consultant and Writer
formerly Lead Coordinator, Pan-Canadian Science Project

Authors

Clayton Ellis
Heart Lake Secondary School
Peel District School Board

Monique R. Muller
Program Facilitator, e-Learning
Durham District School Board

Helen Elena Panayiotou
Leaside High School
Toronto District School Board

Joan C. Sharp
Simon Fraser University, BC

Pauline Webb
Markham District High School
York Region District School Board

Senior Technology Consultant

Josef Martha
Science Education Consultant and Writer
formerly Northern Gateway Public Schools, AB

Contributing Writer

Gabriel Roman Ayyavoo
Notre Dame High School
Toronto Catholic District School Board

Contributing Authors

Neil A. Campbell

Brad Williamson

Robin J. Heyden

PEARSON

PEARSON

Pearson Canada Inc.
26 Prince Andrew Place
Don Mills, ON   M3C 2T8
Customer Service: 1-800-361-6128

ISBN: 978-0-13-705361-2

PUBLISHER: Reid McAlpine
MANAGING EDITOR: Lee Ensor
RESEARCH AND COMMUNICATIONS MANAGER: Martin Goldberg

DIRECTOR OF PUBLISHING: Yvonne Van Ruskenveld (Edvantage Press)
MANAGING EDITOR: Lee Geller (Edvantage Press)
DEVELOPMENTAL EDITORS: Tricia Armstrong (Edvantage Press), Barbara Booth, Louise MacKenzie, Keltie Thomas, Alexandra Venter
COPY EDITORS: Kari Magnuson, Kathy Vanderlinden
INDEXER: Noeline Bridge
PRODUCTION EDITOR: Louise McCauley
PHOTO RESEARCHER: Terri Rothman, M.L.S.
PRODUCTION COORDINATOR: Carol Edwards (ArtPlus Limited)
COVER DESIGN: David Cheung
INTERIOR DESIGN: Alex Li
COMPOSITION AND ART DIRECTION: ArtPlus Limited
COVER PHOTOGRAPH/ILLUSTRATION: Manfred Kage/Science Photo Library
ILLUSTRATORS: Articulate Graphics, ArtPlus Limited, Kevin Cheng, Crowle Art Group, Imagineering Media Services, Quade and Emi Paul (Fivth Media), Jennifer Fairman, Mark Foerster, Kyle Gell, Phillip Guzy, Steven Hall, Matt Mayerchak, Steve McEntee, Stephen McMath, Karen Minot, Laurie O'Keefe, R.G. Kessel/C.Y. Shih/Visuals Unlimited, Theresa Sakno, Nadine Sokol, Greg Williams (Precision Graphics), Jane Whitney
MANUFACTURING COORDINATOR: Karen Alley
VICE-PRESIDENT, PUBLISHING: Mark Cobham

2 3 4 5 TCP 14 13 12 11 10

Printed and bound in Canada

Cover photo: The photo shows a coloured electron micrograph (SEM) of diatoms. The diatoms are a group of photosynthetic, single-celled algae containing about 10 000 species. Diatoms form an important part of the plankton at the base of the marine and freshwater food chains. The characteristic feature of diatoms is their intricately patterned, glass-like cell wall.

ACKNOWLEDGEMENTS

Consultants and Reviewers

Environmental Education

Jane Forbes
Instructor, Science and Technology
Ontario Institute for Studies in Education
University of Toronto

Science, Technology, Society, and the Environment

Gabriel Roman Ayyavoo
Notre Dame High School
Toronto Catholic District School Board

Catholic Education

Kathleen Mack
St. Thomas Aquinas Catholic High School
Catholic District School Board of Eastern
Ontario

ESL/ELL

Jane Sims
Education Consultant
formerly Sir Stanford Fleming Academy
Toronto District School Board

Safety

Dr. Scott Weese
University of Guelph
Ontario Veterinary College

Lab and Activity Testers

Vinay Aggarwal
Emily Carr Secondary School
York Region District School Board

Scott Campbell
Sir Wilfrid Laurier Secondary School
Ottawa-Carleton District School Board

Mustapha Rajab Jr.
Sir Wilfrid Laurier Secondary School
Ottawa-Carleton District School Board

Annette Raper
Holy Trinity Secondary School
Halton Catholic District School Board

Russ Stewart
Sir Wilfrid Laurier Secondary School
Ottawa-Carleton District School Board

Martin Treash
Patrick Fogarty Catholic Secondary School
Simcoe County Roman Catholic Separate
District School Board

Expert Reviewers

Dr. Monika Havelka
University of Toronto

Dr. Nagina Parmar
The Hospital for Sick Children (Toronto)

Dr. Richard Wintle
Assistant Director
The Centre for Applied Genomics
The Hospital for Sick Children (Toronto)

Unit Reviewers

Vinay Aggarwal
Emily Carr Secondary School
York Region District School Board

Gabriel Roman Ayyavoo
Notre Dame High School
Toronto Catholic District School Board

Anna-Marie Boulding
Instructional Services
Simcoe County District School Board

Amanda Curtis
St. Thomas Aquinas Catholic High School
Catholic District School Board of Eastern
Ontario

Susana de Albuquerque
West Humber Collegiate Institute
Toronto District School Board

Angela De Jong
Turner Fenton Secondary School
Peel District School Board

Grant Elliott
Cobourg District Collegiate Institute East
Kawartha Pine Ridge School Board

Michael Faught
Regiopolis-Notre Dame Catholic High School
Algonquin and Lakeshore Catholic District
School Board

Barbara Gaudet
Elmira District Secondary School
Waterloo Region District School Board

Julie Grando
Cardinal Ambrozic Catholic Secondary School
Dufferin-Peel Catholic District School Board

Paul Hatala
Ancaster High School
Hamilton Wentworth District School Board

Doug Jones
Sir Winston Churchill C.V.I.
Lakehead District School Board

Grace Mchaina
Monsignor Doyle Catholic Secondary School
Waterloo Catholic District School Board

Mark McLean
A.B. Lucas Secondary School
Thames Valley District School Board

Bela A.L. Nagy
H.B. Beal Secondary School
Thames Valley District School Board

John Patterson
Bawating Collegiate
Algoma District School Board

Carrie Pilgrim
Lindsay Collegiate
Trillium Lakelands District School Board

Annette Raper
Holy Trinity Secondary School
Halton Catholic District School Board

Rina Sen
Brookfield High School
Ottawa-Carleton District School Board

Lisa Smith
Blenheim District High School
Lambton Kent District School Board

Kevin Spence
Adult High School
Ottawa-Carleton District School Board

Laila Vincze
J Clarke Richardson Collegiate
Durham District School Board

Field Test Reviewers

Tara Archer Teskey
Arnprior District High School
Renfrew County District School Board

Mario Brgan
Lakeshore Catholic High School
Niagara Catholic District School Board

Julio Candeloro
St. Francis Secondary School
Niagara Catholic District School Board

Tammy Connolly
O'Neill CVI
Durham District School Board

Ann Marie Davis
Rick Hansen Secondary School
Peel District School Board

Gurpreet Dhaliwal
Sandalwood Heights Secondary School
Peel District School Board

Stephen Hartman
Notre Dame Secondary
Niagara Catholic District School Board

Stuart Hodson
Bracebridge & Muskoka Secondary School
Trillium Lakelands District School Board

Jim Jamieson
Markham District High School
York Region District School Board

Erin Klein
Innisdale Secondary School
Simcoe County District School Board

Candace Kwan
Etobicoke Collegiate Institute
Toronto District School Board

Melanie Lamonte
Pauline Johnson Collegiate & Vocational School
Grand Erie District School Board

Antonietta Macri
Madonna Catholic Secondary School
Toronto Catholic District School Board

Mark McLean
A.B. Lucas Secondary School
Thames Valley District School Board

Anne Mierzwa
Holy Cross Secondary School
Niagara Catholic District School Board

Barb Murphy
St. Mary Catholic Secondary School
Durham Catholic District School Board

Gracie O'Leary
St. Francis Secondary School
Niagara Catholic District School Board

Michelene Piazza
Lakeshore Catholic High School
Niagara Catholic District School Board

Brendan Polley
Rick Hansen Secondary School
Peel District School Board

Mark Sewell
Markham District High School
York Region District School Board

Nicola Snowden
Lincoln Alexander Secondary School
Peel District School Board

Laura Vanderveen
Cameron Heights Secondary School
Waterloo Region District School Board

Graeme Wyatt
Arnprior District High School
Renfrew County District School Board

Students

The authors and Pearson Canada would like to thank all the students who participated in focus groups and field tests during the development of this book.

CONTENTS

UNIT A

Diversity of Living Things   2

1 Identifying and classifying living things require a common language.   4

2 A diversity of micro-organisms, protists, and fungi is intrinsic to life on Earth.   28

3 Biodiversity evolves over time and is affected by changing conditions on Earth.   56

CONTENTS

CONTENTS

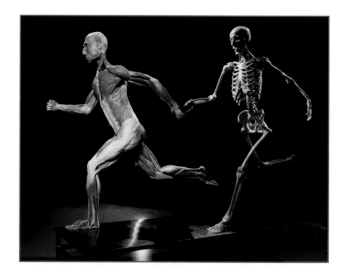

TECHNOLOGY INTEGRATION

BiologySource 11 is a comprehensive Biology 11 program that fully integrates print and online technology.

Throughout the student book, online elements of the program are identified by distinctive banners. Wherever you see the *BiologySource* name, you can find online resources, either as downloads or links to trusted websites. Links are continually tested and updated.

DISCOVERING BIOLOGY

Discovering Biology uses the dramatic image of the unit opener to lead you into an online exploration of content related to the unit you are about to study.

Explore More

Explore More margin features invite you to investigate additional material online that supports a particular concept or topic in the text. The online resources are in the form of readings, simulations, or activities.

Suggested Activity

Suggested Activity margin features indicate appropriate places within the flow of the content to do one or more activities. The information in the margin guides you to the pre-lab summaries and questions for the online activities.

Take It Further

Take It Further margin features introduce intriguing extension topics, leading to reliable online links that you can use for research.

A1 Lab/Activities

A2 Unit Task

Quick Labs, other activities, and the **Unit Task** are introduced in the student book with engaging pre-lab information and questions to help you prepare for the labs/activities. The full activities are available online as interactive simulations or downloadable files.

Biology CAREERS

Biology Careers features introduce a variety of careers related to the topics covered in the student book. More information is available on each one online, with Web links for additional information.

Great CANADIANS in Biology

Great Canadians in Biology profiles a prominent Canadian scientist specializing in biology research. Summaries in the student book lead to links online where you can learn more about these scientists and their work.

For more questions, go to BIOLOGY•SOURCE

"**For more questions, go to *BiologySource***" appears at the end of every Check and Reflect question set and Chapter Review. You will find additional questions online to help you review material in each section and chapter.

BIG IDEAS	FUNDAMENTAL CONCEPTS	OVERALL EXPECTATIONS
UNIT A Diversity of Living Things		
• All living things can be classified according to their anatomical and physiological characteristics. • Human activities affect the diversity of living things in ecosystems.	• Matter • Energy • Systems and Interactions • Structure and Function • Sustainability and Stewardship • Change and Continuity	1. analyse the effects of various human activities on the diversity of living things 2. investigate, through laboratory and/or field activities or through simulations, the principles of scientific classification, using appropriate sampling, and classification techniques 3. demonstrate an understanding of the diversity of living organisms in terms of the principles of taxonomy and phylogeny
UNIT B Genetic Processes		
• Genetic and genomic research can have societal and environmental implications. • Variability and diversity of living organisms result from the distribution of genetic materials during the process of meiosis.	• Structure and Function • Change and Continuity	1. evaluate the importance of some recent contributions to our knowledge of genetic processes, and analyse social and ethical implications of genetic and genomic research 2. investigate genetic processes, including those that occur during meiosis, and analyse data to solve basic genetics problems involving monohybrid and dihybrid crosses 3. demonstrate an understanding of concepts, processes, and technologies related to the transmission of hereditary characteristics
UNIT C Evolution		
• Evolution is the process of biological change over time based on the relationships between species and their environments. • The theory of evolution is a scientific explanation based on a large accumulation of evidence. • Technology that enables humans to manipulate the development of species has economic and environmental implications.	• Systems and Interactions • Structure and Function • Sustainability and Stewardship • Change and Continuity	1. analyse the economic and environmental advantages and disadvantages of an artificial selection technology, and evaluate the impact of environmental changes on natural selection and endangered species 2. investigate evolutionary processes, and analyse scientific evidence that supports the theory of evolution 3. demonstrate an understanding of the theory of evolution, the evidence that supports it, and some of the mechanisms by which it occurs
UNIT D Animals: Structure and Function		
• Groups of organs with specific structures and functions work together as systems, which interact with other systems in the body. • The development and uses of technology to maintain human health are based, in part, on the changing needs of society.	• Energy • Systems and Interactions • Structure and Function	1. analyse the relationships between changing societal needs, technological advances, and our understanding of internal systems of human 2. investigate, through laboratory inquiry or computer simulation, the functional responses of the respiratory and circulatory systems of animals, and the relationships between their respiratory, circulatory, and digestive systems 3. demonstrate an understanding of animal anatomy and physiology, and describe disorders of the respiratory, circulatory, and digestive systems
UNIT E Plants: Anatomy, Growth, and Function		
• Plants have specialized structures with distinct functions that enable them to respond and adapt to their environment. • Plant variety is critical to the survival and sustainability of ecosystems.	• Systems and Interactions • Structure and Function • Sustainability and Stewardship	1. evaluate the importance of sustainable use of plants to Canadian society and other cultures 2. investigate the structures and functions of plant tissues, and factors affecting plat growth 3. demonstrate an understanding of the diversity of vascular plants, including their structures, internal transport systems, and their role in maintaining biodiversity

SAFETY

Science Safety Procedures

You will be doing many activities in this book. When doing an activity, it is very important that you follow the safety rules below. Your teacher may have safety instructions to add to this list.

Before You Begin

1. Read and make sure you understand the instructions in the activity or in any handouts your teacher may provide. Follow your teacher's direction always. Never change or start an activity without approval.

2. Watch for "Caution" notes. These notes will tell you how to take extra care as you work through the activity. Make sure you understand what the cautions mean.

> **CAUTION:** Tie back long hair, and be careful around open flames. Do not touch calcium metal with your bare hands as the metal will react with moisture in your skin.

3. Learn to recognize the safety symbols and the warning symbols for hazardous materials as seen on this page. These include WHMIS symbols. WHMIS is the Workplace Hazardous Materials Information System.

4. Know the location of fire extinguishers and other safety equipment.

5. Always wear safety goggles and any other safety clothing as requested by your teacher or identified in this book.

6. If you have long or loose hair, tie it back. Roll up long sleeves.

7. Inform your teacher if you have any allergies or medical conditions or anything else that might affect your work in the science classroom.

8. Review the Material Safety Data Sheet (MSDS) for any chemicals you use in the lab.

Safety Symbols

 When you see this symbol, wear goggles or safety glasses.

 This symbol tells you that you will be using glassware. Take extra care when handling it.

 When you see this symbol, wear an apron.

 When you see this symbol, wear insulated gloves to protect your hands from heat.

 This symbol tells you that you will be working with sharp objects. Take extra care when handling them.

 When you see this symbol, wear gloves.

 This symbol tells you that you will be working with wires and power sources. Take extra care when handling them.

 This symbol tells you that you will be working with fire. Make sure to tie back loose hair. Take extra care around flames.

WHMIS Symbols

compressed gas

biohazardous infectious material

dangerously reactive material

corrosive material

oxidizing material

flammable and combustible material

poisonous and infectious causing immediate and serious toxic effects

poisonous and infectious causing other toxic effects

©P

During the Activity

9. Report any safety concerns you have, or hazards you see (such as spills) to your teacher.

10. Do not eat, drink, or chew gum in your science classroom.

11. Never taste anything in science class.

12. Never smell any substance directly. Instead, gently wave your hand over it to bring its vapours toward your nose.

13. Handle all glassware carefully. If you see cracked or broken glass, ask your teacher how to dispose of it properly.

14. Handle knives and other sharp objects with care. Always cut away from yourself, and never point a sharp object at another person.

15. If any part of your body comes in contact with a chemical, wash the area immediately and thoroughly with water. If you get anything in your eyes, do not touch them. Wash them immediately and continuously with water for 15 min. Inform your teacher.

16. Wear protective gloves when handling biological specimens.

17. When dissecting, always cut specimens away from you.

18. Treat all living things gently and with respect. Follow your teacher's instructions when working with living things in the classroom or on a field trip.

When You Finish the Activity

19. Make sure you close the containers of chemicals immediately after you use them.

20. Follow your teacher's instructions to safely dispose of all waste materials, including dissected remains.

21. Always wash your hands well with soap, preferably liquid soap, after handling chemicals or other materials. Always wash your hands after touching plants, soil, or any animals and their cages or containers.

22. When you have finished an experiment, clean all the equipment before putting it away. Be careful with hot plates and equipment that have been heated as they may take a long time to cool down.

Ten Themes Unify the Study of Life

With life's many levels of organization and great diversity of organisms, biologists have a huge subject to study. Every year, researchers make new discoveries. How can you make sense of all this information? Fortunately, there are some basic ideas, or themes, that apply to biology at all levels and for all organisms. The ten themes described here will help you connect the many things you will learn as you study biology.

Biological Systems

Have you ever heard the saying "The whole is greater than the sum of its parts?" This saying captures the importance of how a combination of parts can form a more complex organization called a system. A system has properties that are based on the arrangement and interactions of its parts. For example, a bicycle is a mechanical system you can use for exercise or transportation. But just try to get around on a box full of bicycle parts!

Your body, like that of any organism, is a living system. You make use of the interactions among its parts when you type on a keyboard or click a computer mouse (Figure 1). The joints in your fingers and wrist give your hand a wide range of movements. But your bones themselves cannot move. Movement depends on contractions of the muscles attached to the bones. Muscles are coordinated by signals from the brain, carried by nerves. Finally, blood vessels supply all of these parts with oxygen and food. Together, the parts of your body enable you to work the computer. You are certainly more than the sum of your parts, and so are all biological systems.

An ecosystem, such as a forest, is also a biological system. Like your body, an ecosystem has properties that depend on how its parts interact. For example, the organisms in the ecosystem require a steady supply of certain chemicals to live. Plants obtain most of their necessary chemicals from the soil, water, and air. Animals obtain most of the chemicals they need by eating plants or other animals. Chemicals are returned to the soil by bacteria and fungi that decompose the wastes and remains of organisms (Figure 2). The biological systems theme applies to all levels of life, from the biosphere all the way down to the interactions of molecules in cells.

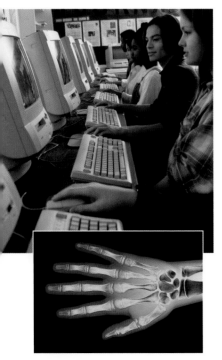

Figure 1 In performing tasks such as using a computer, a person's bones, muscles, nerves, and other parts of the body interact as an organized, living system.

Figure 2 Decomposers, such as these mushrooms, break down wastes and remains of plants and animals, recycling the chemicals in an ecosystem.

The Cellular Basis of Life

All organisms are made of cells. Most multicellular organisms have cells that are specialized for different functions. Two examples of specialized cells in your body are your muscle cells, which contract and enable you to move, and your nerve cells, which transmit impulses that control your muscles.

In most multicellular organisms, cells are organized into higher levels of organization. Beginning with the cellular level, the next level is a tissue, which is a group of similar cells that together perform a specific function. For example, nerve tissue consists of many nerve cells organized into a complex network. Several types of tissue together may make up a structure called an organ. The brain is an organ that consists of nerve tissue and other types of tissues. Finally, several organs that together carry out a major body function make up an organ system. In this example, the brain, spinal cord, and nerves make up the organ system called the nervous system (Figure 3).

A multicellular organism's development and survival are based on the functions and interactions of its many cells. This cellular basis of life is a theme you will encounter often as you explore the living world.

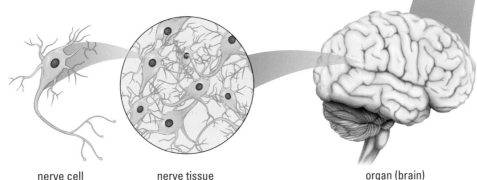

nerve cell   nerve tissue   organ (brain)   nervous system

Figure 3 The human body, like most multicellular organisms, consists of many levels of organization.

Form and Function

Which is the better tool: a hammer or a screwdriver? The answer depends on what you want to do. The heavy head of a hammer is suited to driving in nails, and the thin, flat edge of a screwdriver is suited to turning screws. How something works is related to its structure. In other words, form fits function.

The aerodynamic shape of a bird's wing is a living example of the form-fits-function theme. The structure of the bird's bones contributes to the bird's ability to fly. Inside the bones, an open, honeycomb-like structure provides great strength with little weight. The form-fits-function theme also extends down to the cellular level. Figure 4 on the next page shows the long extensions of the nerve cells that control the bird's flight muscles. These fibres make it possible for the bird's brain to coordinate flying movements. As you explore the structure of life, you will discover many examples of the harmony of form and function.

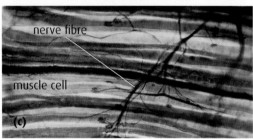

nerve fibre

muscle cell

(c)

Figure 4 A bird's ability to fly provides several examples of how form fits function. (a) The aerodynamic shape of a bird's wing allows it to glide through the air. (b) The honeycomb structure of the bones makes them strong but lightweight. (c) Nerve cells have long fibres that signal the bird's muscles, coordinating its flying movements. (magnification 50×)

Figure 5 This baby Japanese macaque resembles its mother because of their genes.

Reproduction and Inheritance

What explains the similarity between parents and their offspring? For example, the Japanese macaque monkey and her baby closely resemble each other (Figure 5). The baby macaque in turn may grow up and produce similar-looking offspring of its own.

Offspring inherit units of information called genes from their parents. Genes help determine family resemblance.

Genes are made of information-rich molecules called deoxyribonucleic acid (DNA). Each cell in your body contains a copy of all the DNA that you inherited from your mother and father. When a cell divides, it copies its DNA and passes this genetic information on to each of the two cells it produces. How is this information passed from parent organisms to offspring? In humans, an egg cell from the mother fuses with a sperm cell from the father (Figure 6). The result is a fertilized cell containing a combination of DNA from both parents. The inherited DNA directs the development of the fertilized egg into a person, with his or her own eye colour, facial features, and other characteristics.

- How does DNA store information?
- How do cells copy and pass along this information?
- How does the inherited DNA bring about such traits as the colour of the eyes or the shape of a nose?

Later chapters in this book will help you answer these questions. For now, the key point is that inherited information in the form of DNA enables organisms to reproduce their own kind.

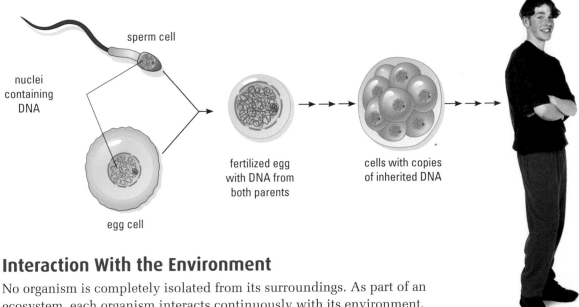

sperm cell

nuclei containing DNA

egg cell

fertilized egg with DNA from both parents

cells with copies of inherited DNA

organism with traits inherited from both parents

Figure 6 When a human egg cell and sperm cell fuse, DNA from each parent is combined in the fertilized egg. The inherited DNA directs the development of the fertilized egg into a person.

Interaction With the Environment

No organism is completely isolated from its surroundings. As part of an ecosystem, each organism interacts continuously with its environment. For example, a plant obtains water and nutrients from the soil, carbon dioxide gas from the air, and energy from sunlight. The plant uses these three "inputs" from its environment for photosynthesis—the process by which the plant makes food.

But the plant also affects its surroundings. For example, as a plant grows, its roots break up rocks and release acids that change the soil. This affects the types of organisms that can live in the soil. Plants also release oxygen as a byproduct of photosynthesis. Other organisms as well as plants use this oxygen for their own survival.

The transfer of chemicals between organisms and their environments is a key process in any ecosystem. Think about your own chemical exchanges with the outside world. You breathe air, drink water, eat food, and get rid of waste products. Living requires a daily balance of such "inputs" and "outputs."

In addition to chemical exchange, there are many other ways you interact with your environment. If you go outside on a bright summer day, the sunlight may cause you to squint. Perhaps the bark of an approaching dog causes you to turn your head quickly. Just as you are constantly sensing and responding to changes in your environment, so are all other organisms. For example, a specialized leaf of the Venus's-flytrap senses the approach of a fly (Figure 7). The plant responds to this environmental stimulus by rapidly folding its leaf. You will discover many such examples of organism-environment interactions as you explore life.

Figure 7 Venus's-flytraps have specialized cells that can detect touch. When an insect lands and stimulates these leaf cells, it may become the plant's next meal.

Energy and Life

Moving, growing, reproducing, and other activities of life require organisms to perform work. Work depends on a source of energy. You obtain your energy in chemical form in the sugars, fats, and other molecules in your food. Your cells use this energy for all their work. You need energy to move, to think, and even to keep your heart beating when you are asleep.

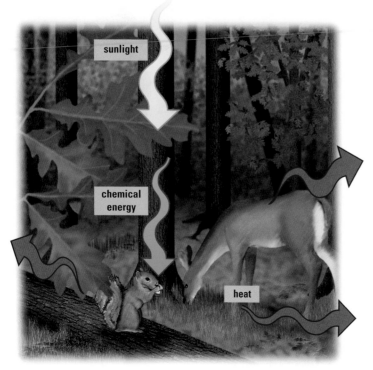

Figure 8 Energy enters an ecosystem as sunlight. Plants are producers that convert light energy to chemical energy stored in food. Animals and other consumers obtain their energy in chemical form by eating. Energy exits an ecosystem as heat, which all organisms generate as they perform work.

On a bigger scale, you can trace energy through an ecosystem. Energy flows into an ecosystem as sunlight and exits in the form of heat. Figure 8 is a simplified diagram of this energy flow through a forest ecosystem. Note how the ecosystem's organisms convert one form of energy to another. For example, in the process of photosynthesis, plants convert light energy to the chemical energy stored in sugars and other foods. Plants and other photosynthetic organisms are an ecosystem's producers, so named because they produce the food upon which the entire ecosystem depends. The plants use some of the food they produce for their own fuel and building material. A portion of the stored energy reaches consumers, which are animals and other organisms that eat (consume) the food made by the producers.

What happens to the chemical energy stored in the food that consumers eat? It is converted to other forms of energy as the organism carries out its life activities. Moving, thinking, breathing, seeing, and everything else you do requires your cells to convert some of the chemical energy of food into other forms of energy (Figure 9). You can compare this energy conversion to a car converting the chemical energy stored in gasoline to the mechanical energy of moving wheels. Whenever an organism or a car performs work, it converts some of its energy supply to heat. The heat is released to the environment. Even when you are sitting still in class, you produce about as much heat as a 100-watt light bulb. Because all organisms lose energy in the form of heat, an ecosystem cannot recycle energy. Life on Earth depends on a continuous supply of energy from the Sun.

Figure 9 Energy is required for all the activities of life. The source of this racer's energy is the chemical energy stored in food.

Regulation

Another theme you will encounter frequently in your study of biology is the ability of organisms to regulate their internal conditions. For example, you have a "thermostat" in your brain that reacts whenever your body temperature varies slightly from 37°C. If this internal thermostat detects a slight rise in your body temperature on a hot day, your brain signals your skin to produce sweat. Sweating helps cool your body.

Panting is another example of a cooling mechanism. You have probably seen a dog pant on a hot day, but did you know that some birds also pant? Panting causes moisture on the large surface of the animal's lungs to evaporate, cooling the body as a result (Figure 10).

The ability of mammals and birds to regulate body temperature is just one example of homeostasis, or "steady state." Mechanisms of homeostasis enable organisms to regulate their *internal* environment, despite changes in their *external* environment.

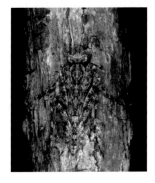

Figure 10 This great blue heron is panting, a mechanism that releases heat from the bird's body.

Adaptation and Evolution

Can you find the three animals in Figure 11? These organisms are three species of insects called mantids. Their shapes and colours enable them to blend into their backgrounds. This camouflage makes the mantids less visible to animals that feed on insects. It also makes them less visible to the insects the mantids feed on!

Figure 11 These mantid species have various adaptations of shape and colour that enable them to blend in with their surroundings.

Adaptations

The unique characteristics that camouflage each mantid species are examples of adaptations. An adaptation is an inherited trait that helps the organism's ability to survive and reproduce in its particular environment.

How do mantids and other organisms adapt to their environments? Part of the answer is the variation among individuals in a population. A population is a localized group of organisms belonging to the same species. Just as you and your classmates are not exactly alike, individuals of all populations, including mantids, also vary in some of their traits. These variations reflect each individual's particular combination of inherited genes. This hereditary variation is the raw material that makes it possible for some individuals to adapt to their environment. If a particular variation is helpful, individuals with the variation may live longer and produce more offspring than those that do not have it. This process is called natural selection because it works by the natural environment "selecting" certain inherited traits.

Figure 12 illustrates a hypothetical example of natural selection in a beetle population. The individual beetles vary in their colouring, from light grey to dark grey. Each beetle's colour is determined by its genes. Now suppose that this beetle population lives on a tree trunk that has dark grey bark. For birds that eat the beetles, it is easiest to spot the beetles that are lightest in colour. On average, the darker beetles have a better chance of surviving and reproducing, passing their genes for dark colour on to their offspring. In contrast, the lighter beetles are more easily spotted and eaten, and fewer survive to produce offspring. Darker colour is an adaptation because it allows dark individuals to survive and reproduce in their environment, a dark tree trunk. After many generations, most of the beetles in the population are dark.

(a) A beetle population includes individuals of different colours.

(b) Birds capture more light beetles than dark beetles.

(c) Survivors, mostly dark beetles, reproduce.

(d) Dark beetles become more frequent in the population over time.

Figure 12 In this hypothetical example of natural selection, darker beetles are more likely to survive and reproduce, passing their genes for dark colour on to their offspring.

Evolution

In biology, the term "evolution" refers to the idea that all species are descendants of ancient species that were different from modern-day species. In other words, species evolve, or change, over time. Natural selection is the mechanism by which evolution occurs. In the beetle example above, as a result of natural selection, dark grey beetles are becoming more common over successive generations of beetles. The beetle population is said to be undergoing evolution, or evolving.

Biology and Society

More than ever before, modern biology is changing humans' everyday lives. New findings about DNA affect such fields as medicine and agriculture (Figure 13). Research on the nervous system is improving the treatment of certain mental illnesses. The study of evolution is helping health professionals understand how disease-causing bacteria become resistant to antibiotic drugs. Environmental issues such as water and air pollution are changing how people think about their relationship to the biosphere. You may be aware of many issues that relate to biology, such as stem cell research, animal cloning, environmental issues, genetically modified crops, and new ways to treat diseases. The concepts you study this year will help you to have informed opinions about the affects of biology's rapid progress.

Figure 13 People apply biology in many ways, including performing complex medical procedures, developing pest-resistant crops, and creating wildlife refuges where species can be protected and studied.

Scientific Inquiry

Biology is a science and, as such, it relies on certain processes of inquiry. Scientific inquiry involves asking questions about nature and then using observations or experiments to find possible answers to those questions. For example, the biologists in Figure 14 are fitting an Atlantic loggerhead turtle with a radio transmitter. Researchers will use signals from the transmitter to monitor the animal as it moves throughout its range. Such research is helping biologists determine how large a nature preserve must be to support a population of Atlantic loggerheads.

In your biology class this year, you will have many opportunities to conduct your own scientific inquiries in laboratory and field settings. The many Online Activities in the *BiologySource 11* program will provide you with additional practice in the process of science. Throughout this adventure, you will find many connections to these ten themes. Enjoy your exploration of life!

Figure 14 This Atlantic loggerhead turtle is being fitted with a radio transmitter that will enable scientists to track its movements.

Concept Check

1. Using examples, describe three biology themes.
2. Describe four ways you have interacted with your environment today.
3. In biological terms are you a producer or a consumer? Explain your answer.

Diversity of
Living Things

Unit Contents

Unit Task

Identifying and classifying the diversity of life is an ongoing endeavour in biology. In fact, the diversity of life is so astounding that almost any organism you can imagine may actually exist. Your task is to design an organism that does not fit into one of the existing groups that scientists use to classify living things and to present the organism to the scientific community. Your presentation may take the form of a multimedia presentation, website, brochure, or written report.

DISCOVERING BIOLOGY

Does the brightly coloured skin of the poison frogs of Central and South America make them a target for predators? Not at all. The bright colours are like a defence system that warns predators the frogs are toxic. Frogs are an integral part of the food web in many of the world's ecosystems. They feed on algae and eat large quantities of insects. In turn, frogs provide prey for a variety of predators, such as fish, snakes, birds, and monkeys. However, nearly one third of the world's frogs and other amphibian species are threatened with extinction, and more than 200 species have already vanished. Although frogs are the most threatened group of animals on Earth, many other animals and plants are also threatened. What is causing these threats to the diversity of life on Earth?

Identifying and classifying living things require a common language.

The **biosphere** is the zone on Earth where all life exists. The biosphere includes the atmosphere, continents, and oceans, and it remains largely unexplored. Scientists have identified 1.75 million organisms in the biosphere but estimate that anywhere from 2 to 10 million more remain to be discovered. The canopies of rainforests and ocean depths are just a few of many areas rich with a diversity of life that is largely undiscovered. In 2005, scientists found 24 organisms in the rainforests and swamps of Suriname that had never been seen before, such as a fluorescent toad, 12 types of dung beetles, six types of fish, and an ant. In 2007, scientists discovered 16 new organisms, including both animals and plants, in the remote forests of Vietnam.

Over the last century, scientists have also discovered many new organisms in the oceans, including 15 new kinds of beaked whales and a creature so unique that at first they could not classify it in any known group of animals. The organism, *Nanaloricus mysticus*, looks a bit like a miniature crawling pineapple (Figure 1.1). *Nanaloricus mysticus* has a large brain for the size of its body and tucks itself inside a shield of body plates when danger threatens. It lives in gravel on the ocean floor, where scientists think it burrows like a mole searching for food. Finding *Nanaloricus mysticus* was a landmark discovery, because scientists had to create several new categories to classify the unusual organism.

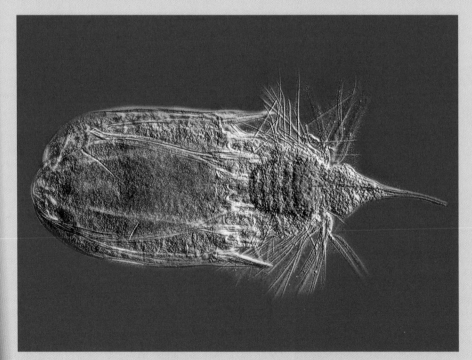

Figure 1.1 A shield of plates surrounds the body of *Nanaloricus mysticus,* and spikes stick straight out of its mouth. This deep-sea creature, which is only as long as 0.5 mm, baffled scientists when they discovered it because it was unlike any other known animal. (magnification 210×)

Section Summary

• Biodiversity has three levels: species diversity, genetic diversity, and ecosystem diversity.

• Biodiversity helps maintain viable ecosystems and contributes to medicine and agriculture.

Whether you snack on sunflower seeds, make guacamole with garlic, or wear cotton T-shirts, you are enjoying the labour of the honeybee (Figure 1.2). In 2007, the work of honeybees came sharply into focus, when North American beekeepers discovered that many of their bees had disappeared. Millions of honeybees were dying, the global population of honeybees appeared to be in jeopardy, and the reason for the massive die-off was unknown.

Figure 1.2 Tiny hairs on the honeybee's body collect pollen from each flower the insect visits. When the honeybee lands on another flower, the pollen rubs off, pollinating the plant.

Spotlight on Honeybees

North America once had more than 4000 different types of native animals that pollinated the continent's plants, such as clover, fruit trees, and field cucumbers. When settlers brought honeybees to North America from Europe in the 1800s, the bees fed on the nectar and pollen of the flowering plants, quickly outcompeting most of the native pollinators. Today, few animals aside from honeybees are left to fill the role of pollinator, and thousands of flowering plants rely on honeybees for pollination in order to reproduce.

If honeybees die out completely, the plants that rely on them for reproduction will also die. Since these plants are the foundation of many food chains in the world's ecosystems, their disappearance would have immediate repercussions on the diversity of life. All organisms that rely on flowering plants as a resource would be threatened, including humans.

Supermarkets would run out of honey and almost all vegetables. They would also run out of all fruit except for pineapples, which hummingbirds pollinate, and bananas, which do not require pollination. Beef, pork, cheese, milk, and ice cream would become luxuries few people could afford, because the cattle and pigs that produce these items rely on flowering plants for food. Coffee and cooking oils would become scarce. Many medicinal plants would become much more difficult to find than usual, and any industry that uses flowering plants would decline.

The Mysterious Disappearance of Honeybees

Why are the honeybees dying? Some scientists and beekeepers attribute it to pesticides used by farmers and homeowners to protect crops and gardens from pests. Since these chemicals are not discriminatory, they will kill almost anything with six legs, including bees.

BIOLOGY•SOURCE

Explore More
When and why did Ontario ban the use of lawn pesticides?

Honeybees may also be dying due to the *Varroa* mite (Figure 1.3). This parasite commonly infests beehives and sucks on bees' blood until the bees become weak and die. The mites also carry several bee viruses, including the Israeli acute paralysis virus (IAPV), which immobilizes bees and ultimately kills them. Over time, the mites become resistant to pesticides developed to eliminate them, and more powerful pesticides are needed to control them.

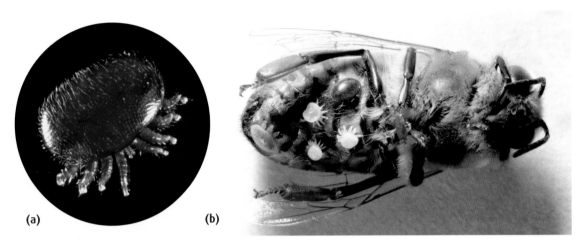

(a) (b)

Figure 1.3 The *Varroa* mite (a) clings to a bee's body (b) with razor-sharp grappling hooks and sucks the bee's blood until the bee dies. (magnification 23×)

Whether it is the mites, a virus, or pesticides behind the demise of the bees, human activity is likely involved. The increasing industrialized farming of bees has created populations of honeybees that have very similar genes. **Genes** are units of inherited information that determine specific characteristics or functions. Parent organisms pass down these characteristics to their offspring through the information in genes. Research shows that honeybee populations with similar genes have limited resistance to parasites, poisons, and pollutants. The vanishing of bees is like an early warning signal. It provides a telling example of how human activity can greatly affect the diversity of life on Earth.

Levels of Biodiversity

Biological diversity, or **biodiversity**, is the variety of life in the world. Biodiversity is a product of millions of years of evolution as organisms adapt to changes in the environment. Since biodiversity allows systems to adapt to changing circumstances over time, it is often used to gauge the health of biological systems. As Figure 1.4 on the next page shows, there are three levels of biodiversity: genetic diversity, species diversity, and ecosystem diversity.

Genetic Diversity

Genetic diversity is the sum of all the different forms of genes present in a particular species. A **species** is a population whose members can breed freely in nature and produce fertile offspring. Within a population, slight differences in genes occur from one individual to another. As genes determine hereditary characteristics, these small differences make each organism unique. They also allow populations to adapt to changes in environmental conditions and evolve over time. Thus, genetic diversity helps ensure the survival of a species.

In contrast, farmers often grow genetically similar crops of wheat, corn, or potatoes to maximize food production. Growing a single type of crop allows farmers to use the same equipment, fertilizers, and techniques on their land. These genetically uniform farms, known as monocultures, are systems with almost no biodiversity. Without the diversity typically found in an ecosystem, monocultures are especially vulnerable to diseases and pathogens. These diseases can decimate populations in which all individuals are equally at risk (Figure 1.5).

Due to this and to help farmers, scientists often use genes from wild populations of corn and other crop plants to introduce important characteristics, such as resistance to disease or pests, into genetically uniform crops. This may also help genetically uniform crops withstand changes in the environment.

Figure 1.5 An infection of fungi rust is especially dangerous on modern corn farms. When one corn plant becomes infected, most of the crop is at risk, because they are all genetically similar.

Figure 1.4 Biodiversity has three levels: (a) genetic diversity, which allows populations to adapt to environmental changes; (b) species diversity, which allows ecosystems to survive environmental changes; and (c) ecosystem diversity, which allows a diverse range of species to thrive.

Species Diversity

Species diversity refers to the variety of species and relative abundance of the species in a given area. Having a variety of species allows ecosystems to survive environmental changes, such as drought, plagues, or disease outbreaks. Each species has a certain set of conditions in which it can survive. Each species also contributes to the whole ecosystem and, without the actions of each species, the ecosystem and other organisms may not be as successful. Figure 1.6 shows examples of different species.

(a)

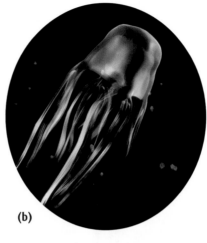
(b)

(c)

Figure 1.6 Our world is home to a diverse range of species, a handful of which are shown here. (a) Tiny micro-organisms called *Sulfolobus archaea* live in hot springs where temperatures exceed 150°C (magnification 33 200×). (b) The sea wasp, or box jellyfish, inhabits tropical or subtropical oceans. (c) Giant sequoia trees, some nearly 100 m tall, grow in North America, Europe, Australia, and New Zealand. (d) Blue green algae live in many environments, including the ocean, soil, bare rock, and the hair of the slow-moving sloth (e). (f) Ants crawl over every continent except Antarctica. (g) Sea turtles hatch on beaches and live in the world's oceans. (h) The blue jay has a variety of habitats in North America, including Ontario's forests.

(d)

(e)

(f)

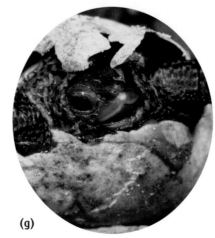
(g)

(h)

Ecosystem Diversity

Ecosystem diversity refers to a diverse range of habitats, the various organisms that live in the habitats, and the relationships that connect them. Figure 1.7 shows a deciduous forest habitat in Ontario, some of its inhabitants, and some of the relationships among them. For example, oak trees drop acorns onto the forest floor, and chipmunks collect the fallen acorns from the oak trees. Mice eat fruit and grain from plants and owls prey on the mice. Wildflowers compete for resources, such as sunlight, water, and nutrients in soil. Banana slugs eat leaves, animal droppings, and dead plants, recycling the nutrients in this organic matter into the soil, and so on.

However, biodiversity is not limited to large ecosystems that extend over vast areas of land. A single cubic metre of soil contains trillions of bacteria and millions of other organisms, such as nematodes, earthworms, mites, protists, algae, and fungi (Figure 1.8). Most animals are also "walking ecosystems" with about 100 trillion micro-organisms living in their intestines. The animals and the micro-organisms have a symbiotic relationship in which they interact for their mutual benefit. Since all parts of an ecosystem are interconnected, any changes to a single part will have some effect on the entire ecosystem and impact the biodiversity of that region.

Figure 1.7 A deciduous forest in Ontario is an ecosystem where an incredible diversity of organisms thrive.

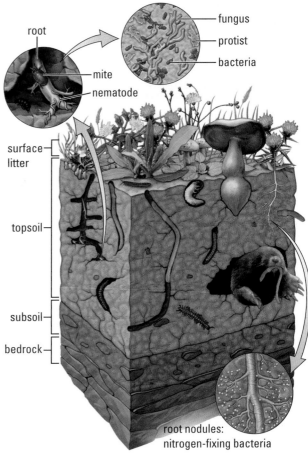

Figure 1.8 A cubic metre of soil is an ecosystem that contains large numbers of a variety of organisms.

Valuing Biodiversity

Ecosystems that have a high biodiversity tend to be healthier and more resilient to changes in the environment. Biodiversity is also important for humans (Figure 1.9). Not only does biodiversity provide the raw materials for medicine, food, and agriculture, but it also helps maintain life-sustaining services, conditions, and processes:

- Insects, bats, birds, and other animals pollinate flowering plants and crops.
- Micro-organisms make nutrients available and break down toxic substances in water and soil.
- Ecosystems cycle carbon, nitrogen, and oxygen.
- Ecosystems clean air, purify water, control erosion, prevent floods, and modify climate.

Often the presence or absence of a single keystone species can have a dramatic impact on an ecosystem. **Keystone species** are species that have a disproportionately large effect on the ecosystems in which they live, such as the honeybee. Sichuan, a small town in China, controlled pest insects by spraying pesticides over their crops. Unfortunately, due to application and misuse of the chemicals, beneficial insects including honeybees were also killed. As the honeybees disappeared from Sichuan, humans had to take over the task of pollinating pear trees (Figure 1.10). Pollination by human hands takes much longer, costs more, and is much less effective than pollination by honeybees. Replicating Sichuan's feat in Canada would cost $20 billion in wages and only a fraction of the plants would be successfully pollinated.

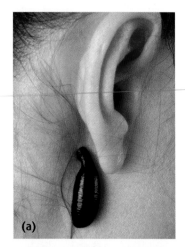

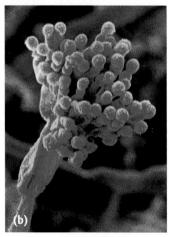

Figure 1.9 Some organisms have evolved chemicals that protect them from disease, infections, and predators and that can be harvested and developed into life-saving medicines. (a) The leech's saliva can be used to treat bruises, rheumatism, hemorrhoids, and blood-clotting disorders. (b) *Penicillium* fungi are used as a general antibiotic to kill many types of bacterial infections. (magnification 11 500×)

Figure 1.10 Each spring, thousands of workers on a large plantation in Sichuan, China, walk around with chicken feathers attached to bamboo sticks and manually pollinate thousands of pear trees. This is the only way to ensure that the trees bear fruit, ever since pesticides destroyed Sichuan's honeybee populations 20 years ago.

BIOLOGY•SOURCE

Take It Further

Look at an unused plant species that could become a star crop for feeding hungry nations. Find out how the Amaranth plant of North America or the winged bean of New Guinea can be used to sustain the human population and minimize impacts on the world's ecosystems. Use a "Know, Wonder, Learned" chart to record your findings.

Concept Check

1. Why is biodiversity important for ecosystems?

2. How is biodiversity important to humans?

3. Define and give examples for each of the following terms: genetic diversity, species diversity, and ecosystem diversity.

Looking at Biodiversity

Purpose
To explore the diversity of life in an ecosystem

Activity Overview
In this Quick Lab, you will examine a diagram of an ecosystem and try to find as many types of organisms in it as possible. You will identify larger groups of organisms to which you think each organism may belong. You will also identify the organisms that have the greatest impact on Earth.

Your teacher will give you a copy of the full activity.

Prelab Questions
Consider the questions below before beginning this activity.

1. Give yourself one minute to write down the names of as many organisms as you can.

2. With a partner, compare lists of organisms and organize all the organisms into groups. Which group of organisms appears to be the largest?

3. Are the organisms in the largest group the most popular type of organisms on the planet? Why do you think that?

Figure 1.11 In this illustration, the size of each organism is roughly proportional to the number of known species in the group to which the organism belongs.

Observing Organisms with a Microscope

Purpose
To use a microscope to help you explore the diversity of life

Activity Overview
In this activity, you will identify the parts of a microscope and learn how to use them to obtain focused images. You will observe four different organisms. You will sketch the organisms as you observe them and make a final drawing of each to indicate their relative sizes.

Your teacher will give you a copy of the full activity.

Figure 1.12 A microscope enables you to see microscopic objects and organisms at different magnifications.

Prelab Questions
Consider the questions below before beginning this activity.

1. When do you use the coarse focus knob on a microscope?

2. Suppose you cannot see anything through the low-power lens. What adjustments could you make without switching to a lens of higher magnification?

Key Concept Review

1. Biodiversity has three levels.
   (a) List the three levels.
   (b) Describe the importance of each.

2. When scientists or farmers selectively breed an organism for certain traits, which type of biodiversity are they manipulating?

3. Products are often developed from living organisms.
   (a) List three such products.
   (b) Identify the organism each was developed from.

4. Name four natural services that ecosystems provide for the biosphere.

Connect Your Understanding

5. How might the loss of biodiversity negatively affect humans?

6. Why is the use of pesticides considered a dilemma for farmers?

7. Coal miners commonly used canaries as an early warning detection system for the presence of methane, an odourless and colourless gas. How might the "canary in the coal mine" analogy relate to the collapse of honeybee populations?

8. Today, the fishing industry locates fish with satellites, spotter airplanes, and sonar systems that detect objects underwater. The industry also uses nets and lines like those shown below. What impact do you think this fishing equipment might have on the diversity of marine species?

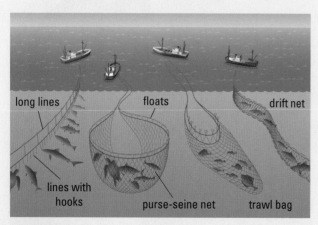

Question 8

9. Create a shopping list for meals for at least three days in a world where insect pollinators no longer exist.

10. Why is it important to maintain wild populations of crop plants such as corn and wheat?

11. Give an example of a type of organism that humans are dependent on for survival. How would our lifestyles change if this organism became extinct?

12. Identify the elements in the illustration below that represent genetic diversity, species diversity, and ecosystem diversity.

Question 12

13. What makes honeybees a keystone species?

14. Imagine you are a conservation biologist who has been given the responsibility of managing a local honeybee population. Write a letter to your supervisor in which you outline your plans to ensure the genetic diversity of the population.

15. Are humans a keystone species? Justify your answer.

Reflection

16. What can you explain about the value of biodiversity that you were not able to explain before reading this section?

For more questions, go to BIOLOGY•SOURCE

1.2 Science of Classification

Section Summary

- Scientists use a systematic method to identify and classify the diversity of life.
- A dichotomous key is a tool for identifying organisms.
- Taxonomy and phylogeny are types of classification systems.
- Phylogenetic trees illustrate how evolution relates to the diversity of life.
- Scientists classify all life into three broad taxa known as domains.
- Prokaryotes and eukaryotes differ fundamentally.

If you have seen one mosquito, you might think you have seen them all. However, as scientists discovered in the 1900s, that is not the case. Find out how their discovery stopped the lethal disease malaria from spreading and revealed the importance of identifying and classifying organisms.

Malaria — A Case for Classification

In the early 1900s, malaria was prevalent throughout Europe. Mosquitoes infected with the deadly disease, which is caused by the microscopic parasite *Plasmodium*, were transmitting malaria through their bites. Insecticide was being used to kill the mosquitoes that carried the disease. However, this effort to control the spread of malaria failed, and scientists had no idea why until they took a closer look at the mosquitoes. Close inspection of the insects revealed several differences in banding patterns of stripes on the insects' bodies, mating patterns, food habits, and other behaviour. Once scientists identified and classified the different types of mosquitoes, they discovered that differences in physiology among the mosquitoes had resulted in the insecticide killing some types but not others, including the type the carry malaria (Figure 1.13). Then scientists were able to use insecticides that targeted the mosquitoes carrying the disease, and malaria was virtually eradicated from Europe. Today, malaria is preventable and treatable, but limited access to medicine and widespread populations of infected mosquitoes make it difficult to control the disease.

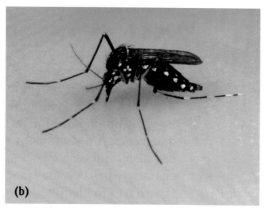

(a)   (b)

Figure 1.13 (a) *Anopheles maculipennis* carries malaria. (b) *Aedes albopictus* is harmless. Without proper classification of mosquitoes, insecticides targeted the wrong type of mosquito and malaria continued to spread through Europe, killing thousands of people.

Identifying Organisms

Scientists use names to identify types of organisms just like we use names to identify individual people. Suppose you wanted to send a package to a friend. Would you address it to "that young woman of medium height with brown hair and brown eyes"? Not if you wanted to ensure your friend received the package since a physical description like that might apply to many different people. You would address the package to her name, Christine, including her last name, Erikson, which we use to help us identify specific individuals. (Long ago, people invented names like Erikson for "Erik's son.") Similarly, scientists have names for specific species of organisms. Often these names honour the scientist who discovered the species and describe distinguishing characteristics of the species, sometimes including ecological relationships. Thus, a species' name may be a key to understanding the species from the structural level to the ecosystem level.

Why are these names important? Many organisms have a common name, such as monkey or pine tree, that is similar to a person's nickname. However, common names often refer to many different species and even organisms that are very different from each other. Consider the names catfish, crayfish, and silverfish — the first is a fish, the second a small freshwater lobster, and the third is an insect. Common names also vary from region to region. So they often can be very confusing to anyone but the locals in the region where they are used. For example, the puma has a range that stretches across the Americas, and people call it a different name in each region, such as mountain lion, cougar, or panther (Figure 1.14).

Then there's the fact that organisms have different common names in different languages. Yet scientists must be able to communicate with one another about the species they study, no matter what language they speak. To reduce this confusion in discussing organisms, scientists assign a universal scientific name to each known species. Scientists also attempt to organize the diversity of life by classifying species into larger groups of related species.

Figure 1.14 Depending on where you live, you might know this animal as a puma, cougar, mountain lion, or panther. This one animal has more than 40 common names. However, it has only one scientific name, *Felis concolor*.

BIOLOGY•SOURCE

Suggested Activity
- A3 Inquiry Activity Overview on page 24

Using a Dichotomous Key

With the enormous diversity of life in our world, it is easy to imagine the confusion that can occur in identifying organisms. A **dichotomous key** is a tool used by scientists and non-scientists to identify organisms with which they are unfamiliar (Figure 1.15). The word *dichotomous* comes from the Greek word for "to cut in two," and aptly describes how the tool works. A dichotomous key poses a series of questions about an organism, and each question asks users to choose between two possible characteristics that the organism may have. On the opposite page, use Figure 1.15 to identify the unknown leaf shown.

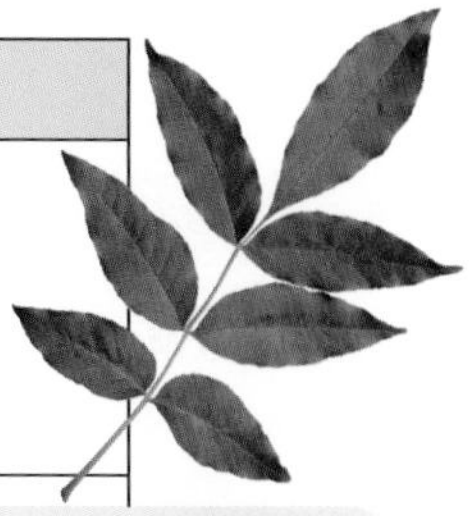

Step	Leaf Characteristics	Tree
1a	Needle-shaped leaf . . . go to Step 2	
1b	Broad leaf and does not persist through winter . . . go to Step 6	
2a	Needles occur in clusters . . . go to Step 3	
2b	Needles occur singly . . . go to Step 4	
3a	Needles occur in clusters of two	Red pine 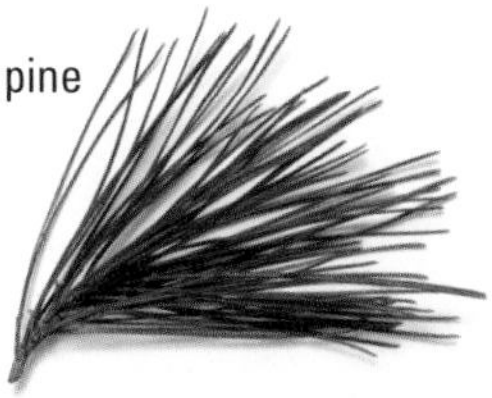
3b	Needles occur in clusters of five	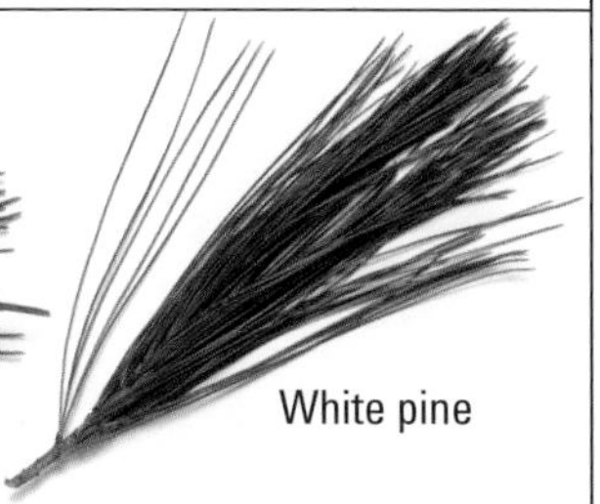 White pine
4a	Needle tapers to sharply pointed tip . . . go to Step 5	
4b	Needle is flat with blunt tips	Balsam fir 
5a	Needles are dark yellowish green	Red spruce 
5b	Needles are bluish green or silvery white	 White spruce
6a	Simple leaf (not divided into leaflets) . . . go to Step 7	
6b	Compound leaf (divided into leaflets) . . . go to Step 8	
7a	Leaf has five lobes with toothed edges and pale green undersurface.	Sugar maple 
7b	Leaf has three sharp-angled lobes and whitish undersurface.	 Red maple
8a	Leaflets taper to a point.	White ash 
8b	Leaflets are oval with rounded tips.	Honey locust

Since your leaf is a broad leaf and does not last through winter, you go to Step 6.

You continue to read the statements to identify your leaf.

Since your leaf has leaflets that taper to a point, you identify it as a white ash leaf.

Figure 1.15 Many field guides use dichotomous keys like this one to help readers identify organisms. Look closely at the leaf shown at the top of the page and use the key to identify it.

What Is Taxonomy?

Taxonomy is the science of naming, identifying, and classifying species. Taxonomy follows well-defined rules that describe how to properly name and classify any species. A good understanding of biodiversity requires a systematic approach to classifying living things that goes beyond the physical appearance of organisms. As you can see in Figure 1.16, problems and challenges may occur when species are classified only by easily observable traits.

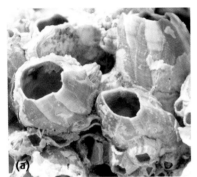
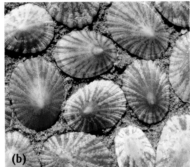

Figure 1.16 If you were to classify (a) barnacles, (b) limpets, and (c) crabs based on easily observable traits, you might group the barnacles and limpets together, because their shells look similar and they both attach to rocks. However, evidence shows that the barnacles are more closely related to the crab than the limpets.

Figure 1.17 When zookeepers successfully cross a male lion with a female tiger, a liger like this one occurs. Ligers do not occur naturally and are sterile.

Recall that a species is a population of organisms whose members can breed freely in nature and produce fertile offspring. Today, many biologists use this biological concept of species to identify individual species. In nature, ecological, behavioural, and physical differences normally keep two different species from interbreeding. However, sometimes zookeepers can cross closely related species (Figure 1.17). As well, biologists cannot rely on the biological concept of species to define all species, because some organisms do not reproduce sexually, have gone extinct, or have not been observed to reproduce (Figure 1.18).

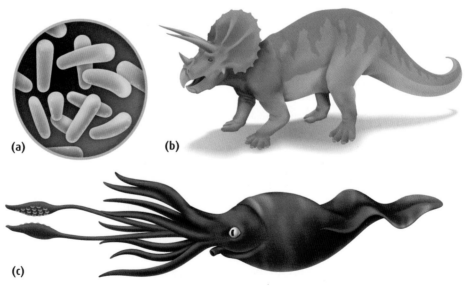

Figure 1.18 To identify species that reproduce asexually, such as (a) bacteria, species that have gone extinct, such as (b) triceratops, or species that have not been observed to reproduce, such as (c) the colossal squid, scientists cannot use the biological concept of species. They must use a different set of rules.

System of Classification

In the 1750s, the Swedish botanist Carolus Linnaeus developed a simple system of naming specific species called **binomial nomenclature**, which became the most widely used classification system in biology. The system has two main characteristics — a two-part Latin name for each species and a hierarchy, or ordering, of species into broader and broader groups.

Linnaeus's system assigns a two-part Latin name, called a **binomial**, to each species. The first part of the name is the **genus** (plural, *genera*) to which the species belongs. The second part of the name refers to one species within the genus. The two words together identify a unique species. Hence, scientists use the two-part Latin name as the **scientific name** of the species. An example of a two-part Latin name is *Panthera pardus,* the scientific name of the leopard. Notice that the first letter of the genus (*Panthera*) is capitalized and that the whole name is italicized. Figure 1.19 shows other examples.

Figure 1.19 (a) The scientific name of the red oak is *Quercus rubra*. The genus *Quercus* consists of all oak trees. The species name *rubra* means "red" in Latin. (b) The scientific name of the red-ruff lemur is *Varecia rubra*.

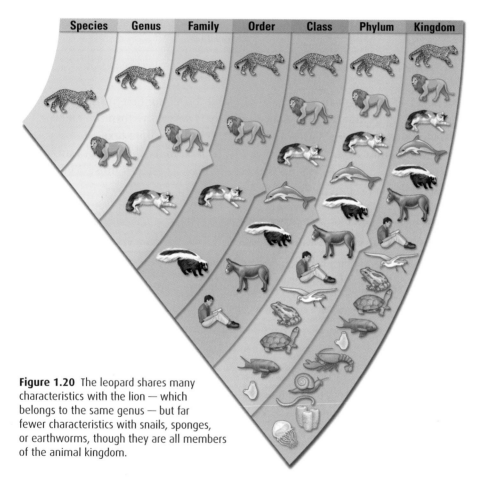

Figure 1.20 The leopard shares many characteristics with the lion — which belongs to the same genus — but far fewer characteristics with snails, sponges, or earthworms, though they are all members of the animal kingdom.

The system also groups species into broader categories, starting with the genus in the two-part Latin name (Figure 1.20). Closely related species are grouped into the same genus. For example, the leopard and the African lion (*Panthera leo*) both belong to the genus *Panthera*. Taxonomists group similar genera in the same **family**. Next, similar families are placed into **orders**, orders into **classes**, and classes into **phyla** (singular, *phylum*). Phyla are grouped into **kingdoms**. Classifying a species by kingdom, phylum, and so on is like placing students in a large school system. First a student might be identified by school, then by specific grade, and finally as a unique individual by name.

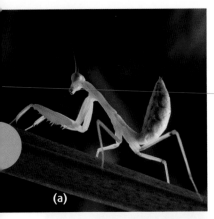

The hierarchy Linnaeus developed has the following sequence: species, genus, family, order, class, phylum, kingdom. Each level in the hierarchy is termed a **taxon** (plural, *taxa*). Table 1.1 shows the taxa used to describe several common organisms.

Table 1.1 Taxonomic Organization of Several Species

Taxon	Grey Wolf	Honeybee	Red Oak
Kingdom	Animalia	Animalia	Plantae
Phylum (Division)	Chordata	Arthropoda	(Magnoliophyta Angiosperms)
Class	Mammalia	Insecta	Magnoliopsida
Order	Carnivora	Hymenoptera	Fagales
Family	Canidae	Apidae	Fagaceae
Genus	*Canis*	*Apis*	*Quercus*
Species	*lupus*	*mellifera*	*rubra*

Note that plant and fungi kingdoms use the taxonomic category Division instead of Phylum.

Most organisms can be classified using the seven taxa initially suggested by Linnaeus. However, diversity is so vast within the class Insecta that taxonomists group insects into intermediate taxa, such as superfamily and suborder (Figure 1.21). In fact, more than half of all named species are insects, and insects are the largest and most diverse group of animals.

Figure 1.21 (a) Praying mantis, cockroaches, and termites belong to the same order. To make classification more manageable, taxonomists place the 2300 species of praying mantis in the suborder Mantodea. (b) Similarly, taxonomists group cicadas, treehoppers, spittlebugs, and leafhoppers in the superfamily Cicadoidea.

Concept Check

1. Why are donkeys and horses considered different species?
2. Why is it important for scientists to use scientific names instead of common names?
3. What is the name of the science of naming and grouping organisms?

Explore More

What does modern classification reveal about how closely birds and reptiles are related?

Modern Classification

Linnaeus grouped species according to their morphology. **Morphology** is the study of form and structure of organisms. However, taxonomists encounter difficulties when they use only anatomical similarities and differences to classify organisms. For example, koala bears, polar bears, and giant pandas look somewhat similar anatomically, but deeper analysis reveals major differences among the three species.

In 1859, Charles Darwin published *The Origin of Species,* describing his theory of how species evolve. The landmark work became the foundation of evolutionary biology and, ever since, biologists have strived to have classification represent the evolutionary relationships among species and to connect evolution to biodiversity. **Phylogeny** is the evolutionary development of a group of organisms. Biologists use phylogenic analysis to compare living organisms to extinct organisms. Based on a shared common ancestor, they group related organisms together into taxa.

©P

Classification and Evolution

Biologists use several types of evidence to help develop hypotheses on how evolutionary taxa should be organized. If fossils are available, fossils can provide the most explicit data to determine common ancestry. However, fossil records are rarely complete enough to do this. In most cases, biologists must rely on the similarities in organisms' morphology and physiology to provide clues to evolutionary relatedness. Analyzing the historical geographical range of a species also gives scientists some insight as to how the species may have developed and evolved. Technological advances have also allowed scientists to analyze proteins and deoxyribonucleic acid (DNA), which provide the clearest link on how closely two species are related (Figure 1.22). Organisms that share a more recent common ancestor will have fewer differences in their proteins and DNA.

raccoons   red pandas   giant pandas   bears

Figure 1.22 Giant pandas share many characteristics with red pandas and raccoons, making the species challenging to classify. After analyzing the DNA of these organisms, scientists have determined that giant pandas are more closely related to bears than red pandas or raccoons.

common ancestor

Phylogenetic Trees

A diagram that reflects the hypotheses of evolutionary relationships is called a **phylogenetic tree**. (The diagram's name comes from the word *phylogeny*, meaning "evolutionary history".) As you can see in Figure 1.23, a phylogenetic tree has a pattern of branches. The tips of the branches represent species as in Figure 1.23 or other descendent taxa. The nodes represent common ancestors of the species, or descendent taxa. In this phylogenetic tree, *Panthera pardus* (leopard), *Mephitis mephitis* (skunk), *Lutra lutra* (European otter), *Canis familiaris* (domestic dog), and *Canis lupus* (wolf) are all descendent species of a common ancestor of the order Carnivora. This tree also shows the genera (*Panthera, Mephitis, Lutra, Canis*), families (Felidae, Mustelidae, Canidae) and order (Carnivora) to which the species belong.

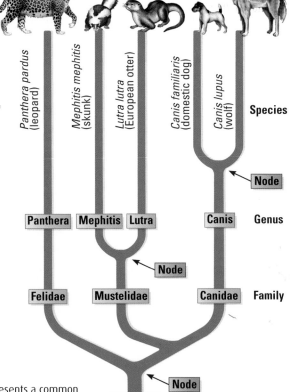

Figure 1.23 In a phylogenetic tree, each node represents a common ancestor of the species above. In this diagram, labels on the branches reinforce how taxonomy reflects the branching pattern of evolution.

Figure 1.24 shows two simple trees constructed from two-way branch points. A particular branching in the cat family could be represented, as in diagram (a). The tree can be expanded to include additional species, as in diagram (b). The "deeper" branch point represents the evolutionary split from a common ancestor of the wolf and cat groups. This phylogenetic tree represents the hypothesis that the wolf and cat groups have a more distant common ancestor than leopards and house cats.

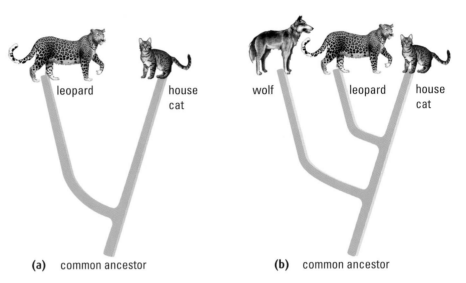

Figure 1.24 (a) Leopards and house cats compose a branch of two species that share a common ancestor. (b) A larger branch that also includes wolves has a common ancestor that would have lived longer ago than the ancestor of leopards and house cats.

Value of Phylogeny

Phylogenetic trees can be used in many ways to solve scientific and practical problems. As honeybee (*Apis melliflera*) populations continue to dwindle, scientists are looking for related species from which they can acquire genetic material to augment honeybee genes for resistance to pests, such as mites. Phylogenic analysis can provide clues as to which species are most closely related to *Apis melliflera*. Phylogenic analysis also has immense value in the development of drugs. The Pacific yew is the original source for the valuable cancer-fighting drug taxol, and harvesting taxol from this tree is very difficult and expensive. By tracing the phylogeny of the Pacific yew, scientists have determined that the more common and accessible European yew might produce a similar compound.

Concept Check

1. How can phylogeny be used to classify organisms?
2. What key features of a phylogenetic tree make it ideal for demonstrating species relatedness?
3. How is the study of phylogeny valuable?

©P

Three Domains

Today, in classifying life forms, many biologists call the broadest taxon a **domain**. According to this classification system, there are three domains: Bacteria, Archaea, and Eukarya (Figure 1.25). The organisms of domains Bacteria and Archaea are microscopic. All of these organisms are **unicellular**, meaning that their entire bodies consist of just a single cell. These cells are relatively simple. For example, they lack nuclei — their DNA is not separated from the rest of the cell. The cells also lack any other organelles bound by a membrane, such as mitochondria and chloroplasts. These organisms are called **prokaryotes**. Thus, the domains Bacteria and Archaea consist of prokaryotic organisms.

All other organisms belong to the domain Eukarya. The major characteristic these organisms have in common is eukaryotic cells, which are more complex than prokaryotic cells and contain membrane-bound organelles, such as nuclei and mitochondria (Figure 1.26). These organisms are called **eukaryotes**. On the next page, Table 1.2 summarizes the major characteristics of prokaryotes and eukaryotes.

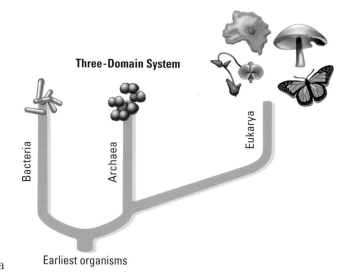

Three-Domain System

Bacteria

Archaea

Eukarya

Earliest organisms

Figure 1.25 Many biologists now prefer this three-domain classification system.

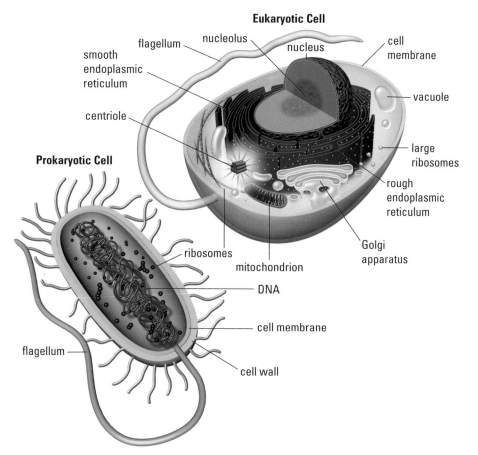

Eukaryotic Cell

flagellum
nucleolus
nucleus
cell membrane
smooth endoplasmic reticulum
centriole
vacuole
large ribosomes
rough endoplasmic reticulum
Golgi apparatus

Prokaryotic Cell

ribosomes
mitochondrion
DNA
cell membrane
flagellum
cell wall

Figure 1.26 A prokaryotic cell is smaller and less complex than a eukaryotic cell. Also there are no membrane-bound organelles in a prokaryotic cell.

Table 1.2 Major Characteristics of Prokaryotes and Eukaryotes

Structure	Prokaryotes	Eukaryotes
Genetic material	DNA is not coated with protein and often occurs in strands or floats freely in cytoplasm.	A nucleus bound by a membrane contains chromosomes made of DNA and proteins.
Cell division	Fission or budding	Splits into two genetically identical cells
Sexual recombination	Transfer of genes from donor to recipient	Often a male and female participate in fertilization
Tissue development	None	Sometimes
Respiration	Some require oxygen and some do not.	Almost all require oxygen.
Size	Microscopic (1–10 µm)	Most are large cells (10–100 µm). Some are micro-organisms.
Energy production	Free-floating enzymes in cytoplasm	Enzymes for energy production are located in mitochondria or chloroplasts.
Flagella	Very simple	Complex

Tree of Life

The classification of Earth's diverse species of life is a work in progress (Figure 1.27). As more is learned about organisms and their evolution, scientists will continue to revise classification systems.

Table 1.3 on the next page shows the three-domain, six-kingdom system of classifying living things. Biologists divide the domain Eukarya into four subgroups: plants, animals, fungi, and protists. Like the prokaryotes, many protists and certain fungi are unicellular and microscopic in size.

BIOLOGY·SOURCE

Take It Further

Find out how researchers at the University of Guelph in Ontario are developing a device to identify organisms by reading a small fragment of DNA like a bar code. Use point-form notes or a graphic organizer to record your findings.

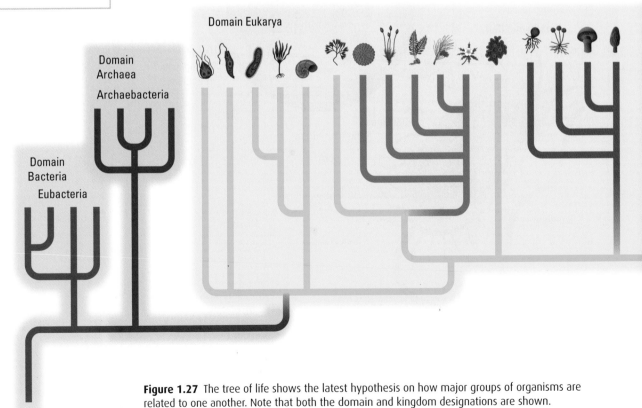

Figure 1.27 The tree of life shows the latest hypothesis on how major groups of organisms are related to one another. Note that both the domain and kingdom designations are shown.

But other protists, most fungi, and all animals and plants are multicellular. **Multicellular** organisms are made of many cells, not just one. Your own body, for example, has trillions of cells.

BIOLOGY•SOURCE

Suggested Activity
• A4 Quick Lab Overview on page 24

Table 1.3 Classification of Living Things

Domain	Bacteria	Archaea	Eukarya			
Kingdom	Eubacteria	Archaebacteria	"Protista"*	Fungi	Plantae	Animalia
Cell Type	Prokaryote	Prokaryote	Eukaryote	Eukaryote	Eukaryote	Eukaryote
Cell Structures	Cell walls with peptidoglycan, a coat of sugars	Cell walls without peptidoglycan	Cell walls of cellulose in some; some have chloroplasts	Cell walls of chitin	Cell walls of cellulose, chloroplasts	No cell walls or chloroplasts
Number of Cells	Unicellular	Unicellular	Most unicellular, some colonial, some multicellular	Most multicellular, some unicellular	Most multicellular, some unicellular	Multicellular
Mode of Nutrition	Makes its own food or eats other organisms	Makes its own food or eats other organisms	Makes its own food or eats other organisms	Breaks down organic matter into nutrients	Makes its own food	Eats other organisms
Examples	*Staphylococcus,* (a) *Salmonella*	(b) *Thermoplasma acidophilum*	(c) Amoeba, *Paramecium,* blue green algae	(d) Mushrooms, mold	(e) Mosses, ferns, conifers, flowering plants	Jellyfish, worms, insects, birds, (f) mammals

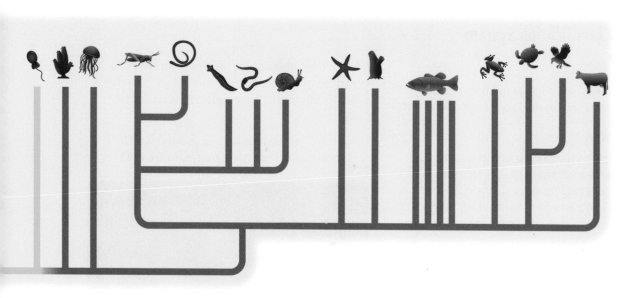

Legend:
■ Eubacteria   ■ Plantae
■ Archaebacteria   ■ Fungi
□ "Protists"*   ■ Animalia

* Note that quotation marks appear around the kingdom "Protista" and "Protists" in Figure 1.27 on this page, because scientists now recognize that there is no way to put all unicellular eukaryotes into one group that contains a single common ancestor. As more evidence of the evolutionary relationships among protists is discovered, most biologists think the traditional kingdom "Protista" will be divided into several kingdoms within the domain Eurakya.

A3 Inquiry Activity
BIOLOGY·SOURCE

Creating a Dichotomous Key

Question

How can you create a dichotomous key to identify organisms?

Activity Overview

In this activity, you will learn how to use and create your own dichotomous keys. Recall that a dichotomous key is a tool used to identify organisms. Each step in a dichotomous key has a set of two choices, or questions, based on observable traits. Each choice leads to another step with a different set of choices, and the steps continue until the organism is identified.

Your teacher will give you a copy of the full activity.

Prelab Questions

Consider these questions before beginning this activity.

1. How can you determine the name of an unfamiliar organism?

2. What types of characteristics might you use to identify a bird, plant, or any other type of organism that is visible to the unaided eye?

Figure 1.28 These students are using criteria to sort objects into groups like scientists use criteria to classify species into groups.

A4 Quick Lab
BIOLOGY·SOURCE

Develop a Classification System

Purpose

To study the features, similarities, and differences among unknown organisms and develop a system to classify them

Activity Overview

Imagine this: In the year 2525, scientists discover a new planet in a new solar system. A space probe lands on the planet, collecting samples of different living organisms and transports them back to Earth. The scientists want you to study the organisms and develop a classification system to help them organize the diversity of life found.

In this activity, you will develop a possible classification system. Your teacher will give you a copy of the full activity.

Prelab Questions

Consider these questions before beginning this activity.

1. With a partner, brainstorm the titles of at least 10 popular songs.

2. Write down three or four genres of music. Place each song into one of the genres. If you disagree on the placement, have a discussion and come to a consensus.

3. What will you be doing in this activity? Why is classification an important process in science?

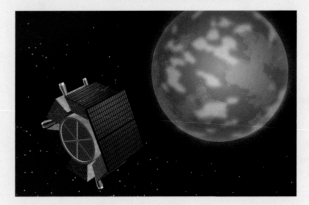

Figure 1.29 A space probe discovers an unknown planet.

Key Concept Review

1. How does the classification of organisms lead to a better understanding of biodiversity?

2. What are some advantages of using binomial nomenclature?

3. What is a dichotomous key and how is it used?

4. Why are common names like daisy and mountain lion often the source of confusion for scientists?

5. List the major taxonomic ranks in Linnaean classification from largest to smallest.

6. What are the six kingdoms of life?

7. What is the major difference between organisms that belong to the domain Eukarya and organisms that belong to the domains Bacteria and Archaea?

8. The scientific name for the brown bear is *Ursus arctos.* What does each part of the name represent?

Connect Your Understanding

9. Classification systems have evolved from a simple two-kingdom system of plants and animals used by Linnaeus to complex 10- and 12-kingdom systems. The following diagrams show three classification systems that have been used to classify organisms over the years. How are these systems different? How are they similar?

Five Kingdoms

Monera	Protista	Plantae	Fungi	Animalia

Six Kingdoms

Eu-bacteria	Archae-bacteria	Protista	Plantae	Fungi	Animalia

Eight Kingdoms

Eu-bacteria	Archae-bacteria	Archezoa	Chromista	Protista	Plantae	Fungi	Animalia

Question 9

10. Explain how the terms "species" and "organism" are similar and different.

11. Explain two different ways that you could classify the following items: banana, lemon, sandwich, milk, orange, meatball, salad.

12. What is a major problem of traditional Linnaean classification? Give an example that demonstrates this problem.

13. The family that contains wolves and foxes is characterized by complex social structures. If dingoes are a part of the same family, what information do you know about these animals?

14. Explain why scientists have had difficulty in classifying the giant panda.

15. Use the diagram below to answer the questions that follow.
    (a) Which species is the common ancestor of all those shown?
    (b) What do 1, 2, and 3 represent?
    (c) To which living species is species H most closely related?

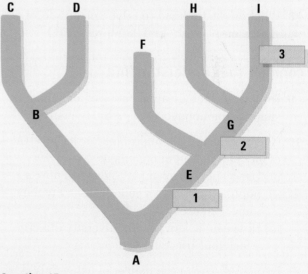

Question 15

Reflection

16. Did anything you learned in this section surprise you? Why?

For more questions, go to   *BIOLOGY•SOURCE*

Key Concept Review

1. Write a definition of the term "biodiversity" that includes all the levels of biodiversity. **k**

2. What is the importance of a hierarchical classification system? **k**

3. Why are common names of organisms inappropriate for identification and classification? **k**

4. Consider the terms "taxonomy," "classification," and "phylogeny," which are often used interchangeably. Write a specific definition for each and give an example to show the appropriate use of each. **k**

5. List the seven hierarchical levels of the Linnaean classification system from smallest to largest. **k**

6. Why do taxonomists sometimes use intermediate taxa, such as superfamily and suborder, to classify organisms? **k**

7. What are two major differences between eukaryotes and prokaryotes? **k**

8. What do the branches on the Tree of Life shown on pages 22 and 23 represent? **k**

Connect Your Understanding

9. How would the disappearance of an animal as small as the honeybee affect biodiversity? **a**

10. Genetic diversity is important for the survival of any population of organisms.
    (a) Use a specific example to explain how a population's lack of genetic diversity may impact an ecosystem. **a**
    (b) How can lack of genetic diversity directly affect your lifestyle? **t**

11. Explain the potential danger of using only a few crops to feed the world's population, and outline how this situation can be avoided. **a**

12. What factors may be contributing to the loss of honeybees? **a**

13. How is maintaining a high level of biodiversity valuable for:
    (a) the environment? **a**
    (b) our society? **a**
    (c) individual people? **a**

14. Compare and contrast the structures and organelles of a prokaryotic cell and a eukaryotic cell. **a**

15. Suppose scientists want to design a chemical that targets mites that cause allergies. How might they go about it? **t**

16. Create a dichotomous key that can be used to identify the beetles shown below. **a**

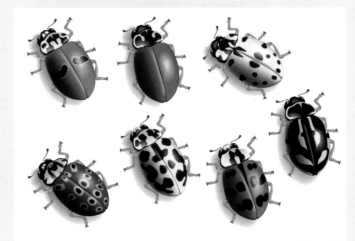

Question 16

17. Consider the biological definition of a species.
    (a) Use the lion and the tiger as an example to explain this definition. **a**
    (b) Would scientists use this definition to classify a dinosaur? Justify your answer. **a**

18. *Felis domesticus* is the two-part Latin name of the domestic cat. Identify the following parts of the name:
    (a) the genus **a**
    (b) the species **a**
    (c) the scientific name **a**

19. The lion and the tiger belong to the same family. The gray wolf and the brown bear belong to the same order. Which pair of animals is more closely related? Justify your answer. *a*

20. Suppose a scientist decides to classify organisms based on their morphology and appearance. Would this scientist be using Linnaean or modern classification strategies? Justify your answer. *a*

21. Why is the Tree of Life diagram shown in Figure 1.27 in the chapter considered a temporary snapshot of the diversity of life? *a*

22. Which kingdom contains organisms with the following characteristics? Refer to Table 1.3 in the chapter to justify your answer.
    (a) cell walls of cellulose *a*
    (b) unicellular cells with cell walls made up of peptidoglycan *a*
    (c) multicellular structure *a*
    (d) breaks down organic matter into nutrients *a*

23. The ermine and the mink are commonly found in the boreal forests of Ontario. Although the two mammals look very similar (see below), they are considered distinct species. Explain why. *a*

Question 23 (a) The mink and (b) the ermine are different species.

(a)

(b)

24. Use the phylogenetic tree below to answer the following questions.
    (a) Which two organisms are most closely related? *a*
    (b) Which two organisms diverged earliest from each other? *a*
    (c) Suppose the letter D represents an organism that is most closely related to organism A. Sketch the tree and include the letter D to show this evolutionary relationship. *a*

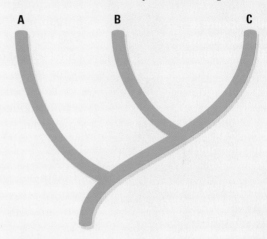

Question 24

Reflection

25. In this chapter, you have learned that ecosystems provide many natural services that support the diversity of life and cannot be easily replicated by human technologies. Think back to your ideas about the impact of human activities on ecosystems. How have your ideas changed? *c*

Unit Task Link

In the Unit Task, you will construct a dichotomous key. Dichotomous keys feature descriptive terms that are specific or measurable. Poor dichotomous keys often have vague terms that are open to interpretation. Review the dichotomous key activities in this chapter, field guides, and online resources, and make a list of suitable terms for dichotomous keys.

For more questions, go to *BIOLOGY•SOURCE*

A diversity of micro-organisms, protists, and fungi is intrinsic to life on Earth.

If you break out in a bull's-eye rash after a hike through the forest, you may have inadvertently picked up *Borrelia burgdorferi*, the microscopic bacteria that cause Lyme disease (Figure 2.1). In southern Ontario, Lyme disease spreads via the life cycles of many forest-dwelling organisms. Oak trees drop acorns rich in fat and proteins that attract large numbers of mice. Often, some of the mice are infected with *Borrelia burgdorferi*. Bloodsucking insects called ticks feed on deer and, as deer pass by, some of the ticks drop off and land on the mice. The ticks feed on the blood of the mice and lay eggs on their skin. The eggs hatch and, as the larvae mature, they pick up the bacteria from infected mice.

To complete their life cycle, ticks need a meal of blood from a large warm-blooded animal like a deer, dog, or human. As the ticks bite these organisms, they transmit *Borrelia burgdorferi*, spreading Lyme disease. Ontario's cold winters limit the northward spread of Lyme disease, which is the most highly-diagnosed tick-borne disease in the world. However, climate change, increased industrialization, and human encroachment on natural areas can all force the organisms that carry Lyme disease to move into previously unaffected areas.

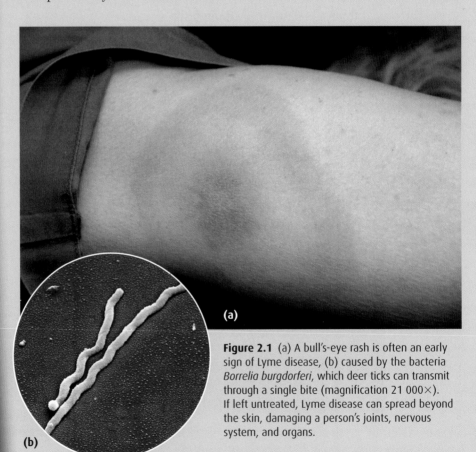

Figure 2.1 (a) A bull's-eye rash is often an early sign of Lyme disease, (b) caused by the bacteria *Borrelia burgdorferi*, which deer ticks can transmit through a single bite (magnification 21 000×). If left untreated, Lyme disease can spread beyond the skin, damaging a person's joints, nervous system, and organs.

©P

Viruses

Do viruses belong on the tree of life you saw in the last chapter? It is easy to mistake viruses for living organisms. Viruses use nucleic acids, such as deoxyribonucleic acid (DNA) and ribonucleic acid (RNA), like living organisms to store genetic information (Figure 2.2). Viruses also adapt to changing conditions like living things by genetically mutating, which can allow them to avoid destruction by medicines. However, unlike living things, viruses are not made of cells and cannot reproduce on their own. Viruses are made of proteins and nucleic acids, and viruses need to use the cells of a host organism to make copies of themselves.

Structure and Function

The structure of a virus is well-suited to its function: entering a host cell and reproducing. A virus is composed of a relatively short piece of nucleic acid, DNA or RNA, surrounded by a protein coat (Figure 2.2). Some viruses also have outer membranes that merge with a host cell's membrane, making it easier for the virus to infect the cell.

Viruses come in many shapes and sizes and are usually classified based on the type of cell they infect. The protein coat that surrounds a virus is like a key to a door. Patterns on the viral coat unlock an entryway into a host cell. These patterns are very specific, and normally a particular virus will open only one type of cell. The HIV virus, which can cause AIDS, for example, can unlock and infect only T cells of the immune system. Viruses called **bacteriophages** attack and infect specific bacterial cells, and scientists often use them in biotechnology as tools to control particular bacterial diseases and in gene therapies. However, sometimes the protein coat of a virus is like a master key, unlocking many different types of cells. The avian flu virus, for example, can infect many different types of birds and mammals.

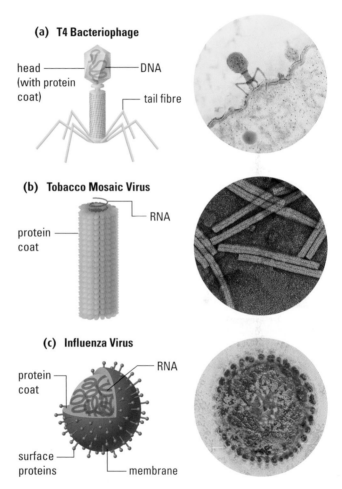

(a) T4 Bacteriophage

head — DNA
(with protein
coat)
— tail fibre

(b) Tobacco Mosaic Virus

— RNA
protein —
coat

(c) Influenza Virus

— RNA
protein —
coat

surface —
proteins
— membrane

Figure 2.2 Viruses come in a variety of types and shapes. But they are not cells. (a) The tail fibres of a bacteriophage enable it to attach to and inject its genetic material into a bacterial host cell as shown. (magnification 60 000×) (b) The tobacco mosaic virus is rod-shaped. (magnification 400 000×) (c) The influenza virus has an additional membrane. (magnification 21 000×)

How Viruses Reproduce

When a virus infiltrates a cell, it unloads its genetic material, takes control of the cell's processes, and replicates. Replication may happen immediately or the viral genes may lie dormant for a period of time before any changes occur to the cell. Early research on bacteriophages uncovered two basic ways that viruses reproduce, the lytic cycle and lysogenic cycle (Figure 2.3).

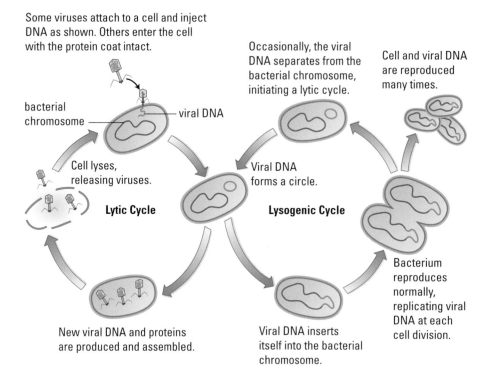

Some viruses attach to a cell and inject DNA as shown. Others enter the cell with the protein coat intact.

bacterial chromosome — viral DNA

Cell lyses, releasing viruses.

Lytic Cycle

New viral DNA and proteins are produced and assembled.

Occasionally, the viral DNA separates from the bacterial chromosome, initiating a lytic cycle.

Viral DNA forms a circle.

Lysogenic Cycle

Viral DNA inserts itself into the bacterial chromosome.

Cell and viral DNA are reproduced many times.

Bacterium reproduces normally, replicating viral DNA at each cell division.

Figure 2.3 Viruses such as a bacteriophage are capable of reproducing in two general ways, the lytic and lysogenic cycles. The word *lyses* means "the disintegration of cells." It comes from the Greek word for "loosen."

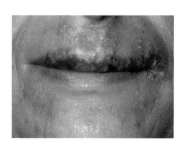

Figure 2.4 Reproduction of the Herpes simplex virus causes cold sores. Blisters like these appear during the lytic cycle.

In the lytic cycle, the bacteriophage attaches to the host cell and injects its DNA. This forces the host cell's enzymes and synthesis machinery to make copies of the viral DNA and viral proteins. The viral proteins and nucleic acids then assemble themselves inside the host cell, making many copies of the original infecting virus. Once there are anywhere from 20 to 500 copies of the virus, the host cell can no longer hold them and bursts open, releasing many new viruses. These go on to infect many new cells, and the cycle is repeated (Figure 2.4).

In the lysogenic cycle, the viral genes are incorporated within the host cell's DNA. Each time the host cell reproduces, the viral DNA is copied along with the host's DNA. Often, an environmental change in temperature or pH triggers the viral DNA to separate from the host DNA and start a lytic cycle. New bacteriophages are then made and released.

Concept Check

1. Is a virus considered a living thing? Justify your answer.

2. How is a virus able to enter a host cell?

3. Draw diagrams of three different types of viruses.

4. Illustrate the lytic and lysogenic reproduction cycles of viruses.

Prokaryotes

Recall that many biologists now classify organisms into three domains: two domains of prokaryotes — the Bacteria and the Archaea — and one domain of eukaryotes — the Eukarya. Before 1977, this system did not exist and biologists divided all living things into two major evolutionary branches: eukaryotes and prokaryotes. All the prokaryotes were bacteria. Then microbiologist Carl Woese discovered a group of bacteria that behave more like eukaryotic cells even though they have typical bacterial components. Eventually, Woese reconstructed the taxonomic tree, and the three-domain system was created with two domains of prokaryotes, the Bacteria and the Archaea.

The word *archaea* comes from a Greek word meaning "ancient." Many archaea live in some of the most extreme environments on Earth, which may resemble conditions that existed on early Earth (Figure 2.5). Archaea are more complex than bacteria. However, the majority of prokaryotes are bacteria, which live in almost every other environment on Earth. These include complex prokaryotes that can convert sunlight into energy or that live in multicellular structures large enough to be seen by the unaided eye.

Figure 2.5 Archaea can survive in some of the most inhospitable places on the planet, like this hot spring, glaciers, methane-saturated swamps, deep sea vents, brine pools, black organic mud devoid of oxygen, and even on the edges of active volcanoes. Often they are the only form of life found in these extreme environments.

Bacteria

Large numbers of bacteria inhabit almost every place on Earth. A millilitre of lake water contains a million bacteria. A pinch of some soils holds more than a billion bacteria, but that is nothing. Your mouth is home to more bacteria than all the humans that have ever lived (Figure 2.6). In fact, your body has approximately 10 times more bacterial cells than human cells.

Some bacteria are well-known because they cause disease in humans. For example, the disease tuberculosis (TB) is caused by an airborne bacterium called *Mycobacterium tuberculosis*. This bacterium causes more deaths worldwide than any other infection. When it is inhaled, *Mycobacterium tuberculosis* grows in the lungs, triggering the body's defence system to destroy large areas of tissue. Other bacteria cause strep throat (*Streptococcus pyogenes*), diphtheria (*Corynebacterium diphtheriae*), many sexually transmitted diseases, and certain kinds of food poisoning.

Figure 2.6 Bacteria are everywhere. This coloured micrograph shows bacteria (blue) on a human tooth (yellow).

Although these diseases may give the impression that all bacteria are harmful, many are harmless and helpful to humans and other organisms. Some of the bacteria in your mouth, for example, prevent other harmful organisms from growing there. You also rely on bacteria in your intestines to break down food and release certain vitamins. In exchange, you house the bacteria and provide them with a regular supply of resources. Many other organisms have similar symbiotic relationships with bacteria.

Bacteria play a key role in the cycling of nutrients throughout the biosphere. They decompose organic matter, releasing nutrients back into ecosystems. Some species convert nitrogen gas from the atmosphere into nitrogen compounds that plants can absorb from the soil.

Plants use these compounds to build proteins, and this nitrogen
passes on to animals when they eat the plants. Cyanobacteria are
producers that play an important role at the start of many food chains.
They also supply a great deal of the world's oxygen. Without bacteria,
larger organisms on this planet could not survive.

Structure and Function of Bacteria

Bacteria are the smallest living cells and can only be studied with the
aid of powerful microscopes. Figure 2.7 shows the basic cell structure of
bacteria. Biologists identify and distinguish bacteria based partly on three
important characteristics:

• cell shape
• cell wall structure
• motility (method of movement)

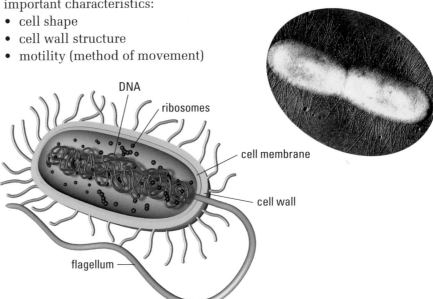

Figure 2.7 Bacteria, such as
E. coli found in your intestine,
have a basic cell structure
that includes a cell wall, cell
membrane, ribosomes, DNA that
is not enclosed in a membrane,
and a flagellum for movement.
(magnification 17 500×)

Cell Shape

Bacteria come in three basic shapes: spherical, rod-shaped, or spiral-
shaped (Figure 2.8). Spherical bacteria, such as the bacteria that cause
pneumonia, are called **cocci** (singular, *coccus*), from the Greek word for
"berries." Some species form clusters of spherical cells, while others,
such as *Streptococcus*, form chains. Rod-shaped bacteria are called
bacilli (singular, *bacillus*), from the Latin word for "stick." The *E. coli*
bacteria in your intestine are bacilli. A third group of bacteria is curved
or spiral-shaped. The largest spiral-shaped bacteria are called **spirochetes**,
from the Greek word for "long hair." The bacteria that cause Lyme disease
and those that cause syphilis are spirochetes.

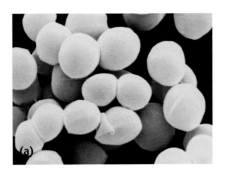 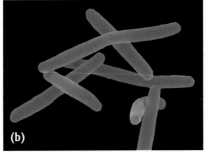 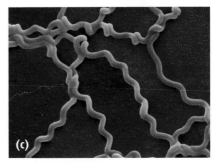

Figure 2.8 Bacteria have three basic shapes. (a) *Staphylococcus aureus* are cocci that can cause
food poisoning. (magnification 1000×) (b) *Capnocytophaga sputigena* are bacilli that can
cause blood poisoning, gum disease, and meningitis. (magnification 5500×) (c) *Leptospira* are
spirochetes that can can cause liver and kidney disease. (magnification 4000×)

Cell Wall Structure

Nearly all bacteria have a cell wall outside their cell membrane (also called the plasma membrane). As in plants, the wall maintains cell shape and protects the cell. But the cell walls of bacteria differ greatly from those of plants, fungi, and protists. Bacteria have one of two types of cell walls. One type is composed mostly of peptidoglycan, a thick coat of sugars. The other has less peptidoglycan and an additional outer membrane. The cell walls of bacteria also differ from those of archaea, which have no peptidoglycan. Differences in structure like these are known as **structural diversity**.

Movement

About half of all prokaryotes lack structures for motility, or movement. Others use long whiplike structures known as **flagella** (singular, *flagellum*) to propel themselves toward food, light, or oxygen. Most motile bacteria have a flagellum. Spiral-shaped bacteria use a corkscrew motion to move. Other bacteria glide on slimy mucous that they secrete.

BIOLOGY•SOURCE

Suggested Activity

• A7 Inquiry Activity Overview on page 36

How Bacteria Obtain Nutrition

Bacteria vary in the way they obtain energy and organic molecules that contain carbon. Table 2.1 summarizes the main nutritional modes of bacteria.

Table 2.1 Main Nutritional Modes of Bacteria

Nutritional Mode	Habitat	Examples
Heterotroph Takes up organic molecules from environment or by eating other organisms	Wide variety of environments	*E. coli* (magnification 2345×)
Photoautotroph Uses sunlight to make carbon dioxide into carbon compounds like sugar	Environments where light is abundant	Cyanobacteria (magnification 100×)
Photoheterotroph Takes up organic molecules from environment and by eating other organisms like basic heterotrophs, and also uses light energy	Environments where light is abundant	*Heliobacter pylori* (magnification 6000×)
Chemoheterotroph Uses energy released through chemical reactions involving ammonia, hydrogen sulphide, and similar chemicals	Dark and/or chemically harsh environments, such as boiling hot springs, deep oceans, mud, digestive systems of animals	*Methanococcus jannaschii* (magnification 100 000×)

Binary Fission

plasma membrane

cell wall

DNA

DNA duplicates.

Cell begins to divide.

Daughter cells separate.

Figure 2.9 Binary fission enables prokaryotes to reproduce very quickly in certain conditions.

How Bacteria Reproduce

All bacteria have the ability to divide, producing two identical cells in a process known as **binary fission** (Figure 2.9). This process allows bacteria to reproduce very quickly. Many bacteria are capable of copying themselves every 20 minutes. In just 12 hours, a single cell could give rise to a bacterial colony containing more than 68 billion cells. However, populations do not grow this large, due to limited food and space. Even so, it is easy to see how a small number of bacteria can spoil food rapidly or make you sick quickly.

Binary fission produces a colony of cells that are genetically identical. Apart from occasional errors in the copying process that result in genetic mutations, binary fission does not allow bacteria to evolve to adapt to changing conditions. However, prokaryotic cells can undergo certain processes that result in genetic mixing, or recombination. Figure 2.10 shows two of these processes: transformation and conjugation.

In **transformation**, some bacteria take up pieces of DNA from the environment. Such pieces of DNA might come from nearby bacteria that have died. In **conjugation**, two bacterial cells temporarily join and directly exchange genetic material. Conjugation usually involves plasmids. Plasmids are separate rings of DNA apart from the cell's main chromosome. **Transduction** is a third method by which bacteria can receive new genetic material. In transduction, viruses that infect bacteria (bacteriophages) carry genes from one cell and inject them into another.

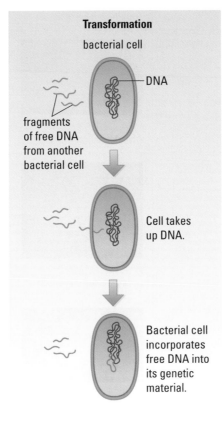

Transformation

bacterial cell

DNA

fragments of free DNA from another bacterial cell

Cell takes up DNA.

Bacterial cell incorporates free DNA into its genetic material.

Figure 2.10 Genetic variation is achieved through the mixing of genetic information between different bacteria.

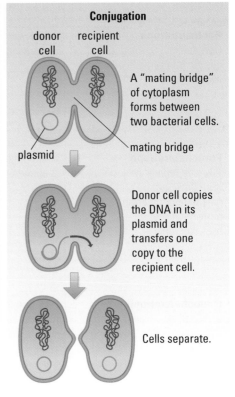

Conjugation

donor cell

recipient cell

A "mating bridge" of cytoplasm forms between two bacterial cells.

plasmid

mating bridge

Donor cell copies the DNA in its plasmid and transfers one copy to the recipient cell.

Cells separate.

©P

When resources are too limited for bacteria to survive, many transform into a dormant stage, called an **endospore** (Figure 2.11). A thick internal wall circles the DNA and a small amount of cytoplasm. The outer cell disintegrates, leaving the highly resistant endospore. Some endospores can survive lack of water and nutrients, heat, cold, and most poisons for many years. When the environment becomes more favourable, endospores can absorb water and grow again. *Bacillus anthracis,* which causes the disease anthrax in cattle, sheep, and humans, is an example of bacteria able to form endospores.

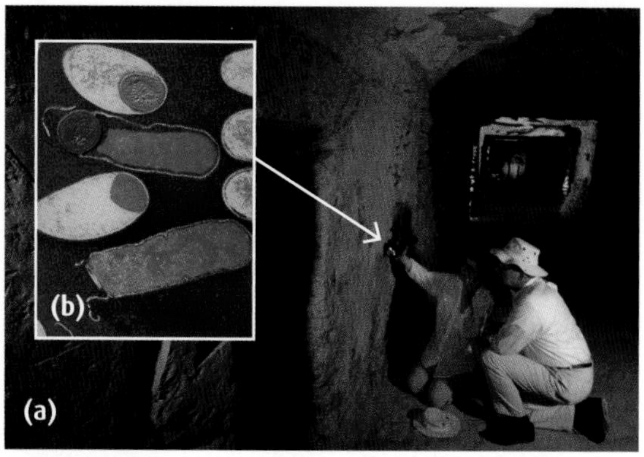

(b)

(a)

Figure 2.11 (a) Archaeologists must take special precautions when opening up long-buried tombs to ensure that they do not become exposed to endospores (b) of dormant bacteria. (magnification 12 500×)

Concept Check

1. What are the three major cell shapes of bacteria?

2. What process alllows bacteria to reproduce very quickly?

3. Name four modes of prokaryotic nutrition. For each, identify the energy source and carbon source.

BIOLOGY•SOURCE

Take It Further

An emerging disease is one that has appeared in a population for the first time, or is rapidly increasing in incidence or geographic range. Research a specific viral or bacterial disease that has recently emerged in Ontario. Map out the range of the virus or bacteria that causes the disease and write point-form notes to describe how the disease spreads from organism to organism.

Climate Change and Prokaryotes

Climate change can have a great impact on the diversity of prokaryotes and their interactions with other organisms. Rising sea levels and vigorous storm surges associated with climate change are driving salt water into peat wetlands (Figure 2.12). The peat soils in these wetland ecosystems contain large populations of methane-producing bacteria that play a critical role in maintaining the ecosystems. The peat is also home to much smaller populations of sulphate-metabolizing bacteria and archaea, which release toxic compounds that kill off surface vegetation and destroy peat. When these bacteria are exposed to salt water, they outcompete and replace the populations of methane-producing bacteria, virtually eliminating the peat and destroying the wetland habitat. Species that live there either die or move to another habitat. The disintegration of peat also releases large volumes of carbon dioxide and methane into the atmosphere, both of which add to global warming, and reduces the amount of peat soil available for farming and gardening.

Figure 2.12 Effects of climate change can eliminate bacteria that maintain peat wetlands and destroy wetland habitats.

Spread of Infectious Disease

Purpose

To simulate the spread of an infectious disease caused by a virus or bacteria

Activity Overview

In this Quick Lab, your class will simulate the spread of an infectious disease throughout a population of organisms. You will use your findings to determine how to minimize and prevent the spread of the disease.

Your teacher will give you a full copy of the activity.

Prelab Questions

Consider the questions below before beginning this activity.

1. In what ways can a disease spread among a population?

2. What steps can you take to prevent a disease from spreading?

3. H1N1 and the avian flu virus have been considered potential sources of a pandemic (countrywide or worldwide outbreak). What steps were taken locally to prevent them from becoming a pandemic?

Figure 2.13 Deer ticks like this one can transmit bacteria, which cause Lyme disease, through their bites.

Drawing Scientific Diagrams

Activity Overview

In this Skill Builder, you will learn how to draw scientific diagrams to record exactly what you observe under a microscope. You will learn guidelines for drawing scientific diagrams.

REQUIRED SKILLS
- Using appropriate equipment and tools
- Drawing conclusions

Classifying Bacteria

Question

Can bacteria be classified by the morphology and chemistry of their cell walls?

Activity Overview

Recall that bacteria have one of two types of cell walls. In this activity, you will use a testing method called Gram staining to distinguish the two types of bacteria. You will use a microscope to study the bacteria and draw scientific diagrams of the bacteria to record your observations.

Your teacher will give you a full copy of the activity.

Prelab Questions

Consider the questions below before beginning this activity.

1. Why is it important to stain cells?

2. How can you determine the size of a cell you are observing under a microscope?

Figure 2.14 These bacteria have been treated with the Gram stain. (magnification 1000×)

Key Concept Review

1. Describe how viruses can be classified.

2. Explain how a virus reproduces itself.

3. Identify three differences between archaea and bacteria.

4. Summarize three mechanisms of genetic recombination in prokaryotes.

5. Explain the role prokaryotes play in nitrogen recycling.

6. Describe how prokaryotes are able to move through the environment.

7. What is structural diversity? Use a specific example to explain your answer.

8. What are the three major types of morphology found in bacteria?

Connect Your Understanding

9. There is disagreement in the scientific world about whether viruses are actually living organisms. Why is there confusion?

10. How is the viral structure well-suited to its function?

11. The rabies virus infects cells of the central nervous system.
    (a) Explain why the virus does not infect the muscle cells in your leg.
    (b) Explain why you need a rabies shot if you are bitten by a rabid dog.

12. Both bacteria and viruses can infect humans. How then is it possible for viruses to infect bacteria cells?

13. Suppose a bacterium has exhausted all the resources in an area and is not able to travel to another area. Describe a process where it may survive to reproduce at a future point in time.

14. Match the following ways bacteria obtain nutrition with the appropriate nutritional classification: heterotroph, chemoheterotroph, photoautotroph, photoheterotroph.
    (a) Bacteria consuming energy from human tissue
    (b) Bacteria receiving all their energy from sunlight

(c) Bacteria using energy from the sun during the day and then consuming other bacteria at night
(d) Bacteria receiving energy from chemical reactions around a deep sea vent

15. Examine the graph below to answer the following questions.
    (a) How many bacteria were produced during the second hour?
    (b) At this rate, how many bacteria would be present at the end of four hours?
    (c) What type of bacterial reproduction that you read about in this chapter would account for this type of rapid growth?
    (d) If one cell became resistant to an antibiotic due to a mutation at the 80-minute mark, how many cells would be resistant at the end of the 120-minute mark? (Assume the same growth rate.)

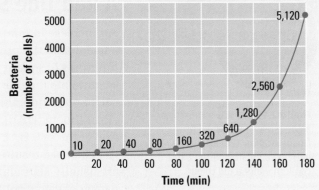

Reproduction of Bacteria

Question 15

16. Describe one way that climate change has affected the diversity of prokaryotes.

Reflection

17. Why do you think it is important to understand the structure, function, and reproduction methods of prokaryotes?

For more questions, go to *BIOLOGY•SOURCE*

2.2 Protists

Section Summary

- Protists are organisms that do not fit into archaea, bacteria, fungi, plant, or animal kingdoms.
- Protists are eukaryotic organisms with nuclei enclosed by a membrane.
- Protists are often classified into plant-like, animal-like, and fungus-like groups based on their behaviour.
- Protists may use pseudopodia, cilia, or flagella to move.
- Protists can reproduce asexually or sexually.
- Climate change has a dramatic impact on the diversity of protists.

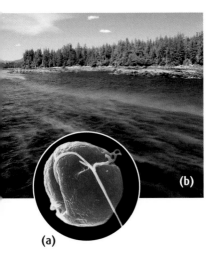

(a)

Figure 2.15 (a) This microscopic algae releases a harmful toxin. (magnification 12 000×) (b) A large accumulation of the algae can turn water a red colour.

The St. Lawrence River, which flows between the Atlantic Ocean and the Great Lakes, is home to many recognizable species of seabirds, fish, and mammals. In 2008, red water swept through the river, leaving a trail of rotting corpses, including 15 endangered beluga whales, that washed up on local beaches. The culprit was a single-celled eukaryote that does not belong to the kingdom of animals, plants, fungi, or even bacteria (Figure 2.15).

A Red Tide Sweeps In

An increase in temperature and rainfall can trigger microscopic algae, a member of the protist kingdom, to reproduce very quickly and cover hundreds of square kilometres of water. So many of the micro-organisms accumulate that the water often appears a different colour. Commonly called a red tide, this phenomenon is more correctly known as a Harmful Algal Bloom (HAB), because it is not always red or associated with the tide of the sea. HABs produce a toxin that can affect animals from fish to mammals, resulting in tissue damage and death. Although humans are usually alert enough to avoid the red water of HABs, we still face the danger of eating contaminated animals, such as shellfish. Paralytic shellfish poisoning can occur when organisms eat shellfish that have eaten algae from a HAB. The shellfish are not affected, but as the toxin builds up in their tissues, it can become highly concentrated and cause paralysis and even death to any mammal (including humans) that eats the shellfish. Over the past several decades, the number of HABs has increased due to climate change. In fact, warmer temperatures and run-off of nutrients from farms and factories after heavy rainstorms create optimal conditions for HABs.

The Most Diverse Eukaryotes

BIOLOGY • SOURCE

Explore More

What makes protists so diverse?

Does your family have a drawer at home where you keep "stuff"? That drawer might contain a flashlight, tape measure, spare keys, rubber bands, or extra stamps. These objects have little in common except that they are kept in the same drawer for convenience. Biologists have a sort of taxonomic "stuff" drawer: the kingdom Protista. Protista is a very diverse kingdom of organisms that do not fit neatly into any of the other kingdoms. All eukaryotes that are not animals, plants, or fungi are classified as **protists**.

©P

Structure and Function of Protists

Protists vary in structure and function more than any other group of organisms and live in a diverse range of habitats, including the bottom of oceans, thermal springs, snowpacks, icebergs, swamps, soil, forest floors, chlorinated swimming pools, sewage treatment plants, and even the atmosphere (Figure 2.16). Most protists are unicellular and free-living (not parasitic). However, some protist species are colonial — organisms consisting of many similar or identical cells. There are even some protists, such as seaweeds like kelp, that are multicellular. These multicellular protists have relatively complex bodies consisting of specialized cells.

Figure 2.16 Protists exhibit extreme diversity occupying many different niches. (a) Brown algae of kelp forests form the foundation of productive ecosystems where sea otters, sea lions, fish, and whales often go to feed. (b) Diatoms, unicellular algae found in freshwater and marine ecosystems, are key members of plankton, an important food source for many marine animals. (magnification 600×) (c) Blepharisma feed on bacteria and decaying organic matter in freshwater. (magnification 290×) (d) Slime moulds, which form super colonies, decompose dead organic matter on forest floors. (magnification 10×)

Protists have the typical eukaryotic cell structure shown in Figure 2.17, including internal membranes, a nucleus bound by a membrane, and organelles such as mitochondria and, in some species, chloroplasts. However, eukaryotic cell structure is a characteristic of all organisms other than bacteria and archaea. So cell structure alone does not define protists.

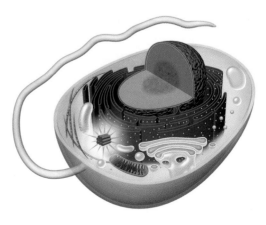

Figure 2.17 Recall that a eukaryotic cell is a complex cell with organelles, such as mitochondria for respiration and chloroplasts for photosynthesis. Unlike plants and animals that have evolved specialized tissues and organs for such tasks, most protists are single cells that have to do all of these specialized jobs.

Most biologists think that with sufficient data the traditional protist kingdom will be divided into several kingdoms within the domain Eukarya. Comparing nucleic acid sequences helps researchers identify these main evolutionary branches of protists. However, evidence of these evolutionary relationships remains incomplete. Until there is a widely accepted division of these diverse organisms into multiple kingdoms, the term "protist" remains useful when studying the group.

The eukaryotic organisms with which you are most familiar are probably large plants and animals, such as the sea otter shown on the previous page. How are these organisms related to protists? And how are protists related to even less complex prokaryotic organisms such as bacteria? Biologists hypothesize that protists evolved from ancient prokaryotes more than a billion years ago. In turn, plants, animals, and fungi evolved from protists hundreds of millions of years ago.

The Origin of Eukaryotes

BIOLOGY•SOURCE

Explore More

What evidence supports the endosymbiotic theory?

Among the most fundamental questions in biology is how the complex eukaryotic cell evolved from much simpler prokaryotic cells. A widely accepted theory is that eukaryotic cells evolved through a combination of two processes (Figure 2.18). In one process, internal membranes such as the endoplasmic reticulum, Golgi apparatus, and nuclear envelope evolved from inward folds of the plasma membrane of ancestral prokaryotic cells. Such internal membranes would allow the cell to carry out more complex chemical reactions in separate compartments.

Evidence suggests that a second, very different process led to the existence of the cellular organelles mitochondria and chloroplasts. Scientists hypothesize that in this process, called serial endosymbiosis, chloroplasts and mitochondria evolved from small symbiotic prokaryotes that lived within other, larger host cells.

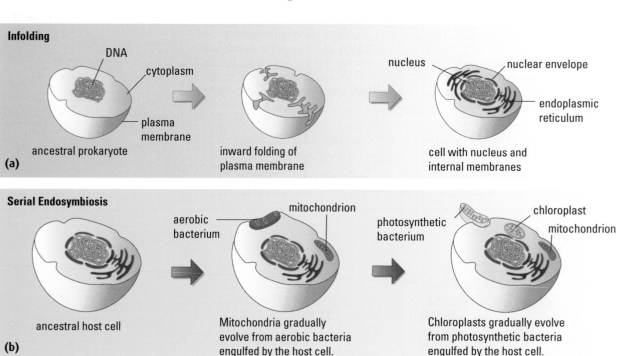

Figure 2.18 Eukaryotic cell organelles may have evolved through a combination of two processes. (a) Infolding of the plasma membrane could have produced internal membranes. (b) Through serial endosymbiosis, certain prokaryotes could have become residents within larger host cells, eventually evolving into mitochondria and chloroplasts.

How Protists Move

Protists have adopted several strategies to move towards food or escape from predators. Amoebas creep slowly by streaming cytoplasm into cellular extensions known as **pseudopodia** in the direction they wish to go (Figure 2.19).

Others swim quickly using hairlike structures called flagella and **cilia** (Figure 2.20). Flagella are long hairlike projections that extend out of the cell membrane. Heterotrophic protists with flagella are called **zooflagellates** and usually have only one or two flagella per cell, but some have hundreds (Figure 2.21). Cilia are much shorter than flagella and occur in large clusters or completely cover the cell membrane. Protists with cilia, such as the rapidly moving *Paramecium* and *Stylonchia*, are called **ciliates** (Figure 2.21).

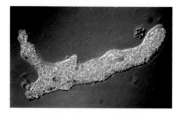

Figure 2.19 Cytoplasm flows from one area of an amoeba cell into a pseudopodium extending outward from the cell, enabling the cell to move in the growing direction of the pseudopodium. (magnification 100×)

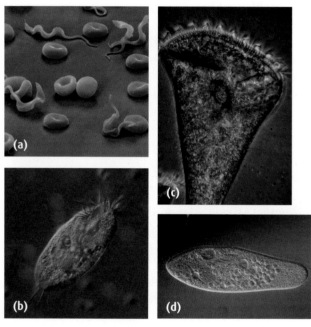

Figure 2.21 (a) Flagella propel *Trypanosoma brucei*, zooflagellates which can cause disease in humans, through red blood cells. (magnification 1750×) (b) The cilia of *Stylonchia* are clumped together in leglike structures used for locomotion. (magnification 57×) (c) The cilia of *Stentor* are used for locomotion and to create a whirlpool-like current that moves food into the cell's mouth. (magnification 200×) (d) Thousands of cilia cover *Paramecium* to propel the organism and gather food. (magnification 1000×)

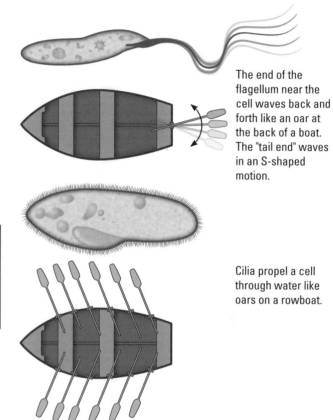

The end of the flagellum near the cell waves back and forth like an oar at the back of a boat. The "tail end" waves in an S-shaped motion.

Cilia propel a cell through water like oars on a rowboat.

Figure 2.20 Flagella and cilia propel some protists through water like oars propel boats.

Still other protists lack the ability to move at all and rely on passive forms of transportation, such as water currents, wind, and passing animals that they may hitch on to. Consider the *apicomplexans*, a group of protists that have an "apical complex" structure at the tip of the cell specialized for penetrating host cells. These protists release reproductive cells called **spores** that can enter the bodies of other organisms and live as parasites. Mosquitoes carry the apicomplexan *Plasmodium*, which causes malaria and is responsible for millions of deaths each year. *Cryptosporidium* produces spores that rely on water currents and is often found in unclean drinking water, causing severe intestinal disease.

How Protists Reproduce

Protists use a variety of strategies to reproduce. Amoebas, paramecia, and most ciliates reproduce by making a copy of their genetic material and dividing into two genetically identical cells. This allows them to reproduce quickly, but the successive generations lack genetic diversity.

Paramecia can circumvent this problem by exchanging genetic material from one organism to another through the process of conjugation. Even though no new paramecia are produced, conjugation enhances genetic variability. Thus, there is a greater chance that the paramecia will be able to survive changes in environmental conditions.

Many other protists alternate between sexual and asexual reproduction in complex life cycles. Slime moulds and *Plasmodium* that causes malaria undergo reproduction in this way (Figure 2.22).

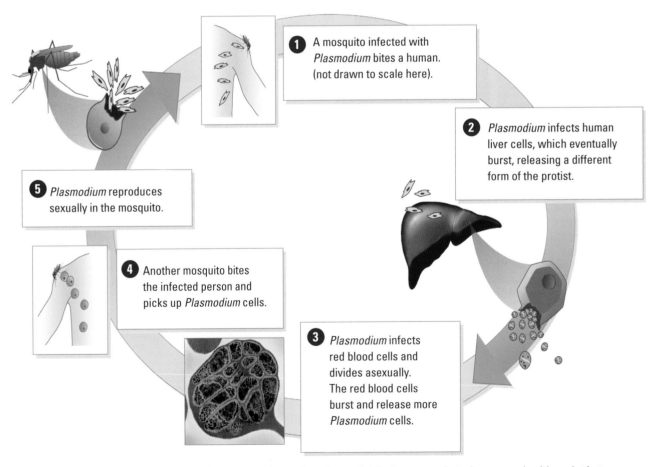

1 A mosquito infected with *Plasmodium* bites a human. (not drawn to scale here).

2 *Plasmodium* infects human liver cells, which eventually burst, releasing a different form of the protist.

5 *Plasmodium* reproduces sexually in the mosquito.

4 Another mosquito bites the infected person and picks up *Plasmodium* cells.

3 *Plasmodium* infects red blood cells and divides asexually. The red blood cells burst and release more *Plasmodium* cells.

Figure 2.22 *Plasmodium*, the protist that causes malaria, has a complex life cycle that alternates between sexual and asexual reproduction and includes multiple hosts.

©P

A Tough Case for Classification

Classifying a group of organisms as diverse as protists is challenging. Recall that classification is ideally based on evolutionary relationships and evidence of these relationships among protists remains incomplete. Thus, in a group as diverse as protists, biologists often use other criteria, such as how organisms obtain food, to informally group the organisms. For example, heterotrophs obtain food from other organisms, and autotrophs make all of their own food. You can think of these methods of obtaining food as different "lifestyles" for protists. Lifestyle is useful to help understand protist adaptations and the roles protists play in ecosystems. In fact, biologists often group protists according to three lifestyles: animal-like, fungus-like, and plant-like.

BIOLOGY·SOURCE

Suggested Activities
- A8 Inquiry Activity Overview on page 45
- A9 Inquiry Activity Overview on page 45

Animal-like Protists

Animal-like protists are heterotrophs that capture and ingest food. The amoeba, for example, slowly engulfs food with pseudopodia (Figure 2.23). Once a pseudopodium surrounds the food, it forms an internal food vacuole, or cavity, that digests the food. The amoeba lives in a variety of aquatic environments, including freshwater, saltwater, and the human mouth. The ciliates, such as *Paramecium*, move very quickly and use their speed to capture food (Figure 2.24). Their hairlike cilia sweep food particles into an oral groove, where the food is pushed into a food vacuole and digested. The vacuole then passes through the organism to an anal pore in the cell membrane, where it releases wastes.

Figure 2.23 This sequence of photos shows how an amoeba uses pseudopodia to surround prey, a group of green algae cells, and produce a food vacuole. (magnification 100×)

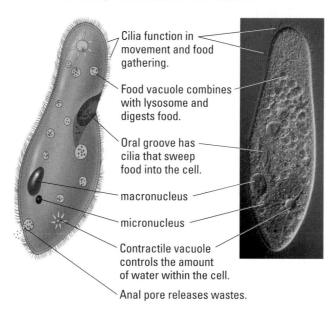

Cilia function in movement and food gathering.

Food vacuole combines with lysosome and digests food.

Oral groove has cilia that sweep food into the cell.

macronucleus

micronucleus

Contractile vacuole controls the amount of water within the cell.

Anal pore releases wastes.

Figure 2.24 *Paramecium* is a freshwater ciliate that feeds mainly on bacteria. It is covered by thousands of cilia that function in locomotion and feeding. (magnifciation 1000×)

Plant-like Protists

Plant-like protists, called **algae** (singular, *alga*) are autotrophs that make their own food. They contain chloroplasts that enable them to carry out photosynthesis as plants do. The algae shown at the beginning of the section that can undergo population explosions producing HABs belong to this group of protists. Many algae are unicellular like that algae, some live in colonies, and still others are multicellular. Most algae have both asexual and sexual mechanisms of reproduction. Biologists classify these protists by differences in cell walls, types of photosynthetic pigments, structure, types of storage carbohydrates, and sequences of nucleic acids.

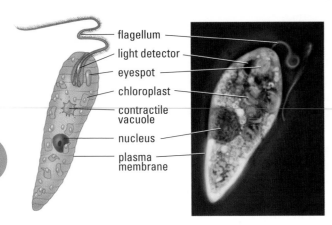

flagellum
light detector
eyespot
chloroplast
contractile vacuole
nucleus
plasma membrane

Figure 2.25 *Euglena* is one of the most common inhabitants of pond water and exemplifies the difficulties with classifying protists. It carries out photosynthesis in the light and, in the dark, it can become heterotrophic and absorb nutrients. (magnification 500×)

Figure 2.26 Plasmodial slime moulds play an important role in recycling organic material. The amoeba-like stage grows as it obtains nutrients from decaying logs and other plant matter.

Even though *Euglena* lacks a cell wall, most biologists include it with algae in this group, because it is mostly photosynthetic (Figure 2.25).

Unicellular protists with a cell wall made of cellulose and two flagella are called **dinoflagellates**. Most but not all are photosynthetic. The dinoflagellates and zooflagellates, as well as amoebas and paramecia, are important parts of plankton in water ecosystems. **Plankton** are communities of mostly microscopic organisms that drift or swim near the surface of ponds, lakes, and oceans. The photosynthetic organisms in plankton are called **phytoplankton**, and they form the base of food chains for most other aquatic organisms.

Fungus-like Protists

Fungus-like protists are heterotrophs that feed mostly on decaying organic matter as fungi do. A **plasmodial slime mould** is a large, branching fungus-like protist that you might see on a decaying log (Figure 2.26). Other fungus-like protists include **cellular slime moulds**, decomposers that live mainly on decaying organic matter, and water moulds. **Water moulds** generally decompose dead plants and matter in freshwater habitats.

Even though this group of protists obtain nutrition like fungi, they have far more in common with unicellular protists. Large and branching as a plasmodial slime mould can be, it is not multicellular like a fungus. Rather, it is a **plasmodium**, a single mass of cytoplasm undivided by membranes or cell walls that contains many nuclei. (Do not confuse this word with the organism *Plasmodium* that causes malaria.) This giant "supercell" behaves somewhat like a large amoeba, extending pseudopodia that engulf bacteria and other bits of organic matter.

Concept Check

1. What process allows some protists to increase their genetic variability?
2. Describe three "lifestyles" that protists have adopted.
3. Name three ways that protists obtain nutrition and describe each.

BIOLOGY•SOURCE

Take It Further

Scientists at the Canadian Barcode of Life Network (BOLNet) are working on classifying all the living things in Canada, including protists. Find out how they are using photosynthetic protists, such as algae, as bioindicators of ecosystem health. Use a graphic organizer to record your findings.

Climate Change and Protists

Climate change has been associated with rising levels of atmospheric and aquatic carbon dioxide. When carbon dioxide dissolves in water, it forms carbonic acid, lowering the pH balance. All organisms have an optimum pH level in which they are able to thrive. Large animals and plants usually have the ability to handle fluctuations in pH. But microscopic phytoplankton, which includes photosynthetic protists, lack this ability. Since these organisms form the base of most aquatic food chains, their disappearance could initiate a cascade of events that lead to the collapse of many ocean food chains.

A8 **Inquiry Activity**   *BIOLOGY·SOURCE*

Sampling Pond Organisms

Question

How do pond organisms reflect ecosystem biodiversity?

Activity Overview

In this activity, you will make a device to sample pond water. You will use the device to collect samples of water from different locations in a pond. You will study the samples with a microscope and classify any organisms you observe. You will compare findings with classmates to determine which location appears to have the greatest biodiversity.

Your teacher will give you a full copy of the activity.

Figure 2.27 At first glance, a pond may appear to have little biodiversity. However, if you look more closely, you may discover that is not the case.

Prelab Questions

Consider the questions below before beginning this activity.

1. Suppose you were very thirsty and came across a pond. The water appears to be clear and you notice no odours. Would this water be safe to drink?

2. Do you think clear or murky water will contain more biodiversity?

3. If you were an organism that requires sunlight to grow, where might you live in a pond?

4. If you were an organism that needs to consume other organisms to obtain energy, where would you want to be in a pond?

A9 **Inquiry Activity**   *BIOLOGY·SOURCE*

Observing Feeding in Protists

Question

How do protists such as *Paramecium* eat?

Activity Overview

In this activity, you will add dyed yeast to *Paramecium* culture and then observe how the paramecia eat the yeast.

Your teacher will give you a full copy of the activity.

Figure 2.28 You will use a toothpick to swirl a speck of yeast paste into a drop of *Paramecium* culture on a slide.

Prelab Questions

Consider the questions below before beginning this activity.

1. A human stomach has two major openings: one where food enters (esophagus) and another where partially digested food exits (small intestine). Describe how food enters and wastes leave paramecia.

2. Many protists are transparent and difficult to spot in water. How can you manipulate a microscope or the environment on the slide to better see these organisms?

Key Concept Review

1. Explain why an amoeba and *Paramecium* are considered "animal-like" protists.

2. Explain the role plankton play in most aquatic habitats.

3. Identify the organism that causes malaria and describe its life cycle.

4. What characteristic do all protists have in common?

Connect Your Understanding

5. What advice about eating would you give to people living near the site of a red tide outbreak? Explain.

6. Contrast three modes of movement among protists.

7. Summarize why protists have traditionally been placed in their own taxonomic kingdom in the six-kingdom system.

8. Why does it no longer seem correct to group all protists in a single kingdom?

9. Describe three examples of structural diversity found in protists.

10. What does the theory of serial endosymbiosis propose about how eukaryotes may have evolved from prokaryotes?

11. Use the photograph below to answer the following questions.
    (a) Explain how the organism in the photograph obtains food.
    (b) Based on this organism's mode of nutrition, what group of protists would you classify it in?

Question 11 (magnification 100×)

12. The graph below indicates the depth that certain wavelengths (colours) of light penetrate water.
    (a) Which colours of light are available for photosynthesis by algae that live at a depth of 10 m? 70 m?
    (b) Some algae grow best when both blue-violet and red light are available for photosynthesis. At what depth range would you expect to find this algae?
    (c) Red algae can grow at depths of 100 m or more. What can you infer about the type of light red algae can use for photosynthesis? Explain.

Penetration of Light in Water

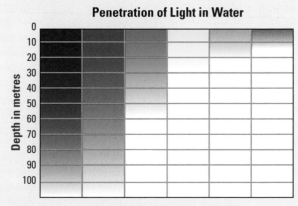

Depth in metres

Wavelengths (colours) of light

Question 12

13. What are the differences between the plasmodium formed by a slime mould and the *Plasmodium* that causes malaria?

14. What characteristics of *Euglena* make it challenging to classify?

Reflection

15. In studying the enormous diversity of structure and function, movement, and reproduction strategies among protists, what did you learn that impressed you the most about this group of organisms?

For more questions, go to **BIOLOGY•SOURCE**

2.3 Fungi

Section Summary

- Fungi are heterotrophic eukaryotes that absorb food and have cell walls made of chitin.
- Fungi provide essential services for ecosystems, such as decomposition, recycling of nutrients, and soil maintenance.
- Fungi have two major structures, hyphae and mycelia.
- All fungi release spores.
- Climate change has an impact on fungi diversity.

Chances are the white button and Portobello mushrooms at your local grocery store were grown in Ontario. Our province is the "mushroom capital" of Canada, producing about 50 percent of the nation's commercial mushrooms.

Figure 2.29 The largest organism in this picture may not be immediately obvious. The mushrooms growing above the ground represent only a small part of the entire fungus.

Fungi — More than Meets the Eye

If you went mushroom hunting in local forests, you might come across a mushroom the size of a beach ball. Ontario's forests have giant puffball mushrooms that grow as large as 70 cm. But even the giant puffball may be small compared to some of its close relatives that you might find known as "fairy rings" (Figure 2.29). Occasionally, some mushrooms grow in a ringlike pattern, getting larger each year. The ring of mushrooms expands outward from a central point as the fungus exhausts the resources in the location. However, as with all fungi, the part you see above ground is only a small part of the entire organism, most of which grows underground. A typical "fairy ring" mushroom like *Marasmius oreades* may be 100 m in diameter, and there are documented cases of mushroom rings growing to a diameter of more than 5.5 km.

Diversity and Importance of Fungi

Seeing fungi growing on wet leaves or a fallen log you might assume they are some type of plant (Figure 2.30 (a)). But evidence shows that fungi are more closely related to animals and even humans than they are to plants. Fungi do not undergo photosynthesis to make their own food as plants do. They are heterotrophic organisms that release powerful enzymes to break down organic matter into nutrients outside their bodies. Then they absorb the nutrients from the environment. As well, almost all fungi need to obtain oxygen from the environment.

Mushrooms, moulds, mildew, yeast, truffles, and rusts like the corn rust shown in the previous chapter are the most common representatives of the fungi kingdom. However, there are more than 100 000 known species of fungi that have a great diversity of size, shape, and colour (Figure 2.30).

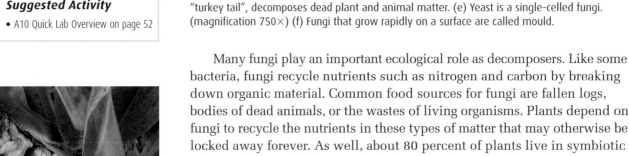

Figure 2.30 (a) *Armillariella mellea,* the "honey mushroom," and (b) *Sparassis crispa,* the "cauliflower mushroom," are parasites that feed on other organisms usually doing some degree of damage. These parasitic fungi use enzymes to break down tissues of their hosts. (c) *Pisolithus arrhizus,* the "dead man's foot" or "dog turd fungus" named for its shape, is an important part of a balanced soil ecosystem. (d) *Trametes versicolor,* the "turkey tail", decomposes dead plant and animal matter. (e) Yeast is a single-celled fungi. (magnification 750×) (f) Fungi that grow rapidly on a surface are called mould.

BIOLOGY•SOURCE

Suggested Activity
- A10 Quick Lab Overview on page 52

Many fungi play an important ecological role as decomposers. Like some bacteria, fungi recycle nutrients such as nitrogen and carbon by breaking down organic material. Common food sources for fungi are fallen logs, bodies of dead animals, or the wastes of living organisms. Plants depend on fungi to recycle the nutrients in these types of matter that may otherwise be locked away forever. As well, about 80 percent of plants live in symbiotic relationships with fungi in which they receive essential nutrients.

Other species of fungi are parasites. They absorb nutrients from the cells or body fluids of living hosts, damaging the host organism. Parasitic fungi cause about 80 percent of all plant diseases, including wheat rust and corn smut (Figure 2.31). Ontario farmers are familiar with several diseases that fungi cause in asparagus, including rot, rust, and blight. You may also be familiar with diseases that fungi cause in humans, such as ringworm and athlete's foot.

Figure 2.31 Corn smut (*Ustilago maydis*) is a parasitic fungus that infects and damages agricultural crops.

Structure and Function of Fungi

Fungi have body structures unlike those of any other eukaryotic organisms. While yeasts are a group of unicellular fungi, most fungi are multicellular. The bodies of most fungi are made of structures called hyphae (singular, *hypha*). **Hyphae** are tiny threads of cytoplasm surrounded by a plasma membrane and covered by a cell wall (Figure 2.32). The cell walls of fungi differ from plants. Most fungi build their cell walls out of chitin. Chitin is a strong, flexible carbohydrate that is also found in the external skeletons of insects.

BIOLOGY•SOURCE

Explore More

How fast can fungal hyphae grow?

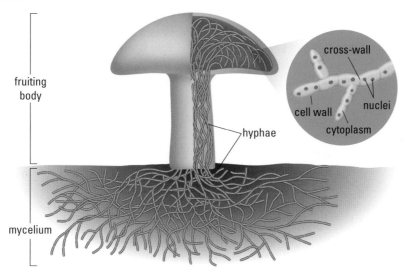
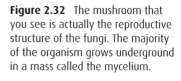

Figure 2.32 The mushroom that you see is actually the reproductive structure of the fungi. The majority of the organism grows underground in a mass called the mycelium.

The hyphae of most fungi have additional cell walls, called cross-walls, that divide the long filaments into many separate end-to-end cells. The cross-walls of many fungi have pores large enough to allow cytoplasm and even organelles, such as nuclei, to flow from cell to cell. The movement of cytoplasm from one cell to another helps a fungus distribute nutrients from one part of its body to another.

The hyphae of a single fungus typically branch as they grow, forming an interwoven mat called a **mycelium** (plural, *mycelia*). In larger mushrooms, the visible part of the fungi that appears above ground is usually the reproductive structure called the **fruiting body** (Figure 2.32). It is an above-ground extension of the mycelium. The mycelium functions as a feeding structure of fungi. Its fibrous structure maximizes contact with the food source. Fungi cannot run, swim, or fly in search of food. But the mycelium makes up for fungi's lack of mobility by its ability to grow rapidly throughout a food source, such as decaying matter in soil. A fungal mycelium can grow as much as a kilometre of hyphae each day as it branches within its food.

Mycorrhizae

Vast networks of fungal mycelia extend throughout many types of soil ecosystems forming **mycorrhizae**. Mycorrhizae are fungus that forms a mutualistic association with plant roots (Figure 2.33). The fungus receives sugars, starches, proteins, and lipids from the plant roots. In return, the fungus acts like an extension of the plant roots, collecting essential nutrients like water and phosphorus. Since the hyphae are only a fraction of the diameter of a plant root, they are able to penetrate into places where plants cannot.

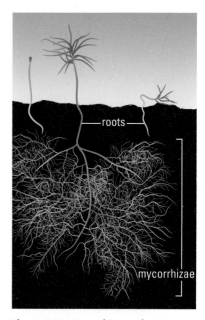

Figure 2.33 Mycorrhizae enhance plants ability to absorb nutrients from the soil by expanding the existing root network.

How Fungi Reproduce

Fungi can reproduce asexually when a piece of the hyphae breaks off or by releasing spores (Figure 2.34). Spores are **haploid** cells that have a single set of chromosomes that contain genetic material. With thick cell walls, spores function as the dispersal stage in the reproduction of fungi. These tough reproductive cells are spread by the wind and can withstand unfavourable conditions for long periods of time. When conditions are favourable spores are capable of germinating and producing hyphae or yeasts.

Most fungi can also reproduce sexually. Fungi exhibit two different sexes termed "+" and "−". Opposite haploid hyphae grow towards each other and fuse to form a **diploid** zygospore that has two sets of chromosomes, one from each "parent" hyphae (Figure 2.35). The zygospore produces haploid spores that are genetically unique. This increases the genetic diversity of the fungi, allowing them to adapt to changing environmental conditions.

In club and sac fungi, such as mushrooms, puffballs, and morels, the joining of two genetically different hyphae produces **dikaryotic** hyphae that contain two nuclei per cell, one from each "parent" hyphae (Figure 2.36). The dikaryotic hyphae grow into a large fruiting body above the ground. Eventually, the dikaryotic nuclei fuse, forming a single diploid nucleus. The diploid nucleus then divides into haploid spores and the cycle repeats.

Figure 2.34 Spore dispersal is critical to the success of fungi. (a) When agitated by a single raindrop or nearby footstep, some species such as this puffball can explode, releasing a cloud containing trillions of spores. (b) This micrograph shows spores of rose rust fungus. (magnification 5600×)

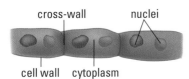

Figure 2.36 Dikaryotic cells that contain two separate nuclei are a unique feature of fungi cells not seen in any other eukaryotic organisms.

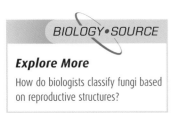

BIOLOGY•SOURCE

Explore More

How do biologists classify fungi based on reproductive structures?

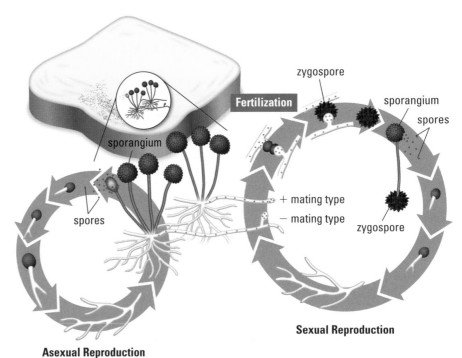

Sexual Reproduction

Asexual Reproduction

Figure 2.35 The black bread mould (*Rhizopus stolonifer*) life cycle is characterized by the presence of a tough zygospore produced during sexual reproduction. Hyphae from two different mating types fuse to form a zygospore. A thick wall develops around the zygospore which allows it to survive long periods of dormancy. When conditions are optimal, the spore germinates and a sporangium appears. During asexual reproduction, spores are produced in the sporangium and released into the environment.

Table 2.2 shows four distinctive reproductive structures that biologists often use to classify fungi into different phyla.

Table 2.2 The Major Phyla of Fungi

Phylum	Reproductive Structure		Examples
Zygomycota (common moulds)	Zygospores that contain sexual spores are able to withstand long periods of either freezing or dry conditions.		*Rhizopus stolonifer* (black bread mould), found on starchy foods like bread, and *Pilobolus* ("hat thrower"), which produces mycelia in horse dung and throws its sporangia 2 m into the air
Basidiomycota (club fungi)	Club-shaped cell called a basidium that contains sexual spores		Mushrooms, club fungi, shelf fungi, puffballs, rusts
Ascomycota (sac fungi)	Sacs called asci that contain sexual spores		Yeasts, truffles, morels
Chytridomycota (chytrids)	Only fungi with flagellated spores		Chytrids

Climate Change and Fungi

As temperatures in North America increase, the range of many organisms is changing. Many plants have begun migrating north, and the southern part of their range is also moving north. The roots of plants are an integral part of soil ecosystems, along with numerous insects, mites, bacteria, and mycorrhizae fungi. Since plant seeds are often spread by wind or animals, plants tend to migrate much faster than the other members of soil ecosystems during climate change. When plants settle in a different location, the soil ecosystem may not match the conditions the plant has evolved to grow in. The symbiotic relationship between the plants and fungi may now be jeopardized and plants may be less likely to be as successful. This is a phenomenon that is under intense study. Air pollution has destroyed 50 percent of the mycorrhizae of western Europe. Ecologists have long wondered what would happen if these fungal webs were removed from soil ecosystems, and it looks like they will soon find out.

Suggested Activity
• A11 Decision-Making Analysis Overview on page 52

BIOLOGY•SOURCE

Take It Further

Many scientists think that global warming associated with climate change is fuelling the spread of chytrid fungi. Find out how chytrid fungi are threatening frogs and other amphibians with extinction. Summarize your findings in a web page or graphic organizer.

Looking at Fungi

Purpose

To observe the diversity of fungi

Activity Overview

In this activity, you will examine different types of fungi and note similarities and differences among them. You will use a microscope to examine and compare the fungi's structures. You will also try to identify the fungi.

Your teacher will give you a full copy of the activity.

Prelab Questions

Consider the questions below before beginning this acitvity.

1. List all the locations where you have seen fungi growing. What similarities do you notice about the locations?

2. What do we use to reduce the growth of unwanted fungi on our food?

Figure 2.37 This photo shows the underside of a button mushroom, a type of club fungi.

REQUIRED SKILLS

- Gathering information
- Stating a conclusion

Climate Change and Fungi Case Study

Issue

Not all fungi mix well with humans. Some species are associated with allergies, diseases, and other human health disorders. As temperatures rise and amounts of precipitation vary in Canada due to climate change, the resulting conditions may favour fungi species that can affect human health.

Activity Overview

In this activity, you will research how climate change affects the diversity of fungi and modifies distribution of species. You will consider the impact of the arrival of the tropical fungus *Cryptococcus gattii* on Vancouver Island. You will also suggest ways this fungus may be controlled.

Your teacher will give you a full copy of the activity.

Prelab Questions

Consider the questions below before beginning this acitvity.

1. List the ways fungi are beneficial. Next, list the ways fungi are harmful.

2. Which of the two lists is longer? Why do you think that is?

3. How do you think the lists might change if you were to research more information about fungi?

Figure 2.38 Climate change has enabled the deadly tropical fungus, *Cryptococcus gattii*, to grow among trees on Vancouver Island, where people, bears, and wolves may come into contact with it.

Key Concept Review

1. What characteristics define fungi?

2. What essential services do fungi provide for ecosystems?

3. How are yeasts different from other fungi?

4. What features of a mycelium make it an efficient structure to obtain food by absorption?

5. What is the purpose of hyphae?

6. State the function of fungal spores.

7. Create a flowchart that describes the reproductive cycle of a typical fungus, such as bread mould.

Connect Your Understanding

8. Create a concept map comparing the reproductive structures and processes of moulds, sac fungi, and club fungi.

9. Suppose you find a fungus growing rapidly on the surface of cheese. How might you classify this organism?

10. Which phyla within the fungi kingdom has a structure most like the endospores of bacteria? Justify your answer.

11. How can you determine the size of the fungus below without digging through the soil? Why do fairy ring mushrooms have this distinctive shape?

Question 11

12. The diagram at the top of the next column shows a cross-section of a fungus.
    (a) What is the name of structure "x"? Describe its function.
    (b) What is the name of structure "y"? Describe its function.

(c) What information would you need to classify this fungus into its correct group?

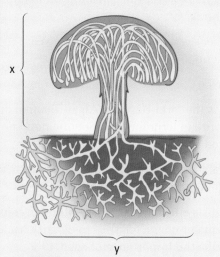

Question 12

13. The picture below shows the results of an experiment performed on pea plants. Plant (a) has been grown in a soil mixture rich with mycorrhizae fungi. Plant (b) has been grown without the benefit of mycorrhizae. Explain why there is a difference in the two plant root systems.

(a) (b)

Question 13

Reflection

14. After reading this chapter, what can you explain about the impact of climate change on fungi that you were not able to explain before?

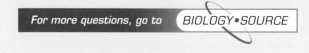

For more questions, go to BIOLOGY•SOURCE

Key Concept Review

1. What structures of a virus help it enter a host cell and take over the cell's reproductive structures? **k**

2. Archaea are a type of prokaryote. What differentiates archaea from bacteria? **k**

3. Describe the process of binary fission. **k**

4. Why is the term Harmful Algal Bloom a more appropriate term for the phenomenon known as a red tide? **k**

5. In a table, compare and contrast the lytic and lysogenic reproductive cycles of viruses. **a**

6. Scientists studying bacteria will often rely on three major characteristics to classify bacteria. Describe the importance of each. **k**

7. What is the taxonomic definition of a protist? **k**

8. On a separate sheet of paper, copy the concept map below and fill in the blank spaces. **k**

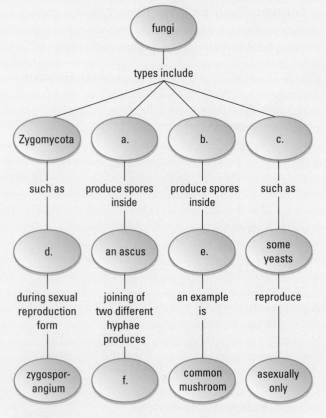

Question 8

9. What is the difference between the terms "hyphae" and "mycelium"? **k**

Connect Your Understanding

10. What feature of the avian flu virus makes containing its spread more difficult than a typical virus like the tobacco mosaic virus? **a**

11. Draw diagrams of specific species of bacteria to illustrate the three main shapes of bacteria. Describe a disease that is associated with each of these three types of bacteria. **a**

12. Why do biologists often classify protists according to "lifestyle"? What problems may be associated with this type of categorization? **a**

13. Suppose you are given a sample of pond water and observe a single-celled organism with the following characteristics: moves through water with the aid of a long whiplike tail; is green in colour; appears to have a number of smaller structures within the cell. Identify the organism. Be as specific as possible and justify your reasoning. **t**

14. Draw a Venn diagram to compare the motility of protists and bacteria. In what ways do they move similarly and differently? **a**

15. Are fungi more closely related to plants or animals? Justify your answer. **a**

16. Protists are described as organisms that do not fit into any of the other kingdoms. Create an analogy to represent this definition. **a**

17. Many bacteria and protists have the ability to switch between sexual and asexual reproduction. Why would this reproductive strategy be successful for these organisms? **a**

18. Describe how conjugation offers a better chance of success for an organism. Use a specific example. **a**

19. Suppose your local environment is undergoing a period of rapid change as temperatures increase and water levels decrease. Describe a bacterial reproductive strategy that would allow the organisms to be successful under these conditions. Which strategy would be the least successful under the conditions? **a**

20. Suppose you are given a bacterial specimen and note the following characteristics: must ingest other organisms to obtain food, moves quickly by whipping around a small tail, has

a very thick cell wall that appears to be within a membrane, is rod-shaped. Use appropriate terminology to describe its motility, shape, cell wall structure, and mode of nutrition. **t**

21. Suppose a person who has been exposed to a virus has blisters on her arm that appear at least once a year and seem to be associated with some type of environmental trigger. Does this virus exhibit a lytic or lysogenic reproductive life cycle? Explain your answer. **a**

22. Suppose you overhear someone say that bacteria are disgusting, dirty organisms that serve no purpose. Critique this statement and provide facts to support your answer. **t**

23. In which of the four fungi phyla does the fungus shown at the right belong? Justify your answer. How can you verify that your answer is correct? **a**

Question 23

24. Identify and classify each of the organisms shown below. Indicate what features allowed you to classify it to the appropriate kingdom. **a**

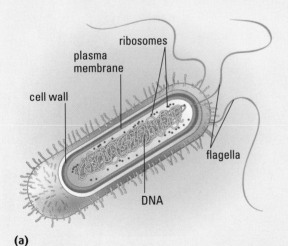

(a)

Question 24

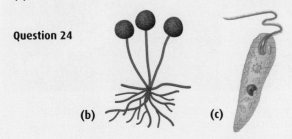

(b)   **(c)**

25. The graphs below show the growth pattern of two plant species. For each species, two plants have been observed: one grown with mycorrhizae and the other without. What pattern do you observe? Write a statement to describe how this fungi affects plant growth. **t**

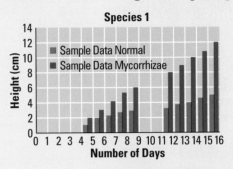

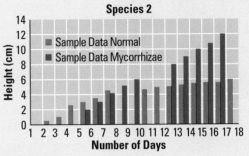

Question 25

26. How might an organism such as bacteria have evolved into the complex structures seen in fungi, plants, and animals? Reference two hypotheses in your answer. **a**

Reflection

27. In this chapter, you learned about viruses, bacteria, protists, and fungi. What is one thing you learned about each that you would like to learn more about? **c**

Unit Task Link

Micro-organisms often form symbiotic partnerships with larger organisms in which one or both organisms benefit. How will the organism you design interact with micro-organisms? Start considering this by making a list of symbiotic partnerships between micro-organisms and plants and animals. Include how the micro-organisms may aid the plants' and animals' growth, reproduction, and survival.

For more questions, go to

Biodiversity evolves over time and is affected by changing conditions on Earth.

Borneo, an Indonesian island in the Pacific Ocean, is home to the world's largest moth, largest carnivorous plant, and largest tree-dwelling animal, the orangutan (Figure 3.1). Borneo's rainforests are some of the most biologically diverse ecosystems on Earth, where flying lizards, flying frogs, and flying snakes glide through tree canopies, and sun bears, clouded leopards, and one of the last populations of wild pygmy elephants creep through underbrush. However, oil palm plantations are displacing Borneo's rainforests and destroying their natural biodiversity.

Palm oil harvested from oil palm plants is a major ingredient of many foods and products, such as bread, margarine, cookies, crackers, lipstick, toothpaste, and soap. Most generic vegetable oils are palm oil, and palm oil is also used to make biodiesel, an alternative fuel source. To meet the demand for palm oil, millions of hectares have been cleared in Indonesia and other parts of the world to plant oil palm plants. Since 1985, the spread of oil palm plantations has wiped out about a third of Borneo's forests, critically endangering orangutans and other animals due to habitat loss (Figure 3.1). The slash and burn techniques used to clear the forests for plantations have also released large amounts of carbon dioxide from peat swamp forests on the island, contributing to climate change. In addition, infectious diseases carried by animals have begun emerging as animals that were previously isolated in the rainforest are now coming into closer contact with humans.

Figure 3.1 (a) The rainforests on Borneo are a last refuge for many species, including the critically endangered orangutan. (b) But deforestation for oil palm plantations threatens to destroy this area rich in biodiversity.

©P

Section Summary

- Plants are eukaryotic, usually photosynthetic, mostly land-dwelling organisms with cell walls made of cellulose.

- Water conservation is a key adaptation that enabled plants to transition from aquatic to terrestrial ecosystems.

- Gymnosperms and angiosperms have adaptations, including seeds, that allow them to thrive in terrestrial habitats.

- Recent DNA evidence has caused green algae to be reclassified as the simplest plant type.

- Climate change has an impact on plant diversity.

The grass in parks, moss that looks like fuzz on rocks, mistletoe, carnivorous pitcher plants that trap flies, climbing vines, and trees that tower high above the ground are all members of the plant kingdom. Except for the most extreme habitats, such as the bottom of deep oceans and the planet's poles, you can find plants everywhere on Earth. Plants grow in soil, grow on other plants, float freely in oceans, and even take root deep below the ocean surface.

The Foundation of Ecosystems

Plants form the foundation of almost all ecosystems and provide essential products and services that sustain life on Earth. Plants are the base of almost all food chains, converting sunlight into chemical energy that other organisms can ingest and use. They provide food, fuel, fibre, and the basis for medicines, such as aspirin, quinine, and morphine. Plants also release oxygen, cycle nutrients, and regulate ecosystem processes to clean air, purify water, absorb carbon, and detoxify soil. Some plants even help clean up pollution that seeps into the environment. The Indian mustard plant, for example, can bind lead, chromium, cadmium, nickel, zinc, copper, and selenium and is used to help clean up major pollution leaks.

What Are Plants?

You might say that you know one when you see one. But plants include an enormous range of very diverse organisms, from tiny algae to mosses to ferns to wildflowers to pine trees. What do they have in common? Plants are mostly land-dwelling organisms that require optimal temperatures and amounts of water, minerals, nutrients, soil, sunlight, and atmospheric gases, such as carbon dioxide and oxygen (Figure 3.2). While a few plants are parasites that obtain nutrition from other organisms, most are autotrophs. In general, plants share three key characteristics:
- Plants are eukaryotic.
- Plants have cell walls that contain the carbohydrate cellulose.
- Plants carry out photosynthesis, using the pigment chlorophyll to transform sunlight into chemical energy.

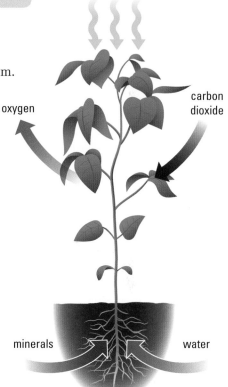

sunlight

oxygen

carbon dioxide

minerals

water

Figure 3.2 A plant lives in two environments: air and soil. It absorbs sunlight, carbon dioxide, and water for photosynthesis. Soil or another medium provides a place for it to root and to obtain the nutrients and minerals necessary for growth.

BIOLOGY•SOURCE

Explore More

What challenges did plants have to overcome to move from aquatic habitats to land?

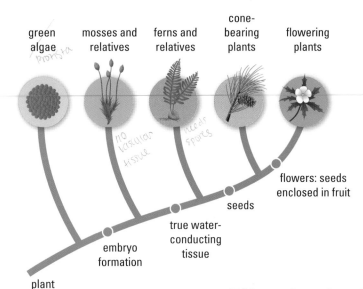

green algae *Protista*

mosses and relatives — *no vascular tissue*

ferns and relatives — *needs spores*

cone-bearing plants

flowering plants

flowers: seeds enclosed in fruit

seeds

true water-conducting tissue

embryo formation

plant ancestor

Figure 3.3 Fossil and biochemical evidence indicate that green algae are the oldest group of plants and flowering plants the youngest.

Evolution of Plants

Evidence shows that ancestors of modern-day plants were aquatic organisms similar to green algae (Figure 3.3). To grow successfully on land, plants developed several adaptations, including:

- the formation of an **embryo**, a reproductive structure that develops into a plant
- the ability to stand upright and grow tall to get as much sunlight as possible
- tissues to transport nutrients, waste, and water
- strategies to reduce water loss
- strategies to disperse reproductive structures without water currents

Table 3.1 shows how the evolutionary history of plants reflects their transition from life in aquatic environments to life on land, where water conservation is very important.

Table 3.1 Major Periods of Plant Evolution

475 Million Years Ago	425 Million Years Ago	365 Million Years Ago	135 Million Years Ago
Primitive plants lacking leaves, stems, seeds, or any rigid tissue evolve from algal ancestors and begin to colonize areas where water and land meet.	Plants begin to develop **lignin**, a chemical that hardens cell walls, allowing them to stand upright, and **vascular tissues** to transport water and nutrients. This allows plants to move farther away from water bodies.	The development of **seeds**, plant embryos encased in a protective covering along with a food supply, helps plants spread to diverse terrestrial habitats by allowing plant embryos to be dispersed without drying out.	The final major period of plant evolution begins with the appearance of flowering plants. **Flowers** are a reproductive structure that attracts animals to help spread plants' seeds farther afield.
Mosses represent these plants today	Ferns represent these plants today	Seed plants (gymnosperms) represent these plants today	Flowering plants (angiosperms) represent these plants today

Alternation of Generations

Most plants have a life cycle that alternates between diploid and haploid forms (Figure 3.4). Recall that diploids have two sets of chromosomes, one from each parent, and haploids have just one set. In the life cycles of plants, the haploid and diploid forms are distinct, multicellular generations. In some plants, the haploid individual is actually larger than the diploid one. The haploid generation produces egg and sperm cells called gametes and is called the **gametophyte**. The diploid generation produces spores and is called the **sporophyte**. (The suffix –*phtye* comes from the Greek word for "plant.") In a plant's life cycle, each of these generations "takes turns" giving rise to the other. The alternation between the haploid and diploid forms is called **alternation of generations**.

In contrast, the haploid stage in mammals, including humans, is either a single sperm or egg cell. When these gametes fuse, they produce a diploid **zygote**, which eventually develops into a distinct individual.

Plants typically reproduce through gametes and spores. As reproductive cells, spores differ from gametes in two ways. First, a spore can develop into a new organism without fusing with another cell. In contrast, two gametes must fuse to form a zygote. Second, spores of some plants have tough coats that enable them to resist harsh environments. Gametes are not adapted to resist harsh conditions.

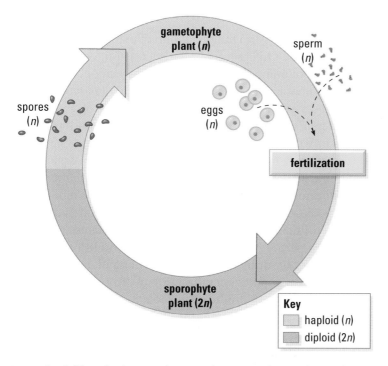

Figure 3.4 A plant's life cycle alternates between the gametophyte and sporophyte generations.

Concept Check

1. What key characteristics do plants share?
2. Describe four adaptations plants developed that allowed them to grow on land.
3. A plant life cycle shows alternation of generations. What does this look like?
4. List the differences between the sporophyte and gametophyte plant generations.

Major Groups of Plants

As Figure 3.5 shows, five major groups of plants exist today:

- green algae
- mosses and relatives
- ferns and relatives
- seed plants
- flowering plants

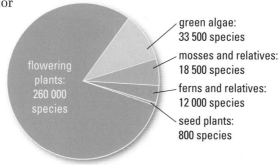

Figure 3.5 Flowering plants are the largest group of the five main groups of plants that exist today.

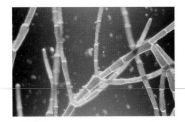

Figure 3.6 This branching green alga is one of the closest relatives of plant ancestors.

Figure 3.7 This mat of moss consists of many gametophyte plants growing in a tight pack, holding one another up. The stalks are the sporophytes. The mat has a spongy quality that enables it to absorb and retain water. Flagellated moss sperm swim to the eggs through a film of water on the surface of the mat.

Figure 3.8 Ferns have vascular tissue to transport water and dissolved nutrients from the ground to leaves and shoots.

Figure 3.9 Each brown "dot" on the underside of this fern leaf is made up of many capsules that each contain large numbers of spores.

Green Algae — Modern Relatives of Plant Ancestors

Many species of green algae, the closest living relatives of plant ancestors, are found in shallow fresh water around the edges of ponds and lakes (Figure 3.6). At first, biologists classified green algae in the kingdom Protista along with other algae. However, since recent evidence revealed that green algae have cell walls and photosynthetic pigments identical to plants, biologists have reclassified green algae in the kingdom of plants. Unlike most plants though, green algae do not undergo alternation of generations.

Mosses and Relatives — Seedless Non-vascular Plants

Mosses and their relatives were the first group of plants to diversify from the aquatic algal ancestors. This group of plants, called the **bryophytes**, grow close to the ground in damp locations where they can obtain water easily. The bryophytes do not have seeds or stems. Nor do they have any rigid support structures, such as lignin-reinforced cell walls or vascular tissues that allow most modern terrestrial plants to stand tall and transport water great distances upward against the force of gravity to leaves and shoots. So mosses cannot grow tall and are sometimes called **non-vascular plants**.

However, this lack of complexity does not impede their success. Mosses and other non-vascular plants, such as hornworts and liverworts, comprise nearly 10 percent of all plant species. In certain habitats, they are more successful than modern terrestrial plants, because they can withstand long dry periods and harsh tundra-like conditions.

Mosses and other bryophytes are unique among plants in having the gametophyte as the dominant generation (Figure 3.7). Male and female gametes (sperm and eggs) are produced in separate reproductive structures. Sperm are flagellated and must swim through water to the eggs.

Ferns and Relatives — Seedless Vascular Plants

Imagine a huge population of plants growing close to the ground, competing for any open space where they can capture sunlight for photosynthesis. In such a crowded habitat, any plant able to grow higher than its neighbours would be able to capture more sunlight and be more successful. **Vascularization,** the formation of tubes to carry fluid throughout an organism, was the next step in plants' invasion of land, allowing plants to reach greater heights by connecting above-ground shoots and underground roots (Figure 3.8).

Today, biologists divide seedless vascular plants into three phyla: ferns, club mosses, and horsetails. Seedless vascular plants reproduce much like mosses. On the underside of the gametophyte are sperm- and egg-producing structures. Sperm are flagellated and must swim through a film of water to fertilize eggs. In contrast to mosses, the sporophyte is the dominant fern generation. Perhaps you have seen what look like brown "dots" on the

underside of mature fern fronds, or leaves (Figure 3.9). In fact, each "dot" is made up of many spore capsules — small spore-filled containers. Each capsule releases a large number of tiny haploid spores that drift down to the ground and grow into tiny gametophytes on or just below the soil surface.

Seed Plants — Gymnosperms

Gymnosperms are plants that bear "naked" seeds — seeds that are not protected and enclosed in an ovary. The most common gymnosperms are conifers, such as pine, fir, spruce, redwood, and cedar trees. These vascular plants with seeds represent the next step in plant evolution. Seeds are plant embryos packaged in a protective coat along with a food supply. In addition to seeds, gymnosperms have two other adaptations that make survival in diverse land habitats possible: smaller gametophytes than ferns, and pollen.

In gymnosperms, the diploid sporophyte generation is much more highly developed and obvious than the haploid gametophyte generation. A pine tree, for example, is actually a sporophyte on which the smaller gametophytes live in cones (Figure 3.10). This contrasts with ferns, where the small gametophytes live on their own, without the protection of the larger sporophyte.

A second adaptation of seed plants to dry land was the evolution of pollen. **Pollen grains** are small male gametophytes that contain cells that develop into sperm. In the case of conifers, wind carries pollen from male to female cones, where eggs develop within the female gametophyte. The evolution of pollen allowed sperm to reach eggs by travelling through a dry environment rather than swimming through water.

Figure 3.10 (a) A pine tree's cones contain its gametophytes. (b) The inset photo shows male pollen cones at the left and female seed cones at the right.

Flowering Plants — Angiosperms

Angiosperms, or flowering plants, were the last major group of plants to evolve. The rise of angiosperms coincides with the rise of mammals in the animal kingdom. Both have structures that prevent water loss and improve their ability to reproduce on land. In angiosperms, the reproductive structures are flowers. The word *angiosperm* means "enclosed seed." In fact, ovaries within flowers completely enclose and protect the seeds of flowering plants. The gametophytes of angiosperms develop within the flowers of the sporophyte.

Flowers are the most effective reproductive and seed dispersal structures found in the plant kingdom. Flowers have many adaptations that attract insects or other animals to transfer pollen directly from one flower to another flower. The great variety of flower size, shape, odour, texture, and colour reflects the diversity of interactions that angiosperms have with animal pollinators. Angiosperms that are wind-pollinated, such as grasses, also have flowers, but their flowers are typically smaller and simpler than those of angiosperms pollinated by animals.

Once pollination occurs, the ovary often develops into a fruit. A **fruit** is the ripened ovary of a flower (Figure 3.11). Fruits provide a very effective means of dispersing seeds. Some fruits attract animals, and the animals ingest them. However, the seeds usually remain undigested and pass through the animals unharmed, landing in new locations. Other fruits, such as burrs, stick to animals. Still others, such as maple keys, are adapted for wind dispersal, and others, such as coconuts, for water dispersal.

Figure 3.11 (a) Some flowers attract animal pollinators like this hummingbird. (b) Other flowers develop into fruit like this blackberry that attract animals that eat the fruit and disperse the seeds as the seeds pass through them.

Concept Check

1. What are the major groups (or phyla) of plants?
2. What advantage does vascularization provide to plants?
3. What advantage does the seed provide?
4. What is the most effective reproductive and seed-dispersal structure in the plant kingdom?

Climate Change and Plants

As plants transpire, they give off water vapour. This process, known as **transpiration**, moves an enormous amount of water from the ground to the atmosphere (Figure 3.12). In fact, rainforests get their name from all the water vapour in the air around them. Much of this water vapour becomes precipitation. Thus, changes in plant growth and destruction of rainforests can alter precipitation and weather patterns. For example, as landowners clear large areas of the Amazon rainforest in Brazil, agricultural land near the rainforest will receive less precipitation and farmers will have to look for artificial methods of irrigation. In addition, microclimates in areas that receive shade or surface cooling from the rainforest may change, affecting the diversity of local species. In many cases, when impacts from human activities like this cease, ecosystems may repair themselves and return to normal. However, extensive deforestation can reduce rainfall so much that rainforests may not be able to re-establish themselves.

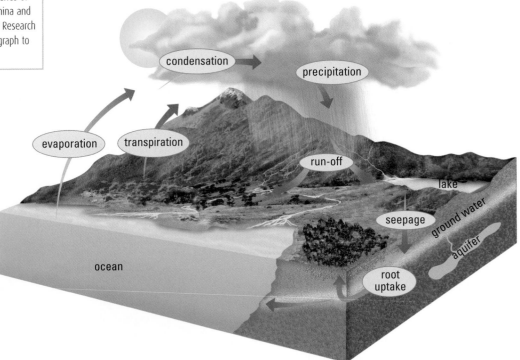

Figure 3.12 Trees are an important part of the water cycle as they transport water from the soil into the atmosphere through a process known as transpiration.

Looking at Plants

Purpose

To explore the diversity and features of plants

Activity Overview

In this activity, you will examine several different types of plants. You will look for distinct features of each and the presence of seeds. You will also identify reproductive structures of the plants and draw scientific diagrams of the plants to record your observations.

   Your teacher will give you a copy of the full activity.

Figure 3.13 Boston fern

Prelab Questions

Consider the questions below before beginning the activity.

1. What characteristics do you predict that you will observe in each plant?

2. What are two reproductive structures of plants that you will look for?

Figure 3.14 Daffodil

REQUIRED SKILLS
- Designing an experimental procedure
- Analyzing patterns

Climate Change and Plants

Question

How can climate change affect plants?

Figure 3.15 Like all plants, these mustard plants require optimal temperatures and amounts of water, nutrients, sunlight, and atmospheric gases to grow.

Activity Overview

In this activity, you will conduct your own investigation. You will write a hypothesis and identify all of the variables and how to control the appropriate variables. You will then carry out your investigation, analyze your results, and conclude whether your results support your hypothesis.

   Your teacher will give you a copy of the full activity.

Prelab Questions

Consider the questions below before beginning the activity.

1. A symbiotic relationship is a close interaction between species in which one species lives on or in the other. Describe three symbiotic relationships that involve a plant and an organism from another kingdom.

2. With a partner, brainstorm a list of environmental variables that are affected by climate change.

3. What are ideal characteristics for a live specimen that is the subject of experimentation?

Key Concept Review

1. What differentiates a plant from the species of other kingdoms?

2. What group of algae is most closely related to plants?

3. Why must a bryophyte have open water to be successful?

4. List the five main groups of plants and describe two characteristics of each.

5. What is the function of the vascular tissue in plants?

6. What resources are necessary for a plant to grow?

7. Why are plants considered the foundation of most ecosystems?

Connect Your Understanding

8. Why are green algae but not brown algae considered part of the plant kingdom?

9. Which group of plants appears to be the most successful? Justify your answer.

10. Most plants have roots, but mosses do not. Name and describe the function of the underground growth in mosses.

11. Why can ferns grow several metres tall but mosses cannot?

12. List two key adaptations that distinguish angiosperms from earlier plants.

13. Alternation of generations is a key characteristic common to most plants. Which group of plants does not exhibit this life cycle?

14. Describe the process of alternation of generations. Use a specific type of plant in your description and be sure to identify which parts of the life cycle are haploid and which are diploid.

15. Describe the trend in gametophyte size as plants become more removed from water.

16. Suppose you were given a plant that is haploid, small, and has flagellated sperm. What type of plant would it be? Explain how you came to this conclusion.

17. Why is the gymnosperm seed a less successful reproductive strategy than the angiosperm seed?

18. Why is the dispersal of the seed a key factor in the success of angiosperms?

19. Evolutionary trends show that plants have moved from aquatic to terrestrial environments. However, a number of angiosperms, such as the water lily or duckweed, have adapted to aquatic ecosystems. Why would it not be appropriate to reclassify these plants as bryophytes, considering that they no longer live on land?

20. Suppose a bacterium that targets the production of lignin tissue were to infect all plants. How might this affect the evolution of future plants?

21. Suppose your little sister picks up some green fluff from the playground, notes that it is living, and says it is a plant. Would she be correct? What further analysis might you need to do to determine if it is a plant?

22. Researchers have used mosses to study biological damage that might be caused by radiation leaks from nuclear power plants. (Recall that radiation damages organisms by causing mutations.) Suggest why the researchers might be able to observe the genetic effects of radiation in mosses more quickly than in other plants.

23. Describe how deforestation can contribute to climate change.

Reflection

24. In reading about the adaptations of plants that allowed them to move from water to land, what did you learn that impressed you the most about plants?

For more questions, go to *BIOLOGY•SOURCE*

3.2 Exploring Animal Diversity

Section Summary

- Animals are multicellular, heterotrophic, eukaryotic organisms with cells that lack cell walls.

- Each animal has a unique body plan that reflects its evolutionary history.

- Animals are often classified as invertebrates or vertebrates.

- Chordates are the group of animals most closely related to humans.

Coral reefs are home to more than 25 percent of the world's marine species, including parrotfish, grouper, sponges, starfish, worms, shrimp, crabs, lobsters, and sea turtles (Figure 3.16). Tiny coral animals, called polyps, create these elaborate reef structures underwater by secreting limestone.

Figure 3.16 As one of the most complex ecosystems on the planet, coral reefs are home to more than 250 000 known species.

Coral Reefs — Biodiversity Hot Spots

Coral polyps receive most of their nutrients through symbiotic partnerships with photosynthetic protists, such as dinoflagellates. Since sunlight is necessary for the protists to photosynthesize, coral reefs normally grow only as deep as sunlight penetrates. Today, mining, overfishing, pollution, and other human activities that result in the rising levels of carbon dioxide that cause climate change pose the greatest threat to coral reefs. Slight temperature fluctuations, for example, can stress coral polyps, causing them to expel the protists they rely on for nutrients. Since coral polyps derive their colour from the protists, stressed coral polyps appear bleached — a clear sign that a coral reef is in trouble (Figure 3.17). Without the protists, coral polyps can slowly starve to death. Also, as carbon dioxide dissolves in water, it forms carbonic acid, lowering the pH balance. Recall that all organisms have an optimum pH level in which they thrive. The acidification of seawater interferes with the formation of coral polyps and also leads to bleaching. Even though bleached coral can recover, the impact of climate change combined with the impacts of other human activities makes it unlikely to happen any time soon. If coral reefs disappear, many species will be left without a home, and those that cannot find or adapt to a new habitat will die.

Figure 3.17 Climate change caused by rising levels of carbon dioxide can bleach coral like this and threaten the reef ecosystem.

What Are Animals?

You know an animal when you see one — or do you? Can you explain why the sea anemone and the coral shown on the previous page are considered animals (Figure 3.18)?

More than a million living species of animals are organized into about 35 major groups (phyla). (Different biologists have different views on the exact number of animal phyla.) But as diverse as they are, animals share six key characteristics that taken together separate them from other organisms:

- Animals are eukaryotic.
- Animal cells lack cell walls.
- Animals are multicellular.
- Animals are heterotrophs that ingest food.
- Animals are motile at some point in their life cycle.
- Animals form a hollow ball of cells, called a **blastula**, during embryological development.

Figure 3.18 Though it may look like a plant, this sea anemone is classified as an animal because it has all six key characteristics listed at the right.

Evolution of Animals

Animals and plants have similar evolutionary histories that trace the movement of an ancestral organism from the water onto land. However, we will not cover all 35 animal phyla. We will focus on animal phyla that exhibit important evolutionary steps that include changes to the body plan.

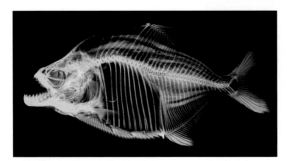

Figure 3.19 This stained skeleton of a piranha reveals the backbone in its body plan. It also shows the presence of a head and placement of fins.

Body Plans

Each species has a unique body structure that is often called a **body plan**. A body plan is like a blueprint of a building. It includes structural details and features, such as type of symmetry, presence of a body cavity, embryological development, segmentation, presence of a head, placement and number of limbs, mobility, and presence of a backbone (Figure 3.19).

Levels of Organization

Cells are one of the simplest levels of organization in animals. In many animals, cells become specialized and organized into tissues. **Tissues** are groups of cells that perform a particular function. Animals often have muscle, nervous, and connective tissues. Groups of tissues can form organs, and organs can work together in systems to carry out specific functions. Some animals have a digestive system to process food.

BIOLOGY•SOURCE

Explore More

Can the symmetry found in animals change throughout their lives?

Body Symmetry

Symmetry can give you insight into an animal's movement, evolution, and interaction with prey and predators. Some animals, such as sponges, have no symmetry at all and are called **asymmetrical**. Most animals shaped like a cylinder or bowl have **radial symmetry**, in which their body parts are arranged like pieces of a pie around an imaginary central axis (Figure 3.20(a)). Any imaginary slice passing longitudinally through this central axis divides the organism into identical pieces. Animals with radial symmetry lack a head and have no real front or back. Thus, they are able to interact with the environment from any direction. This is especially effective for sessile animals that are anchored in place and cannot move to obtain food.

©P

An animal with **bilateral symmetry** has mirror-image right and left sides (Figure 3.20(b)). Bilateral symmetry is the most common form of symmetry in the animal kingdom. A bilaterally symmetrical animal has a distinct head (anterior end), and tail (posterior end). It also has a back (dorsal) surface, a bottom (ventral) surface, and two side (lateral) surfaces.

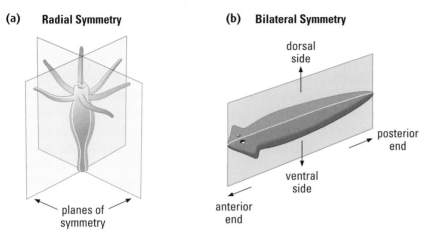

(a)   Radial Symmetry

planes of symmetry

(b)   Bilateral Symmetry

dorsal side

posterior end

ventral side

anterior end

Figure 3.20 Symmetry is part of an animal's body plan that determines how the animal interacts with the environment. (a) Radial symmetry enables the hydra and other cnidarians to interact with the environment from all sides. (b) Bilateral symmetry helps flatworms, sea-dwelling relatives of earthworms, move in a particular direction in the environment.

Bilaterally symmetrical animals are well-adapted for movement. Whether they wiggle, slither, hop, walk, or fly, their bodies are usually streamlined to move quickly. In most bilateral animals, eyes and other sense organs are located up front, on a head. This allows the animals to detect prey and predators in the direction that the animals are moving. The development of a distinct head with sense organs is known as **cephalization**.

Embryological Development

All animals begin life as a zygote that forms when a sperm fertilizes an egg. The zygote splits into two cells, then four, and so on. Eventually, a hollow ball of cells, known as a blastula, forms and an infolding of cells occurs at a particular spot in the ball. The infolding eventually pushes all the way through the hollow ball, forming a tube that connects both ends. This tube develops into a digestive tract.

Depending on the type of animal, the first opening in the digestive tract may become a mouth or an anus. This opening is called a **blastopore** (Figure 3.21). If the blastopore develops into a mouth, the animal is a **protostome** (protos = "first," stoma = "mouth"). If it develops into an anus, the animal is a **deuterostome**. Biologists use this sequence of development to determine how closely species of animals are related.

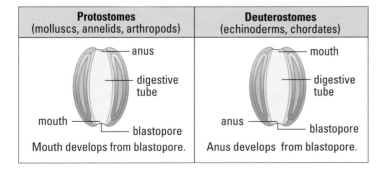

Protostomes
(molluscs, annelids, arthropods)

anus

digestive tube

mouth

blastopore

Mouth develops from blastopore.

Deuterostomes
(echinoderms, chordates)

mouth

digestive tube

anus

blastopore

Anus develops from blastopore.

Figure 3.21 This diagram depicts the differences in early embryonic development between protostomes, such as molluscs and annelids, and deuterostomes, such as echinoderms and chordates (the phylum that includes humans).

Figure 3.22 Segmentation of body parts is especially noticeable in segmented worms.

Segmentation: Repeating Parts

Many bilaterally symmetrical animals have numerous repeating parts called **segments** in their bodies. Earthworms and other segmented worms known as annelids have segments that are all very similar except for a distinct head and tail as shown in Figure 3.22. In fact, the name *annelid* means "little rings." Different segments like the head, thorax, and abdomen of insects can also become specialized for specific functions.

Limbs: Legs, Flippers, and Wings

Animals with bilateral symmetry and cephalization also tend to have **paired limbs**, external appendages that extend from their bodies. They may use the limbs for movement, defence, or gathering sensory information. Animal phyla can be characterized by the types of appendages they have: antennae, mouthparts, wings, gills, legs, fins, arms, and certain parts of a tail.

Phylogenetic Tree of Animals

The features of animal body plans help biologists sort animals into phyla and build a phylogenetic tree of animals (Figure 3.23). Due to the relatively short period of time during which animals diversified, it is difficult from the fossil record to sort out the sequence of branching in the evolutionary history of animals. So how can biologists test hypotheses about evolutionary relationships among animal phyla? They use data from comparative anatomy, embryology, genetics, and molecular studies of living species to search for clues about common ancestry.

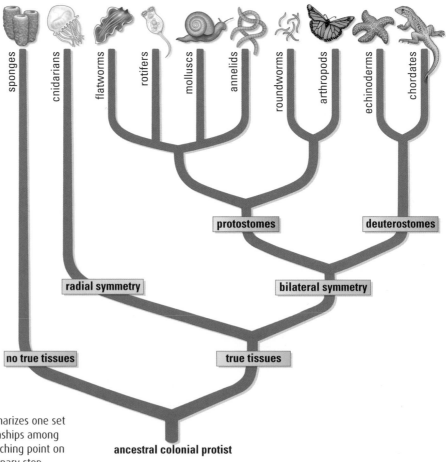

Figure 3.23 This phylogenetic tree summarizes one set of hypotheses about evolutionary relationships among several of the 35 animal phyla. Each branching point on the tree represents an important evolutionary step.

©P

The phylogenetic tree in Figure 3.23 is based upon the best available data from these sources. It represents one hypothetical view of the evolutionary history of the animal kingdom. At the bottom of the tree is the hypothetical colonial protist that may have given rise to the earliest animals. The tree has a series of branching points. The first branching splits the sponges, which lack true tissues, from all other animals, which do have tissues. Among the "tissue animals," the next branching divides the radial animals, such as cnidarians, from animals with bilateral symmetry. The bilateral animals are then split into protostomes and deuterostomes. Like other phylogenetic trees, this tree serves as a hypothesis to stimulate further research and discussion. The hypothetical tree of animal origins will undoubtedly be revised to be compatible with new information as research continues.

BIOLOGY·SOURCE

Suggested Activities
- A14 Quick Lab Overview on page 74
- A15 Inquiry Activity Overview on page 74

Concept Check

1. What characteristics do all animals have?
2. List several evolutionary steps biologists use to place different types of animals on the phylogenetic tree.
3. What types of symmetry are found in animals?

Major Groups of Animals

One common way to group animals is based on whether they have a backbone. Animals with a backbone are called **vertebrates** and those without, **invertebrates**. Even though invertebrates comprise more than 98 percent of all animals, you are probably more familiar with vertebrates (Figure 3.24). The vertebrate group of animals includes: most pets, such as cats, dogs, reptiles, birds, and fish; all beasts of burden, such as horses, donkeys, and mules; and livestock, such as cows, pigs, and sheep. Since invertebrates are a group based on a lack of a trait, they are not an evolutionary branch on the tree of animals in Figure 3.23. Table 3.2 on the next page shows body systems of invertebrates.

Figure 3.24 If you examined a tide pool, you would find yourself in a world of invertebrates. Most invertebrate animals, such as the sea anemones, sea stars, and sea urchins visible here, live in aquatic or moist habitats.

Table 3.2 Invertebrate Body Systems

Phylum (with examples)	Body Support/Movement	Nervous Control	Reproduction
Porifera: Sponges	Cells called amoebocytes produce a protein called spongin or mineral-based, needle-like structures for support. Adults are sessile, or anchored in place.	None	Asexual: budding Sexual: male and female structures are present in same individual; zygotes develop into flagellated larvae
Cnidaria: Jellyfish, hydras, and anemones	Fluid in a gastrovascular cavity (digestive sac) gives the body shape. Microfilaments within cells are arranged into fibres that contract.	Nerve net	Asexual: budding Sexual: male and female structures are present in same individual
Platyhelminthes: Flatworms	True muscle tissue — muscles run along the length of the animal (longitudinally).	Primitive brainlike ganglia (nerve clusters) and ventral nerve cords	Asexual: fragmentation and regeneration Sexual: male and female structures are present in same individual
Nematoda: Roundworms	Exoskeleton — called the cuticle — has to be shed as animal grows. Muscles are all longitudinal, causing thrashing movements.	Central brainlike ganglion with nerve cords extending to the front and rear	Sexual: most species have separate males and females; internal fertilization in most species
Annelida: Segmented worms	Fluid-filled compartments provide support; two sets of muscles — circular and longitudinal	Two ventral nerve cords connect to ganglia in each segment; pair of cerebral ganglia in the head	Sexual: male and female structures are present in same individual (except in polychaetes); internal fertilization (external in polychaetes)
Mollusca: Snails, clams, squids	Mantle produces a shell in most species; muscular foot	Nerve ring around the esophagus with attached nerve cords	
Arthropoda: Insects, crustaceans, spiders	Exoskeleton of protein and chitin; muscles attached to knobs on interior of exoskeleton	Ventral nerve cord with several ganglia. In the head region, the two cords meet and fuse into a larger ganglion (brain).	Sexual: separate males and females; internal fertilization
Echinodermata: Sea stars, sea urchins, sea cucumbers	Endoskeleton of hard plates; water vascular system	Nerve ring plus nerve cords along each arm	Sexual: separate males and females; gametes are released externally in water

Digestion	Circulation	Excretion	Gas Exchange
Digestion, circulation, excretion, and gas exchange are accomplished by multi-purpose amoebocytes. Amoebocytes ingest food particles, and digest and transport the nutrients throughout the sponge. Gas exchange also occurs at the cellular level, primarily by diffusion.			
Digestion takes place in a gastrovascular cavity (digestive sac), which has a single opening that is both mouth and anus. The nutrients are distributed to cells that line the cavity. In flatworms, the gastrovascular cavity is finely branched, helping the distribution of nutrients throughout the body.		Expulsion from gastrovascular cavity; simple diffusion of wastes from cells into surrounding water	No specialized structures. Diffusion across cell membranes helped by circulation in the gastrovascular cavity.
		Most wastes diffuse from cells into the surrounding water. Ciliated cells move fluid containing wastes through branched ducts opening to the outside.	
Complete digestive tract (tube) with opening at both ends — mouth and anus; digestive tract has specialized regions for digestion, the stomach and intestine.	No specialized circulatory system. Nutrients are transported by fluid in the body cavity	A ventral gland or a tubular system is connected to an excretory pore; mostly used for maintaining water balance	Diffusion across cell membranes
	Closed circulatory system; dorsal and ventral vessels connected by two vessels per segment; blood with oxygen-carrying hemoglobin; accessory hearts	Tubular structures called metanephridia in each segment remove wastes from blood.	The moist skin serves as the organ for gas exchange; oxygen absorbed across the skin is transported by the circulatory system.
	Open circulatory system in most species; dorsal heart circulates fluid to body cavities	Specialized structures called nephridia remove wastes from blood.	Mantle cavity with gills in aquatic species; mantle cavity can serve as a lung for terrestrial species.
	Open circulatory system with a dorsal heart; bloodlike fluid transports materials	In insects and arachnids, Malpighian tubules remove wastes from the bloodlike fluid.	Feathery gills in aquatic species; tracheal tubes inside the body in terrestrial species; book lungs in spiders
Short digestive tract with mouth and anus	Fluid in the body cavity transports nutrients through the body.	No specialized excretory system; wastes are removed by diffusion from the fluid in the body cavity and the water vascular system.	Water vascular system

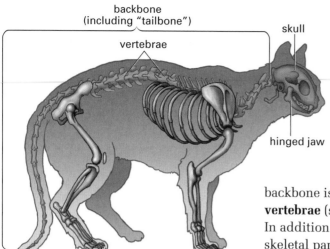

backbone
(including "tailbone")

skull

vertebrae

hinged jaw

Figure 3.25 A cat's skeleton shows two distinguishing characteristics of vertebrates: a backbone of segmented units (vertebrae) and a skull enclosing the brain. Like most vertebrates, cats also have hinged jaws.

Vertebrates

Vertebrates make up most of the chordates phylum you saw on the phylogenetic tree of animals earlier in the chapter. Vertebrates include fish, amphibians, reptiles, birds, mammals, and humans. Figure 3.25 illustrates two unique features of vertebrates: a skull and a backbone. These skeletal features protect the main parts of the animal's nervous system. The skull forms a hard case for the brain. The backbone is composed of a series of skeletal segments called **vertebrae** (singular, *vertebra*), which enclose the nerve cord. In addition to the skull and vertebrae, most vertebrates have skeletal parts, such as shoulders and a pelvis, that support paired limbs, such as pairs of legs.

Phylogenetic Tree of Vertebrates

You can see the diversity of vertebrates in the phylogenetic tree on the opposite page (Figure 3.26). This tree is based on one set of hypotheses for the evolutionary history of living vertebrates. To construct this diagram, biologists relied on a combination of anatomical, molecular, and fossil evidence. The branching points represent important steps in vertebrate evolution.

The first two branching points near the bottom of the diagram lead to two animal groups thought to be most closely related to the ancestors of vertebrates: hagfishes and lampreys. All vertebrates other than hagfishes and lampreys have hinged jaws. The evolution of hinged jaws in sharks and rays enabled vertebrates to capture and eat a wide variety of prey. The development of paired limbs in these fish also helped vertebrates catch prey and move around.

The next evolutionary step shown on the tree, lungs and lung derivatives such as air sacs that give fish buoyancy, developed in bony fishes. Until recently, all bony fishes were grouped together in the class Osteichthyes. Most biologists now recognize three separate classes of bony fishes: ray-finned fishes (class Actinopterygii), lobe-finned fishes (class Actinistia), and lungfishes (class Dipnoi).

All the other jawed vertebrates shown on the tree are *tetrapods,* a term that means "four-footed." The tetrapods include amphibians, reptiles, birds, and mammals. A tetrapod has two sets of paired limbs such as legs that can support the animal. This evolutionary step made it possible for vertebrates to inhabit the land.

Reptiles, birds, and mammals make up the evolutionary branch of the tree called the **amniotes**. This branch is named for the adaptation of the **amniotic egg**, a waterproof egg with a shell, which allowed vertebrates to reproduce on land (Figure 3.27). In mammals, the shell-covered egg has been replaced by internal embryo development. Unlike reptiles, birds and mammals generate body heat from their cell metabolism. Feathers are modifed scales that may have evolved as insulation to conserve heat.

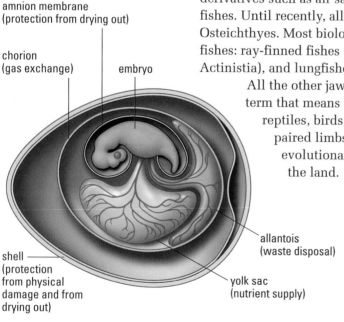

amnion membrane
(protection from drying out)

chorion
(gas exchange)

embryo

allantois
(waste disposal)

shell
(protection from physical damage and from drying out)

yolk sac
(nutrient supply)

Figure 3.27 This diagram shows a cross-section of a generalized amniotic egg. The shell and the amnion membrane protect the embryo from drying out.

©P

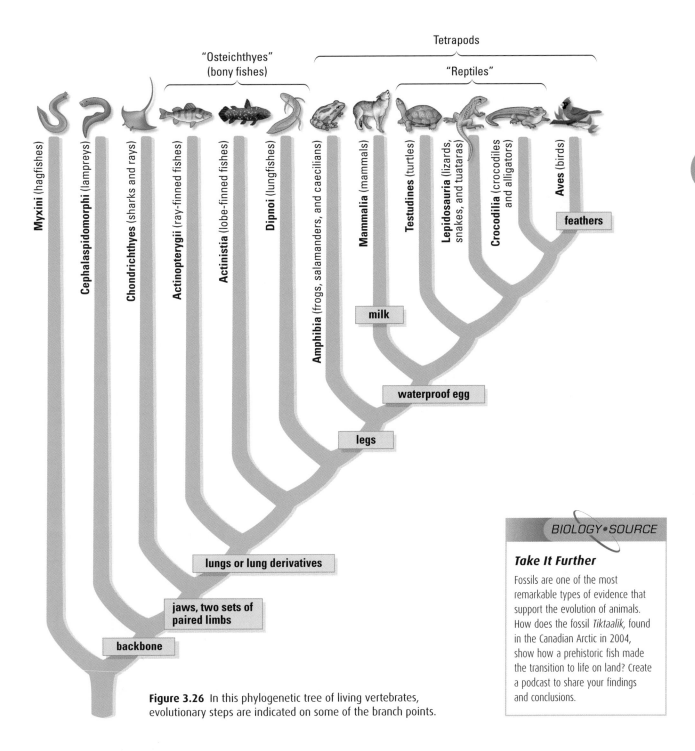

Figure 3.26 In this phylogenetic tree of living vertebrates, evolutionary steps are indicated on some of the branch points.

BIOLOGY•SOURCE

Take It Further

Fossils are one of the most remarkable types of evidence that support the evolution of animals. How does the fossil *Tiktaalik*, found in the Canadian Arctic in 2004, show how a prehistoric fish made the transition to life on land? Create a podcast to share your findings and conclusions.

Concept Check

1. Which phylum has the simplest animal?

2. What two general categories are often used to classify animals?

3. What are three evolutionary steps in vertebrates? Why is each significant?

Dichotomous Key to the Kingdoms

Purpose

To create and apply a dichotomous key to identify organisms from each kingdom

Figure 3.28 (a) A sea star and (b) a cat

Activity Overview

In this activity, you will choose one organism from each kingdom. You will identify a distinguishing characteristic for each organism and create a dichotomous key to identify the organisms. Then you will exchange keys with a classmate to test them.

Your teacher will give you a copy of the full activity.

Prelab Questions

Consider the questions below before beginning this activity.

1. What are the six kingdoms?

2. How do you use a dichotomous key to identify organisms?

3. What type of questions does a dichotomous key ask you to consider at each step?

REQUIRED SKILLS
- Using appropriate equipment and tools
- Recording and organizing data

Wanted: Worms

Question

How are the adaptations and behaviour of flatworms and segmented worms suited to their lifestyles and environments?

Activity Overview

In this investigation, you will closely observe a living flatworm (*planarian*) or a segmented worm (*lumbriculus*). You will study the anatomy of the worm, draw a biological diagram of the worm, and discover how it moves and responds to stimuli. You will research the type of worm you are observing, then create a "wanted poster" describing it.

Prelab Questions

Consider the questions below before beginning this activity.

1. What are two differences between flatworms and segmented worms?

2. Do you predict that touching the head of the worm will initiate the same response as touching the tail end? Why or why not?

Figure 3.29 (a) A flatworm and (b) a segmented worm

Key Concept Review

1. What is the definition of an animal?

2. What distinguishes an animal from animal-like protists?

3. What is the difference between invertebrates and vertebrates?

4. What is the significance of the blastula during embryological development?

5. Describe the types of symmetry evident in the animal kingdom, and give an example animal for each.

6. Give one example of a vertebrate without hinged jaws, and one example of a vertebrate with hinged jaws.

7. What characteristics are unique to vertebrate animals?

Connect Your Understanding

8. What advantage does cephalization give bilaterally symmetrical animals?

9. The flatworm's body plan is well-suited to the animal's lifestyle. Justify this statement.

10. Use the pie chart below to answer the following questions.

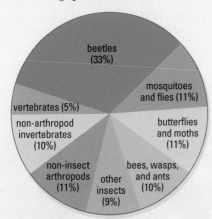

Question 10

(a) What general conclusion about arthropods can you draw from this pie chart?
(b) Which arthropod group is most diverse?
(c) Name at least three groups that fall within the "non-insect arthropod" category.

11. Explain the evolutionary significance of the amniotic egg.

12. Describe how embryonic development can indicate the evolutionary relationships between different invertebrates.

13. Given that 98 percent of animals are invertebrates, why do you think animals are typically classified as invertebrates or vertebrates?

14. Compare and contrast the evolutionary steps that allowed plants and animals to transition from water to land.

15. Suppose you are a zoologist working in a laboratory. An animal you are observing has the following characteristics: bilateral symmetry, an open circulatory system, a mantle cavity, and a complete digestive tract. In which phylum does this animal belong? Explain.

16. Compare and contrast the process of digestion in flatworms, roundworms, and annelids.

17. Animals with radial symmetry and bilateral symmetry tend to interact differently with their environments. Compare and contrast how they interact with their environments and describe how the structural details of their body plans influence these interactions.

18. Describe how tetrapods may have evolved from fish-like ancestors.

Reflection

19. Describe three things that you did not know about animals before working on this section of the chapter.

20. In this section you have learned about the diversity of animals. Has this changed your point of view about the importance of biodiversity? If so, how? If not, why?

For more questions, go to *BIOLOGY•SOURCE*

Section Summary

- Major threats to biodiversity caused by human activity include habitat loss, pollution, invasive species, overexploitation, and climate change.
- Climate change has both positive and negative effects on biodiversity.
- Conservation biology focusses on protecting ecosystems and species.

Do you like to jump in the lake at the cottage, wakeboard, go fishing, listen to waves roll ashore, or have a room with an ocean view? Whatever draws you to the water, you're not alone. The most developed regions of our continent are on the coasts.

On the Waterfront

More than half the population of North America live on the continent's coasts, and the shorelines of the Great Lakes are also major areas of development (Figure 3.30). Coastal areas and shorelines are also major areas of biodiversity. As human populations grow in these areas, more land is needed for agriculture, roads, and communities, and the resultant human activities often have impacts that reduce biodiversity. Establishing more agricultural lands may lead to more fertilizer runoff that flows into the water, creating **dead zones**, areas with low levels of oxygen that cannot support life. Building more roads and communities may displace wildlife and increase sewage, polluting the water when released partially treated. In turn, new communities may spur developers to dredge wetlands to build desirable waterfront properties, destroying more wildlife habitats. Fortunately, evidence shows that with proper care shorelines can recover from this damage caused by human activity. The Great Lakes Water Quality Agreement between Canada and the United States has reduced fertilizer runoff, improved sewage treatment, and helped protect the Great Lakes ecosystem.

Figure 3.30 The northern shore of Lake Ontario is a major area of urban development.

Threats to Biodiversity

Throughout Earth's history, species have become **extinct** — the last members of the population on the planet have died. Periods of mass extinction most likely occurred as a result of drastic climate change caused by volcanic eruptions or asteroid collisions. You are probably familiar with the story of one such event during the Cretaceous period, which scientists hypothesize resulted in the extinction of Earth's many dinosaur species.

There is currently another period of mass extinction taking place on Earth. Its exact scale is uncertain since the 1.5 million living species known to biologists are probably only a fraction of the total number of species on Earth. But there are signs that species are disappearing at a dramatic rate:

- About 12 percent of the 9900 known bird species in the world are endangered.
- Of approximately 20 000 known plant species in North America, at least 300 are at risk. Mosses face the highest risk with 86 percent in danger of extinction.
- Conservation biologists estimate that about 37 percent of the known fish in the world have become extinct during historical times or are at risk.

What is causing these threats to biodiversity? The main factors are:
- habitat loss
- invasive species
- pollution
- overexploitation
- climate change

(b)

Habitat Loss

Habitat loss is the greatest threat to the biodiversity of life. According to studies by the International Union for Conservation of Nature (IUCN), habitat loss is the major factor that endangers 50 percent of all threatened species. As human populations grow and develop land for communities, roads, farms, and obtaining natural resources, such as lumber, coal, and minerals, they may harm and destroy natural ecosystems. If the species that inhabit those ecosystems cannot adapt or move to new areas, they will not survive.

Some developments split habitats into fragments, leading to habitat fragmentation. **Habitat fragmentation** alters small areas within a large region, creating a patchwork of altered and original habitats. For example, building a road through a forest creates a barrier that may prevent species from using resources in all parts of the forest. The smaller the habitat fragments become, the fewer species each fragment can support.

In southern Ontario, a soaring population, intense agricultural use of land, and a high density of roads have all destroyed natural ecosystems, significantly reducing biodiversity. Species such as the eastern cougar have vanished and others have become endangered (Figure 3.31). The movement of people into natural undisturbed areas, advanced tree-harvesting technologies, government subsidies for clearcutting forests, and human indifference have all contributed to these impacts on biodiversity.

(c)

Figure 3.31 (a) The eastern cougar requires an extensive range to survive. As land has been cleared for settlement and agriculture, the cougar has mostly disappeared from Ontario and much of its North American range. (b) Loss of habitat due to these human activities has also endangered the loggerhead shrike in Ontario. (c) Similarly, loss of habitat due to logging and replanting of different tree species has endangered the wood turtle.

(a)

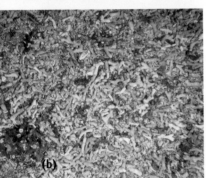

(b)

Figure 3.32 These photos show a coral reef before (a) and after (b) a deep-sea trawler has dragged a net through the area.

BIOLOGY•SOURCE

Explore More

How has the leafy spurge changed the face of cattle country in the Prairies?

Figure 3.35 Zebra mussels are voracious filter feeders that remove food and matter particles from water as they feed, making the water appear more transparent. One zebra mussel can filter several litres of water a day, allowing it to outcompete native mussels.

Today, however, several regions of our province practise sustainable forestry, including replanting cut trees with seedlings. Organizations such as the Forest Stewardship Council also work to conserve and protect forest habitats.

Around the world, deep-sea trawling destroys marine habitats much like deforestation. As deep-sea trawlers drag nets across the ocean floor to capture fish, they cut down everything in their path, including deep-sea coral (Figure 3.32). The coral grows slowly and, like a rainforest, it is home to a wealth of biodiversity.

Invasive Species

After habitat loss, invasive species pose the largest threat to biodiversity. **Invasive species** are non-native species that harm ecosystems where they are introduced. Invasive species often prey on native species or outcompete them for resources. Humans usually introduce these organisms into new geographic areas intentionally or accidentally as people travel around the globe. In the 1930s, people planted the Japanese plant kudzu in the American south to help control erosion, especially along irrigation canals (Figure 3.33). But kudzu soon grew out of control, taking over vast expanses of landscape. By 2009, kudzu had crept as far north as Ontario.

More than 160 invasive species have entered southern Ontario and the Great Lakes region. Examples include the emerald ash borer, which migrated from Michigan where it arrived in wood packing material in cargo ships or airplanes from Asia; plum pox virus, which damages agricultural crops; purple loosestrife, which clogs wetland habitats; and several species of Asian carp, which also damage wetlands (Figure 3.34).

Figure 3.33 Growth of the kudzu vine, which is often described as "out of control," smothers native trees and plants.

Figure 3.34 The emerald ash borer alters ecosystems, killing ash trees as its larva eat the trees' inner bark.

Invasion of the Zebra Mussels

When ocean tankers release ballast water in the Great Lakes, as many as 3000 to 4000 non-native species often pour out along with the water. Many die or do not cause problems, but not the zebra mussel, native to the Caspian Sea in Asia. In 1988, ballast water introduced microscopic larva of this organism into Lake St. Clair near Windsor. Lacking any natural predators in the new locale, zebra mussels reproduced much faster than native mussels, quickly spreading through the Great Lakes and associated waterways. Today, zebra mussels are a familiar sight in Ontario, growing on anything they can cling to, including boats, piers, docks, turtles, crayfish, and even other mussels (Figure 3.35). Some areas have more than one million mussels per square metre — enough to lower oxygen levels in the lake and thereby reduce biodiversity.

©P

Pollution

Many human activities pollute Earth's atmosphere, soil, and water. Burning coal to produce electricity is one of the greatest contributors to pollution impacting biodiversity. Coal-fired power plants emit more carbon dioxide that contributes to global warming than all the vehicles in North America. As temperatures rise, species must adapt, find new homes or die. Generating electricity from coal also emits sulphur dioxide and mercury that combine with water vapour to form acid rain. Acid rain damages forests, fresh water, and soil. It also changes pH levels and organisms that cannot adapt die off. In addition, to be used as fuel, coal must be washed to remove impurities. The resulting waste water contains toxins, such as mercury, lead, and arsenic. Sludge lagoons or slurry ponds capture and store this toxic waste water. However, increases in precipitation caused by climate change can make the water overflow and spill into neighbouring ecosystems (Figure 3.36).

Pesticides are chemicals used to control pests that harm livestock, crops, and gardens. Widespread use of pesticides has inadvertently killed many organisms besides those targeted. In South America, pesticides sprayed to control grasshoppers also killed 6000 Swainson hawks. Today, many areas in Ontario have banned pesticides. Once a pesticide enters an ecosystem, it can harm diversity through the food chain. The herbicide atrazine, for example, accumulates in sublethal doses in amphibians, even changing the sex of species, such as leopard frogs. As top predators in the food chain eat the tainted animals, lethal doses of pesticides build up in their tissues.

Figure 3.36 This worker is removing coal sludge that overflowed from a slurry pond in Inez, Kentucky, and spilled into a local river.

Overexploitation

Humans harvest many natural resources and organisms faster than the resources can be replenished and the organisms can reproduce. This unsustainable use of resources is called **overexploitation,** and it is a major cause of the current global species decline. The rosy periwinkle used to treat cancer was almost picked to extinction in Madagascar before people began growing it artificially. The most dramatic example of overexploitation in Canada, and perhaps the world, is the collapse of the North Atlantic cod fisheries. Between 1988 and 1995, the annual catch dropped from 479 141 tons to 12 490 tons, prompting the close of the fisheries. After a decade, the cod population had not recovered. Canadian scientists have recommended that cod be placed on the Government of Canada's Species at Risk list.

Climate Change

Many human activities contribute to climate change by emitting carbon dioxide (CO_2) into the atmosphere, which increases global warming. Examples include burning fossil fuels, clearing land by slashing and burning forests, burning peat forests, raising livestock, and draining wetland ecosystems. Table 3.3 on the next page summarizes some of the potential effects of climate change on biodiversity.

BIOLOGY·SOURCE

Explore More

How do cattle add to global warming by belching?

Table 3.3 Potential Effects of Climate Change on Biodiversity

Disease Outbreaks	Insects adapt to changing climate conditions quickly and will come into increasing contact with humans. Since insects often carry disease, epidemics like SARS and H1N1 are more likely to occur.
Plant Migration	All plants have an optimal range of temperatures. As climate becomes more temperate in northern Ontario, grasslands will replace boreal forests.
Animal Migration	Animals have ideal climates where they are most successful. White-tailed deer and Virginia possum are now found hundreds of kilometres north of where they were 50 years ago. As animals migrate to new habitats, they change the natural balance of both their old and new ecosystems.
Extreme Weather	Climate change has increased the number of extreme weather events throughout Canada, including major ice storms, droughts, and floods. Extreme weather events can change the composition of an ecosystem and dramatically reduce levels of biodiversity in a short period of time — literally overnight.
Increased CO_2 Levels	As increased CO_2 levels dissolve in water, they can change the pH of the water. Since aquatic organisms require a specific range of pH to survive, they may die off.
Water Availability and Quality	Climate patterns will reduce the availability and quality of water in many arid (dry) and semi-arid regions.

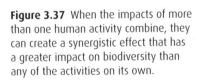
BIOLOGY•SOURCE

Suggested Activities
- A16 Quick Lab Overview on page 83
- A17 Decision-Making Analysis Overview on page 83

In some areas, the impacts of several human activities combine, producing **synergistic effects** that result in greater damage. For example, habitat fragmentation and climate change can pack a "one-two punch" that substantially reduces the biodiversity in many regions. Figure 3.37 shows another example of a synergistic effect.

Climate change modifies the pattern of water runoff and precipitation in northwestern Ontario, increasing the number of droughts. Organic matter that is normally deposited into the lakes with runoff is much reduced.

Synergistic Effect

Pollution from coal mining releases sulphur and nitrous oxides into the surrounding air, causing acid rain. The acidification of the water decreases the amounts of algae that float in and on the lake.

Without the algae and organic material in the lake, lake water becomes much clearer, allowing harmful UV radiation to penetrate deeply into the water and further harm organisms. This includes aquatic plants, small animals, and protists — all integral parts of the food chains in northern Ontario's lakes.

Figure 3.37 When the impacts of more than one human activity combine, they can create a synergistic effect that has a greater impact on biodiversity than any of the activities on its own.

Concept Check

1. List five threats to biodiversity.
2. Which threat represents the greatest problem for biodiversity?
3. Why would a province or municipality ban the use of pesticides?

©P

Conserving Biodiversity

What measures can we take to protect ecosystems and species? Finding solutions and carrying them out are two goals of **conservation biology**, the application of biology to counter the loss of biodiversity. Since plants and animals do not recognize national boundaries, countries around the world need to work together to conserve biodiversity. The Convention on Biological Diversity is an international treaty signed by 161 countries, including Canada, to sustain the diversity of life on Earth. A major goal of the convention is to protect the genetic diversity of species through two strategies:

- **ex-situ conservation**, protecting species by removing them from their natural habitats
- **in-situ conservation**, protecting species in their natural habitats

Protecting Species Beyond Their Habitats

Conservation biologists use ex-situ conservation when a species' habitat is threatened or no longer exists, or the existing population of the species is very small. They have the at-risk individuals live in zoos, botanical gardens, and reserves. They also store seeds, frozen cuttings of plants, and living plants in seed and gene banks (Figure 3.38).

Today, zoos play an active role in preserving biological diversity through breeding programs and other efforts. Many zoos across North America, including the Metro Toronto Zoo, participate in Species Survival Plans (SSPs). SSPs are breeding programs specifically for species threatened with extinction. The Metro Toronto Zoo breeds and maintains a population of black-footed ferrets, which no longer exist in the wild in Ontario. In 2009, the zoo and other organizations reintroduced the ferrets into the wild in a national park in Saskatchewan and began to monitor the population.

Protection of Species in Their Habitats

Biologists consider ex-situ conservation a strategy of last resort. In-situ conservation focusses on conserving species in their natural habitats by establishing protected areas, restoring habitats, and adopting laws to protect threatened species. Restoring habitats is part of the Lake Ontario Atlantic Salmon Restoration Program. In an effort to bring back salmon to Lake Ontario and its surrounding waterways, the program has stocked close to a million young salmon in three Lake Ontario streams, the Credit River, Duffins Creek, and Cobourg Brook (Figure 3.39).

Understanding the habitat requirements of a species can help biologists manage its existing habitat or create new habitat areas. Consider the example of the Karner blue butterfly (*Lycaeides melissa samuelis*), an endangered species once found in Ontario but now only found in rare populations in the northeastern United States. The species breeds on or near the savanna grass wild lupine (*Lupinus perennis*). This grass requires open space to grow and does not tolerate shade. Periodic fires that sweep through pine forests keep the trees from dominating the landscape and allow the undergrowth to proliferate. With the increasing control of forest fires to prevent damage to human property, these ecosystems became endangered and populations of Karner blue butterflies (Figure 3.40) became extirpated in Ontario. Extirpated means that a species no longer exists in a particular region but still occurs elsewhere.

Figure 3.38 Constructed 120 m below the ice on an island in the Arctic Ocean, the Svalbard Global Seed Vault can conserve up to 4.5 million seeds. These seeds can act as a backup for any plants that have been lost due to mismanagement or natural disasters.

Figure 3.39 The Lake Ontario Atlantic Salmon Restoration program is one of the largest freshwater conservation projects in North America.

Figure 3.40 The Karner blue butterfly is being reintroduced into its natural range in Ontario.

Today, the butterflies exist only in small populations south of the border. However, efforts are underway through species survival plans, recovery teams, conservation of natural oak savanna ecosystems, and controlled burns to reintroduce these butterflies back to their natural range in Ontario.

Taking Action to Conserve Biodiversity

Today, many countries are taking action to conserve biodiversity. Some, such as Costa Rica, protect wildlife habitats by enforcing a heavy tax on any industry that releases large amounts of nutrient pollution. Others develop incentives, such as South Africa's Working for Water Programme, for people to help remove invasive species. In South America, programs encourage landowners to leave "corridors" of forested land between cleared areas as migration routes for animals with large ranges. This has greatly improved the survival of mammals like the jaguar.

You can also conserve biodiversity by reducing your ecological footprint on the biosphere. An **ecological footprint** is an estimate of all the land and water needed to produce the resources you consume and to absorb the wastes you produce (Figure 3.41). The average Canadian requires 8.9 ha to maintain his or her lifestyle. This is equivalent to about 17 football fields. It is not sustainable. If everyone on Earth had the same ecological footprint, we would need 5.7 Earths.

The goal of sustainable development is to develop natural resources so that they can renew themselves and be available for the future. Sustainable development depends on the continued research and applications of basic ecology and conservation biology. The challenge for individuals and nations is to find a way to meet the needs of Earth's human population, while conserving ecosystems and resources to meet the needs of the planet's other populations as well. By exploring the diversity of life in your biology class this year, you and your classmates have taken an important step toward an understanding of nature that is essential to the future of the biosphere.

BIOLOGY•SOURCE

Take It Further

We are currently in a period of mass extinction. Scientists think it is the sixth period in Earth's history when a large number of species were wiped out. When did these other mass extinctions occur? Draw a timeline to record your findings. Look for patterns on the timeline and discuss any with a classmate.

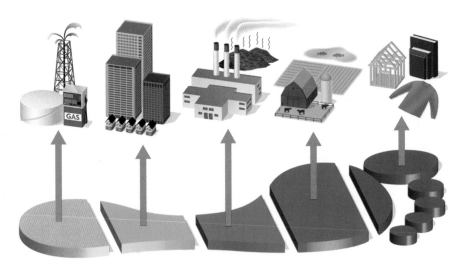

Figure 3.41 A person's ecological footprint includes the space needed for extracting energy, living and working, manufacturing and waste disposal, growing food, and extracting resources, such as timber, textiles, pulp and paper.

©P

Looking at Human Interventions

Purpose

To determine how human interventions can positively or negatively impact biodiversity

Activity Overview

In this activity, you will consider five scenarios that describe human impacts on biodiversity. You will analyze the risks and benefits of each and justify your conclusions.

Your teacher will give you a copy of the full activity.

Prelab Questions

Consider the questions below before beginning this activity.

1. Why is biodiversity important?

2. What might happen to your local ecosystem if biodiversity continues to be threatened?

3. What is a human intervention that affects biodiversity?

Figure 3.42 Workers unload beehives off a transport truck, so the bees can be used to pollinate local crops.

REQUIRED SKILLS
- Asking questions
- Stating a conclusion

Costs and Benefits of Human Intervention

Issue

Biodiversity contributes directly to the health and well-being of all ecosystems. However, human intervention in the biodiversity of ecosystems has impacts. Are the benefits of improving biodiversity greater than the costs?

Activity Overview

In this activity, you will research how a particular human intervention affects the biodiversity of a terrestrial or an aquatic ecosystem. You will evaluate the costs and benefits of the intervention. You will summarize your findings and conclusions in a short report and present your report to the class.

Your teacher will give you a copy of the full activity.

Prelab Questions

Consider the questions below before beginning this activity.

1. In this unit, you have learned about many impacts that affect the diversity and success of honeybees. What types of human interventions may be contributing factors to the reduced diversity of honeybees?

2. To decide on a course of action, people often weigh the costs and benefits of proceeding. Give an example of a cost and a benefit of taking a particular route to school in the morning.

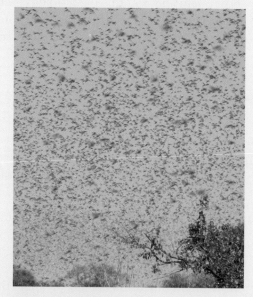

Figure 3.43 This photo shows a swarm of grasshoppers. Recall that in South America, spraying pesticides to control grasshoppers inadvertently killed 6000 Swainson hawks.

Key Concept Review

1. What is an ecological footprint?

2. What types of strategies are in place to protect the Great Lakes ecosystems?

3. Why do lakes that have been exposed to acid rain usually appear clear and lifeless?

4. List some problems that affect biodiversity from the use of pesticides.

5. How does habitat fragmentation contribute to habitat loss?

6. What are five human threats to global biodiversity? Give a specific example of each.

Connect Your Understanding

7. Biodiversity hot spots are ecosystems that contain high numbers of species not found anywhere else. Why do you suppose that human impacts at biodiversity hot spots are especially concerning to conservation biologists?

8. Trace the removal of honeybees from an ecosystem and describe the various cascading effects that may occur. Make specific reference to how biodiversity would be reduced and include at least four other organisms in your description.

9. Coal is an important source of fuel. How does the use of this resource impact biodiversity?

10. The Karner blue butterfly feeds exclusively on wild lupine, a plant that grows after forest fires. How has human encroachment on their habitat affected biodiversity in these areas?

11. The New Zealand mistletoe relies on birds to transport its seeds from one tree to the next. Its habitat is large forests, and it is not able to survive in open plains, or sparse woodland. How might the following factors affect the populations of New Zealand mistletoe?
    (a) invasive species that prey on birds
    (b) deforestation

12. Analyze the pie chart and bar graph below to answer the following questions:
    (a) What percentage of Ontario is covered by forest?
    (b) What percentage is covered by water?
    (c) Which action is potentially more damaging to Ontario's biodiversity — water pollution or deforestation? Justify your answer with at least three supporting points.
    (d) Suppose an invasive insect from Antarctica wiped out the world's forests. According to the graph, which area of the world would suffer the greatest impact? Hypothesize how this would affect global biodiversity.

Percentage of Land Types and Water Areas in Ontario

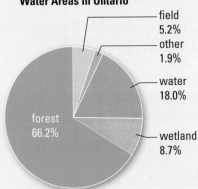

- field 5.2%
- other 1.9%
- water 18.0%
- wetland 8.7%
- forest 66.2%

Proportion of Forest Compared to Total Land Area

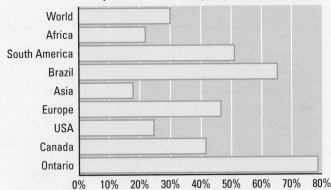

Question 12

Reflection

13. You have learned about human impacts on biodiversity in this chapter. How do you think the loss of biodiversity would impact humanity? How would it impact you?

For more questions, go to BIOLOGY·SOURCE

©P

Ethnobotanist Dr. Memory Elvin-Lewis is one of Canada's leading experts in evaluating the use of traditional medicines from plants. But that's not all. She is also an infectious disease microbiologist. In 1969, Dr. Elvin-Lewis came across a strange case of a 16-year-old boy diagnosed with chlamydia, a common but curable sexually transmitted disease. Although doctors prescribed antibiotics, the boy's muscles shrank and his lungs filled with fluid. He soon died and no one could figure out why. Thinking that medical advances might one day solve the mystery, Dr. Elvin-Lewis froze samples of the boy's blood, brain, and other organs. About 20 years later, when acquired immune deficiency syndrome (AIDs) was identified, Dr. Elvin-Lewis thought the symptoms of AIDs matched those of the boy. She had the boy's frozen remains analyzed and the results confirmed her idea. Now the case is recognized as the first documented case of AIDs in North America.

Today, the pressing concern for Dr. Elvin-Lewis is the rapid destruction of the world's tropical rainforests. She and her husband, Dr. Walter Lewis who is also a notable biologist, are working to create an inventory of medicinal plants used by cultural indigenous groups in the Amazon region of South America before this knowledge disappears.

Figure 3.44 Dr. Elvin-Lewis is a professor of microbiology and ethnobotany at Washington University in St. Louis.

Biology CAREERS   *Environmental and Wildlife Officer*

Who do you call when a company releases toxic waste into a local river or someone takes an endangered turtle from a protected wetland to keep as a pet? Your local environmental and wildlife officer. This officer's job is to enforce the laws of the Canadian Environmental Protection Act along with other environmental and wildlife regulations. When infractions of these occur, the officer works to correct the situation by educating those involved, issuing written warnings, and developing programs to address areas or laws that are frequently misinterpreted.

Environmental and wildlife officers also gather intelligence and conduct investigations into activities that harm the environment and wildlife. They may sample and collect soil, plant, or animal tissues and analyze them in the lab. In addition, since the environment and wildlife know no borders, the officers often work with provincial, territorial, federal and international governments and agencies, such as the United States' Environmental Enforcement Agency and Interpol.

Figure 3.45 When the water in this creek near Kingston, Ontario, suddenly turned bright green, an environmental officer took samples to investigate the source of contamination.

To find out more, visit   BIOLOGY•SOURCE

Key Concept Review

1. What does the term "alternation of generations" describe? **k**

2. Describe two differences between spores and gametes. **k**

3. What information is used to create phylogenetic trees? **k**

4. Which plant phyla have a dominant gametophyte generation? **k**

5. Why is the term invertebrate not considered a taxonomic rank? **k**

6. What is the purpose of conservation biology? How does the Convention on Biological Diversity conserve biodiversity? **k**

7. Describe how five outcomes of human activity threaten plant and animal populations. **k**

8. What evolutionary step is present in ferns but not mosses? Describe how it is an advantage. **k**

9. Apart from animals, do other organisms have symmetry in their form and structure? **k**

Connect Your Understanding

10. Analyze two adaptations plants evolved to grow on land. Why were they necessary for plants to be successful in terrestrial environments? **a**

11. Do phylogenetic trees represent fact, fiction, or something in between? Explain your answer. **a**

12. Identify the following as either in-situ or ex-situ conservation:
    (a) Zoos participating in species survival plans by protecting endangered species that no longer exist in local ecosystems **a**
    (b) Royal botanical gardens protecting natural populations of water lilies from damage by recreational water enthusiasts **a**
    (c) Storing specific seeds of historical wheat crops from the Prairies in an Arctic seed vault **a**

13. Propose a reason why mosses and amphibians are extremely susceptible to changes in the environment. **t**

14. How is the description of "naked seed" an appropriate label for gymnosperm gametes? **a**

15. Create a concept map that shows the progression of early aquatic animals to modern terrestrial environments. **a**

16. What characteristics of the organism shown below define it as an animal? **a**

Question 16

17. Suggest how the distribution of a pesticide over a small farm may affect the local biodiversity of a neighbouring forest, stream, and lake. **a**

18. Create a concept map that connects the various impacts associated with climate change. Include at least five specific effects, and for each one reference specific organisms that are impacted. **a**

19. How is the life cycle of the protist *Plasmodium* similar to the life cycle of a plant? **a**

20. Green algae has been recently moved from the protist kingdom to the plant kingdom. What features of green algae make it hard to classify? **t**

21. Both angiosperms and mammals have evolved several adaptations for life in terrestrial environments. Compare the features of these two groups that allow them to thrive on land using the terms: reproduction, water conservation, gas exchange structures, vascularization, and symbiosis. **a**

22. Describe how climate change and pollution from coal mining can combine to create a synergistic effect in Ontario. **a**

23. The red-cockaded woodpecker (*Picoides borealis*) is an endangered species found in very specific locations in the southeastern United States. The species prefers to nest in longleaf pines. Fungi soften the wood of these trees, making it easy for the woodpecker to drill its nest. The woodpecker also relies on low-growing vegetation surrounding the pines.

The birds benefit by having a clear flight path between their home trees and neighbouring feeding grounds. How might the suppression of forest fires impact the diversity of this species and the region? ⓐ

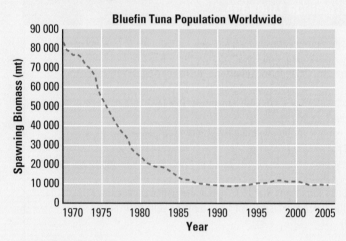

Bluefin Tuna Population Worldwide

Question 24

24. Use the graph above to answer the following questions.
   (a) Extrapolate the data to determine the size of the bluefin tuna population in 2010. ⓣ
   (b) What human activity is likely driving the decimation of the bluefin tuna population? ⓣ
   (c) What strategies may help the bluefin population recover over the next 20 years? ⓣ

25. West Nile virus has been resident in bird populations for many years. But it was not until 1999 that West Nile virus was first observed in North America. The maps below show the geographic range and spread of West Nile over 10 years. What phenomenon is likely a major contributor to the pattern in the map? Justify your answer. ⓣ

Reflection

26. In this section you have explored human impacts on biodiversity. How will you take action to reduce your impact? Write a short paragraph outlining the action you will take. ⓒ

Unit Task Link

In the Unit Task, you will create a new plant or animal. What are the defining characteristics of plants and animals? What are the major classes of plants and animals? Create a table for each group of organisms that includes the group's defining characteristics and major classes.

For more questions, go to BIOLOGY•SOURCE

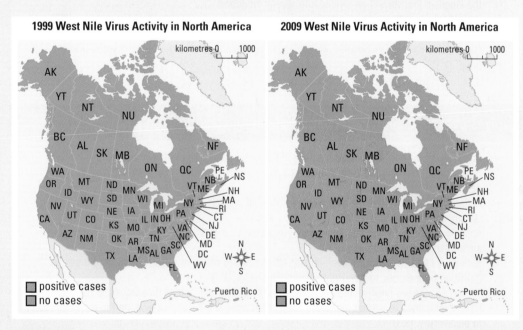

Question 25

KEY CONCEPTS	CHAPTER SUMMARY

1   Identifying and classifying things require a common language.

- Biodiversity
- Taxonomy
- Phylogeny
- Prokaryotes
- Eukaryotes

- Species diversity, ecosystem diversity, and genetic diversity are key components of biodiversity. (1.1)
- Taxonomy is the science of naming, identifying, and classifying species. (1.2)
- All organisms are classified into one of six kingdoms: Eubacteria, Archaebacteria, Protista, Fungi, Plantae, or Animalia. (1.2)
- Phylogeny is the evolutionary development of a group of organisms. Biologists use phylogenic analysis to compare living organisms to extinct organisms. (1.2)
- Phylogenetic trees are a visual hypothesis of the evolutionary history of a species and show its relationships to other species. (1.2)
- Classification systems continually evolve as new evidence about the evolutionary relationships among organisms is discovered. (1.2)
- Prokaryotes are microscopic unicellular organisms that lack membrane-bound organelles. (1.2)
- Eukaryotes are unicellular and multicellular organisms that have complex cells that contain membrane-bound organelles. (1.2)

2   A diversity of micro-organisms, protists, and fungi is intrinsic to life on Earth.

- Viruses are not alive.
- Archaea and bacteria are prokaryotes.
- Protists are a diverse kingdom of eukaryotes.
- Fungi are heterotrophic eukaryotes.

- Viruses are not considered living things even though they have many characteristics of living organisms. (2.1)
- Prokaryotes are divided into two domains: archaea and bacteria. (2.1)
- Archaea are complex prokaryotic organisms often found in extreme environments. (2.1)
- Bacteria have a cell wall, DNA, and can divide into two cells through binary fission. (2.1)
- The kingdom Protista contains all the eukaryotic organisms that do not fit into the other five kingdoms. (2.2)
- As more evidence of the evolutionary relationships among protists is discovered, most biologists think the kingdom Protista will be divided into several kingdoms. (2.2)
- Most fungi are composed of two main structures: thread-like hyphae and mat-like mycelia. (2.3)
- Fungi can reproduce sexually or asexually. (2.3)
- Climate change has both positive and negative impacts on the diversity of prokaryotes, protists, and fungi. (2.3)

3   Biodiversity evolves over time and is affected by changing conditions on Earth.

- Plants are autotrophic eukaryotes.
- Animals are multicellular, heterotrophic, eukaryotes.
- Alternation of generations
- Threats to biodiversity
- Conservation of biodiversity

- Green algae, mosses, ferns, seed plants, and flowering plants are the five major groups of plants. (3.1)
- Plants have a reproductive cycle that alternates between a haploid generation and a diploid generation. (3.1)
- Animal body plans reflect the evolutionary history of animals and provide key characteristics used to classify animals into taxa. (3.2)
- Animals are often divided into two groups: vertebrates, animals with a backbone, and invertebrates, animals without a backbone. (3.2)
- Both plants and animals have evolutionary adaptations to conserve water that allowed them to transition from aquatic to terrestrial environments. (3.1, 3.2)
- Climate change has positive and negative impacts on plant and animal diversity. (3.1, 3.2, 3.3)
- Habitat loss, invasive species, pollution, overexploitation, and climate change are the major threats to biodiversity. (3.3)
- Sustainable development is important for the conservation of biodiversity. (3.3)

©P

Key Terms Review

1. Create a concept map, with the term "biodiversity" at the centre that links all the terms in the list below. Use additional words from the unit to clarify your understanding. **c**

   - biosphere
   - species
   - genetic diversity
   - species diversity
   - ecosystem diversity
   - eukaryotes
   - prokaryotes
   - binary fission
   - endospore
   - alternation of generations
   - gymnosperms
   - angiosperms
   - vertebrates
   - invertebrates
   - dead zones
   - habitat fragmentation
   - invasive species
   - overexploitation
   - climate change
   - conservation biology

Key Concept Review

CHAPTER 1

2. What are the kingdoms in the six-kingdom classification system? **k**

3. What purpose does sexual reproduction serve for bacteria, protists, and fungi? **k**

4. What is the purpose of an endospore? **k**

5. *Cyanocitta cristata* is the two-part Latin name for the blue jay. Identify the the following parts of the name:
   (a) genus **k**
   (b) species **k**
   (c) scientific name **k**

6. What is the difference between taxonomy and phylogeny? **k**

7. Construct a concept map that shows how genes, species, and ecosystems can be used to define biodiversity. **k**

8. In this unit, you have studied the Linnaeus classification system that has seven taxonomic levels. Another top-level taxon has recently been added to classification systems. What is this level called and what are its components? **k**

9. What are prokaryotes? What are eukaryotes? Describe the major characteristics of each. **k**

CHAPTER 2

10. Propose an argument for classifying viruses as living organisms. What argument would a scientist make to counter it? **k**

11. Why do most biologists think the protist kingdom will eventually be divided into several kingdoms? **k**

12. Compare and contrast the types of reproduction that occur in bacteria and protists. **k**

13. What advantage does conjugation give paramecia? **k**

14. What characteristics of slime moulds cause them to be classified as fungus-like protists? **k**

15. What are the defining characteristics of fungi? **k**

16. What is the significance of mycorrhizae? **k**

CHAPTER 3

17. Which plant phyla have a dominant sporophyte generation? **k**

18. Which group of animals have a backbone and which do not? **k**

19. What is the significance of evolutionary steps for animal phyla? **k**

20. Recall that biologists think that an ancestral protist may have given rise to the earliest animals. Draw a phylogenetic tree to show the next three major steps in animal evolution.

21. Use the illustration below to answer the following questions.

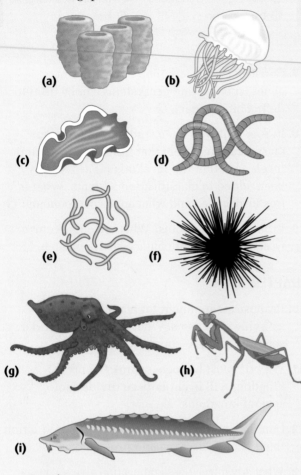

Question 21

(a) Which of the animals shown is classified as a vertebrate? **k**

(b) Which animal has only two tissue layers? **k**

(c) Which animal undergoes deuterostome embryological development? **k**

(d) Which animal represents the most diverse and densely populated phylum on the planet? **k**

(e) Which animals are segmented? **k**

(f) Which animals have radial symmetry? **k**

(g) Which animals are most closely related to birds? Justify your answer using evolutionary steps. **k**

(h) What evolutionary steps distinguish roundworms from flatworms? **k**

(i) To which phylum does each animal belong? **k**

22. What is sustainable development? How can it be used to lessen the negative impacts of human activities? **k**

23. Contrast the terms "sustainable forestry" and "deforestation." **k**

Connect Your Understanding

24. The photos below show (a) the Kaibib squirrel and (b) the Abert's squirrel. The two squirrels look very similar and can be easily confused. What conventions do scientists use to clearly identify and distinguish the two types of squirrels? **a**

Question 24

25. Early classification systems categorized all living organisms as plants or animals. What are the limitations of such a system? What advances have allowed the reclassification of organisms into distinct kingdoms? **a**

26. The biological species definition has some weaknesses. In each instance below, identify the weakness and suggest a modification of the species definition that would allow the organisms to be defined as a unique species.
(a) Mules, the offspring of a male donkey and a female horse **a**
(b) Asexually reproducing prokaryotes such as bacteria **a**
(c) Extinct dinosaurs and prehistoric mammals **a**

27. Given that bacteria can reproduce very quickly, what prevents them from overpopulating the world? **a**

28. Some traditional classification systems classify protists based on the organisms' lifestyles. What problems may be associated with this type of categorization? **a**

29. Increasing amounts of UV radiation have been associated with climate change. Many protists are sensitive to UV radiation and will no longer grow under such conditions. What long-term effects might this have on ecosystems? **a**

30. Some bacteria can produce endospores. Compare and contrast these structures to spores produced by fungi. **a**

31. Why would it be easy to mistake a fungus-like protist for a fungus? How are the two types of organisms different? **a**

©P

32. Identify the lifestyle of each protist shown below. ⓐ

  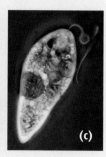

(a)   **(b)**   **(c)**

Question 32

33. Fungi cannot produce their own food or move to capture food. What adaptations allow fungi to quickly absorb food when they come in contact with a source of nutrients? ⓐ

34. In which phylum does the fungus shown below belong? Justify your answer. How can you verify that your answer is correct? ⓐ

Question 34

35. Define the term "alternation of generations" without using the terminology haploid, diploid, or zygote. ⓐ

36. Contrast how the gametophyte and sporophyte generations of vascular plants obtain nutrients. ⓐ

37. Suppose you observe an animal that does not have a distinct head. What type of symmetry and lifestyle do you think it might have? Explain your reasoning. ⓣ

38. What features of southern Ontario make it challenging to maintain high levels of biodiversity? ⓐ

39. Rank the following features in order of their appearance in evolution: tissues, vertebrate development, multicellular organisms, and protostome development. ⓐ

40. Why are some pollutants more harmful to organisms near the top of the food chain than those near the bottom that are directly exposed to the pollutants? ⓚ

41. Bioindicators are living organisms that are very sensitive to changes in the environment. Describe an organism that might be a good bioindicator, and describe a situation where they might be useful as a bioindicator. ⓐ

42. Vascularization occurs in plants and animals. Explain how this evolutionary step allowed both animals and plants to invade land. ⓐ

43. Suppose a marine biologist returns from exploring the deep-sea and presents the scientific community with an unknown animal. What are some characteristics scientists could use to determine in which phylum the animal might belong? ⓣ

Skills Practice

44. Create a dichotomous key that can be used to identify the leaves shown below. ⓣ

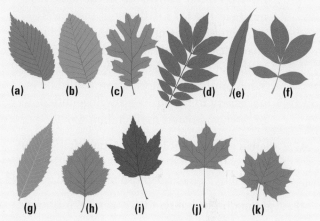

(a)   **(b)**   **(c)**   **(d)** **(e)**   **(f)**

(g)   **(h)**   **(i)**   **(j)**   **(k)**

(a) American elm   **(g)** chestnut
(b) beech   **(h)** scarlet hawthorn
(c) black oak   **(i)** red maple
(d) black walnut   **(j)** sugar maple
(e) black willow   **(k)** sycamore
(f) shagbark hickory

Question 44

45. Eating salmon steaks was once a rare delicacy. Now many grocery stores carry several varieties of salmon steaks. Even though wild salmon fisheries are being depleted, more fish are making it to market largely due to an increase in salmon aquaculture farming. Do a cost benefit analysis to determine if providing salmon for people is more important than the conservation of local ecosystems connected with wild salmon runs and aquaculture. ⓣ

46. Use the following table to answer the questions below.

Common Name	Scientific Name
Polar bear	*Ursus maritimus*
American black bear	*Ursus Americanus*
Grizzly bear	*Ursus arctos horribills*
Giant panda	*Ailuropoda melanoleuca*
Sun bear	*Helarctos malayanus*
Sloth bear	*Melursus ursinus*

(a) What taxonomic ranks are represented in this table? **a**

(b) What is the genus of the grizzly bear? **a**

(c) The kinkajou is a rainforest mammal found in Central America. Locals also call it the sun bear, and its scientific name is *Potos flavus*. Which bear listed in the table is it most similar to? Justify your answer. **a**

(d) The scientific name for the Asiatic black bear is *Ursus thibetanus*. Which bears listed in the table are most closely related to it? **a**

(e) What additional information would be necessary to construct a phylogenetic tree of the bears listed in the table? **a**

47. Create a new classification system that can be used to categorize different types of arthropods. Explain why you chose those taxonomic ranks. **t**

48. Use the photos below to answer the following questions.

(a) The sea cucumber has deuterostome development and no appendages. The bumblebee has protostome development and appendages. Humans have deuterostome development and appendages, such as arms and legs. Which of the two organisms are more closely related? Explain your answer. **t**

(b) Create a phylogenetic tree to represent your hypothesis. **a**

(c) What further evidence could you collect to support your hypothesis? **t**

(d) Why is this considered only a hypothesis? **t**

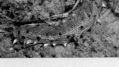

Question 48

49. Create a phylogenetic tree that shows the evolution of plants from their algal ancestors to flowering plants. Identify the nodes and label them with evolutionary steps that state how the branching organisms have adaptations for better terrestrial success. **t**

Revisit the Big Ideas and Fundamental Concepts

50. Explain how a warming ocean trend may affect the biodiversity of coral reefs. **a**

51. An understanding of natural interactions and the diversity of life are key for sustaining ecosystems. What role does fungi play in ecosystems? Justify your answer. Include the organisms that fungi interact with and the organisms that benefit from the interactions. **a**

52. Describe the potential effects of climate change on ecosystems and ultimately the diversity of life. **a**

53. Plants and animals have evolved similarly to transition from aquatic to terrestrial environments. Consider the following groups of animals and plants — mammals, amphibians, flatworms, reptiles, bryophytes, conifers, flowering plants, ferns — and use a table like this one to answer the questions below:

Animal	Plant	Justification

(a) Match up the groups of animals and plants that have similar evolutionary steps. **t**

(b) Justify your pairings by using the terms or phrases, such as the following: **t**
- development of water-resistant covering
- amphibious lifestyle
- strategies to protect and disperse reproductive structures in terrestrial environments
- elaborate, enclosed structures capable of both protecting and nourishing embryos
- dependent on open water for reproduction, growth, and metabolism

54. List the five major threats to biodiversity and describe the role that human activities play in each. **c**

Science, Technology, Society, and the Environment

55. Most actions have both positive and negative impacts. From the unit, choose a human intervention that directly impacts biodiversity. Do a cost-benefit analysis to determine if the benefits of the intervention outweigh the costs. **t**

56. Throughout history a number of mass extinctions have wiped out large numbers of species. After each, a rich diversity of organisms has bounced back and thrived. The current period of mass extinction has been attributed to a variety of human impacts, including climate change. How has climate change had this effect on species? Explain your response and include an opinion on whether climate change is a consequence of human activity or a cycle that occurs naturally. **c**

57. Antibiotics are medicines that destroy micro-organisms that cause disease and infections. Humans often produce antibiotics from chemicals naturally produced by organisms. Fungi cultivated by leaf cutter ants produce an antibiotic crucial to the survival of the ant colony. Why might organisms other than humans produce antibiotics? **a**

58. Today, many governments offer financial incentives to encourage corporations and industries to respect the environment. Can a monetary value be placed on biodiversity? Justify your answer. **t**

Reflection

59. In this unit, you have learned many things about how organisms are identified, named, and classified. What is the most important thing you learned about the science of taxonomy? Why do you think it is the most important? **c**

60. In this unit, you have learned about many impacts that climate change might have on biodiversity. Has your learning prompted you to become more involved in community actions and organizations to reduce humans' contribution to climate change? Explain the reasoning for your response. **c**

61. In this unit, you have learned about the diversity of livings things. Choose one of the six kingdoms of life and describe the influence its organisms have on your life. Next, describe the influence you have on the organisms. What steps can you take to ensure the existence of these organisms? **c**

Classifying a New Organism

The sole job of some scientists is to classify organisms. When an animal or plant new to science is discovered, these scientists study the organism and identify characteristics it shares with known organisms in the vast database of identified species. The scientists must conduct a great deal of analysis and planning to classify and name a new species.

Question

How can you classify a newly discovered animal or plant that does not fit into any taxonomic class?

Task Overview

In this activity, you will create a new animal or plant that fits into an existing taxonomic phylum but does not fit into an existing class. You will identify, name, and classify the organism and communicate your results to the class in the form of a sketch, model, and presentation.

Your teacher will give you a copy of the full task.

Figure 3.46 The tongue-eating isopod *Cymothoa exigua* consumes the tongue of the snapper fish and replaces the tongue. The fish uses the parasite like a tongue, and the parasite feeds on the fish's blood or mucus. Scientists place the isopod in the phylum Arthropoda, subphylum Crustacea, and class Malacostraca.

UNIT B

Genetic Processes

Unit Contents

Unit Task

Genetic testing allows us to find out if we are carrying disease-associated variations of genes. It also allows us to assess the risk of passing down genetic conditions to the next generation. For your unit task, you will play the role of a genetic counsellor. You will provide a genetic risk assessment for a hypothetical family to help them make an informed decision about relevant genetic tests.

DISCOVERING BIOLOGY

Our genes are made of information-rich molecules called DNA. Shown in the photo is a DNA sequencing gel, a technology that reveals the chemical sequence in a cell's DNA. Each coloured bar represents one part of the sequence. Like an instruction book written in code, the chemical sequence in DNA tells our cells how to grow and function. The DNA instruction booklet is also passed down from generation to generation. Geneticists study the information in DNA sequences to identify genes and their functions and, in doing so, to better understand the complexity of the human body.

What can we learn from DNA sequence data to improve human health and quality of life?

The cell's genetic material determines inherited characteristics.

Learning Expectations

By the end of this chapter, you will:

Relating Science to Technology, Society, and the Environment

- analyze, on the basis of research, some of the social and ethical implications of research in genetics and genomics

- evaluate, on the basis of research, the importance of some recent contributions to knowledge, techniques, and technologies related to genetic processes

Developing Skills of Investigation and Communication

- use appropriate terminology related to genetic processes

- investigate the process of meiosis, using a microscope or similar instrument, or a computer simulation, and draw biological diagrams to help explain the main phases in the process

Understanding Basic Concepts

- explain the phases in the process of meiosis in terms of cell division, the movement of chromosomes, and crossing over of genetic material

- explain the concepts of DNA, genes, chromosomes, mitosis and meiosis, and how they account for the transmission of hereditary characteristics

- describe some genetic disorders caused by chromosomal abnormalities

Your body developed from a single cell that formed when a unique sperm fertilized a unique egg cell. A fertilized egg cell, called a zygote, undergoes many successive rounds of cell division. As each cell divides, the number of cells doubles. After about four days of development, the zygote becomes an early embryo called a blastocyst. The blastocyst is a hollow ball of cells surrounding an inner cluster of cells. As the inner cells of the blastocyst divide, they also begin to specialize, becoming various types of body tissue (Figure 4.1). Some cells will make up the brain. Others will form the digestive tract. Still others will become lung tissue, heart tissue, or skin.

It is difficult to imagine, but it is through the processes of cell division that one single cell eventually gives rise to the trillions of cells that make up the body. Even now there are cells in your body that are dividing. Your cells make genetically identical copies of each other to repair damage and to enable your body to grow. When each cell divides, it must duplicate and distribute its genetic information to the new cells. This genetic information, passed down from one generation of cells to another, contains all the instructions that a cell needs in order to function.

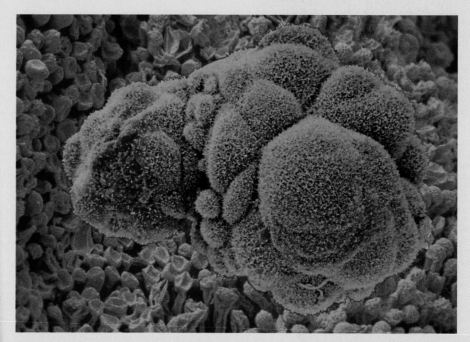

Figure 4.1 This orange cluster of cells is an early human embryo, shown next to the cells of the womb.
(magnification 1200×)

4.1 Structure and Replication of the Genetic Material

Section Summary

- The genetic material is deoxyribonucleic acid (DNA). DNA is packaged into chromatin, which condenses to form chromosomes.

- During interphase of the cell cycle, the cell lives, grows, and replicates its DNA. In mitotic phase (M phase), the chromosomes distribute to daughter cells.

- A duplicated chromosome consists of two sister chromatids.

Each family member in Figure 4.2 looks unique, although the younger members share a certain likeness with their parents. The children also resemble one another much more than they would an unrelated person. Their similarities and uniqueness both result — at least in part — from genetic information inherited from their parents.

Inherited Characteristics

In sexually reproducing species, offspring obtain a unique combination of genetic information from their parents, resulting in a unique combination of characteristics. The resemblances found among family members are due to shared characteristics inherited from their biological parents.

A **trait** is a characteristic of an organism, such as hair colour or the sound of a person's voice. Some traits, such as sun-bleached hair, we acquire as we live. Other traits, such as naturally curly hair, we inherit. Before anyone understood how traits could be inherited, people thought there must be a material that controlled these biological characteristics and was passed down from one generation to the next.

Figure 4.2 Parents pass down some of their traits to their offspring.

The Genetic Material

Until the mid 1900s, the chemical nature of the genetic material remained unknown. Scientists hypothesized that the genetic material consisted of proteins. Proteins could have great variation in their chemical makeup and physical properties, features that the genetic material would also have. However, after a series of experiments with bacteria and viruses, scientists had an incredible breakthrough. They demonstrated that the genetic material was composed of a molecule called **deoxyribonucleic acid (DNA)** (Figure 4.3). DNA was transferred between generations of organisms and had the ability to transform the properties of a cell.

Every cell's DNA is organized into genes. **Genes** are units of inherited information that carry a code for specific traits or functions. Many genes code for proteins. The information contained in genes is responsible for inheritance — the passing down of traits from parent organisms to their offspring.

Figure 4.3 Purified DNA

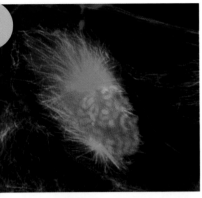

Figure 4.4 Chromosomes in a kangaroo rat kidney cell just before cell division (magnification 1600×)

Packaging of DNA

Plants, fungi, and animals belong to a group of organisms called the eukaryotes. A eukaryotic cell has a nucleus and other internal organelles enclosed by membranes. The nucleus contains the cell's DNA. For much of a cell's life, its DNA exists as a mass of very long fibres called **chromatin,** a combination of DNA and protein. Chromatin is very thin and not usually visible with a light microscope.

As a cell is preparing to divide, its chromatin fibres condense, becoming visible compact structures called chromosomes. A **chromosome** consists of one long, condensed DNA molecule containing hundreds or thousands of genes. A human body cell contains enough DNA to stretch about 2 m in length! In the stained animal cell shown in Figure 4.4, each dark-orange bar is an individual chromosome in the nucleus. The number of chromosomes varies among different species. Human body cells generally have 46 chromosomes, while the body cells of dogs generally have 78 chromosomes.

The DNA in chromatin is tightly coiled around proteins called **histones** (Figure 4.5). The DNA and histone packages form structures resembling beads, called **nucleosomes**. The organization of the DNA prevents it from tangling and being damaged, much as winding thread around a spool keeps the thread in good shape.

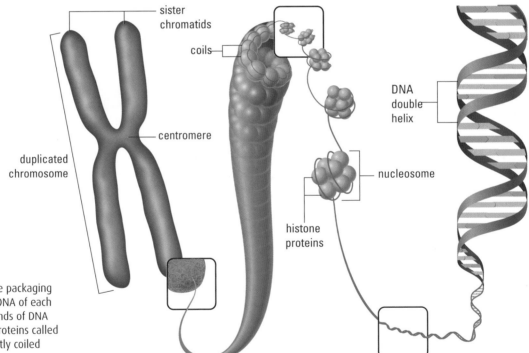

Figure 4.5 An intricate packaging system compacts the DNA of each chromosome. The strands of DNA are wrapped around proteins called histones and then tightly coiled to form chromosomes.

DNA's Structure

In the early 1950s, scientist Rosalind Franklin began to study the structure of DNA. Using a method called X-ray crystallography, a technique that uses X-rays to determine the geometry or arrangement of atoms in a molecule, Franklin determined that DNA had the form of a spiral, or helix. Using Franklin's findings and other research, scientists James Watson and Francis Crick modelled DNA's structure as a twisting shape called a double helix (Figure 4.6). Their model placed sugar-phosphate backbones on the outside of the double helix and subunits called nitrogenous bases on the inside. This model successfully represented DNA's structure.

The Components of DNA

DNA consists of a long chain of subunits called **nucleotides**. A nucleotide has three parts (Figure 4.7):

1. A ring-shaped sugar called deoxyribose

2. A phosphate group

3. A **nitrogenous base** (or base, for short): a single or double ring of carbon and nitrogen atoms

There are four types of nucleotides in DNA, which differ only in their nitrogenous bases. The bases thymine (T) and cytosine (C) are single-ring structures called **pyrimidines** (Figure 4.8). Adenine (A) and guanine (G) are larger, double-ring structures called **purines**. Nucleotides are joined to one another by covalent bonds that connect the sugar of one nucleotide to the phosphate group of the next. This repeating pattern of sugar-phosphate is called the sugar-phosphate backbone.

Scientists noticed very specific pairings between the nucleotides of the two strands of the double helix. They discovered that there are bonds between specific base pairs that provide enough force to hold the two strands in the helix together. It is the placement of these bonds that twists DNA into a spiral shape. The purine adenine pairs with the pyrimidine thymine, and the purine guanine pairs with the pyrimidine cytosine, as shown in Figures 4.8 and 4.9. The bases are called "complementary" bases. A is complementary to T, and G is complementary to C.

Along the strands of the double helix, each base is paired up with its complementary base. Therefore, if the sequence of one strand is known, the sequence of the other strand can be determined. These base-pairing rules set the stage for understanding how the information in DNA is replicated and passed through generations.

Figure 4.6 Watson (left) and Crick with their model of DNA

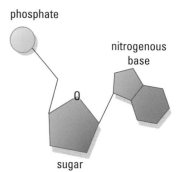

Figure 4.7 A nucleotide

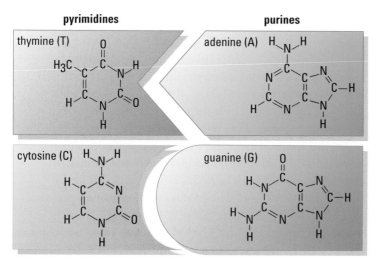

Figure 4.8 DNA contains four different nitrogenous bases.

Figure 4.9 In the DNA double helix, bases pair up between two intertwined sugar-phosphate backbones.

DNA Sequences

We use the 26 letters of the alphabet to spell an almost countless number of words. Like letters of the alphabet, nucleotides can combine in various sequences. For example, the single DNA strand shown in Figure 4.10 has nine nucleotides arranged in the order CTGCTATCG. This arrangement is only one of many possible. Since nucleotide chains also vary in length, from only a few hundred nucleotides to millions of nucleotides, the number of possible nucleotide sequences is essentially unlimited.

Like the arrangement of letters and words in an instruction book, the arrangement of nucleotides in DNA stores information. The genes included in this information code for specific cell proteins and functions.

Figure 4.10 A single DNA strand

Concept Check

1. Define "gene."
2. What are the three main components of a DNA molecule?
3. What is another term for "DNA sequence"?

The Cell Cycle

DNA contains all the instructions a cell needs to function throughout its life. Passing on this genetic information to new cells is an essential part of cell division. Over the course of a eukaryotic cell's life, it will go through an orderly sequence of events known as the **cell cycle** (Figure 4.11). The cell cycle consists of two main stages: a growing stage and a cell division stage.

The growing stage of the cell cycle is called **interphase**. During interphase the cell carries out its metabolic processes and performs its regular cellular activities. A cell may spend as much as 90 percent of the cell cycle in interphase. During this stage, the cell prepares for cell division by increasing its protein supply, creating more cytoplasmic organelles, and growing in size. It is in interphase that the DNA of the cell's chromosomes is duplicated. This period of interphase is called the S phase (S stands for DNA synthesis). The interphase periods before and after the S phase are called the G_1 and G_2 phases (G stands for gap).

The stage of the cell cycle in which the cell divides is called the M phase (M stands for mitotic phase). The M phase includes two processes: mitosis and cytokinesis. During **mitosis**, the nucleus and the duplicated chromosomes divide and are evenly distributed between two "daughter" nuclei. (Mitosis will be discussed in greater detail in section 4.2.) **Cytokinesis** is the process by which the cytoplasm is divided in two. Cytokinesis usually begins before mitosis is complete.

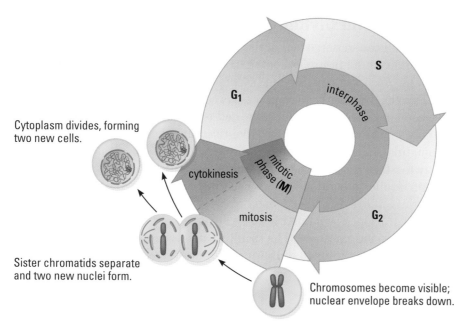

Cytoplasm divides, forming two new cells.

cytokinesis

mitotic phase (M)

G₁

S

interphase

G₂

mitosis

Sister chromatids separate and two new nuclei form.

Chromosomes become visible; nuclear envelope breaks down.

Figure 4.11 During the cell cycle, the cell lives, grows, duplicates its DNA, prepares for cell division, and then divides into two daughter cells.

Cytokinesis

In animal cells, cytokinesis occurs along a cleavage furrow (Figure 4.12). A ring of protein under the plasma membrane contracts, making the cleavage furrow deeper. The cell membrane pinches off the cytoplasm into two halves to form two cells.

Plant cells have cell walls surrounding their cell membranes, so they must use a different process to divide. A structure called a cell plate forms inside the plant cell undergoing mitosis (Figure 4.13). The cell plate contains new cell membrane and cell wall material. As the cell plate grows, daughter cells form on either side of it. Eventually, each cell is bounded by its own continuous membrane and its own cell wall.

Once cytokinesis is complete, two genetically identical daughter cells have been produced. Each daughter cell has a single nucleus, surrounding cytoplasm and organelles, and a plasma membrane.

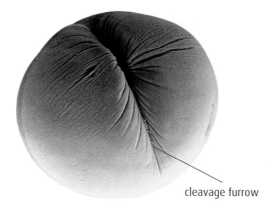

cleavage furrow

Figure 4.12 Cytokinesis in a frog cell (magnification 20×)

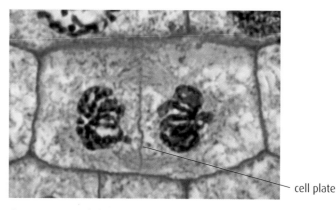

cell plate

Figure 4.13 Cytokinesis in a plant cell (magnification 3200×)

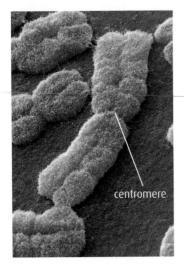

Figure 4.14 Electron microscope image of a human chromosome. Each chromosome consists of two identical chromatids attached at the centromere. (magnification 7000×)

Preparing and Dividing the DNA

Before a cell can undergo cell division, it must duplicate all the genetic information stored in its DNA so that each new cell will have a complete copy. The process of copying the DNA molecule is called DNA replication.

Once the DNA replication process is complete and the chromatin fibres have condensed into chromatids, the cell is ready to undergo division. Each chromosome now consists of two identical joined copies called **sister chromatids** (Figure 4.14). The region where the two chromatids are joined tightly together is called the **centromere**. A dividing human cell starts with 46 duplicated chromosomes, each made up of two sister chromatids. When the cell divides, the 92 sister chromatids separate from each other (Figure 4.15). Once separated from its sister, each chromatid is considered a full-fledged chromosome. The result of the division is two offspring nuclei, each containing 46 individual chromosomes.

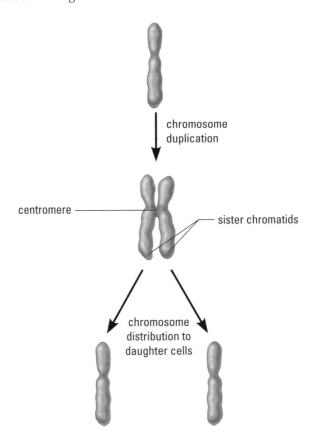

chromosome duplication

centromere — sister chromatids

chromosome distribution to daughter cells

Figure 4.15 Each chromosome in a reproducing cell is duplicated to form a pair of sister chromatids. The sister chromatids then separate to form two individual chromosomes.

BIOLOGY•SOURCE

Explore More

How does DNA replicate?

Every time a eukaryotic cell's DNA replicates, the ends of each chromosome lose a small amount of DNA. However, chromosomes have protective end caps called **telomeres**. Telomere DNA does not contain information for making proteins. When a cell's DNA replicates, the telomeres shorten slightly, but the chromosomes will not lose essential information if enough telomere DNA remains. With successive rounds of cell division, the telomeres eventually become too short, and cells can no longer divide. The ability to replace telomere DNA allows some cells to divide frequently. Cells that the body continually replaces (such as blood cells, skin cells, and the cells lining the intestine) and cells that form sperm and eggs can divide again and again. In contrast, there is a limit to how many times most adult cells can divide.

1. What is a centromere?

2. Why is interphase important?

3. Contrast cytokinesis in animal cells and plant cells.

B1 **Quick Lab**   *BIOLOGY·SOURCE*

Explore DNA's Storage System

Purpose

To examine how DNA is stored in the cell

Figure 4.16 There are many levels of DNA structure.

Activity Overview

It is difficult to imagine how the vast amount of information coded in the DNA molecule can fit inside the nucleus of a cell (Figure 4.16). In this activity, you will review the intricate packing system of DNA.

Your teacher will give you a copy of the full activity.

Prelab Questions

Consider the questions below before beginning this activity.

1. What organelle contains the chromosomes?

2. What is the approximate length of the DNA in a human cell?

3. Why must DNA in a cell be tightly coiled?

B2 **Quick Lab**   *BIOLOGY·SOURCE*

Examine the Stages in the Cell Cycle

Purpose

To examine how cell processes are regulated in the cell cycle

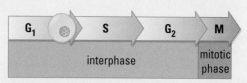

Figure 4.17 Checkpoints after G_1 and G_2 regulate the cell's passage through the cell cycle.

Activity Overview

Biologists study how cells grow and divide in the cell cycle. This process is almost identical in all eukaryotic cells, from yeast to human. In the cell cycle, the cell undergoes four main processes: growth, replication of DNA, mitosis, and division. In this activity, you will discover how these processes are regulated at a number of checkpoints (Figure 4.17).

Your teacher will give you a copy of the full activity.

Prelab Questions

Consider the questions below before beginning this activity.

1. What are some of the limits to cell growth?

2. Describe the necessary preparations a cell must make before it divides (Figure 4.18).

3. What are the main stages in the cell cycle?

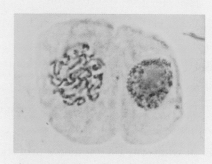

Figure 4.18 The cell on the left is about to divide, while the cell on the right is still in S phase.
(magnification 1500×)

4.1 Check and Reflect

Key Concept Review

1. What does DNA stand for?

2. Describe the components and structure of a DNA molecule.

3. List the four types of nitrogenous bases found in DNA.

4. Summarize what happens during the process of cell division.

5. Describe how a cell's chromatin changes as the cell prepares to divide.

6. What is the role of interphase in cell division?

7. List the following phases of the cell cycle in sequence and briefly describe what occurs in each: M phase, S phase, G_2 phase, G_1 phase.

8. Explain why DNA's structure is called the double helix.

9. List two human traits.

10. Give two reasons that cells divide.

Connect Your Understanding

11. How are the following terms related to one another: DNA, chromatin, chromatid, chromosome?

12. What is the role of DNA in a cell that is not dividing?

13. If the six bases on one strand of a DNA double helix are AGTCGG, what are the six bases on the complementary section of the other strand?

14. Why is it necessary for a cell to replicate its DNA prior to cell division?

15. What is the main difference between a histone and a nucleosome?

16. How many ways can the nucleotide sequence GAT be arranged?

17. What is the difference between a nitrogenous base and a nucleotide?

18. In what way do telomeres protect genetic information?

19. How many chromosomes does a human body cell contain in each of the following periods? Explain.
    (a) G_1 phase
    (b) just before M phase
    (c) just after cytokinesis

20. Interphase is sometimes described as a "resting phase." Why is this description inaccurate?

21. How is it possible for a strand of DNA as long as your arm to fit inside the nucleus of a cell?

22. Suggest what would happen to a single-celled organism if it were to go through many rounds of mitosis but did not go through cytokinesis.

23. Use the table below to answer the questions that follow.

Life Spans of Various Human Cells

Cell Type	Life Span	Cell Division
Red blood cells	< 120 days	Cannot divide
Cardiac (heart) muscle	Long-lived	Cannot divide
Smooth muscle	Long-lived	Can divide
Neuron (nerve cell)	Long-lived	Most do not divide

(a) Which type or types of cells listed in the table would undergo mitosis? Explain.
(b) Red blood cells do not contain nuclei. Explain how this fact relates to red blood cells' inability to divide.

24. Draw and label the following structures:
    (a) an individual chromosome
    (b) sister chromatids

25. Suggest reasons why blood cells and skin cells reproduce more often than other cells in the body.

Reflection

26. How has your understanding of the term "gene" changed since completing this section?

27. Describe three things about DNA that you did not know before working on this section.

For more questions, go to BIOLOGY•SOURCE

Section Summary

- Mitosis is a process of asexual reproduction that produces genetically identical cells. Mitosis distributes the diploid number of chromosomes to daughter cells.

- The stages of mitosis are prophase, metaphase, anaphase, and telophase.

- Meiosis occurs in sexual reproduction. It distributes an assortment of chromosomes to the gametes.

- In meiosis I, homologous chromosomes exchange pieces of DNA and then separate to new, haploid cells. In meiosis II, sister chromatids separate to new, haploid cells.

The timing and regulation of cell division are critical for normal growth and development. A control system that depends on specific proteins within the cell regulates the sequence of events in the cell cycle. If a cell reproduces at the wrong time, or in the wrong place, it may end up forming a mass of cells called a tumour. Malignant tumours are especially dangerous. They are masses of cells that result from the reproduction of cancer cells (Figure 4.19).

Cancer is a disease caused by the severe disruption of the mechanisms that regulate the cell cycle. The disruption leads to uncontrolled cell division, which if unchecked can affect the entire body and even become fatal. The most dangerous characteristic of cancer cells is their ability to spread. A malignant tumour displaces normal tissue as it grows. If the malignant tumour is not killed or removed, it can metastasize. This means that the cancer cells spread into other tissues or organs of the body. Many different biochemical changes can affect the cell cycle and result in cancer. For this reason, there is no single "cure," but rather multiple approaches to controlling or halting the progress of the disease.

Figure 4.19 Cancer cells may be abnormally large and have more than one nucleus each. In this light microscope image of liver cancer cells, the red cells are undergoing mitosis. (magnification 1200×)

Mitosis and Asexual Reproduction

Cell division — when it occurs correctly — is essential for living and is the basis of reproduction for every organism. The *Paramecium* in Figure 4.20 is undergoing cell division. Single-celled organisms often reproduce by simple cell division, in which a single cell or group of cells splits into two new genetically identical cells. The two new cells rapidly grow and develop into organisms that are genetic clones of one another. Under ideal conditions, a *Paramecium* can divide as often as three times a day. This process, known as **asexual reproduction,** produces offspring that inherit all their genetic material from just one parent. As a result, the offspring are genetically identical to each other and to their parent.

Asexual reproduction also enables multicellular organisms to grow and to repair and replace worn-out or damaged cells. Cells of the body are known as **somatic cells**. How often a somatic cell divides depends on the type of cell and its role in the body. Some cells, such as skin cells, divide every few days. Other cells, such as highly specialized muscle cells, do not divide at all. When a single-celled organism or somatic cell divides, it must go through a precise sequence of steps in order to create daughter cells that are genetically identical to the original parent cell.

Explore More

What happens when the control system of the cell cycle malfunctions?

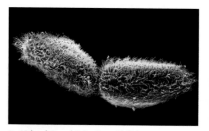

Dr. Richard Kessel & Dr. Gene Shih/ Visuals Unlimited, Inc.

Figure 4.20 A *Paramecium* reproduces by simple cell division, producing offspring that are genetically identical to the parent. (magnification 100×)

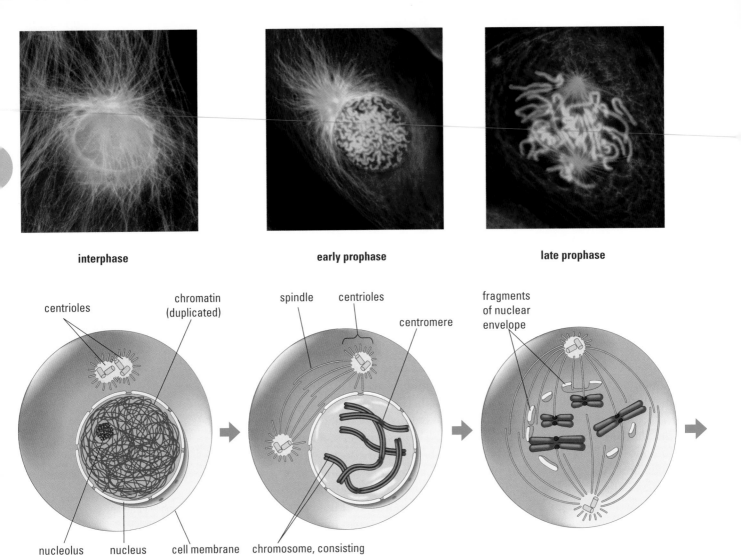

interphase   **early prophase**   **late prophase**

centrioles   chromatin (duplicated)

spindle   centrioles

centromere

fragments of nuclear envelope

nucleolus   nucleus   cell membrane

chromosome, consisting of two sister chromatids

Figure 4.21 Mitosis begins after the chromosomes have duplicated in interphase and ends when telophase is complete. There are four main phases: prophase, metaphase, anaphase, and telophase. (magnification 1450×)

Phases of Mitosis

After interphase, the cell's DNA has been replicated and the M phase can begin. Mitosis distributes the duplicated sets of chromosomes to two daughter nuclei, and cytokinesis divides the cytoplasm, producing two daughter cells. The events of mitosis include four continuous phases: prophase, metaphase, anaphase, and telophase (Figure 4.21). The length of time a cell remains in mitosis depends on the type of cell and can vary from a few minutes to several days.

During interphase, the cell replicates its DNA and makes other new molecules and organelles. At this stage the individual chromosomes are not yet visible because they are still loosely packed fibres of chromatin. The presence of the nucleolus, a dark-staining region of the nucleus, indicates that the cell is actively making proteins. In **prophase**, the first stage of mitosis, the sister chromatids become visible. In animal cells, the centrioles, two tiny structures located in the cytoplasm, separate and move to opposite sides of the nucleus. The sister chromatids attach to the long fibres of the spindle. By the end of this stage, the nucleolus disappears and the nuclear envelope breaks down.

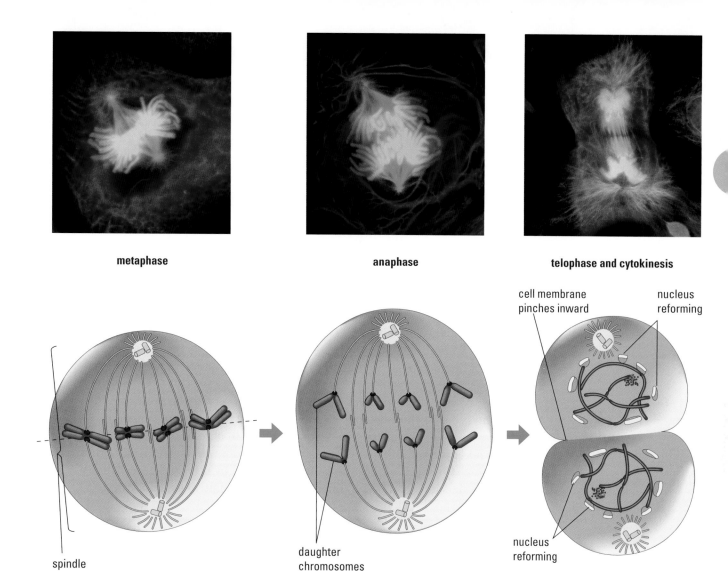

metaphase

anaphase

telophase and cytokinesis

cell membrane
pinches inward

nucleus
reforming

spindle

daughter
chromosomes

nucleus
reforming

During **metaphase**, the second stage of mitosis, the sister chromatids are fully attached to the spindle fibres. The spindle fibres move the chromatids and line them up across the middle of the cell. **Anaphase** is the third stage of mitosis. During this stage, the sister chromatids separate from their partners to become individual chromosomes. The spindle fibres pull the chromosomes to opposite ends of the cell, as if reeling in fishing lines. Once the chromosomes have reached the poles and are in two separate groups, anaphase is complete.

The final stage of mitosis is **telophase**. During this stage, the chromosomes begin to uncoil and take the form of chromatin, the spindle fibres disappear, and nuclear envelopes re-form around each set of daughter chromosomes. At the end of this stage, mitosis is complete. Cytokinesis completes cell division by dividing the cytoplasm into two daughter cells, each with its own nucleus. This process usually occurs at the same time as telophase.

Concept Check

1. What is the role of mitosis?

2. Summarize the events that occur during mitosis and cytokinesis.

3. At the end of cell division, how does the number of chromosomes in the two new daughter cells compare with the number in the original parent cell?

Meiosis and Sexual Reproduction

The process in which two parents provide genetic material in order to produce offspring is called **sexual reproduction**. With sexual reproduction, some of the genetic material from each parent combines, producing offspring that differ genetically from both parents. Each of the offspring inherits a unique combination of traits.

Sexual reproduction depends on a specialized type of cell division called meiosis. **Meiosis** is a form of cell division that produces four cells, each containing half the number of chromosomes as the parent cell. In animals, meiosis occurs in the sex organs — testes in males and the ovaries in females.

Almost all cells in an individual organism have the same number and types of chromosomes. For example, a typical human somatic cell has 23 pairs of chromosomes, for a total of 46 chromosomes. Figure 4.22 is a **karyotype**, a display of all the chromosomes in a cell or individual. Notice that each of these chromosomes has a near twin that resembles it in size and shape. You inherit one chromosome of each pair from

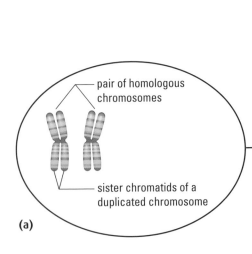

pair of homologous chromosomes

sister chromatids of a duplicated chromosome

(a)

Figure 4.22 (a) An illustration of how a homologous pair of chromosomes would look if you could distinguish the sister chromatids. (b) A display of the 46 chromosomes (or 23 pairs of chromosomes) in an individual. Each chromosome actually consists of two chromatids, but these cannot be distinguished. (magnification 1300×)

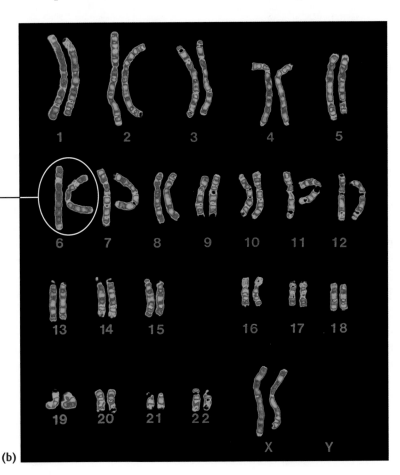

(b)

©P

your mother and the other from your father. The two chromosomes of each matching pair are called **homologous chromosomes**. Each member of a pair of homologous chromosomes carries the same series of genes controlling the same inherited traits.

Most human cells are **diploid**, meaning they contain two sets of chromosomes. The total number of chromosomes, 46 in humans, is called the diploid number. The diploid number is often represented by $2n$. So, in humans, $2n = 46$. An exception to diploid cells are the sex cells. The sex cells (egg cells and sperm) are also known as **gametes**. Each gamete has only a single set of chromosomes, one from each homologous pair. A cell with a single set of chromosomes is called a **haploid** cell. For humans, the haploid number (represented by n) is 23. The haploid gametes are produced through the process of meiosis.

Meiosis Maintains the Correct Number of Chromosomes

In the life cycle of sexually reproducing organisms, the nucleus of a haploid sperm from the father fuses with the nucleus of a haploid egg cell from the mother (Figure 4.23). The fusion of the nuclei along with the cytoplasm from the gametes is called fertilization. The resulting fertilized egg is called a **zygote**.

The zygote is diploid because it contains pairs of homologous chromosomes ($2 \times 23 = 46$), one set from each parent. In other words, the zygote is diploid because the gametes were haploid. Had the gametes been diploid, the zygote would have twice the number of chromosomes that it should ($2 \times 2 \times 23 = 92$). Meiosis, therefore, enables the zygote to have the correct number of chromosomes. Eventually the diploid zygote will develop into a sexually mature adult with trillions of cells produced by mitosis (Figure 4.24).

BIOLOGY•SOURCE

Explore More

What happens to the chromosomes during meiosis?

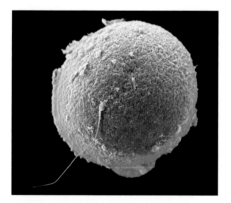

Figure 4.23 Sperm entering an egg during fertilization. (magnification 380×)

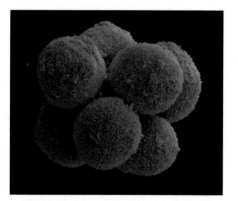

Figure 4.24 After three rounds of mitosis and cytokinesis, an embryo consists of eight cells. (magnification 600×)

The Sex Chromosomes

One set of chromosomes, called the **sex chromosomes**, determines an individual's sex. All other chromosomes are called **autosomes**. In humans, the 23rd pair of chromosomes are the sex chromosomes. These chromosomes have different forms, called X and Y. In mammals, females have two X chromosomes, while males have one X chromosome and one Y chromosome (Figure 4.25). An egg cell contains an X chromosome. A sperm, however, may contain either an X or a Y. If a sperm with an X chromosome fertilizes an egg, the zygote will typically develop into a female. If the sperm has a Y chromosome, the zygote will develop into a male.

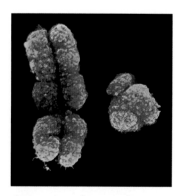

Figure 4.25 In humans, the X chromosome (left) is much larger than the Y chromosome (right). (magnification 7600×)

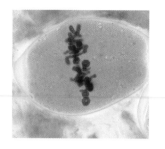

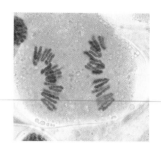

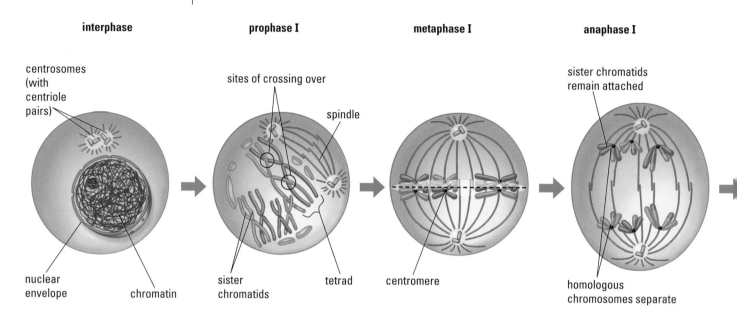

meiosis I: homologous chromosomes separate

| interphase | prophase I | metaphase I | anaphase I |

interphase

centrosomes (with centriole pairs)

nuclear envelope   chromatin

prophase I

sites of crossing over

spindle

sister chromatids   tetrad

metaphase I

centromere

anaphase I

sister chromatids remain attached

homologous chromosomes separate

Figure 4.26 The stages of meiosis. Meiosis I begins with a diploid cell with duplicated chromosomes. Meiosis II ends with four haploid daughter cells. The microscope images show stained cells from a lily plant. (magnification 350×)

BIOLOGY•SOURCE

Explore More

What does the motion of chromosomes in meiosis look like and what are the results?

Phases of Meiosis

Many phases of meiosis are similar to those of mitosis. And as with mitosis, the DNA replicates before meiosis begins. However, unlike mitosis, this single round of DNA replication is followed by two distinct cell division stages: meiosis I and meiosis II. By the end of meiosis II, the original diploid cell has become four haploid cells. Figure 4.26 shows the phases of meiosis in detail.

Similar to prophase of mitosis, **prophase I** begins with two complete sets of duplicated chromosomes in the form of sister chromatids. During prophase I, each duplicated chromosome pairs with its corresponding homologous chromosome, forming a tetrad. The homologous chromosomes then exchange portions of DNA. The exchange of DNA segments is called **genetic recombination**. During **metaphase I**, the tetrads move to the middle of the cell and line up.

In **anaphase I**, homologous chromosomes separate from the tetrad and migrate to opposite poles of the spindle. Sister chromatids remain attached at their centromeres. In **telophase I**, the nuclear membrane re-forms around each cluster of chromosomes. At this stage, the chromosomes of each daughter cell are present in duplicate (as sister chromatids), although each cell is considered haploid. The cells must go through a second division in order to have the correct number of chromosomes.

©P

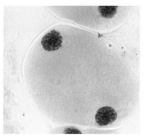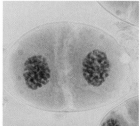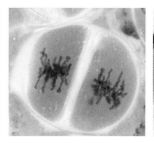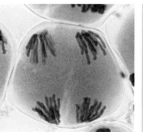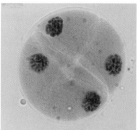

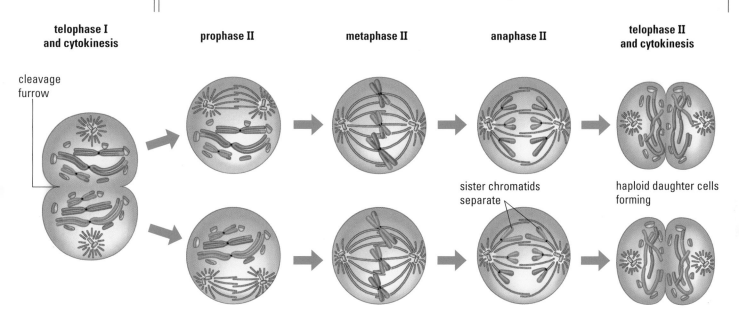

meiosis II: sister chromatids separate

| telophase I and cytokinesis | prophase II | metaphase II | anaphase II | telophase II and cytokinesis |

cleavage furrow

sister chromatids separate

haploid daughter cells forming

Unlike prophase I, prophase II is not preceded by a round of DNA replication. During **prophase II**, in each haploid daughter cell, a spindle forms and attaches to the centromeres of the sister chromatids. In **metaphase II**, the spindle, attached to the centromeres, moves the sister chromatids so that they line up in the middle of the cell.

In **anaphase II**, the sister chromatids separate and move to opposite poles of the cell. Once separated, they are considered individual chromosomes. When **telophase II** begins, the chromosomes are at the poles. Separate nuclei begin to form around each group of chromosomes. Cytokinesis splits the cells one more time. The process of meiosis is complete, with four haploid daughter cells the final result.

BIOLOGY•SOURCE

Suggested Activity
• B3 Inquiry Activity Overview on page 114

New Gene Combinations

Offspring that result from sexual reproduction are genetically different from their parents and from one another. The genetic variety in offspring arises through the processes of meiosis and fertilization. Each parent contributes a unique combination of genes to the offspring, and this set of genes codes for a unique combination of traits.

The way in which chromosomes assort or distribute during meiosis contributes to variation in the gametes. How the chromosomes in each homologous pair (tetrad) line up and separate in metaphase I occurs by chance. Therefore, the assortment of chromosomes in the resulting gametes is random. In the example shown in Figure 4.27, the original cell contains only two pairs of homologous chromosomes. Even so, there are four possible combinations of chromosomes in the gametes.

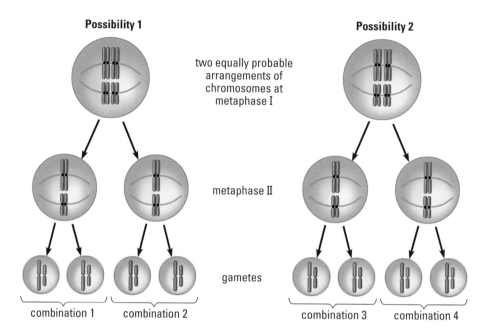

Possibility 1

two equally probable arrangements of chromosomes at metaphase I

metaphase II

gametes

combination 1   combination 2

Possibility 2

combination 3   combination 4

Figure 4.27 Random assortment of chromosomes in meiosis results in gametes with different combinations of chromosomes.

BIOLOGY•SOURCE

Suggested Activity

• B4 Quick Lab Overview on page 114

Crossing Over

In addition to the random assortment of chromosomes, in prophase I of meiosis there is an exchange of genetic material between homologous chromosomes. This exchange is called **crossing over**. Figure 4.28 shows crossing over in one tetrad. When crossing over takes place, homologous chromosomes are closely paired along their lengths. Each gene on one pair of sister chromatids is precisely lined up with the corresponding gene on the adjacent pair of sister chromatids. This close association between homologous chromosomes in early meiosis is known as **synapsis**. At regions called chiasmata, chromatids from different pairs are attached and segments of the chromatids are exchanged.

Genetic recombination results in chromosomes with new combinations of genetic information different from those carried by the original chromosomes. Without this process, every chromosome produced by meiosis would be purely of maternal origin or purely of paternal origin. One single cross-over event can affect many genes on a chromosome. Since more than one cross-over event can occur in each tetrad, it is no wonder that the resulting gametes and offspring can be so varied.

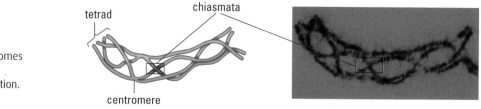

tetrad

chiasmata

centromere

Figure 4.28 Crossing over between maternal chromosomes and paternal chromosomes produces genetic recombination. (magnification 2200×)

©P

Comparing Mitosis and Meiosis

Figure 4.29 compares two types of cell reproduction in eukaryotic organisms: mitosis and meiosis. Mitosis, which provides for growth, repair, and asexual reproduction, produces diploid daughter cells that are genetically identical to their parent cell. Meiosis, on the other hand, produces the specialized egg cells and sperm of sexually reproducing organisms. Unlike mitosis, meiosis produces haploid daughter cells with the haploid number of chromosomes. Chromosome assortment and crossing over during meiosis produce a large variety of possible gene combinations in the gametes.

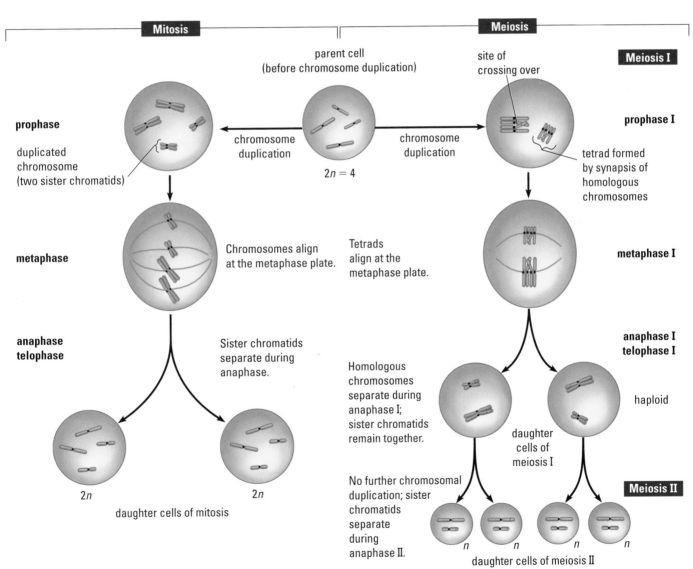

Figure 4.29 Comparison of mitosis and meiosis

B3 Inquiry Activity · BIOLOGY·SOURCE

REQUIRED SKILLS
- Using appropriate equipment and tools
- Recording and organizing data

Observe Meiosis

Question

How can you recognize the different phases of meiosis?

Activity Overview

Meiosis is the process of cell division that produces sperm and egg cells. Meiosis has two distinct divisions, meiosis I and meiosis II. In this investigation, you will use prepared slides to investigate the process of meiosis, and draw biological diagrams to help explain the main phases in the process (Figures 4.30 and 4.31).

Your teacher will give you a copy of the full activity.

Prelab Questions

Consider the questions below before beginning this activity.

1. How do the process and genetic results of meiosis differ from those of mitosis?

2. What type of cells undergo meiosis?

3. What is one advantage of meiosis in sexually reproducing organisms?

4. What are the two elements of meiosis that contribute to genetic variation?

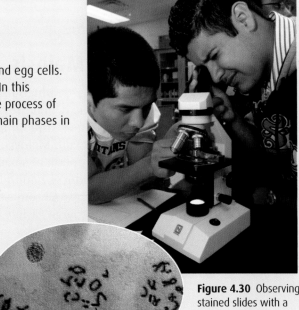

Figure 4.30 Observing stained slides with a light microscope

Figure 4.31 Microscope image of cells in anaphase I of meiosis (magnification 625×)

Analyze the Process of Crossing Over

Purpose

To visualize how crossing over leads to new gene combinations on chromosomes

Activity Overview

This activity models how new combinations of genes are formed when two homologous chromosomes exchange pieces during meiosis (Figure 4.32). You will observe how this process, called crossing over, increases genetic variation.

Your teacher will give you a copy of the full activity.

Prelab Questions

Consider the questions below before beginning this activity.

1. What are regions of chiasmata?

2. During what stage of meiosis does crossing over occur?

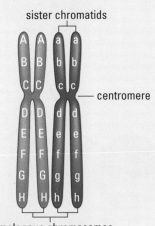

Figure 4.32 A pair of homologous chromosomes

Key Concept Review

1. List the four stages of mitosis in the correct sequence and briefly describe what happens in each stage.

2. What is the function of the spindle during mitosis?

3. What is the special name for the 23rd pair of chromosomes in humans?

4. Where does the process of meiosis occur in organisms?

5. How does meiosis I differ from meiosis II?

6. What is a tetrad composed of?

7. What stage in meiosis is represented by the illustration below? How do you know?

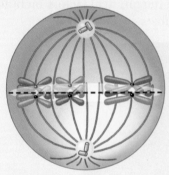

Question 7

(a) prophase I
(b) anaphase II
(c) telophase I
(d) metaphase I

8. List the following events in the correct sequence and describe what happens during each event: anaphase I, metaphase II, prophase I, telophase II.

9. Name two factors that introduce genetic variation during the process of meiosis.

10. Explain how genetic recombination occurs between homologous chromosomes.

Connect Your Understanding

11. What is the consequence to a human gamete if there is no crossing over in meiosis I?

12. How does the process of crossing over during meiosis in an individual organism recombine the genetic material of the organism's two parents?

13. Each type of eukaryotic organism has a characteristic number of chromosomes. Human somatic cells generally have 46 chromosomes in their nuclei, while fruit flies generally have 8 chromosomes. If there was only one round of cell division in meiosis, how might this affect the chromosome numbers in offspring? Explain.

14. Human nerve cells rarely undergo mitosis. On the basis of this information, why do you think complete recovery from a nervous-system injury is rare?

15. Compare the number of sets of chromosomes in human gametes with the number of sets in other cells of the body.

16. If an organism generally has 8 chromosomes in its somatic cells, how many chromosomes will its gametes contain?

17. During meiosis only chromosomes, not individual genes, assort randomly. Why?

18. Given what you have read in this section, explain why it is so important to stay away from substances that may alter or damage the DNA in your cells.

19. When organisms reproduce through asexual reproduction, mitosis occurs but not meiosis. Now that you have studied the process of meiosis, suggest the role of sexual reproduction in producing genetically varied offspring.

Reflection

20. What is the most important concept you learned about cell division from this section? Why do you think it is the most important?

21. How has your understanding of the role of chromosomes in the human body changed since completing this section?

For more questions, go to BIOLOGY•SOURCE

4.3 Alterations in Chromosome Structure and Number

Section Summary

- Errors in meiosis can lead to errors in chromosome number in gametes. Embryos that develop from these gametes will have missing or extra chromosomes.
- Duplication, deletion, inversion, and translocation are types of damage that can occur to chromosomes during meiosis.
- Genetic testing can be an important part of diagnosing, treating, or preventing particular genetic conditions.

The photograph in Figure 4.33 is taken from a scene in a performance by the Famous PEOPLE Players. The actors use a theatrical black light show to create stunning visual effects. Founded in 1974, this theatre company is dedicated to employing people who have developmental disabilities. A **developmental disability** is a lifelong disability due to mental or physical impairment. Developmental disabilities can be caused by social, environmental, or physical factors. Some of the physical factors include abnormalities in genes or chromosome numbers.

Figure 4.33 The Famous PEOPLE Players

Atypical Chromosome Numbers

In most cases, a human embryo with an atypical number of chromosomes does not survive and the mother has a miscarriage (loses the pregnancy). Some embryos with atypical chromosome numbers do survive, depending on which chromosomes are affected. **Trisomy**, for example, is a condition in which an individual has three copies of a particular chromosome.

Down syndrome is a condition in which the individual carries an extra copy of chromosome 21 (Figure 4.34). Also known as trisomy 21, this syndrome is characterized by mild to severe developmental delays, characteristic facial features, and below average height. Other traits typically include heart defects and an impaired immune system. Though people with Down syndrome have life expectancies shorter than average, they can live to middle age or beyond and have productive, happy lives.

Figure 4.34 The man conducting this orchestra has Down syndrome.

©P

Non-disjunction

Meiosis occurs repeatedly in a person's lifetime as the testes produce sperm or the ovaries complete production of eggs. Almost always, the meiotic spindle distributes chromosomes to the daughter cells without error. Occasionally, accidents can occur during meiosis that alter chromosome number. When homologous chromosomes do not separate during anaphase I or II of meiosis, **non-disjunction** occurs. This results in gametes with either missing or extra chromosomes. If an abnormal gamete produced by a non-disjunction event unites with a normal gamete in fertilization, the result is a zygote that contains an atypical number of chromosomes. Mitosis will then carry this number of chromosomes to all of the embryonic cells.

Down syndrome is one condition that can result from non-disjunction during meiosis (Figure 4.35). Table 4.1 lists some others.

BIOLOGY•SOURCE

Suggested Activity
• B5 Quick Lab Overview on page 122

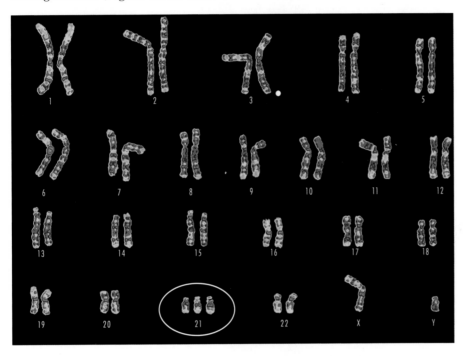

Figure 4.35 People with Down syndrome have an extra copy of chromosome 21, as shown in this karyotype. (magnification 1000×)

Table 4.1 Conditions Caused by Non-disjunction of Chromosomes

Chromsome Number	Condition	Traits
Trisomy 13	Patau syndrome	Affects approximately 1 in 16 000 live births. This condition results in severe intellectual disability and physical abnormalities. Individuals often have heart defects, brain or spinal cord abnormalities, small or poorly developed eyes, extra fingers and/or toes, a cleft lip, and weak muscle tone. Only 5–10% of babies survive past their first year.
Trisomy 18	Edwards syndrome	Affects approximately 1 in 5000 live births. This condition is associated with severe intellectual disability and low birth weight; a small, abnormally shaped head; a small jaw and mouth; clenched fists; heart defects; and other organ abnormalities. Only 5–10% of babies survive past their first year.
Trisomy 21	Down syndrome	Affects approximately 1 in 800 live births. This condition is associated with a mild to moderate intellectual disability, a characteristic facial appearance, and poor muscle tone (hypotonia) in infancy.
XXY	Klinefelter syndrome	Affects approximately 1 in 500 to 1 in 1000 males. This condition affects male sexual development and results in small testes that do not produce enough testosterone. The shortage of testosterone can lead to breast enlargement, reduced facial and body hair, and infertility. Some affected boys are very shy and/or have learning disabilities. Testosterone injections help treat the condition.

Figures 4.36 and 4.37 illustrate two ways that non-disjunction can occur. What causes non-disjunction? The answer is not fully known. It is clear, however, that there is a direct correlation between a woman's age and the likelihood of non-disjunction occurring (Figure 4.38). Meiosis begins in the female's ovaries before she is born but is not completed until meiosis resumes during ovulation. Since only one egg is released each month, egg cells may remain stopped in the middle of meiosis for decades. Some research suggests that damage to the cell during this lag time may contribute to errors in meiosis.

Occurrence of Down Syndrome vs. Age of Mother
Infants with Down Syndrome (per 1000 births)
90
80
70
60
50
40
30
20
10
0
20 25 30 35 40 45 50
Age of Mother

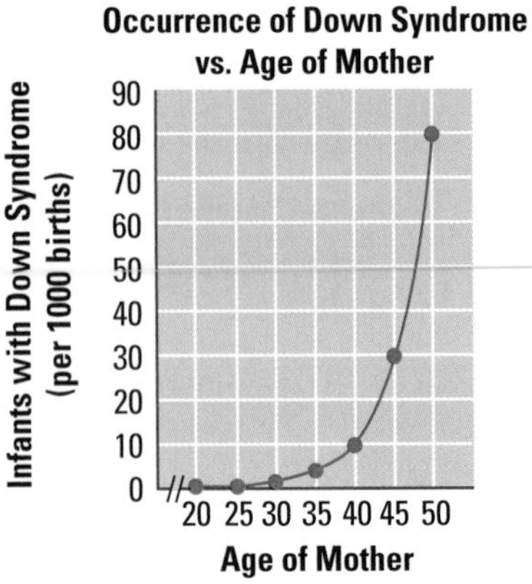

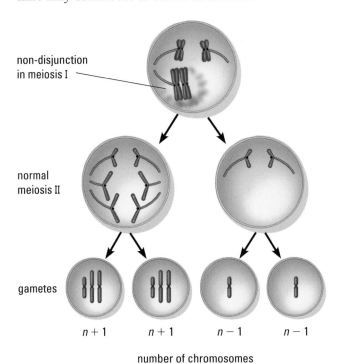

Figure 4.38 The chance of having a baby with trisomy 21 increases with the mother's age.

non-disjunction in meiosis I
normal meiosis II
gametes
n + 1
n + 1
n − 1
n − 1
number of chromosomes

Figure 4.36 Non-disjunction in meiosis I

normal meiosis I
non-disjunction in meiosis II
gametes
n + 1
n − 1
n
n
number of chromosomes

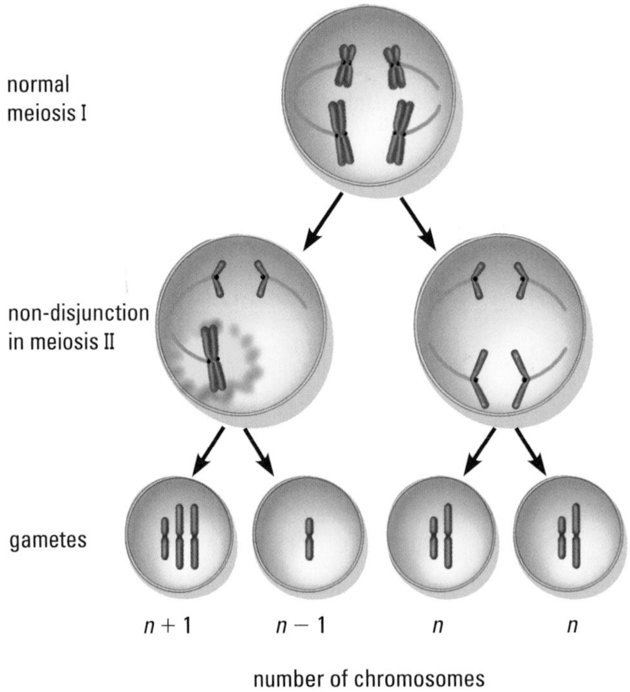

Figure 4.37 Non-disjunction in meisosis II

BIOLOGY•SOURCE

Explore More

How does non-disjunction contribute to the evolution of plants?

Damage to Chromosome Structure

A **mutation** is any change to the DNA of a cell. Some mutations change only one or a few base pairs in a DNA sequence. Other mutations occur at the level of chromosomes. Large-scale mutations that damage chromosome structure can occur when something unusual happens during crossing over. One such chromosomal change is translocation. A **translocation** occurs when a fragment of one chromosome attaches to a nonhomologous chromosome (Figure 4.39). Translocation Down syndrome, for example, is a condition that results when translocation occurs between chromosomes 21 and 14. With translocation Down syndrome, a person inherits two normal copies of chromosome 14 and one that has a piece of chromosome 21 attached to it. The extra material from chromosome 21, like trisomy 21, causes Down syndrome.

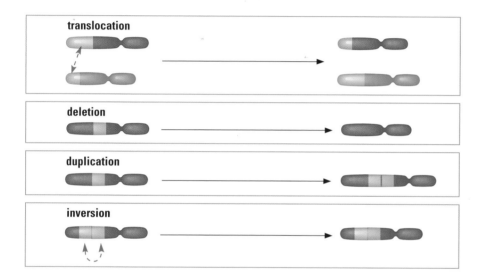

Figure 4.39 Changes to a chromosome's structure may have various effects. Part of the chromosomes may be duplicated, deleted, inverted, or translocated to another chromosome.

Sometimes translocations result in deletions. A **deletion** occurs when a fragment of a chromosome is lost. Because much of our DNA does not contain genes, small deletions are not usually harmful. However, if the lost fragment contains one or more genes, then the instructions for making certain proteins may be lost. Those proteins have specific functions in the body. Large deletions, therefore, typically have serious effects on the body. Prader-Willi syndrome, for example, results from a deletion in chromosome 15. Affected children have developmental delays and learning disabilities, behavioural problems, obesity, short stature, decreased muscle tone, and sex glands that produce little or no hormones (Figure 4.40).

A **duplication** is a chromosomal change that occurs when part of a chromosome is repeated. The repeated region sometimes includes an entire gene. Interestingly, if a region is only repeated once, the duplication may have no effect. If a region is repeated three or more times, as sometimes occurs on chromosome 15, the impact may include seizures and developmental delays. Another type of change, an **inversion**, reverses a fragment of the original chromosome. Most of the genes are still present in their normal number and some may function. However, inversions can cause problems with the synapsis of chromosomes during meiosis, so someone with a chromosomal inversion may have difficulties conceiving a baby.

Figure 4.40 Individuals with Prader-Willi syndrome can benefit from highly structured learning environments, therapy to improve muscle tone, and having their food intake closely monitored to prevent severe obesity.

Concept Check

1. What causes translocations?

2. List one condition associated with non-disjunction.

3. List four types of damage to chromosome structure that can cause disorders.

Genetic Testing

Modern technologies offer many ways to obtain information about the genetic makeup of an individual. This can be an important part of diagnosing, treating, or preventing a particular illness (Figure 4.41). There are several types of genetic tests available.

In addition to karyotype analysis, genetic testing can include screening for specific gene sequences. For example, people considering having children may suspect that they are carrying mutations for a genetic condition such as cystic fibrosis or Tay-Sachs disease. These diseases are due to base pair changes. Cystic fibrosis causes debilitating disease of the lungs and digestive system. Tay-Sachs disease, which is most common among French Canadians and certain Jewish populations, attacks an infant's nervous system and results in death by five years of age. Couples may wish to know their risk of passing down such a condition before they have children. **Carrier testing** can determine if an individual carries a copy of a mutation that his or her children could inherit.

A person with a family history of a genetic condition may want to undergo genetic testing to find out his or her risk of developing the condition. This type of testing is called predictive or **presymptomatic testing** and is usually done for disorders that appear after birth or later in a person's life. **Diagnostic genetic testing** is used to confirm a diagnosis when symptoms for a particular genetic condition are present. Slurred speech and shaking, for example, are symptoms of many unrelated conditions, including Huntington's disease. Diagnostic testing could be used to confirm that Huntington's disease is the cause. This type of testing can be conducted at any time during a person's life.

Figure 4.41 A genetic counsellor helps a couple to interpret genetic tests.

Prenatal Testing

A human embryo becomes a fetus about seven weeks after fertilization. **Prenatal testing** is used to detect small-scale mutations or chromosomal alterations in a fetus. Spina bifida and Down syndrome are two genetic conditions that are often screened for using prenatal genetic testing. Spina bifida is a birth defect that involves the incomplete development of the spinal cord and may result in a protrusion from an opening in the spine. In some cases this condition has a genetic component that can be detected through genetic screening.

Amniocentesis is a prenatal screening procedure performed between weeks 14 and 20 of pregnancy (Figure 4.42, left). A physician inserts a needle into the mother's uterus and extracts some of the amniotic fluid that surrounds the developing fetus. The fetal cells are then tested for genetic disorders, through a process of karyotyping or biochemical tests.

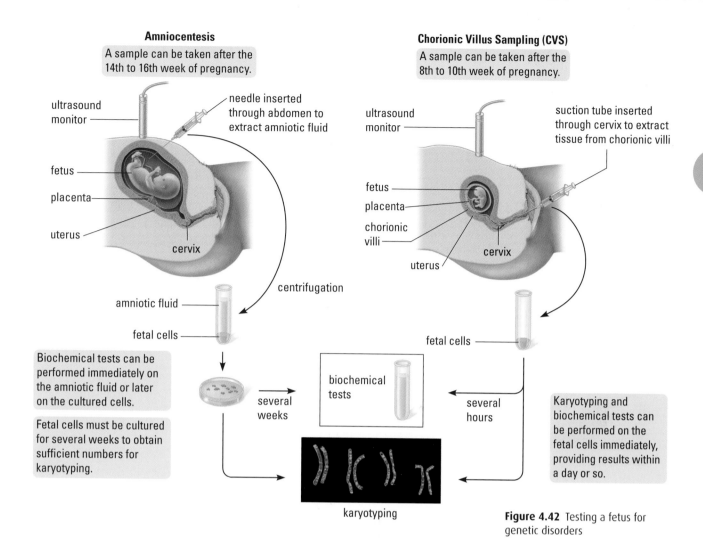

Amniocentesis

A sample can be taken after the 14th to 16th week of pregnancy.

ultrasound monitor

needle inserted through abdomen to extract amniotic fluid

fetus

placenta

uterus

cervix

amniotic fluid

centrifugation

fetal cells

Biochemical tests can be performed immediately on the amniotic fluid or later on the cultured cells.

Fetal cells must be cultured for several weeks to obtain sufficient numbers for karyotyping.

several weeks

biochemical tests

karyotyping

Chorionic Villus Sampling (CVS)

A sample can be taken after the 8th to 10th week of pregnancy.

ultrasound monitor

suction tube inserted through cervix to extract tissue from chorionic villi

fetus

placenta

chorionic villi

cervix

uterus

fetal cells

several hours

Karyotyping and biochemical tests can be performed on the fetal cells immediately, providing results within a day or so.

Figure 4.42 Testing a fetus for genetic disorders

Chorionic villus sampling (CVS) is another procedure used for fetal testing (figure 4.42, right). Chorionic villi are fingerlike projections that protrude from the tissue surrounding the fetus. A physician extracts a small sample of chorionic villi by inserting a narrow, flexible tube into the mother's uterus. This procedure can be conducted as early as the 8th week of pregnancy, enabling earlier detection than amniocentesis. Unfortunately, both of these procedures pose some risk of complication and can lead to maternal bleeding, miscarriage, or premature birth. Therefore, these procedures are usually conducted only if there is a high risk of genetic disorder.

Newborn Screening

Newborn screening can detect some genetic disorders at birth through simple tests performed in hospitals. Shortly after birth, newborns are screened for phenylketonuria (PKU). PKU is an inherited disorder that results in the inability of children to break down the naturally occurring amino acid phenylalanine. An accumulation of phenylalanine may lead to severe developmental delays. Therefore, the detection of this condition in a newborn can prevent retardation. A diet low in phenylalanine is usually sufficient to prevent the onset of developmental delays.

BIOLOGY SOURCE

Take It Further

Non-disjunction of chromosomes during meiosis can also affect sex chromosomes. The effects of this can vary from no visible symptoms to severe symptoms. Research two different syndromes caused by non-disjunction of sex chromosomes and report your findings.

Construct and Analyze Karyotypes

Purpose

To construct and analyze karyotypes

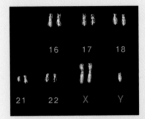

Figure 4.43 Part of a karyotype for someone with chromosome alterations (magnification 500×)

Figure 4.44 Constructing a karyotype

Activity Overview

A photographic display of chromosomes is called a karyotype (Figure 4.43). A typical human karyotype shows that each somatic cell contains 46 chromosomes in 23 pairs. You inherit one member of each chromosome pair from each of your parents. In this activity, you will construct a human karyotype (Figure 4.44).

Your teacher will give you a copy of the full activity.

Prelab Questions

Consider the questions below before beginning this activity.

1. Define the term "autosome."

2. What type of information can be obtained from an individual's karyotype?

3. What type of genetic alteration would be the most identifiable from a karyotype? Explain.

REQUIRED SKILLS
- Selecting and recording information
- Stating a conclusion

Who Controls Your Genetic Information?

Issue

With the rapid development of genetic tools, the ability to test individuals for genetic conditions has dramatically improved. Are laws protecting genetic privacy necessary?

Activity Overview

An issue that arises with genetic-testing technology is how to regulate the use of, storage, and access to the information obtained from testing. Should third parties such as employers, insurance companies, health-care providers, and governments have access to your genetic information (Figure 4.45)?

You will research this issue and then present your findings.

Your teacher will give you a copy of the full activity.

Prelab Questions

Consider the questions below before beginning this activity.

1. Define the term "mutation."

2. List the types of chromosomal alterations that can occur.

3. What types of mutations can genetic testing detect?

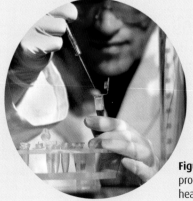

Figure 4.45 Genetic testing provides information about our health risks.

4.3 Check and Reflect

Key Concept Review

1. What is a chromosomal mutation?

2. What is a karyotype?

3. Describe two conditions that result from chromosome changes.

4. (a) What are the primary benefits of prenatal genetic testing using CVS?
   (b) What are some risks associated with this procedure?

5. What are some of the characteristics of Prader-Willi syndrome?

6. Give an example of a genetic condition that can result from errors in meiosis.

7. Which of the following shows an inversion?

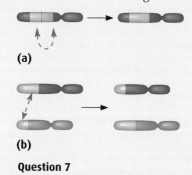

   (a)

   (b)

   Question 7

8. What is the karyotype of an individual with Klinefelter syndrome?

9. What are the main differences between the tests done in carrier testing and in newborn screening?

10. What populations in Canada are most affected by Tay-Sachs disease?

Connect Your Understanding

11. (a) How is a mother's age related to the probability of non-disjunction of chromosomes in her egg cells?
    (b) Why might non-disjunction be less likely in a male?

12. (a) What is the relationship between Down syndrome and the karyotype trisomy 21?
    (b) Describe how meiosis can lead to trisomy 21.

13. What are some ethical considerations related to advancements in genetic screening technology?

14. Suppose an animal has a diploid number of 6 chromosomes ($2n = 6$). If a trisomy were to occur in one of this animal's gametes, how many chromosomes would that gamete contain?

15. Draw and label a diagram showing how non-disjunction in meiosis II could result in an egg cell without an X chromosome.

16. Suppose an individual has the karyotype XXX. Explain what might have occurred in her parents' gametes that resulted in this karyotype.

17. (a) Draw and label a diagram of a chromosome with an inversion next to a homologous chromosome without an inversion.
    (b) Explain why problems might arise in meiosis in an individual with a chromosomal inversion.

18. Why are current treatments for Klinefelter syndrome successful?

Reflection

19. How has your understanding of the concept of genetic variation changed after completing this section?

20. Describe two interesting facts you learned about developmental disabilities from reading this section.

For more questions, go to **BIOLOGY•SOURCE**

Key Concept Review

1. Define the term "trait." ⓚ

2. What are the subunits of DNA? ⓚ

3. What cellular process does a single-celled organism, such as *Paramecium*, undergo in order to reproduce asexually? ⓚ

4. List the stages of the cell cycle in order. ⓚ

5. What proportion of the cell cycle does a cell spend in interphase? What happens in this stage? ⓚ

6. What is the function of the spindle during meiosis? ⓚ

7. Define "somatic cell." ⓚ

8. What cells undergo meiosis? ⓚ

9. During what stages of the cell cycle does a cell contain sister chromatids? ⓚ

10. How many autosomes does a human somatic cell contain? How many autosomes does a human gamete contain? ⓚ

11. What form does DNA have during (a) replication and (b) cell division? ⓚ

12. How does mitosis differ from cytokinesis? ⓚ

13. How many pairs of homologous chromosomes does a human somatic cell contain? How many chromosomes does a human somatic cell contain? ⓚ

14. How many X chromosomes are normally present in a somatic cell of a male mammal? ⓚ

15. What is non-disjunction? How can non-disjunction lead to developmental disabilities in a person's children? ⓚ

16. (a) What causes cystic fibrosis? ⓚ
    (b) What is one way that cystic fibrosis affects the body? ⓚ

17. Describe the effects of one condition caused by non-disjunction of chromosomes. What is the karyotype for an individual with this condition? ⓚ

18. Briefly describe amniocentesis and its associated risks and benefits. ⓚ

Connect Your Understanding

19. Differentiate between pyrimidines and purines. ⓣ

20. Draw a diagram to show the levels of DNA packaging in the nucleus. ⓒ

21. Explain what is happening to the cell in this diagram. ⓐ

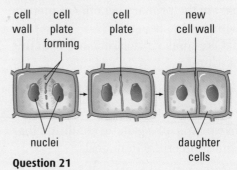

cell wall   cell plate forming   cell plate   new cell wall

nuclei   daughter cells

Question 21

22. How does the cell cycle ensure that the daughter cells will have the same number of chromosomes as the parent cell? Why is this important? ⓣ

23. (a) The diploid number of chromosomes for a bean plant is 22. What is *n* for a bean plant? ⓐ
    (b) In ferrets, 2*n* = 40. Give the haploid number of chromosomes for a ferret. ⓐ
    (c) The diploid number of chromosomes for shrimp is 254. How many more chromosomes does a shrimp somatic cell have than a human somatic cell has? ⓐ

24. Compare the content of the genetic material in a cell in prophase I with that of a cell just after telophase II. ⓣ

25. For each of the diagrams below and on the next page, name the stage of mitosis, identify the numbered structures, and briefly describe what is happening. ⓐ

(a)

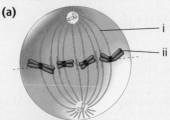

i

ii

(b)

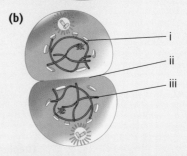

i

ii

iii

(c)

(d)

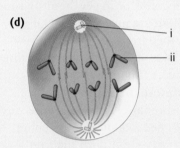

Question 25

26. How might drugs that interfere with mitosis be effective in treating cancer? 🄣

27. Describe one key process that introduces genetic variation to daughter cells during meiosis. 🄣

28. Why is it necessary for meiosis to have two division stages? 🄣

29. Create a table to compare and contrast the process of mitosis and meiosis. Use the following headings: Stages, Number of Cellular Divisions, Chromosome Number After Completion, Type of Cells. 🄒

30. If an organism has six chromosomes in each cell after meiotic division, what is its diploid chromosome number? 🄐

31. A dog somatic cell has 78 chromosomes.
    (a) How many sister chromatids will a dog cell have between S phase and metaphase I? 🄐
    (b) How many chromosomes will each new dog cell have after mitosis? 🄐

32. How long do cells in a woman's ovaries spend in meiosis before they become haploid egg cells? What might explain the link between maternal age and the chance of having a baby with trisomy 21? 🄣

33. Explain why a chromosomal mutation usually leads to a genetic disorder. 🄣

34. Suppose a strand of DNA contains the nucleotide sequence ATGCATCATGCCGCC. What is the sequence of the complementary strand? 🄐

35. Explain how chromosome duplications would affect the length of someone's DNA. 🄣

36. (a) Use a diagram to show what could happen in meiosis I that would produce a human gamete with two copies of chromosome 13. 🄒
    (b) If this gamete becomes part of a zygote that develops into a fetus, what will be the karyotype of this individual? 🄣
    (c) What are the name and effects of the condition that this individual will have? 🄐

37. How can karyotype analysis help parents to care for a child with the symptoms of Prader-Willi syndrome? 🄐

38. How might it help prospective parents to undergo genetic testing for the Tay-Sachs disease mutation? 🄐

39. Phenylketonuria (PKU) is a genetic disease that eventually causes brain damage if the person eats foods containing the compound phenylalanine. Why is it important to screen newborns for the PKU mutation? 🄐

Reflection

40. What is one topic related to this chapter that you would like to know more about? Why? 🄒

Unit Task Link

For your Unit Task, you will suggest appropriate genetic tests for particular genetic conditions. To prepare for this activity, make a table of genetic conditions and related mutations and tests. Identify mutations as DNA sequence mutations or mutations in chromosome structure. Suggest the most appropriate type of test to use in each case (carrier, diagnostic, presymptomatic, or prenatal testing or newborn screening).

For more questions, go to BIOLOGY•SOURCE

Mendelian laws and chromosome theory help explain inheritance patterns.

Learning Expectations

By the end of this chapter, you will:

Developing Skills of Investigation and Communication

- use appropriate terminology related to genetic processes

- use the Punnett square method to solve basic genetics problems involving monohybrid crosses, incomplete dominance, codominance, dihybrid crosses, and sex-linked genes

- investigate, through laboratory inquiry or computer simulation, monohybrid and dihybrid crosses, and use the Punnett square method and probability rules to analyze the qualitative and quantitative data and determine the parent genotype

Understanding Basic Concepts

- explain the concepts of DNA, genes, chromosomes, alleles, mitosis, and meiosis, and how they account for the transmission of hereditary characteristics according to Mendelian laws of inheritance

- explain the concepts of genotype, phenotype, dominance, incomplete dominance, codominance, recessiveness, and sex linkage according to Mendelian laws of inheritance

Dog breeding is one of the longest-running genetic experiments. For thousands of years, people have kept and bred dogs to suit their particular needs. We have dogs that guard property, herd livestock, hunt, or provide companionship. Today, there are more than 400 dog breeds, each with distinctive traits. They range from the massive great Danes and Weimaraners to the tiny Chihuahuas, and from the curly-haired poodles to the short-haired Labrador retrievers (Figure 5.1).

To be entered in a show, a dog must conform to a set of specific standards before it can qualify. The breed standards for a golden retriever, for example, are medium-large, round eyes, acceptable colours being dark brown or brown. The ears should be fairly short with the front edge flopping close to the cheek, and the nose should be filled with pigment so that it is dark brown or black. The coat should be a rich golden colour.

In order to achieve these standards, show-dog owners and breeders are careful to breed only those dogs that exemplify the desired traits. Over time, this selective breeding process has produced the variety of dog body types and temperaments that now exist. Each breed has a distinct genetic makeup that influences its physical and behavioural traits. The inheritance of these traits can be explained by the science of heredity: genetics.

Figure 5.1 Each dog breed has a characteristic body type and temperament.

©P

Section Summary

- Mendel's genetic experiments helped explain simple inheritance patterns. He suggested that heritable factors (now known as alleles) account for different inherited traits.

- A dominant allele is expressed in the traits of a heterozygous individual, while the recessive allele for the same gene is hidden. An individual must carry two copies of a recessive allele in order to express it as a trait.

- The Punnett square is a method to predict probabilities of offspring from genetic crosses.

- A monohybrid cross is between individuals that differ in one trait. A dihybrid cross is between individuals that differ in two traits.

Pet snakes come in many colours and patterns, but as reptile enthusiasts will tell you, the rarest varieties are the most prized. Among the most highly sought-after snake varieties is the black-eyed leucistic ball python (Figure 5.2). This python is valued for its stunning snow-white skin and jet-black eyes. Other ball pythons may have yellow stripes, brown blotches, or black-on-orange spots. These different genetic varieties of the same species are known as morphs.

Figure 5.2 The black-eyed leucistic ball python is a rare morph.

Producing morphs takes patience. Breeders experiment by crossing one variety with another to obtain offspring with new or unusual colour combinations. In much the same way, people have experimented with flower crosses or livestock breeds in order to bring about offspring with particular traits.

Inheritance Patterns

In some cases, it is possible to predict the outcome of a genetic cross. For example, a white-flowered pea plant crossed with another white-flowered pea plant will produce seeds for white-flowered plants. However, a white-flowered pea plant crossed with a purple-flowered pea plant may produce a few seeds for white flowers but more seeds for purple flowers. **Inheritance patterns** are the predictable patterns seen in the transmission of traits from one generation to the next. Inherited traits are also known as **hereditary** traits.

In the 1850s, an Austrian monk named Gregor Mendel (1822–1884) began a series of experiments that helped explain basic inheritance patterns and paved the way for the modern science of genetics (Figure 5.3). For seven years, Mendel bred pea plants and recorded inheritance patterns in the offspring. He hypothesized that parents pass down separate and distinct factors to their offspring, and that these factors are responsible for hereditary traits. Mendel believed that the inherited factors retain their identity generation after generation. Today we know these factors as genes.

Figure 5.3 A memorial of Mendel shows the scientist with his pea plants.

Figure 5.4 Some flowers can be self-fertilized with their own pollen to produce a true-breeding line of plants.

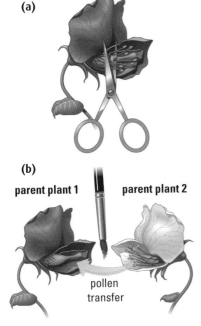

(a)

(b)

parent plant 1   parent plant 2

pollen
transfer

Figure 5.5 (a) To prevent self-fertilization, Mendel removed the pollen-carrying structures from one flower. (b) To cross-fertilize the plants, he brushed pollen from a second flower onto the first.

Mendel's Experiments

To begin his experiments, Mendel identified pea plants that were true-breeding. A **true-breeding** plant, when self-fertilized, produces offspring identical in appearance to itself, generation after generation (Figure 5.4). For example, a true-breeding purple flower, if self-fertilized, would only produce offspring with purple flowers.

Mendel also conducted a series of **cross-fertilization** experiments, in which sperm from the pollen of one plant fertilizes the eggs in the flower of a different plant (Figure 5.5). The parental plants in a genetic cross are known as the P generation (P stands for parental). The first generation of offspring from a genetic cross is called the F_1 generation, or first filial generation. (F stands for *filius* and *filia*, the Latin words for "son" and "daughter.") If the offspring from the F_1 generation are crossed with each other, then their offspring are called the F_2 generation, or second filial generation.

Hybrids are offspring that result from crossing two true-breeding varieties of the same species. Figure 5.6 shows how Mendel produced hybrids by crossing tall-stemmed pea plants with short-stemmed pea plants. The offspring are known as **monohybrids** because their parents differ in just one trait. Mendel observed that all of the F_1 hybrids were tall, not short, and not of intermediate height. In other words, the tall and short plant traits were not blended in the offspring. He wondered if the short plant's genetic contribution was lost as a result of crossing, or if it was just hidden. In order to test this idea, Mendel observed what happened when he allowed the F_1 plants to self-fertilize. He found that the factor for short stems did not disappear after all — about ¼ of the F_2 generation plants were short. Mendel reasoned that there must be two factors for stem length carried by the plants: one for tall and one for short.

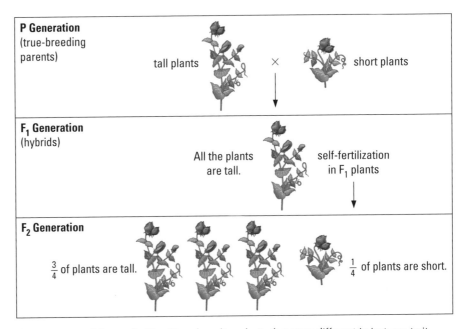

Figure 5.6 Mendel cross-fertilized true-breeding plants that were different in just one trait. He then allowed the monohybrids to self-fertilize.

Mendel's Monohybrid Crosses

In a **monohybrid cross**, hybrids with parents that differ in one trait are crossed with one another. Mendel used monohybrid crosses to study at least seven categories of pea-plant traits, such as stem length and seed colour (Figure 5.7). He observed the same inheritance pattern for each category: one of the two parents' traits disappeared in the F_1 generation but then reappeared in about ¼ of the F_2 generation.

		Flower Position	Seed Colour	Seed-Coat Colour	Seed Shape	Pod Shape	Pod Colour	Stem Length
P		axial	yellow	grey	round	inflated	green	tall
		×	×	×	×	×	×	×
		terminal	green	white	wrinkled	constricted	yellow	short
F₁		axial	yellow	grey	round	inflated	green	tall

Figure 5.7 Mendel examined the inheritance patterns of seven different pea-plant traits. Each of the monohybrids displayed only one of the parental traits.

The Mendelian Model of Inheritance

Mendel completed his work without any knowledge of chromosome structure or DNA. Even so, he used his experimental results to formulate a model to explain basic inheritance patterns. His model is summarized here using modern terminology.

1. Genes can exist in different forms. For example, there are two versions of the gene for seed colour in peas: yellow and green. An **allele** is an alternative version of a gene. So, in the example, peas have a yellow-seed allele and a green-seed allele.

2. For each gene, an individual organism inherits two alleles, one from each parent. If the two alleles are the same, the individual is said to be **homozygous** for that gene. If the two alleles are different, the individual is **heterozygous** for that gene.

3. An allele may be expressed (appear) as a trait or else hidden in a heterozygous individual. The **dominant** allele determines the trait that a heterozygous individual expresses. The **recessive** allele is not expressed in a heterozygous individual. There must be two copies of the recessive allele for it to be expressed as a trait. In pea plants, the yellow-seed allele is dominant, and the green-seed allele is recessive. That's why the F_1 generation in Figure 5.7 has yellow seeds.

4. Each gamete (sperm or egg) carries only one allele for each hereditary trait due to the separation of allele pairs when the gametes form. Allele pairs are re-formed in fertilization.

Mendel's Law of Segregation

Mendel's first law is known as the law of segregation. The **law of segregation** states that the two alleles for a trait or gene segregate (separate) during the phases of meiosis. Figure 5.8 shows the segregation of alleles on homologous chromosomes due to meiosis. With fertilization, each gamete donates one allele to make up the allele pair.

Alleles, like the traits they determine, are said to be **heritable** because they can be inherited.

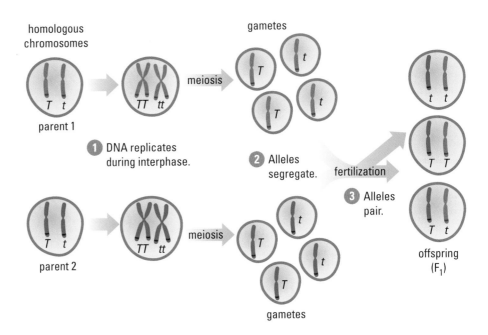

Figure 5.8 Allele pairs segregate during meiosis and re-form during fertilization.

Genotypes and Phenotypes

BIOLOGY•SOURCE

Suggested Activity

• B7 Quick Lab Overview on page 137

The genetic makeup or combination of alleles for an individual is its **genotype**. For example, a pea plant with two alleles for long stems has a homozygous dominant genotype. Genotype influences which inherited traits an individual will show. **Phenotype** refers to an individual's expressed traits, including physical appearance. In the stem length example, the actual height (tall) is the phenotype.

In an individual with a heterozygous genotype, the dominant allele is expressed in the phenotype, while the recessive allele is masked. In general, uppercase letters are used to represent the dominant allele (in the stem-length example, *T*). The lowercase version of the same letter is used for the recessive allele (for example, *t*).

Some genetic crosses produce predictable proportions of genotypes and phenotypes in the offspring. Table 5.1 summarizes the results of Mendel's monohybrid cross with heterozygous tall pea plants. About ¼ of the offspring from the monohybrid cross were homozygous dominant (*TT*) for height. These plants are tall because they carry two dominant alleles for height. The letters *TT* represent their genotype. Their physical trait of being tall is their phenotype. In this same cross, ½ of the offspring are heterozygous for height (*Tt*) and carry one dominant allele and one recessive allele. Because the dominant *T* allele for long stems masks the recessive *t* allele for short stems, these plants with the genotype *Tt* will also be tall. The remaining ¼ of the plants are *tt*, homozygous recessive for height. The genotype for these plants is *tt*, and their phenotype is short stems.

Table 5.1 Results of Mendel's Monohybrid Cross

Phenotypes	Genotypes
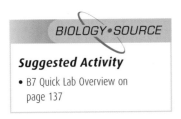 3 tall	1*TT*, 2*Tt*
1 short	1*tt*

Concept Check

1. Describe the pattern of inheritance Mendel observed when he crossed tall pea plants with short pea plants.

2. How does a homozygous genotype differ from a heterozygous genotype?

3. What is the difference between an organism's genotype and its phenotype?

Probability and the Punnett Square

When two gametes unite to form a zygote, it is not certain which of the alleles for a gene will be inherited from the parents. However, we can predict the probability for the inheritance of each allele. **Probability** is the likelihood that a particular event will occur. When Mendel conducted his experiments with the pea plants, he was careful to categorize and record the traits of the parents and offspring. This provided Mendel with a good range of data to analyze. Once he began to look at the data, he realized that the basic principles of probability could be used to explain the results.

Consider the process of flipping a coin. There are two possible outcomes: the coin will land with heads up, or the coin will land with tails up. The probability of either outcome is equal, or ½ (50%) for each. Suppose you flip two coins. What is the probability of a particular combination occurring? To find out, you can construct a grid that shows the probability of each combination (Figure 5.9). The probability of a particular outcome is equal to the product of the individual probabilities. For example, the probability of two heads showing up is $\frac{1}{2} \times \frac{1}{2} = \frac{1}{4}$ (25%).

Similarly, if we know the genotypes of both parents in a genetic cross, we can use a grid to calculate the probabilities of different combinations of alleles that could occur. This type of grid is called a Punnett square. It is named after English geneticist Reginald C. Punnett (1875–1967), who devised the approach. A **Punnett square** is a diagram that shows the expected proportions of all possible outcomes of a genetic cross. In Figure 5.10, the gametes of the heterozygous plants pair randomly, making the possible allele combinations TT, Tt, or tt. Of these plants, ¼ are TT, ½ are Tt, and ¼ are tt. The ratio of the phenotypes (phenotypic ratio) is three tall to one short (3:1).

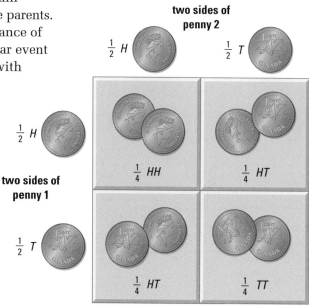

Figure 5.9 The grid makes it simple to predict the probabilities of certain combinations. The probability of a penny landing heads up once is ½. The probability of two pennies landing heads up is ¼.

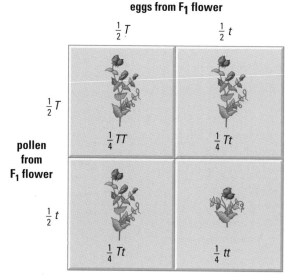

Figure 5.10 Punnett square showing the probability of outcomes from a cross between heterozygous tall pea plants

Constructing a Simple Punnett Square

When constructing a Punnett square, keep in mind the law of segregation. Table 5.2 gives the steps to follow.

Table 5.2 Constructing a Punnett Square for One Gene with Two Alleles

Step	Example
1. Draw a square with a 2 by 2 grid.	
2. Consider all possible gametes produced by the first parent. Write the alleles for these gametes across the top of the square.	
3. Consider all possible gametes produced by the second parent. Write the alleles for these gametes down the side of the square.	
4. Complete the square by writing all possible allele combinations from the cross.	
5. Determine the genotypic and phenotypic proportions of the offspring.	

Example 5.1   Using Simple Punnett Squares

A geneticist crosses two pea plants. One of the plants is heterozygous for the dominant inflated pea pod trait, and the other plant has constricted pea pods. What would be the expected genotypic and phenotypic proportions of the offspring?

Given
Inflated pod (*I*) is dominant to constricted pod (*i*).
II or *Ii* produce inflated pods.
ii produces constricted pea pods.
The cross is *Ii* × *ii*.

Required
• expected proportions of F_1 plants with genotypes *II*, *Ii*, and *ii*
• expected proportions of plants with inflated pods and plants with constricted pods

Practice Problems

Use the Punnett square method to analyze the following crosses. What would be the expected genotypic and phenotypic proportions of the offspring in each cross?

1. A brown snake heterozygous for the skin-colour gene (*Bb*) is crossed with an albino (colourless) snake (*bb*).

2. A man with dimples (*DD*) has children with a woman who is heterozygous for the dimples/no dimples gene (*Dd*).

Analysis

Determine the gametes from the parental genotypes.

Construct a Punnett square for this cross to determine the allele combinations and phenotypes of the offspring.

Solution

The *Ii* parent produces gametes *I* and *i*.

The *ii* parent produces gametes *i* and *i*.

	I	*i*
i	*Ii*	*ii*
i	*Ii*	*ii*

Paraphrase

From the Punnett square, $\frac{1}{2}$ of the offspring would be heterozygous (*Ii*) and $\frac{1}{2}$ would be *ii*. Therefore, $\frac{1}{2}$ of the offspring would have inflated pods, and $\frac{1}{2}$ would have constricted pods.

Practice Problems

3. Some people have the ability to taste the bitter chemical PTC. A PTC-tasting woman (*Tt*) has children with a PTC-tasting man (*Tt*).

Answers

1. $\frac{1}{2}$ *Bb*, $\frac{1}{2}$ *bb*; $\frac{1}{2}$ brown, $\frac{1}{2}$ white

2. $\frac{1}{2}$ *DD*, $\frac{1}{2}$ *Dd*; all children would have dimples

3. $\frac{1}{4}$ *TT*, $\frac{1}{2}$ *Tt*, $\frac{1}{4}$ *tt*; $\frac{3}{4}$ tasters, $\frac{1}{4}$ non-tasters

The Test Cross

A question that breeders and geneticists often have is "what is the genotype of an organism that displays the dominant phenotype?" For example, a purple-flowered pea plant could have either of two possible genotypes: *PP* or *Pp*. To determine whether the purple-flowered plant is homozygous (*PP*) or heterozygous (*Pp*), it is necessary to perform a test cross. A **test cross** breeds an individual of unknown genotype but dominant phenotype (your purple-flowered mystery plant) with a homozygous recessive individual — in this case a white-flowered plant (*pp*).

The phenotypes of the offspring resulting from the test cross will reveal the genotype of the mystery plant. Because the homozygous recessive parent can contribute only the recessive allele to the offspring, their phenotypes will indicate the allele from the other parent (the mystery plant). If the purple-flowered parent were homozygous (*PP*), it would contribute only the *P* allele to the offspring (Figure 5.11). We would therefore expect all of the offspring to be purple-flowered *(Pp)*. However, if the purple-flowered parent were heterozygous *(Pp)*, it would contribute both *P* and *p* to the next generation, and we would expect both purple-flowered (*Pp*) and white-flowered (*pp*) offspring.

BIOLOGY•SOURCE

Explore More

How can we test if inheritance follows rules of chance?

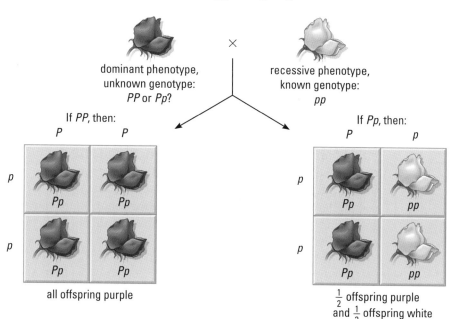

Figure 5.11 A test cross can reveal whether an organism that displays the dominant phenotype is homozygous or heterozygous.

©P

Concept Check

1. What is probability?

2. What are the two possible gametes that could be produced by a plant with the genotype *Aa*? Give the probability of producing each gamete.

3. In guinea pigs, rough coat is dominant to smooth coat. How could you determine the genotype of a rough-coated guinea pig?

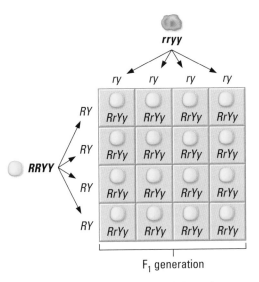

Figure 5.12 When Mendel crossed plants that were homozygous dominant for round yellow peas with plants that were homozygous recessive for wrinkled green peas, all of the resulting offspring had round yellow seeds.

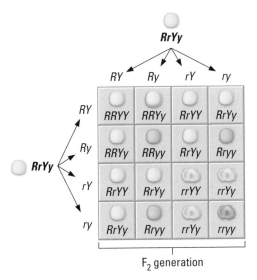

Figure 5.13 Mendel crossed the F₁ plants that were heterozygous for round yellow peas. He found combinations of alleles not present in the parental genotypes. This indicated that alleles segregate independently.

Inheritance Patterns Involving Two Genes

So far we have examined inheritance patterns and crosses involving only one category of trait (or one gene). Mendel also followed the inheritance of two categories of traits (or genes) at a time. He wanted to know, for example, if the inheritance of seed colour would affect the inheritance of seed shape, or vice versa. In one experiment, he crossed true-breeding pea plants that produced two different types of seeds: round yellow seeds and wrinkled green seeds (Figure 5.12). The parents' genotypes are written *RRYY*, for round and yellow, and *rryy*, for wrinkled and green. As the diagram shows, all of the F₁ generation produced round yellow seeds (*RrYy*). Such offspring are called **dihybrids**, because their parents differed in two traits.

Based on the results of the first cross, it was apparent that the smooth seed trait was dominant to wrinkled, and that the yellow seed trait was dominant to green. Even so, Mendel could not tell if the alleles for seed colour and shape were inherited together, or if they segregated independently. He decided to cross the dihybrid plants to produce an F₂ generation (Figure 5.13). In a **dihybrid cross**, hybrids with parents that differ in two traits are crossed with one another. In total, his experiment produced 556 seeds. Of these, 315 seeds were round and yellow, and 32 seeds were wrinkled and green, both parental phenotypes. However, the remaining seeds had a combination of phenotypes not observed in either parent, and thus new combinations of alleles: 108 were round and green, and 101 were wrinkled and yellow. To confirm their genotypes, Mendel conducted test crosses with the F₂ generation and pea plants with wrinkled green seeds.

Mendel's results were very close to the 9:3:3:1 phenotypic ratio predicted by the Punnett square in Figure 5.13. He concluded that the allele pairs for seed shape do segregate independently of the allele pairs for seed colour. Mendel's second law, the **law of independent assortment**, states that genes that segregate independently in meiosis do not influence each other's inheritance.

Constructing a Punnett Square with Two Genes

When constructing a Punnett square for the inheritance of two genes, keep the law of independent assortment in mind. You should include every possible combination of alleles for the gametes from each parent. Table 5.3 gives the steps to follow.

BIOLOGY•SOURCE

Suggested Activity

• B8 Inquiry Activity Overview on page 137

Table 5.3 Constructing a Punnett Square for Two Genes

Step	Example
1. Draw a square with a 4 by 4 grid.	
2. Consider all possible gametes produced by the female parent. Write the alleles for these gametes across the top of the square.	AaTt → AT, At, aT, at
3. Consider all possible gametes produced by the male parent. Write the alleles for these gametes down the side of the square.	AaTt → AT, At, aT, at
4. Complete the square by writing all possible allele combinations from the cross.	AaTt
5. Determine the genotypic and phenotypic proportions of the offspring.	AaTt: AATT AATt AaTT AaTt / AATt AAtt AaTt Aatt / AaTT AaTt aaTT aaTt / AaTt Aatt aaTt aatt

Take It Further

BIOLOGY•SOURCE

Genotype does not only affect physical appearance. In 1931, a chemist named Arthur Fox made an intriguing discovery about the sense of taste after accidentally spilling a bottle of phenylthiocarbamide (PTC) in his laboratory. Research how geneticists determined that there is an inherited component that influences the ability to taste PTC. Write a news story about the discovery of PTC tasting and the inheritance pattern for this trait.

Example 5.2   Two-Gene Crosses

Practice Problems

Use the Punnett square method to analyze the following crosses involving two genes.

1. A black mouse with a short tail (*BBll*) is mated with a brown mouse with a short tail (*bbll*). What proportion of their offspring will be black with short tails?

2. A tall, purple-flowered pea plant (*TTPP*) is crossed with a short, purple-flowered pea plant (*ttPp*). What proportion of the offspring will be heterozygous for flower colour? What proportion of the offspring will be tall with white flowers?

3. A black-eyed, long-haired rabbit (*BBss*) is mated with a red-eyed, short-haired rabbit (*bbSS*). What proportion of the offspring will have black eyes and short hair? What proportion will have red eyes and long hair?

Answers

1. 1 or 100% black with short tails

2. $\frac{1}{2}$ *Pp*; 0% tall with white flowers

3. 100% black-eyed with short hair; 0% red-eyed with long hair

In mice, the normal long-tail phenotype is dominant to the short-tail trait, and black coat colour is dominant to brown coat colour. If two long-tailed black mice, heterozygous for both traits, are mated, what proportion of their offspring will be brown with short tails?

Given

Long tail (*L*) is dominant. Short tail (*l*) is recessive.
LL or *Ll* produce long tails.
ll produces short tails.

Black coat colour (*B*) is dominant. Brown coat colour (*b*) is recessive.
BB or *Bb* produce black coat colour.
bb produces brown coat colour.

The cross is *BbLl* × *BbLl*.

Required

• expected proportion of offspring that will be brown with short tails

Analysis

Determine the gametes from the parental genotypes.
Construct a Punnett square for this cross to determine the allele combinations and phenotypes of the offspring.

Solution

The *BbLl* parents produce gametes *BL*, *Bl*, *bL*, *bl*.

	BL	Bl	bL	bl
BL	BBLL	BBLl	BbLL	BbLl
Bl	BBLl	BBll	BbLl	Bbll
bL	BbLL	BbLl	bbLL	bbLl
bl	Bbll	Bbll	bbLl	bbll

Paraphrase

Mice with brown coats and short tails have the genotype *bbll*. From the Punnett square, $\frac{1}{16}$ of the offspring will be brown with short tails.

Applying Mendel's Laws

Mendel's laws of inheritance apply to animals as well as plants. In the early 1900s, an American geneticist named Thomas Hunt Morgan (1866–1945) turned to a different model organism, the common fruit fly (Figure 5.14). The fruit fly, *Drosophila melanogaster*, is a useful genetic model because it produces large numbers of offspring relatively quickly. Since the time of Morgan's studies, geneticists have used fruit flies to test Mendel's laws of inheritance and have learned that these principles also apply to many other organisms, including humans.

Figure 5.14 *D. melanogaster*, the common fruit fly, is a useful model organism.

Genetic Variation in the Classroom

Purpose

To observe various hereditary traits and calculate the frequency of traits in the classroom population

Figure 5.15 Curly hair is a hereditary trait. So are red hair and freckles.

Figure 5.16 A pointed hairline (also known as a widow's peak) is a hereditary trait.

Activity Overview

Everyone has a distinct set of traits. Some of these traits are hereditary (Figures 5.15 and 5.16). In this activity, you will examine your own features to see what traits you have. You will also calculate the frequency of particular traits in the classroom population.

Your teacher will give you a copy of the full activity.

Prelab Questions

Consider the questions below before beginning this activity.

1. What are some advantages and disadvantages of genetic variation in human populations?

2. What would be the best way to represent the results from this survey for visual analysis?

3. Some traits are purely genetic, while others reflect an interaction between genetic and environmental factors. Brainstorm a few human traits that you think are affected by both genes and the environment.

REQUIRED SKILLS
- Analyzing patterns
- Reporting results

Determining P Phenotypes from F_1 and F_2 Phenotypes

Question

How can you determine the traits of a plant from the P generation by observing the traits of the F_1 and F_2 generations?

Activity Overview

In this investigation, you will germinate seeds from two consecutive crosses of Fast Plants®. By observing the stem colour (purple or non-purple) and height (dwarf or tall) of the seedlings, you will determine the patterns of inheritance and the phenotypes of the P generation.

Your teacher will give you a copy of the full activity.

Figure 5.17 A Fast Plant® (*Brassica rapa*)

Prelab Questions

Consider the questions below before beginning this activity.

1. How are seeds produced to grow the F_1 and F_2 generations?

2. If some plants grown from the F_2 generation had the dwarf phenotype and others had the tall phenotype, what could you infer about the genotype and phenotype of the F_1 plants?

3. Fast Plants® do not normally self-pollinate. Why is this helpful to scientists performing genetic crosses with these plants?

Figure 5.18 Sorting seeds

5.1   Check and Reflect

Key Concept Review

1. Differentiate between self-fertilization and cross-fertilization of plants.

2. Define the term "hybrid" and give an example.

3. What is meant by the terms "homozygous" and "heterozygous?" Give an example to explain each term.

4. A pea plant that produces yellow seeds may have either one or two copies of the allele for yellow seeds. Differentiate between the plant's genotype and phenotype.

5. Which allele will determine the trait that shows up in a heterozygous individual: the dominant allele or the recessive allele? Why?

6. What is the purpose of a test cross?

7. What are separated during meiosis, according to the law of segregation?

8. Name two types of organisms that have been used to study laws of inheritance. What makes them useful as model organisms for genetic studies?

Connect Your Understanding

9. Mendel used stocks of pea plants that were true-breeding. What is meant by this term? Give an example and explain why it was necessary to use these particular plants in the crosses.

10. How does the law of independent assortment help explain the inheritance pattern for seed colour and shape in pea plants?

11. What is the difference between a monohybrid and a dihybrid?

12. What is a monohybrid cross?

13. How do Punnett squares help us to predict the probable outcomes of genetic crosses?

14. List all possible allele combinations in the gametes of an individual with genotype *AaBb*.

15. How did Mendel show that traits were not blended in offspring?

16. If the phenotype for a plant is tall, and the long-stem allele is dominant to the short-stem allele, describe how to determine the exact genotype of this plant. Show an example cross.

17. The allele for cystic fibrosis is recessive. Suppose both members of a couple are heterozygous for the gene related to cystic fibrosis. What is the probability that their first child will have cystic fibrosis?

18. Suppose a man has one copy of the dominant allele for Huntington's disease. What is the probability that one of his children will inherit the Huntington's disease allele from him? What is the probability that two of his children will inherit the allele from him?

19. In Labrador retriever dogs, the allele for a black-coloured coat (*B*) is dominant to the allele for a chocolate-coloured coat (*b*). Suppose a heterozygous male is mated with a homozygous recessive female. Determine the genotypes and phenotypes of the offspring from this cross and give their proportions.

20. In rabbits, the black coat-colour allele (*B*) is dominant to the chocolate coat-colour allele (*b*). The Agouti allele (*A*) for a white belly is dominant to the allele for a coloured belly (*a*). Suppose two dihybrids for coat colour and belly colour are mated. Determine the expected genotypes and phenotypes from this cross. State the phenotypic ratio.

21. Draw a diagram to show how allele pairing is related to the behaviour of chromosomes during gamete formation and fertilization.

Reflection

22. It is often said that "we inherit our parents' genes." How has your understanding of this statement changed now that you have completed this section?

23. List one topic that interests you or a question that you have related to this section.

For more questions, go to   BIOLOGY•SOURCE

Section Summary

- Not all inheritance patterns can be explained by dominant and recessive alleles.
- In the case of incomplete dominance, heterozygous individuals have traits that are intermediate between their parents' traits. In the case of codominance, codominant alleles are equally expressed in a heterozygous individual.
- A single trait can be influenced by many genes, each with two or more alleles.
- The environment usually influences an organism's phenotype.

What do you get when you cross a black chicken with a white chicken? If they are Andalusians, a blue chick. In the Andalusian breed of chickens, a cross between a black bird and a white bird produces hybrid offspring called blues, which have grey-blue feathers (Figure 5.19). This phenomenon cannot be explained by dominant and recessive alleles. Dominance and recessiveness explain some simple forms of inheritance. For most traits, however, inheritance patterns are more complex, as in the case of blue Andalusian chickens.

Figure 5.19 A blue Andalusian chicken

Incomplete Dominance

In Mendel's pea plant crosses, the F_1 heterozygous offspring always resembled the homozygous dominant parent. For each trait, one dominant allele was expressed. This inheritance pattern is known as complete dominance. In the case of **complete dominance**, one allele is expressed and the other is not. In contrast, the alleles controlling feather colour in Andalusian chickens are neither dominant nor recessive. Instead, heterozygous individuals have an in-between phenotype. **Incomplete dominance** is an inheritance pattern in which the phenotype of a heterozygous individual falls between the two parental phenotypes.

Allele Pairing Explains Incomplete Dominance

Figure 5.20 shows how alleles pair in the case of incomplete dominance. When true-breeding red snapdragons are crossed with white snapdragons, the resulting F_1 hybrids have pink flowers. Although the offspring are pink — an intermediate between red and white — this does not mean that the alleles are physically blended. A cross between two pink snapdragons from the F_1 generation produces F_2 offspring in the ratio of one red to two pink to one white (1:2:1). This ratio of phenotypes indicates that the red-flower allele and white-flower allele segregate during gamete formation.

Incomplete dominance is just one of many variations in Mendelian inheritance patterns.

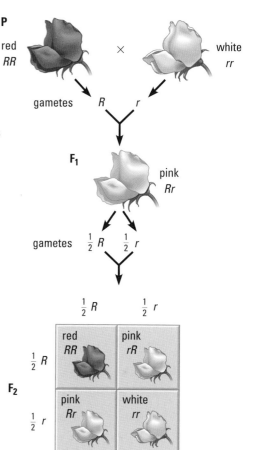

Figure 5.20 Snapdragons exhibit incomplete dominance for flower colour.

Codominance

Similar to incomplete dominance, codominance is an inheritance pattern in which neither allele is dominant to the other. In the case of **codominance**, both alleles are completely expressed at the same time, and so a heterozygous individual has a mixture of the two parental phenotypes. For example, in cattle, a cross between a true-breeding red bull and a white cow will produce roan calves. Roan cattle have patches of white hair intermingled with patches of coloured hair (Figure 5.21). This mixed phenotype results from the expression of the white-hair allele in some patches, and the coloured-hair allele in other patches.

Figure 5.22 is a Punnett square showing how codominant alleles pair to produce the roan coat phenotype. A similar set of alleles produces roan coats in horses.

Figure 5.21 Roan cattle exhibit codominance in coat colour.

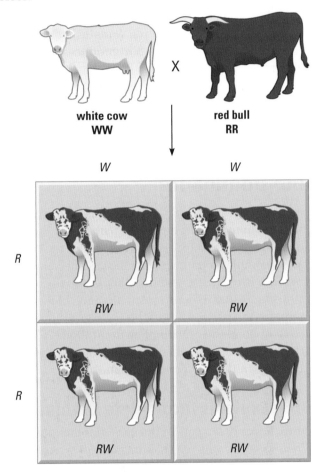

Figure 5.22 In roan cattle, the expression of one allele is not masked by the expression of the other. Instead, the alleles are said to be codominant.

Genes with Multiple Alleles

So far we have discussed traits that involve only two alleles per gene. But for most genes, more than two alleles exist in a population. The existence of multiple alleles means that there may be many possible genotypes for a particular gene, and many possible phenotypes. For example, ABO blood type in humans involves three alleles. A person can have one of four blood types: A, B, AB, or O. The letters of the blood type refer to two types of carbohydrates, A and B, that are found on the surface of red blood cells. A person's red blood cells may be coated with either carbohydrate A (blood type A) or carbohydrate B (blood type B), both carbohydrates (blood type AB), or neither (blood type O).

Table 5.4 shows how the four ABO blood types result from various combinations of three alleles, symbolized by I^A (for carbohydrate A), I^B (for carbohydrate B), and i (for neither A nor B). Everyone inherits one of these alleles from each parent. There are six possible ways to pair the alleles — in other words, there are six possible genotypes. The alleles I^A and I^B are codominant, meaning that an $I^A I^B$ heterozygous individual expresses both the I^A and the I^B traits, and thus has blood type AB.

BIOLOGY•SOURCE

Suggested Activities

- B9 Quick Lab Overview on page 144
- B10 Quick Lab Overview on page 144

Table 5.4 ABO Blood Types: Genotypes, Phenotypes, and Cross-Reactions

Blood Type (Phenotype)	Genotypes	Red Blood Cells	Antibodies Present in Blood	Reaction When Blood from Types Below Is Mixed with Antibodies from Types at Left			
				0	A	B	AB
0	ii		anti-A anti-B				
A	$I^A I^A$ or $I^A i$	carbohydrate A	anti-B				
B	$I^B I^B$ or $I^B i$	carbohydrate B	anti-A				
AB	$I^A I^B$		—				

Blood Types

When someone requires a blood transfusion, it is critical to match the recipient's blood type with a compatible donor blood type. If the blood types are incompatible, the recipient will have a potentially fatal immune response. The immune system detects cells that appear foreign to the body. For example, someone with blood type A has an immune system that recognizes red blood cells with carbohydrate B as foreign and will try to destroy them. Immune system proteins called antibodies will bind to the foreign carbohydrates, causing the donor red blood cells to clump together. Similarly, someone with blood type B has antibodies against carbohydrate A. Someone with blood type O has antibodies against both A and B carbohydrates. Table 5.4 shows the different cross-reactions that occur between the ABO blood types.

Humans are not the only animals to have different blood types. Dogs, cats, horses, and chimpanzees are among the species with known blood type variations (Figure 5.23).

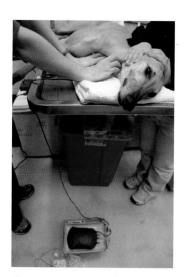

Figure 5.23 Most greyhounds are considered universal blood donors for other dogs.

Concept Check

1. What is the difference between incomplete dominance and codominance?

2. How many genotypes exist for human ABO blood type?

3. What blood types can be donated to a person with blood type B?

Example 5.3 Incomplete Dominance and Codominance

In humans, blood type AB is a codominant trait. Suppose Jim has blood type AB ($I^A I^B$) and his wife, Rebecca, has blood type O (*ii*). What are the possible genotypes and ABO blood types of their children?

Given

I^A and I^B are codominant. Both are dominant to *i*.
The father's blood type is AB and his genotype is $I^A I^B$.
The mother's blood type is O and her genotype is *ii*.

Required

• possible genotypes and ABO blood types of the children

Analysis

Determine the possible gametes from the parental genotypes.

Construct a Punnett square for this cross to determine the allele combinations and phenotypes of the offspring.

Solution

The mother produces gametes *i* and *i*.
The father produces gametes I^A and I^B.

	i	*i*
I^A	$I^A i$	$I^A i$
I^B	$I^B i$	$I^B i$

Paraphrase

From the Punnett square, Jim and Rebecca's children could have blood type A, due to the $I^A i$ genotype, or blood type B, due to the $I^B i$ genotype.

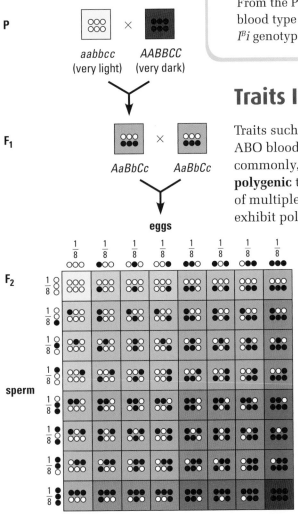

P

aabbcc (very light) × *AABBCC* (very dark)

F₁

AaBbCc × *AaBbCc*

F₂

eggs

sperm

Figure 5.24 A polygenic inheritance model for skin colour

Traits Influenced by Multiple Genes

Traits such as pea plant height, snapdragon flower colour, and ABO blood type are each under the control of a single gene. More commonly, however, a trait is influenced by two or more genes. A **polygenic** trait has a range of phenotypes due to the additive effects of multiple genes. In humans, eye colour, skin colour, and height exhibit polygenic inheritance.

As many as 60 genes are thought to influence skin colour — exactly how many is not known. The interaction of these genes controls the amount of pigment in the skin. To understand this interaction, it is useful to consider a simplified model with three genes. Each gene has a dark-skin allele (represented by *A*, *B*, and *C*). Each of these alleles contributes one "unit" of pigment to the phenotype. These alleles exhibit incomplete dominance with corresponding light-skin alleles (*a*, *b*, and *c*). Therefore, a person who is *AABBCC* would have dark skin, while a person who is *aabbcc* would have light skin (Figure 5.24, P generation). Their children (the F₁ generation) would have the genotype *AaBbCc* and an intermediate phenotype.

©P

Figure 5.24 also shows all possible genotypes for the children of *AaBbCc* parents (triple heterozygotes). This model predicts a spectrum of phenotypes from the various allele combinations. A graph of the predicted proportions of each phenotype is a bell-shaped curve (Figure 5.25). The curve is similar to the actual variation in skin colour observed in some populations.

The more genes that are involved a polygenic trait, the larger the number of possible allele combinations, and the smoother the bell-shaped curve of phenotypes. Dozens to hundreds of genes are thought to influence polygenic traits such as susceptibility to certain diseases.

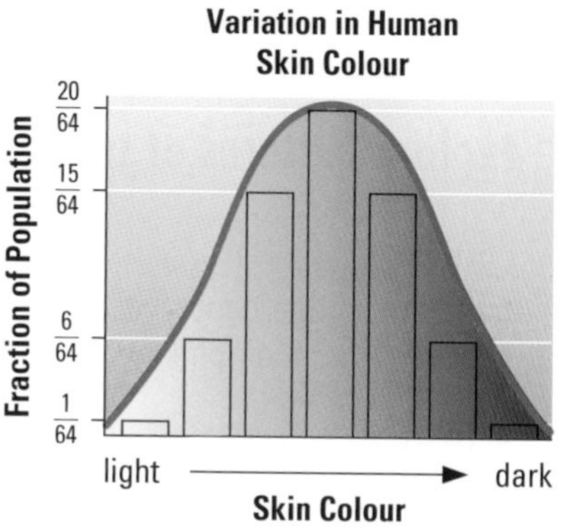

Variation in Human Skin Colour

Y-axis: Fraction of Population — $\frac{20}{64}$, $\frac{15}{64}$, $\frac{6}{64}$, $\frac{1}{64}$

light ⟶ dark

Skin Colour

Figure 5.25 Most individuals in a population will have an intermediate phenotype for a polygenic trait.

The Environmental Influence

Different allele combinations account for a great variety of phenotypes. However, for most traits, the product of a genotype is not a single, rigidly defined phenotype, but a range of possibilities arising from the combination of heredity and environment.

In genetics, "environment" refers to the conditions in which a cell or organism lives. For example, although a tree's genotype does not change throughout its lifetime, the shape, size, and colour of its leaves greatly depend on the tree's exposure to sunlight and humidity. Similarly, flower colour can be influenced by the nutrients and pH of the soil. Hydrangeas grown in slightly acidic soil have blue flowers, but if grown in slightly basic soil have pink flowers.

Temperature can also have a very interesting effect on phenotypes. The Siamese cat pictured in Figure 5.26 is covered in creamy white fur, except on its ears, face, feet, and tail. The pattern is due to a mutation in a gene for pigment production. As a result of the mutation, the enzyme responsible for black fur is sensitive to heat. The enzyme is active only in the cooler temperatures found at the cat's extremities, giving the Siamese cat its characteristic appearance. Other breeds of cats do not have the mutant allele that produces the Siamese phenotype.

Figure 5.26 Due to a mutant allele, in Siamese cats, fur colour is affected by temperature.

Environmental Effects on Human Traits

Whether genes or environment has the greatest influence on human traits is a very old and contested topic. In cases such as ABO blood types, genes determine the phenotype with no influence from the environment. However, as geneticists take a closer look at genes, they are finding that many human phenotypes, such as blood-cell counts and cholesterol levels, are sensitive to environmental influences. Blood count depends on such factors as the presence of an infection, a person's level of physical activity, and the altitude at which the person lives. Diet and lifestyle, as well as genetics, influence cholesterol levels. Other environmental factors that influence phenotypes include stress and exposure to toxins.

BIOLOGY•SOURCE

Take It Further

Offspring inherit their genetic makeup from their parents. But the way in which traits are expressed is usually due to a combination of genetic and environmental factors. Epigenetics studies how genes are turned on and off. Find out how environmental factors can influence the expression of one trait in a particular type of organism.

Quick Lab

Explore Patterns of Inheritance

Purpose

To determine the genotypes of parents and their offspring from their phenotypes

Activity Overview

Traits that exhibit complete dominance, incomplete dominance, or codominance have distinct inheritance patterns. In this activity, you will investigate the inheritance patterns for a hypothetical species (Figure 5.27). You will also predict genotypes and phenotypes from various genetic crosses.

    Your teacher will give you a copy of the full activity.

Figure 5.27 A genetic cross between hypothetical organisms

Prelab Questions

Consider the questions below before beginning this activity.

1. What are the five primary inheritance patterns?

2. How could you determine the pattern of inheritance for a particular trait?

Quick Lab

Modelling Allele Segregation and Pairing

Purpose

To model how alleles segregate in meiosis and pair in a genetic cross

Activity Overview

During meiosis, genes on different chromosomes assort independently, and alleles separate to different gametes. With fertilization, alleles pair once more. In this activity, you will use clay chromatids to simulate chromosome assortment and allele segregation and pairing (Figures 5.28 and 5.29). You will determine the possible outcomes when different genes are on the same or on different chromosomes.

    Your teacher will give you a copy of the full activity.

Figure 5.28 Modelling sister chromatids

Prelab Questions

Consider the questions below before beginning this activity.

1. How is genetic variation produced during the process of meiosis?

2. How do you think the location of different genes on a chromosome will influence allele combinations in the gametes?

Figure 5.29 Modelling homologous chromosomes

Key Concept Review

1. Define "complete dominance" for a genetic trait.

2. Give examples of the following types of inheritance.
   (a) codominance
   (b) incomplete dominance
   (c) polygenic inheritance

3. What form of inheritance does ABO blood type in humans exhibit?

4. Give an example of a human physical trait influenced by the environment.

5. If two parents have blood type O, what are the possible ABO blood types of their children?

6. What is the form of inheritance in which a heterozygous individual has a phenotype that is in between the parental phenotypes?

Connect Your Understanding

7. Use a Punnett square to explain why parents who are heterozygous for a codominant trait can have offspring that show one of three phenotypes.

8. Give the phenotypes of the F_1 generation from a cross between a white snapdragon and a pink snapdragon.

9. The hydrangeas in the following photo all have the same genetic makeup. Explain why the plants have different phenotypes.

Question 9

10. Some fruit flies have long wings and some have short wings. Suggest an experiment that could be used to find out the mode of inheritance for wing length in fruit flies.

11. Four o'clocks are flowering plants. Suggest why a cross between two pink four o'clocks would produce an F_1 generation of red flowers, pink flowers, and white flowers.

12. Cats can have one of three different blood types, depending on which carbohydrates coat their red blood cells. Blood type A has carbohydrate A, blood type B has carbohydrate B, and blood type AB has both carbohydrates. The alleles for the different carbohydrates are codominant. Suggest symbols to represent the genotypes of the different blood types. If two heterozygous cats mate, what are the possible genotypes of their offspring?

13. Suppose that a newly discovered species exhibits an inheritance pattern that cannot be explained by dominant and recessive alleles. Describe the phenotypes of the trait in question and suggest symbols for the corresponding genotypes. Use a Punnett square to show the form of inheritance.

14. Suggest a model of how various allele combinations could produce a range of human heights, from short to tall.

15. The size of a chicken's eggs is partly under genetic control.
    (a) Use the data in the following table to graph egg weights versus numbers of chickens.

Weights of Eggs from Different Hens

Egg Weight (g)	Number of Chickens	Egg Weight (g)	Number of Chickens
49	1	63	14
51	2	65	13
52	3	68	12
56	6	71	9
56	9	73	5
59	12	75	3

(b) From your graph, what is the form of inheritance for chicken-egg weight?

Reflection

16. Many different factors influence inheritance. How has what you learned in this section changed your view of the concept of heredity?

For more questions, go to  BIOLOGY•SOURCE

5.3 Inheritance Patterns for Linked Genes

Section Summary

- The segregation and assortment of chromosomes are responsible for inheritance patterns.
- Genes are located at specific chromosome locations called loci (singular, locus).
- Genes located in close proximity to each other on a chromosome tend to be genetically linked.
- Traits linked to a particular sex chromosome exhibit unique inheritance patterns.

Figure 5.30 Many of Queen Victoria's male descendants, including Alexei Romanov (front, centre) of the Russian royal family, inherited hemophilia.

BIOLOGY•SOURCE

Explore More

What can you learn from a pedigree diagram?

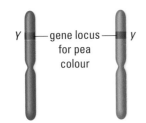

Figure 5.31 A gene locus on homologous chromosomes

Many historical artifacts and documents contain references to humans with excessive and unexplained bleeding. It was not until the early 1800s that the term hemophilia was used to describe this disorder. Hemophilia was often referred to as the "royal disease" due to its spread to the royal families of Europe through Queen Victoria's descendants (Figure 5.30). In fact, Queen Victoria (1819–1901) began to worry about the quality of the blood lines in the British royal family. The blood disorder was thought to be an inherited disease that affected males. An interesting observation about the royal lineage was that non-affected mothers were somehow passing the disease on to their sons, although no one had a clear understanding of its transmission. In the early 1900s, geneticists discovered that some traits, such as hemophilia, are linked to sex chromsomes and so deviate from traditional Mendelian inheritance patterns.

Meiosis Explains Mendel's Laws

Mendel's findings did not gain recognition until many years after his work was published. In the late 1800s, when cell biologists began to study the role of chromosomes in cell reproduction, similarities were found between the behaviour of chromosomes and the behaviour of Mendel's heritable factors. From this discovery emerged the chromosome theory of inheritance. The **chromosome theory of inheritance** states that genes are located at specific positions on chromosomes, and the segregation and assortment of these chromosomes during meiosis is responsible for inheritance patterns.

In Figure 5.31, chromosomes from one parent are shown in blue and from the other parent in red. The alleles of a gene reside at the same location, or locus, on homologous chromosomes. A **gene locus** (plural gene loci) is a site on a chromosome that a specific gene occupies.

Homologous chromosomes may bear either the same alleles or different ones at a particular locus, making an organism either homozygous or heterozygous for each gene. Figure 5.32 shows the gene loci in a dihybrid pea plant that is heterozygous for both seed shape and seed colour. The gene loci for seed shape and seed colour are on different chromosomes. The chromosomes assort independently during meiosis, producing four possible genotypes in the gametes.

©P

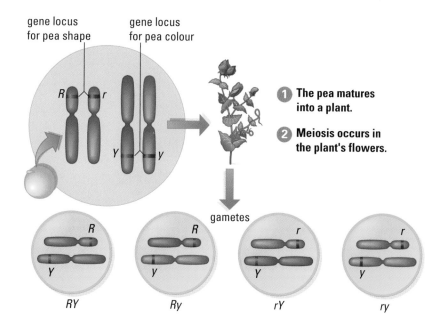

Figure 5.32 A pea plant has gene loci for shape and colour on different chromosomes. The chromosomes and gene loci shuffle during meiosis.

① The pea matures into a plant.

② Meiosis occurs in the plant's flowers.

gametes

RY · Ry · rY · ry

Genetic Linkage

A chromosome contains hundreds of different genes lined up along its length at specific loci. If genes are located on separate chromosomes, they assort independently of each other during meiosis. But what happens when genes are located on the same chromosome? The alleles for these genes are less likely to assort independently, and instead stay together during meiosis. The only way such alleles can assort independently is if crossing over during meiosis separates them.

The tendency for alleles for different genes on the same chromosome to be inherited together is called **genetic linkage**. Genes with loci that are close together are known as linked genes. For example, black fruit flies commonly have short wings whereas grey fruit flies commonly have long wings. In fruit flies, the genes for body colour and wing length are linked. The closer two genes are on a chromosome, the greater the degree of genetic linkage (Figure 5.33). The farther apart the genes are, the more likely it is that crossing over will separate them. In Scenario 2 of Figure 5.33, allele Q can be found with either allele M or m.

Because the distance between loci is directly related to genetic linkage, scientists sometimes look at the frequency with which certain genes turn up together. This value, called the recombination frequency, can be used to map the distance between gene loci on a chromosome. These values allow geneticists to create a **gene map**, a diagram that shows the relative locations and distances of genes on a chromosome. The first studies of this kind were conducted on fruit flies (Figure 5.34 on the next page). This technique has since been used to map the chromosomal location of many genes from various species.

BIOLOGY•SOURCE

Explore More

How does the chromosome theory of inheritance help us to interpret Mendel's laws?

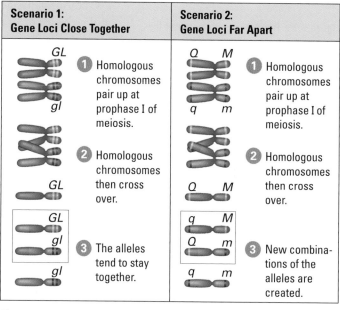

Scenario 1: Gene Loci Close Together	Scenario 2: Gene Loci Far Apart
GL / gl — ① Homologous chromosomes pair up at prophase I of meiosis.	Q M / q m — ① Homologous chromosomes pair up at prophase I of meiosis.
② Homologous chromosomes then cross over.	② Homologous chromosomes then cross over.
GL / GL / gl / gl — ③ The alleles tend to stay together.	q M / Q m / q m — ③ New combinations of the alleles are created.

Figure 5.33 Crossing over can recombine gene loci on homologous chromosomes.

BIOLOGY•SOURCE

Suggested Activity

• B11 Design a Lab Overview on page 150

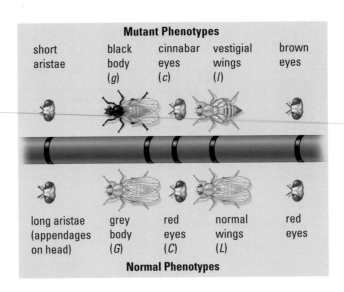

Figure 5.34 Gene map showing the location of genes on chromosome 2 of the fruit fly

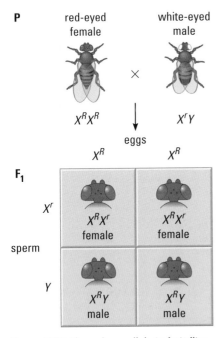

Figure 5.35 The red-eye allele in fruit flies is dominant to the white-eye allele.

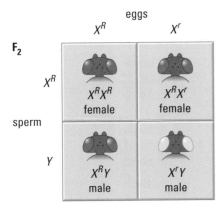

Figure 5.36 Male fruit flies that inherit one copy of the white-eye allele will have white eyes.

Inheritance Patterns of Sex-Linked Traits

Sex-linked genes were discovered by Thomas Hunt Morgan while he was studying the inheritance of white eye colour in fruit flies. White eyes are very rare in natural fruit fly populations. When Morgan crossed a white-eyed male fly with a red-eyed female fly, all of the F_1 offspring had red eyes (Figure 5.35). This result suggested that the allele for red eyes was dominant. When the F_1 offspring were bred together, the resulting F_2 offspring showed both phenotypes, in the ratio of three red-eyed flies to one white-eyed fly, or 3:1. An unexpected result was that all the flies with white eyes were males (Figure 5.36). Morgan realized that in fruit flies, there must be a relationship between eye colour and sex.

From this and other experimental evidence, Morgan discovered that the gene involved in the white-eye inheritance pattern is located only on the X chromosome. There is no corresponding gene for eye-colour on the Y chromosome. Females have two X chromosomes (they are XX), therefore females carry two copies of the red or white eye-colour gene. Males have only one X chromosome (they are XY) and so carry only one copy of the gene. Since the white-eye trait is recessive, a female will have white eyes only if both X chromosomes carry the white-eye allele ($X^r X^r$). On the other hand, if a male inherits a single copy of the white-eye allele on his X chromosome, as there is no other copy of the gene, he will have white eyes ($X^r Y$).

Any gene that is located on a sex chromosome is called a **sex-linked gene**. In humans, most sex-linked genes are found on the X chromosome, which is considerably larger in size than the Y chromosome. Genes on the X chromosome are said to be X-linked.

Concept Check

1. What is the chromosome theory of inheritance?

2. Define the term "gene locus."

3. What are sex chromosomes?

Sex-Linked Disorders

The genetics of fruit fly eye colour helps explain the inheritance of sex-linked traits in humans. Red-green colour blindness, for example, is an X-linked recessive trait. The condition affects about 4 to 8% of males and about 0.4% of females. People who have red-green colour blindness cannot distinguish between the colours of the dots in Figure 5.37 to make out the number 70. The two main types of hemophilia are also X-linked. Hemophilia is sometimes called the "bleeder's disease" because the blood fails to clot normally. About 1 in 10 000 babies are born with hemophilia, most of them boys.

The fruit fly model shows why recessive sex-linked traits are much more common in males than in females. Like a male fruit fly, if a human male inherits a sex-linked recessive allele from his mother, this allele will be expressed (Table 5.5 and Figure 5.38). In contrast, a female must inherit two such alleles — one from each parent — to exhibit the trait.

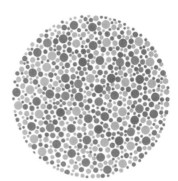

Figure 5.37 Test for red-green colour blindness

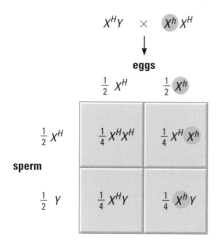

Figure 5.38 A female carrier for hemophilia who has children with an unaffected male may have affected sons. None of their daughters will have hemophilia.

Table 5.5 Genetics of Hemophilia

Genotype	Phenotype
$X^H Y$	Normal male
$X^h Y$	Affected male (hemophiliac)
$X^H X^H$	Normal female
$X^H X^h$ (carrier)	Normal female
$X^h X^h$	Affected female (very rare)

Other recessive X-linked disorders include an immune system disorder and Duchenne muscular dystrophy, which causes progressive muscle weakness (Figure 5.39(a)). Although many sex-linked genes are located on the X chromosome, some genes are located on the Y chromosome and are passed down from the father. Y-linked disorders are caused by mutations in genes located on the Y chromosome. Although rare, these mutations tend to be in regions related to male sex determination. SRY, which stands for sex-determining region on the Y chromosome, is the gene for testis-determining factor (Figure 5.39(b)). A mutation in this region results in XY females with disorders in the development of the reproductive system.

BIOLOGY • SOURCE

Take It Further

Research the role of hemophilia in European history. Locate a pedigree diagram that shows hemophilia's transmission among royal family members. Why do you think this disorder was so prevalent in Europe's royal families?

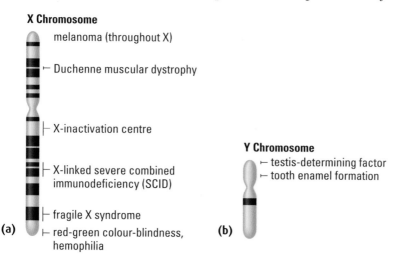

Figure 5.39 Some of the genes on the X and Y chromosomes

Practice Problems

Give the genotypic and phenotypic proportions (including sex) for the offspring of the following crosses.

1. A red-eye female fly ($X^R X^r$) is mated with a white-eyed male fly ($X^r Y$).

2. A red-green colourblind woman ($X^c X^c$) has children with a man who has normal vision ($X^C Y$).

3. A man with hemophilia ($X^h Y$) has children with a woman who is a carrier ($X^H X^h$).

Answers

1. $\frac{1}{4}$ heterozygous red-eyed females ($X^R X^r$), $\frac{1}{4}$ white-eyed females ($X^r X^r$), $\frac{1}{4}$ red-eyed males ($X^R Y$), $\frac{1}{4}$ white-eyed males ($X^r Y$)

2. $\frac{1}{2}$ heterozygous females with normal vision ($X^C X^c$), $\frac{1}{2}$ red-green colourblind males ($X^c Y$)

3. $\frac{1}{4}$ female carriers ($X^H X^h$), $\frac{1}{4}$ females with hemophilia ($X^h X^h$), $\frac{1}{4}$ normal males ($X^H Y$), $\frac{1}{4}$ males with hemophilia ($X^h Y$)

Example 5.4 Sex-Linked Inheritance Patterns

Hemophilia is an X-linked recessive disorder. If a woman who is a carrier for hemophilia has a child with a man who does not have hemophilia, what is the chance that the couple will have a son affected with hemophilia?

Given
Hemophilia is X-linked and recessive.
The mother's genotype is $X^H X^h$.
The father's genotype is $X^H Y$.

Required
• the probability of the parents having a son with hemophilia

Analysis
Determine the gametes from the parental genotypes.
Construct a Punnett square for this cross to determine the genotypes and phenotypes of the offspring.

Solution
The mother produces gametes X^H and X^h.
The father produces gametes X^H and Y.

	X^H	X^h
X^H	$X^H X^H$	$X^H X^h$
Y	$X^H Y$	$X^h Y$

Paraphrase
A son with hemophilia would have the genotype $X^h Y$. From the Punnett square, the probability of the couple having a son with hemophilia is $\frac{1}{4}$ or 25%.

REQUIRED SKILLS
■ Predicting
■ Drawing conclusions

Fruit Fly Genetics Lab

Question

How can you use fruit fly crosses to determine genotypes and the effects of mutant alleles?

Activity Overview

You can trace the inheritance of several fruit fly genes by studying the phenotypes of mutant alleles (Figures 5.40 and 5.41). In this activity, you will design and perform crosses between fruit flies and determine the ratios of genotypes and phenotypes of the offspring.

Your teacher will give you a copy of the full activity.

Prelab Questions

Consider the questions below before beginning this activity.

1. Describe three different inheritance patterns for sex-linked traits.

2. What sex is most affected by X-linked traits?

3. What are some genes on fruit fly chromosome 2?

4. How could you recognize the inheritance of a recessive trait in fruit flies?

Figure 5.40 Eye colours and body colours in fruit flies

Figure 5.41 Fruit flies with vestigial wings, a recessive trait

©P

Key Concept Review

1. How are chromosomes related to the inheritance of traits?

2. What is the relationship between alleles and gene loci?

3. Describe two differences between X and Y chromosomes in humans.

4. Define "sex-linked trait."

5. How is distance between gene loci related to genetic linkage?

6. What inheritance pattern would you expect to see for a Y-linked trait in humans?

7. Which human chromosome carries most of the genes for sex-linked traits?

Connect Your Understanding

8. The diagram below shows the inheritance of hemophilia in a family. Examine the diagram and answer the questions that follow.

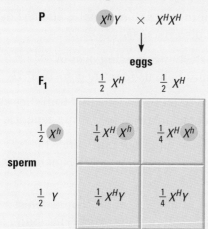

P $X^h Y$ $\times$ $X^H X^H$

eggs

F$_1$ $\frac{1}{2} X^H$ $\frac{1}{2} X^H$

$\frac{1}{2} X^h$ | $\frac{1}{4} X^H X^h$ | $\frac{1}{4} X^H X^h$ |

sperm

$\frac{1}{2} Y$ | $\frac{1}{4} X^H Y$ | $\frac{1}{4} X^H Y$ |

Question 8

(a) What is the genotype of the father?
(b) What is the probability that one of the daughters will inherit the allele for hemophilia?
(c) Suppose one of the daughters starts her own family. Her husband does not have hemophilia. Draw a Punnett square to show all possible genotypes of the F$_2$ offspring.
(d) From your Punnett square, what is the probability that the woman will pass down the hemophilia allele to her children?

(e) From your Punnett square, how many of the sons with the hemophilia allele will also have the condition?

9. Duchenne muscular dystrophy is a recessive sex-linked trait. Suppose a man who does not have the condition has children with a woman who is a carrier. Give all possible genotypes and phenotypes for the children. What is the probability of each phenotype occurring?

10. Using a diagram, explain why the farther apart two genes are on a chromosome, the more likely they are to separate during meiosis.

11. The following table shows the results of a cross between two red-eyed fruit flies. Some of the offspring have "ruby" (deep pink) eyes.

Numbers of Offspring from Fruit Fly Cross

Eye Colour	Numbers of Males	Numbers of Females
Red	77	151
Ruby	75	0

(a) Are ruby-coloured eyes dominant or recessive?
(b) How do the results of the cross indicate that ruby eye colour is sex-linked?
(c) Using X^R for the dominant allele and X^r for the recessive allele, write the genotypes of the two parents.
(d) Do the female offspring all have the same genotype? List the likely genotypes(s) of the female offspring.
(e) List the genotype of the red-eyed males and the genotype of the ruby-eyed males.

12. Male birds have two Z chromosomes (ZZ), while female birds have a Z chromosome and a W chromosome (ZW). Suggest why birds would make poor model organisms for understanding the inheritance of human sex-linked traits.

Reflection

13. Describe two things that you learned about inheritance patterns from reading this section.

14. What do you feel is the most important topic you learned about in this section? Why?

For more questions, go to   BIOLOGY•SOURCE

Key Concept Review

1. Define "dominant allele" and "recessive allele." **k**

2. What is meant by a true-breeding organism for a particular trait? Give an example. **k**

3. Distinguish between the terms "genotype" and "phenotype." Give an example of each. **k**

4. Give the phenotype for each of the following pea plants.
   (a) a plant that is homozygous for the dominant tall allele **k**
   (b) a plant that is heterozygous for the dominant tall allele **k**
   (c) a plant that is homozygous for the recessive yellow pod colour allele **k**
   (d) a plant that is heterozygous for both the dominant axial flower allele and the dominant round seed allele **k**

5. List the four main principles of the Mendelian model of inheritance. **k**

6. What is the difference between a dihybrid cross and a monohybrid cross? **k**

7. State the law of independent assortment. **k**

8. What is genetic linkage? How does linkage affect the inheritance of certain traits? **k**

9. What is the difference between multiple alleles and polygenic inheritance? **k**

10. Give an example of a sex-liked disorder. Describe how this disorder is inherited. **k**

11. Differentiate between codominance and incomplete dominance, using an example for each. **k**

Connect Your Understanding

12. Explain why it was necessary for Mendel to use true-breeding plants in his crosses. **t**

13. How did Mendel explain why offspring inherit traits from previous generations? **t**

14. (a) Explain the concept of independent assortment. **t**
    (b) What evidence from Mendel's experiments demonstrated independent assortment? **t**

15. How are Punnett squares used to predict the probability of genetic outcomes from a cross? **a**

16. Use an example to explain how a test cross can be used to determine the genotype of an organism with a dominant trait. **a**

17. The fruit fly phenotype depicted in the following photograph helped Thomas Morgan with an important genetic discovery. Explain what that discovery was and describe the observations that led Morgan to his conclusion. **a**

Question 17

18. If a trait has a continuous range of phenotypes, what is the most likely mode of inheritance? Explain. **a**

19. Why are more males than females affected by sex-linked disorders? **t**

20. How does studying crossing over of chromosomes help us identify gene loci? **t**

21. Suggest two or more reasons that fruit flies are good model organisms for studying genetics. **t**

22. How can the environment influence the expression of a particular trait? Explain using an example. **t**

23. After eating asparagus, some people detect a sulphurous smell in their urine. The ability to detect this smell is thought to be a dominant trait. Explain why two people with the smelling trait could have children who lack the trait. **a**

24. People with achoo syndrome sneeze in response to bright light. Suggest what observations of human populations might have led researchers to conclude that achoo syndrome is a dominant trait? **a**

25. (a) Draw a Punnett square to represent a cross between a true-breeding tall pea plant with green seeds and a short pea plant with yellow seeds. **ⓒ**
    (b) What are the possible genotypes and phenotypes from the above cross? **ⓐ**
    (c) Give the phenotypic ratio for the F_1 generation. **ⓐ**

26. Suppose a horse with a roan coat colour is crossed with a true-breeding white horse.
    (a) Draw a Punnett square to represent this cross. **ⓐ**
    (b) What would be the expected genotypes and phenotypes of the F_1 generation for this cross? **ⓐ**

27. Suppose an organism has the genotype *AaBBCC*. List all possible allele combinations in the gametes for this individual. **ⓒ**

28. Using your knowledge of ABO blood types, is it possible for a woman with blood type A and a man with blood type B to have a child with blood type O? Explain using a Punnett square to support your answer. **ⓒ**

29. What are the possible genotypes of the parents for a daughter that is affected with hemophilia? **ⓒ**

30. The flowers in the photograph below are snapdragons. Explain why a cross between two pink snapdragons would produce an F_1 generation of red flowers, pink flowers, and white flowers. **ⓣ**

Question 30

31. Suggest why it might be helpful for parents to know if their child has a mutation in the SRY region of the Y chromosome. **ⓐ**

32. People with albinism lack an enzyme needed to make melanin, a pigment that colours the eyes, skin, and hair. The trait can skip generations.
    (a) Suggest why albinism can skip generations. **ⓣ**
    (b) What observations would lead you to conclude that the gene for the melanin enzyme is on an autosome rather than a sex chromosome? **ⓐ**

33. The results of a test cross between green corn plants and true-breeding albino (colourless) corn plants are given in the data table below. Use the data to answer the questions that follow.

Phenotypes of F_1 Offspring from Corn Plant Cross

Phenotype	Number of Plants
Green leaves	310
Albino leaves	90

    (a) What is the phenotypic ratio of green corn plants to albino corn plants? Show your calculations. **ⓒ**
    (b) Which trait is dominant: green leaves or albino leaves? How do you know? **ⓐ**
    (c) What is the genotype of the green corn plants from the parental generation? **ⓐ**

34. Having a pointed hairline is a dominant trait, yet it is uncommon in most human populations. How is dominance different from frequency? **ⓣ**

Reflection

35. What have you learned about the inheritance of human traits by completing this chapter? **ⓒ**

36. List three things from this chapter that apply to your own life. **ⓒ**

Unit Task Link

For your Unit Task, you will need to create Punnett squares for particular genetic conditions. To prepare for this activity, add to your table of common genetic conditions and list the mode of inheritance for each. Create a sample Punnett square for each condition to demonstrate the mode of inheritance and the probability of parents who are carriers having affected offspring.

For more questions, go to   **BIOLOGY•SOURCE**

Genetic and genomic research and technologies have social and ethical implications.

This genetically engineered mouse is helping scientists study retinitis pigmentosa, a disease that affects one in every 3000 people worldwide (Figure 6.1). The disease begins in the teens with loss of peripheral vision, then progresses over many years to tunnel vision and blindness. The single largest cause of retinitis pigmentosa is mutation of a gene for a light receptor pigment at the back of the eye.

In order to study the disease and develop treatments, researchers constructed a mouse model with human gene mutations. First, they fused the mutated human gene with a jellyfish gene for green fluorescent protein, or GFP. They then replaced the light receptor gene in mouse cells grown in a culture dish with the fused human-GFP gene. The mouse cells were injected into mouse embryos, which developed into mice with the new gene. Genetic treatments for retinitis pigmentosa are tested on the mice. If a treatment works, the eyes of the mice light up with GFP. The degree of fluorescence in the eyes indicates how effective the treatment is.

The mouse is a favoured model organism because of its many genetic similarities to humans. Along with knowledge of DNA sequences and the ability to manipulate DNA, mouse models are invaluable in genetic research.

Figure 6.1 Mice with green fluorescent eyes are helping us to understand retinitis pigmentosa.

©P

6.1 Studying the Human Genome

Section Summary

- DNA can be manipulated with restriction enzymes and analyzed using gel electrophoresis and DNA sequencing.

- The Human Genome Project completed the nucleotide sequence for the entire human genome.

- Much of current genetic research involves genomics and bioinformatics, specifically the exploration of the human genome in order to identify the locations and functions of human genes.

- *Escherichia coli* bacteria, nematodes, yeast, fruit flies, and mice are common model organisms for genetic studies.

Even the smallest human chromosome contains about five million nucleotide pairs. It may seem like an impossible task to determine the entire nucleotide sequence for every human chromosome. However, in 1990, over a century after Mendel's work, scientists launched the most ambitious genetics project to date: the Human Genome Project. This international collaboration had two main goals: first, to determine the nucleotide sequence of all the DNA in human chromosomes, and second, to identify the location and sequence of every human gene. Other goals included exploring gene functions, studying variations among different people's DNA, and comparing human DNA with DNA from other species.

Dissecting Genomes

A **genome** is the full DNA sequence of an organism. The completion of the first draft of the human genome in June 2000 made history. The details of the work were later announced in two highly respected scientific journals, *Nature* and *Science* (Figure 6.2). People often ask whose DNA was sequenced for the Human Genome Project. The answer is, not any one person's DNA in particular. The human genome sequenced in the project was compiled from a group of individuals.

The Human Genome Project uncovered some interesting and unexpected information. For example, only about 1.5–2% of the human genome contains genes. The remaining 98% includes repeated nucleotide sequences, regions that regulate genes, and even DNA sequences inserted from viruses.

Figure 6.2 In February 2001, *Science* and *Nature* announced the details of the human genome.

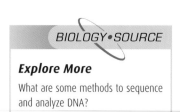
Manipulating DNA

Most DNA molecules in organisms are very long, and so before they can be analyzed, they must be cut into smaller pieces. The "molecular scissors" used to cut DNA comes from bacteria. **Restriction enzymes** are bacterial proteins that cut DNA wherever a particular nucleotide sequence occurs. Figure 6.3 shows how one restriction enzyme cuts DNA at the recognition sequence CTTAAG. The pieces of DNA made by cutting it with restriction enzymes are called **restriction fragments**.

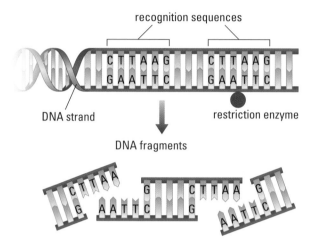

Figure 6.3 Restriction enzymes cut DNA at precise recognition sequences.

Once DNA has been cut into restriction fragments, the pieces can be sorted and analyzed using a technique called gel electrophoresis (Figure 6.4). A DNA gel, which looks and feels like a slab of gelatin, is porous. DNA fragments are added to one end of the gel, and electric current is applied. DNA molecules are negatively charged and so move to the positively charged end of the gel. The smaller the fragment, the faster it moves through the pores in the gel. When the electric current is turned off, some fragments will have moved farther along the gel than others. The resulting pattern of bands on the gel represents the various fragment sizes. Finally, a stain is applied to the DNA to make the bands visible (Figure 6.5).

1 A pipette is used to load DNA samples into wells in the end of a gel.

2 Electric current is applied to the gel to separate the DNA fragments.

3 When electrophoresis is complete, the gel can be stained.

Figure 6.4 Using gel electrophoresis to separate restriction fragments

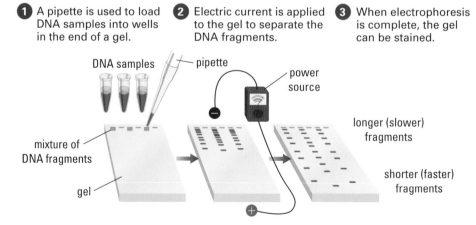

Figure 6.5 A restriction fragment gel

DNA from different organisms will produce different restriction fragments. This is why a restriction fragment gel can be used to identify the source of a disease outbreak. For example, if bacteria that are making people ill produce the same restriction fragments as bacteria in a food sample, the food can be identified as the source of the illness. The pattern of restriction fragments is sometimes called a DNA fingerprint.

©P

DNA Sequencing

Determining the order of nucleotides in DNA is known as **DNA sequencing**. To complete the human genome, it took hundreds of automated DNA sequencing machines (Figure 6.6). These machines use robotics to work with the DNA. Computer programs then analyze the results (Figure 6.7).

More recently, even more efficient sequencing technologies have been developed. Many use nucleotides that are labelled with different colours of fluorescent dyes. First, the two strands of a DNA helix are separated. Then, one of the strands is used as a template to make a complementary strand of DNA. The complementary strand grows one nucleotide at a time — adenine, thymine, guanine, or cytosine. In one method, as each nucleotide adds on, there is a bright flash of light from the dye. The system detects the light and records which nucleotide was added.

Figure 6.6 Hundreds of people have worked on the Human Genome Project. This researcher is monitoring a DNA sequencing machine.

Bioinformatics

One of the new fields to emerge from the Human Genome Project is bioinformatics. **Bioinformatics** is the science of handling and analyzing biological data (Figure 6.8). This area of study involves the creation, development, and operation of databases and other computational tools to collect, organize, and interpret data. For example, nucleotide sequences are stored in searchable databases. Researchers then use specialized computer programs to recognize and align overlapping nucleotide sequences.

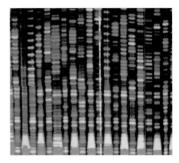

Figure 6.7 Results from an automated DNA sequencer. Each coloured band represents one of the four nucleotides.

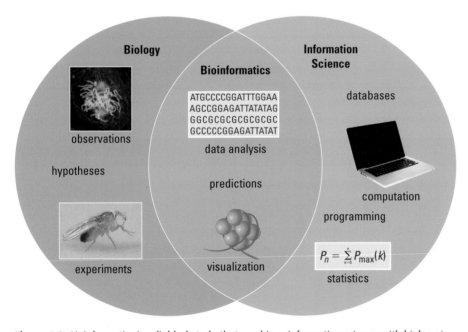

Figure 6.8 Bioinformatics is a field of study that combines information science with biology in order to study and interpret genomes.

Along with the human genome, the genomes of various microorganisms, plants, and animals have been completed (Table 6.1 on the next page). Many of these sequences have proven to be very valuable in understanding human gene functions. The DNA sequences obtained from the Human Genome Project are all housed in a central repository called GenBank. This database is publicly available on the Internet, enabling researchers and students to search, browse, and compare DNA sequences from thousands of species.

BIOLOGY•SOURCE

Explore More

Which genes are linked to particular genetic disorders?

Not everyone agrees that nucleotide sequences should be made publically available, free of charge. Some people argue that scientists should own DNA sequences that they have worked out. Others argue that this knowledge rightfully belongs to all.

Table 6.1 Some Completed Genomes

Species	Genome Size (Base Pairs)	Approximate Number of Genes
Haemophilus influenzae (bacterium)	1.8 million	1 700
Escherichia coli (bacterium)	4.6 million	4 400
Saccharomyces cerevisiae (yeast)	12 million	6 200
Caenorhabditis elegans (nematode)	96 million	19 000
Arabidopsis thaliana (mustard plant)	125 million	25 500
Drosophila melanogaster (fruit fly)	170 million	13 700
Oryza sativa (rice plant)	470 million	60 000
Mus musculus (mouse)	2.6 billion	30 000
Rattus norvegius (lab rat)	2.8 billion	25 000
Macaca mulatta (macaque)	2.9 billion	22 000
Pan troglodytes (chimpanzee)	3.1 billion	22 000
Homo sapiens (human)	3.2 billion	21 000

BIOLOGY•SOURCE

Take It Further

DNA profiling is often used in forensics, but not only to identify humans. Forensic investigations are also conducted on trucks and fishing boats to check for DNA from endangered or protected wildlife species. The Wildlife Forensic DNA Laboratory is a Canadian service and research facility. How does the laboratory collect samples and how does it use genetic information from their databases to catch poachers?

Concept Check

1. What is the Human Genome Project?
2. What can you learn by comparing restriction fragment gels?
3. Why did the field of bioinformatics emerge as a science?

Start
→
...CTCCTGGGAA**ATG**TGCTGGTGA

CCGTTTTGGCAATCCATTTCGGCA

AAGAATTCACCCCTGAGGTGCAG

GCTTCCTGGCAGAAGATGGTGAC

TGCAGTGGCCAGTGCCCTGTCCT
Stop
CCAGATACCAC**TGA**GCCACTTGC

CCATGATTCAGAGCTTT...

Figure 6.9 Start codons and stop codons can be used to locate genes.

Genomics

Much of human genetics research today involves exploration of data from the Human Genome Project. The study of genomes is called **genomics**. One goal of genomics is to map the location of genes within a genome. Scientists use key identifier regions to map genes. These identifiers include switches that turn genes on or off, start codons at the beginning of genes, and stop codons at the end of genes (Figure 6.9).

Some regions of genes contain the instructions for making particular proteins. These regions are known as coding regions. For example, the alpha globulin gene contains a coding region for part of the hemoglobin protein. Other regions that can be used to locate genes are noncoding, and their roles are not fully understood.

Mapping genes enables researchers to identify genes associated with diseases. An example is Parkinson's disease. This progressive disease gradually destroys brain cell function, causing tremors, speech difficulties, and rigid muscles.

Prior to the Human Genome Project, scientists were unsure if genetics played a role in Parkinson's disease. To find out, researchers examined DNA sequences from people with Parkinson's disease and compared these to sequences from other people. There were some important differences. In a number of cases, the people with Parkinson's disease had a mutation in a particular gene (Figure 6.10). Further study of this gene and the protein it codes for indicated links to Alzheimer's disease, suggesting a relationship between the two diseases. Other mutations that may cause Parkinson's disease have also been discovered.

healthy gene

...CATGGTGTGGCAACA...
...CATGGTGTGACAACA...

mutated gene

Figure 6.10 A mutation on chromosome 4 linked to Parkinson's disease

BIOLOGY•SOURCE

Suggested Activity
• B12 Case Study Overview on page 160

Model Organisms

Cross-species comparisons can help us understand the functions of particular genes. For example, if a nucleotide sequence in the human genome is similar to a particular mouse gene with a known function, this gives us insight into the function of the human sequence. When comparing genomes, researchers look for regions of similarity and the locations of genes. For example, cross-species comparisons show that a gene for sense of smell in rats and a gene involved in song-learning in zebra finches are similar to a human gene affected in Parkinson's disease. The gene's role in rats and zebra finches provides clues about the gene's role in humans and what happens when this function is missing. Understanding the role of such genes helps people to develop therapies and potential cures for genetic diseases.

Functional genomics is a specific branch of study in genomics. In this field, researchers study model organisms, such as mice, in order to understand the functions of genes and other parts of the genome. Model organisms enable scientists to follow the inheritance of genes through many generations in a relatively short time. Some common model organisms include the bacterium *Escherichia coli* (*E. coli* for short), a nematode (*Caenorhabditis elegans*) (Figure 6.11), baker's yeast (*Saccharomyces cerevisiae*) (Figure 6.12), the fruit fly (*D. melanogaster*), and the laboratory mouse (*Mus musculus*).

The mouse is a particularly special model organism for genetic studies. Mouse development and genetics have been well studied. Mice and humans have a similar number of nucleotides in their genomes and a comparable number of genes. In most cases, for a particular human gene a mouse counterpart can be found.

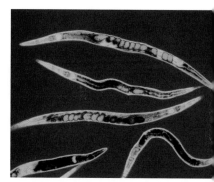

Figure 6.11 The nematode *C. elegans* (magnification 80×)

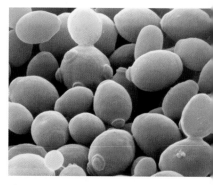

Figure 6.12 Baker's yeast: *S. cerevisiae* (magnification 4000×)

Concept Check

1. What are the goals of genomics?

2. How do scientists identify gene regions in DNA?

3. Name two model organisms.

Applying Genomics

Genomics has made possible new types of genetic testing, such as DNA chip tests. A **DNA chip** is a small glass wafer or slide spotted with an array of single-stranded DNA fragments. Some spots, for example, could contain DNA with mutations known to cause cystic fibrosis. The person undergoing genetic testing provides a DNA sample that is cut into pieces. The pieces are then tagged with a fluorescent dye to make a series of probes. Wherever there is a match between a probe and a spot of DNA on the chip, the probe will bind. Its fluorescent tag marks the spot (Figure 6.13). DNA chips can be made that span large regions of the human genome and include mutations for various genetic conditions. For this reason, gene chips could become a useful tool in personalized health care.

Knowledge about genomes can have useful applications in agriculture as well as medicine. For example, sequencing the rice genome has led to ways of making it a more nutritious food source. Perhaps the most challenging and important aspect of genetic research today is to understand how all genes and proteins work together to create complex living organisms.

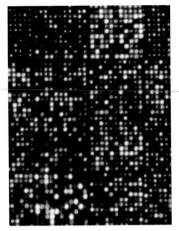

Figure 6.13 A DNA chip

B12   Case Study   *BIOLOGY·SOURCE*

REQUIRED SKILLS
- Asking questions
- Summarizing information

Identifying Disease-Associated Variations of Genes

Issue

Human genomics has had an enormous impact on both science and society. In many cases, we can identify disease-associated variations of genes when someone has no symptoms, or when treatments are radical or not yet available. What are the benefits and problems with testing for disease-associated alleles?

Activity Overview

Genetic testing gives people the ability to learn if they carry disease-associated alleles, and in some cases, the likelihood of developing a life-threatening condition (Figure 6.14). While testing for disease-associated alleles can give people foresight, test results may be distressing. There is also a concern that test results would be used to deny people life insurance. In this activity, you will examine opposing viewpoints on genetic testing and give your own opinion on the issue.

Your teacher will give you a copy of the full activity.

Prelab Questions

Consider the questions below before beginning this activity.

1. Begin a list of genetic diseases that a person could be tested for.

2. Brainstorm the possible advantages of learning that you or a family member has a disease-associated allele.

3. List three concerns you might have about learning that you or a family member has a disease-associated allele.

Figure 6.14 Actress Christina Applegate elected to have a double mastectomy (removal of the breast tissue) when she learned that she had cancer in one breast. A breast cancer-associated gene variation runs in her family.

Key Concept Review

1. What is the difference between a gene and a genome?

2. What were the primary goals of the Human Genome Project?

3. How are restriction enzymes used to manipulate DNA?

4. What does DNA sequencing determine?

5. What fraction of the human genome contains genes?

6. Which areas of science does bioinformatics bring together?

7. What term is used for the study of genomes?

8. How are DNA chips used for genetic testing?

9. (a) Which species has more genes in its genome: the mustard plant or the nematode *C. elegans*?
   (b) Which species has more DNA in its genome: the rice plant or the fruit fly?

Connect Your Understanding

10. Describe two ways in which model organisms are used to understand the function of human genes.

11. Describe three benefits of having a complete map of the human genome.

12. (a) What are three reasons that mice are used as model organisms in genetic studies?
    (b) Suggest one or more drawbacks to using mice in genetic studies.

13. How are DNA sequencing and gene mapping related?

14. Describe any patterns or similarities you notice among the genomes in Table 6.1 on page 158.

15. Outline an experiment to determine whether a disease is primarily due to environmental factors or a genetic mutation. Assume you have access to DNA sequence data from the human genome.

16. Should anyone have the right to own DNA sequence data? Justify your response.

17. The following diagram shows a simplified restriction fragment gel of bacterial DNA. The DNA in lane A is from bacteria isolated from an ill child. The DNA in lanes B, C, and D are from bacteria isolated from different food samples.
    (a) Which of the bacteria (A, B, C, or D) are the same?
    (b) Which of the bacteria may share some of the same genetic content?
    (c) Which food sample contained the bacteria that made the child ill? Explain.

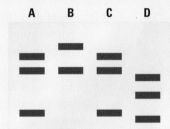

Question 17

18. People planning on having children may choose the option of having their DNA screened for over 100 genetic disease mutations with DNA chip technology. Draw a Venn diagram to illustrate some of the implications of using DNA chips this way, including the positives, negatives, and mixed implications.

Reflection

19. How has learning about the Human Genome Project affected the way you think about genetic disease?

20. List two questions or concerns you have about the implications of genomics and related technologies.

For more questions, go to BIOLOGY•SOURCE

Section Summary

- Biotechnology is the use of organisms to make useful products. Some forms of biotechnology involve genetic engineering.
- Recombinant DNA technology can be used to modify an organism's genome.
- Bacteria containing recombinant DNA can be used for gene cloning or to produce proteins used in industry or medicine.

Blue jean manufacturers are going green, thanks to modern genetic technologies. An important change is in the fabric dying process. Traditionally, the indigo dye that gives blue jeans their characteristic colour was derived from plants. Synthetic production involving coal or oil then became standard practice, although it produces potentially toxic by-products. A newer and environmentally friendly substitute is bio-indigo from bacteria (Figure 6.15).

Alterations to the genome of *E. coli* have resulted in a strain that makes high levels of tryptophan, a molecule that can be converted into indigo in a series of steps. The engineered bacterial strain also contains a gene from a soil bacterium. The gene is for an enzyme that completes the last step in the conversion of tryptophan to indigo. Making bio-indigo is less energy intensive than standard methods and does not result in harmful by-products.

Biotechnology

Historically, humans have relied on other species to do certain jobs. People used yeast to make bread long before they understood the chemistry of fermentation. Farmers bred animals and plants to produce offspring with desired traits without knowing about the activities of DNA and chromosomes. Breeders would sometimes try to introduce variation into a genetic line by breeding organisms with unusual phenotypes. However, the resulting phenotypic changes were unpredictable and often not reproducible.

The use of organisms to make useful products is called **biotechnology**. For example, micro-organisms are used to produce vaccines, antibiotics, hormones, food products, and enzymes that are added to detergents. Much of biotechnology today makes use of our ability to analyze and manipulate genomes at the molecular level.

As we learn about biology at the molecular level, people are developing astonishing ways to modify organisms in the laboratory. We can increase genetic variation in a population by transferring certain genes from one organism to another. **Genetic engineering** is the intentional production of new genes and alteration of genomes by the substitution or introduction of new genetic material. With genetic engineering we can tailor the abilities of living organisms to meet specific needs in agriculture, industry, and medicine.

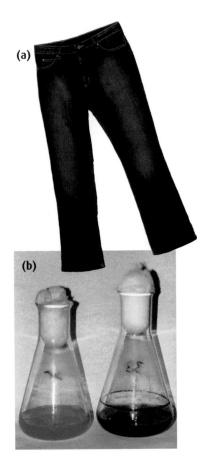

Figure 6.15 (a) Indigo dye is one of many microbial products that can be used to make blue jeans. (b) The *E. coli* cells on the right have been genetically engineered to produce indigo dye.

©P

Genetic Recombination

Bacteria are organisms essential to modern biotechnology. By genetically engineering bacteria, we can use them to mass produce useful genes and proteins. Many of the developments in genetic engineering have come from research with the common bacterium *E. coli*. Chapter 4 describes how sexual reproduction can lead to new combinations of genetic information in offspring. Unlike plants and animals, bacteria do not undergo meiosis, produce gametes, or reproduce by fertilization. Yet they have their own means of genetic recombination. Scientists have been able to apply these processes to transfer DNA into bacteria.

Through their experiments in the 1940s, American scientists Joshua Lederberg and Edward Tatum demonstrated that two bacterial cells can form a direct connection. One bacterial cell can then transfer genes to the other (Figure 6.16). Researchers later identified two other ways that bacteria acquire new genes. Viruses can carry bacterial genes from one bacterial cell to another, or bacteria can take up loose pieces of DNA from their surroundings. Using knowledge of the different ways that DNA can be transferred and recombined, people have developed a set of laboratory techniques called recombinant DNA technology. **Recombinant DNA technology** combines genes from different sources — even different species — into a single DNA molecule.

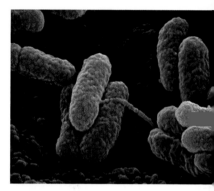

Figure 6.16 A connection between bacterial cells can draw them together so that one cell can directly transfer DNA to the other. (magnification 12 000×)

Concept Check

1. How has the bacterium *E. coli* played a role in the development of biotechnology?

2. Describe one use of genetic engineering.

3. List three ways genetic recombination occurs in bacteria.

Making Recombinant DNA

To understand the process of recombinant DNA technology, it is helpful to learn how bacteria naturally transfer genes among themselves. Many bacteria contain a small circular DNA molecule called a **plasmid**. This plasmid is separate from the much larger bacterial chromosome (Figure 6.17). A plasmid may carry a number of genes and can make copies of itself. Bacteria can share genes by passing a copy of a plasmid from one bacterial cell to another.

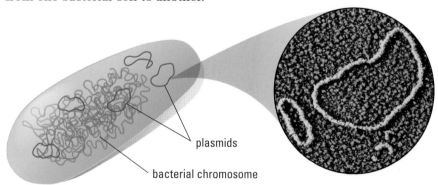

plasmids

bacterial chromosome

Figure 6.17 In addition to their main chromosomes, many bacterial cells contain small circular DNA molecules called plasmids. (magnification 50 000×)

In some instances, plasmids transfer genes for traits that help bacteria survive, such as genes that make bacteria resistant to antibiotics. The plasmids carrying these antibiotic-resistance genes can quickly spread throughout a bacterial population. As a result, an increasing variety of bacteria that cause human disease are resistant to antibiotics.

Although plasmids can spread antibiotic resistance, they can also be used for human benefit. Plasmids can be used to move pieces of DNA, such as the genes for producing indigo dye, into bacteria. To do this, a plasmid is removed from a bacterial cell, and the desired gene — from any kind of cell — is inserted into the plasmid (Figure 6.18). The result is a recombinant plasmid — a combination of the original plasmid and the new DNA. The recombinant plasmid is put back into a bacterial cell, where the DNA can replicate many times as the cell reproduces. By putting the gene in bacterial cells that can express the gene as protein, the biologist sets up a system for making large amounts of the protein.

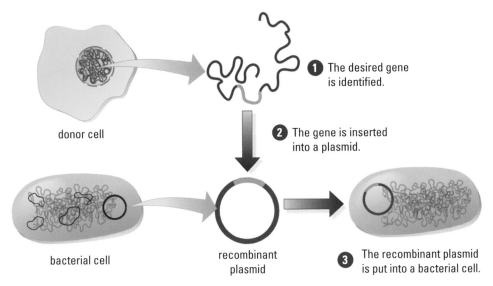

① The desired gene is identified.

donor cell

② The gene is inserted into a plasmid.

bacterial cell

recombinant plasmid

③ The recombinant plasmid is put into a bacterial cell.

Figure 6.18 Plasmids can serve as carriers of genetic information. This diagram shows the basic technique for producing a genetically engineered bacterial cell with a recombinant plasmid.

"Cutting and Pasting" DNA

To make a recombinant plasmid requires two main steps, which can be described as "cutting and pasting." First, a piece of DNA containing the desired gene must be "cut" out of a much longer DNA molecule. Restriction enzymes are used for cutting the DNA. Most restriction enzymes make staggered cuts that leave single-stranded DNA at the ends of the fragments (Figure 6.19). The single-stranded portion of a DNA fragment is called a "sticky end" because it is available to bind to any sequence that is complementary to it. Sticky ends are useful for recombining DNA, such as plasmid DNA and a human gene. The complementary sticky ends of two DNA fragments can join together by base-pairing with each other. Another enzyme, called DNA ligase, "pastes" the sticky ends together.

sticky end

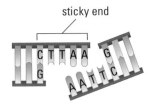

Figure 6.19 DNA fragments with sticky ends

Cloning Recombinant DNA

Recombinant DNA technology is not only useful in biotechnology. In some cases, it is used to obtain mass quantities of the DNA itself. Gene cloning is the process of putting a recombinant plasmid into a bacterial cell to make copies of a particular gene.

©P

A Glowing Transformation

Question

How can you genetically engineer bacteria to contain a jellyfish gene?

Activity Overview

Some bacteria can pick up "naked" DNA from their surroundings in a process called transformation. In this investigation, you will discover what happens if you add recombinant plasmid DNA containing the gene for green fluorescent protein (GFP) to *E. coli*. You will culture the bacteria and then check for glowing clones of bacteria that have the fluorescence gene and produce GFP (Figure 6.20).

Your teacher will give you a copy of the full activity.

Prelab Questions

Consider the questions below before beginning this activity.

1. What is the difference between the gene for GFP and GFP itself?

2. What happens when bacteria undergo transformation?

3. How could you test for antibiotic resistance in bacteria?

4. How could you find out what substances activate a gene on a plasmid?

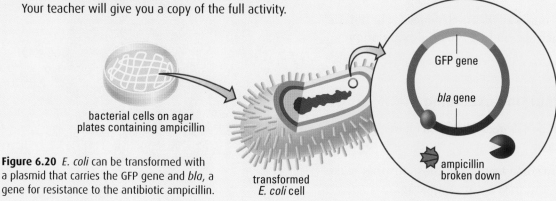

bacterial cells on agar plates containing ampicillin

GFP gene

bla gene

ampicillin broken down

transformed *E. coli* cell

Figure 6.20 *E. coli* can be transformed with a plasmid that carries the GFP gene and *bla*, a gene for resistance to the antibiotic ampicillin.

Cut and Paste DNA

Purpose

To create recombinant DNA using simulated restriction enzymes and plasmids

Activity Overview

Each type of restriction enzyme cuts DNA at a specific nucleotide sequence. By cutting two types of DNA with the same restriction enzyme, you can create DNA fragments that will stick together (Figure 6.21).

Your teacher will give you a copy of the full activity.

Prelab Questions

Consider the questions below before beginning this activity.

1. What is complementary base pairing?

2. If one strand of DNA has the sequence GATACA, what is the complementary sequence of the other strand?

3. What is a plasmid?

4. In what way are restriction enzymes "molecular scissors"?

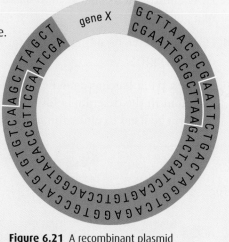

DNA ligase

gene X

Figure 6.21 A recombinant plasmid

Key Concept Review

1. What is biotechnology? List two specific examples.

2. Summarize the process of recombinant DNA technology.

3. How does recombination occur naturally in bacteria?

4. What is a recombinant plasmid?

5. Why is it useful to have sticky ends on DNA fragments?

6. What is one way in which genes for antibiotic resistance spread in a bacterial population?

7. What are two uses for recombinant DNA?

Connect Your Understanding

8. What is the difference between cloning a gene and expressing a gene?

9. What are some features of plasmids that make them useful in genetic engineering?

10. Is genetic engineering the same as biotechnology? Explain.

11. (a) How is bio-indigo produced?
    (b) What are the advantages of bio-indigo over other sources of indigo?

12. What could you use as an indicator that bacterial cells have picked up recombinant plasmids?

13. How could you use bacteria to make copies of a gene?

14. How is seletive breeding similar to genetic engineering?

15. Explain what has happened to the DNA fragment in the diagram below. How could bacteria be used to clone the fragent?

restriction
enzyme

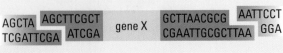

AGCTA AGCTTCGCT   gene X   GCTTAACGCG AATTCCT
TCGATTCGA ATCGA   CGAATTGCGCTTAA GGA

Question 15

16. Rennin is an animal protein used to make cheese. Traditionally, people obtained rennin from the stomach of a calf, lamb, or young goat. Today, many cheese producers use a form of rennin made by genetically engineered micro-organisms. The recombinant rennin is used in "vegetarian cheese." Which food product would you rather eat: one from an animal source or a product of genetic engineering? Justify your response.

Question 16

17. (a) If you could genetically engineer bacteria to produce a protein for medical, agricultural, or industrial use, what product would you choose to make? Why?
    (b) Outline the steps you would take to genetically engineer the bacteria.
    (c) Suggest a procedure for collecting the product from the bacteria. What are some of the challenges you might face?
    (d) What are some possible risks to using genetically engineered bacteria to make the product? What questions could you ask to help assess those risks?

Reflection

18. How has your understanding of the term "genetic engineering" changed since reading this section?

19. List three ways in which biotechnology impacts your life.

For more questions, go to BIOLOGY•SOURCE

6.3 Applications of Genetic Technologies

Section Summary

- Genetic engineering is used to genetically modify crop plants to give them useful traits, such as improved nutritional content or pest resistance, or for biotechology.

- Transgenic animals are engineered to have desirable traits. Mammals can be genetically modified to produce medically important human proteins in their milk.

- Nuclear transplantation and in vitro fertilization are techniques for cloning an animal's entire genome.

- Mouse models help us to investigate human genetic conditions.

- Gene therapy is an experimental treatment to alter a person's genome if a gene is missing or malfunctioning.

Heavy-metal contamination of water threatens both our health and the environment. Technologies that use bacteria to clean out heavy metals from water are an active area of research. One candidate for this task is the bacterium *Caulobacter crescentus*. *C. crescentus* is a natural inhabitant of Lake Erie and other lakes. The bacterial cells form an adhesive stalk-like structure that binds to solid surfaces, such as rocks, and create a layer of cells known as a biofilm (Figure 6.22).

Using recombinant DNA technology, genetic engineers have given *C. crescentus* a very useful property: surface molecules that bind heavy metals. Researchers hope that this genetically engineered bacterium will provide a safe and inexpensive way to remove heavy metals from a lake that provides drinking water for millions of people (Figure 6.23).

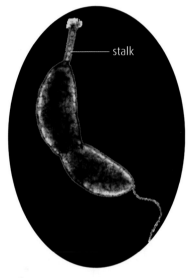

stalk

Figure 6.22 *C. crescentus* is an aquatic bacterium. (magnification 22 000×)

Genetically Modified Organisms

Genetic engineers have made thousands of types of bacteria. Putting such bacteria into the environment, or using them to make food, medicines, or industrial products could have great benefits — and unknown consequences.

Genetic engineering goes well beyond developing new strains of bacteria. Today we can custom design plants and animals that carry particular mutations or genes from other organisms. A **genetically modified organism** (GMO) is any organism with genetic material that has been altered through genetic engineering. A GMO is said to be **transgenic** if it has acquired one or more genes from a different type of organism.

GMOs have many applications in agriculture and medicine. However, their use also raises important issues. For example, releasing GMOs into the natural environment could have unexpected effects.

Figure 6.23 Millions of people depend on Lake Erie for their drinking water.

Producing Genetically Modified Plants

Using recombinant DNA technology, genetic engineers can improve the characteristics of crop plants. For example, there are genetically modified (GM) plants with new genes for delayed ripening, improved nutritional content, stress tolerance, or resistance to spoilage or disease. Genetic engineering is replacing traditional methods of plant breeding in many situations. It is used most often when a plant's useful traits are determined by one or only a few genes.

If you've ever grown a plant from a cutting, you know that some new plants can be easy to grow without actually planting seeds. For many species, a new plant can be grown in the laboratory from just one adult plant cell. Taking advantage of this fact, biologists can produce a genetically engineered plant cell that grows into an entire plant with new traits.

Recombinant DNA technology can be used to create transgenic plant cells. Biologists often use a plasmid from the soil bacterium *Agrobacterium tumefaciens* to introduce new genes into plant cells. Figure 6.24 outlines this procedure for producing a transgenic plant. This technique has been used to create transgenic varieties of tomato, potato, tobacco, soybean, walnut, and apple. Another technique, which works to modify corn, is to use a "DNA gun" to shoot DNA-coated particles into plant cells.

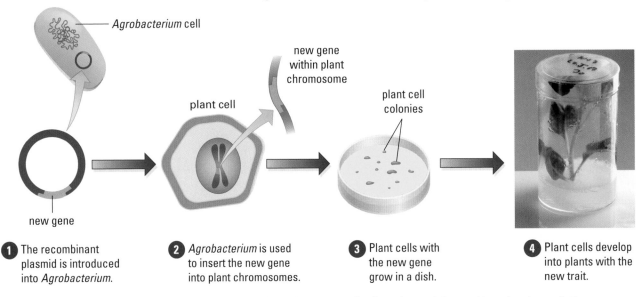

Agrobacterium cell

new gene within plant chromosome

plant cell

plant cell colonies

new gene

1. The recombinant plasmid is introduced into *Agrobacterium*.

2. *Agrobacterium* is used to insert the new gene into plant chromosomes.

3. Plant cells with the new gene grow in a dish.

4. Plant cells develop into plants with the new trait.

Figure 6.24 A plasmid containing the desired gene is inserted into the plant cell. The engineered plant cell then grows into a transgenic plant.

Pest-Resistant Crops

One genetic modification to plants is the incorporation of genes for a bacterial toxin produced by *Bacillus thuringiensis* (Figure 6.25). The Bt toxin kills specific types of insects, such as corn borers and cotton bollworms, without harming humans or most other animals. Upon ingesting Bt toxin, the enzymes of the insect's digestive system convert the toxin to a form that kills the insect. Corn and other crop plants carrying the toxin gene produce high yields without having to be sprayed with chemical pesticides. Insect resistance is just one of the many traits that are engineered into crop plants. Other traits include tolerance to herbicides (chemicals that destroy weeds) and resistance to viral infections.

Figure 6.25 Bt toxin-producing corn

©P

Plants As Factories

GM plants are used in biotechnology for the production of pharmaceuticals, industrial products, or biofuels (renewable fuels from plant matter or other organic materials). For example, genetic engineers have developed lines of safflower plants that produce a wide variety of products (Figure 6.26). One of these products is insulin, for the treatment of diabetes. Transgenic safflower can efficiently produce authentic molecules of human insulin. Insulin is then extracted from the oily seeds of the safflower plant.

The demand for insulin is high because the number of people with type 2 diabetes is increasing dramatically. Typically, insulin is produced from genetically engineered yeast or bacteria. One problem with this technique is that it is challenging to purify the insulin. Biotechnologists believe that the development of plant-made insulin will reduce production costs and increase yield to meet the exploding demand.

Figure 6.26 A safflower plant (*Carthamus tinctorius*). Some GM varieties produce human insulin, which is extracted from the plant's seeds.

Producing Genetically Modified Animals

Recombinant DNA technology is used extensively to make vaccines and growth hormones for farm animals. However, the animals themselves can also be genetically modified. This process is more difficult than producing GM plants. Methods to genetically modify mammals typically involve in vitro fertilization. **In vitro fertilization** is the process of fertilizing an egg in a test tube or laboratory dish and transferring the embryo to the uterus (womb). One procedure is to extract an egg cell from a female. Sperm from the same species is then used to fertilize the egg in a test tube or laboratory dish. Then the desired gene is injected into the fertilized egg. After a few rounds of cell division, the early embryo is transferred to an animal's uterus, where it can develop further.

It usually takes many attempts before a fertilized egg will incorporate DNA from another source. If the embryo develops successfully, the result is a GM animal. The offspring contains one or more genes from a third "parent" that may even be of a different species.

Farm Animals and "Pharming"

The goals of genetically modifying an animal are often the same as the goals of traditional breeding. For instance, people may try to make a sheep with better-quality wool, a pig with leaner meat, or a fish that will mature in a shorter time (Figure 6.27).

In other cases, the goal is to make a transgenic animal that produces a large amount of a rare biological substance for medical use. Using transgenic animals to produce pharmaceuticals is sometimes called "pharming." Most cases involve adding a gene for a desired human protein, such as a hormone, to the genome of a farm mammal. The gene is added in such a way that the desired human protein is secreted in the animal's milk. The human protein can then be purified. This is a good method when a human gene is not expressed well in bacteria, meaning that the transgenic bacteria cannot make the human protein properly, or at all.

Figure 6.27 These two salmon are the same age, but the GM salmon (top) is larger because it grew at about twice the rate of the unmodified salmon (bottom).

Chapter 6 Genetic and genomic research and technologies have social and ethical implications.　169

Animal Cloning

Cloning is not limited to cloning individual genes in bacteria, yeast, plants, or animals. Entire genomes can also be cloned. In 1997, Scottish scientist Ian Wilmut announced the birth of Dolly the sheep (1996–2003), the first mammal to be successfully cloned from a somatic cell (Figure 6.28). Since Dolly, biologists have cloned a number of mammals, including goats, cows, mice, pigs, cats, and rabbits.

Special techniques are required to clone an entire animal that normally reproduces sexually. One method is nuclear transplantation. The nucleus of a single cell is obtained from the donor, the adult animal to be cloned (Figure 6.29). The donor nucleus from the adult cell replaces the nucleus of an unfertilized egg cell from another animal of the same species. The procedure is similar to that described for producing a GM animal, except that instead of inserting a single gene into the egg cell, an entire foreign nucleus (including all its genes) replaces the egg's own nucleus. The egg then develops into an animal that has the same genome as the donor. The new animal is a clone of the animal that supplied the nucleus.

Some of the difficulties with using somatic cells to clone mammals are that many embryos do not survive, and the clones can have serious health problems. However, cloning offers the potential to mass-produce an animal with a desirable set of traits. This is much faster than using traditional animal breeding to select for a certain set of traits over several generations of animals. One application is cloning a GM animal so that its genes are not altered by breeding.

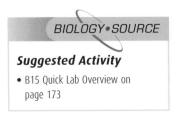

Figure 6.28 Dolly the cloned sheep

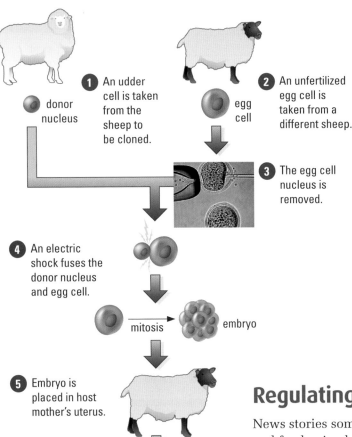

① An udder cell is taken from the sheep to be cloned.

donor nucleus

② An unfertilized egg cell is taken from a different sheep.

egg cell

③ The egg cell nucleus is removed.

④ An electric shock fuses the donor nucleus and egg cell.

mitosis → embryo

⑤ Embryo is placed in host mother's uterus.

⑥ Embryo develops into a cloned sheep.

cloned lamb

Figure 6.29 Animal cloning involves the insertion of a donor nucleus into an egg cell. (magnification 80×)

BIOLOGY•SOURCE

Suggested Activity
• B15 Quick Lab Overview on page 173

Regulating the Use of GMOs

News stories sometimes question the safety of GM crop plants and food animals. There are concerns that transgenic species could be harmful to human health or to the environment. For example, people are concerned that GM salmon could escape and compete with wild salmon. Another concern is that GM crops could pass their new genes to closely related plants in nearby wilderness areas. Pollen from crop plants carrying genes for resistance to herbicides might fertilize the flowers of wild plants. The offspring might then become "super weeds" that would be very difficult to control.

From time to time, GM crop plants have been found in fields where the farmer only sowed non-GM seeds. However, studies have not shown that crops genetically modified to resist pests pose significant health or environmental risks. Even so, strict regulations are recommended on how GM crops are grown and used, and scientists continue to research this area.

©P

Another concern is that GM plant or animal products could have unknown risks to human consumers. Some consumers think labelling that clearly identifies GM products should be required (Figure 6.30). Pharmaceuticals produced from transgenic farm animals may also pose certain risks. For example, human proteins produced in the milk of a transgenic mammal can differ slightly from natural human proteins. For this reason, transgenic products used in medicines or foods have to be tested very carefully. It is important to make sure that the proteins produced by GMOs will not cause allergic reactions or other negative health effects in people.

Figure 6.30 GM flax seeds and non-GM flax seeds look the same

Regulatory Agencies

Governments and regulatory agencies throughout the world are dealing with issues of how to ensure that new biotechnology products and procedures are safe. In Canada, the Canadian Food Inspection Agency (CFIA) is responsible for regulating the environmental release of plants with novel traits, including GM plants. Evaluators from the CFIA and Health Canada assess the safety of new agricultural products made with modern biotechnology, such as food products for people and livestock feed. Developers of these products are required to follow regulations and guidelines, and must supply evaluators with detailed information about their products.

BIOLOGY•SOURCE

Suggested Activity
• B16 Decision-Making Analysis Overview on page 173

Concept Check

1. How is producing a GM plant different from producing a GM animal?
2. Compare the techniques for producing a GM mammal and a cloned mammal.
3. Give an example of a potential risk posed by GMOs.

Genetic Technology in Medical Research

Model organisms are often used to help determine gene function and to develop therapies. Genetic technologies make it possible to add or delete genes at specific locations in a model organism's genome. In doing so, researchers can target specific genes that they want to either inactivate or turn on. Knockout mice are transgenic mice used in medical research. The genome is altered in knockout mice so that a gene no longer functions (the gene is "knocked out"). This technique is sometimes compared to removing a part from a car engine, then driving the car to find out what the part was for. Once the alteration is made in the mice, they are bred in captivity in order to create a population referred to as a "line" of mice with the new trait.

Researchers have used knockout mice to better understand obesity. The researchers cloned and bred mice with a defect in the so-called obese (*ob*) gene (Figure 6.31). These mice were unable to control their appetites and became obese. By studying these mice, researchers discovered that the *ob* gene codes for a protein called leptin, which sends the brain signals of feeling full. Leptin plays in important role in fat and glucose metabolism. With knowledge gained from the *ob* knockout mice studies, researchers are working on treatments for childhood obesity disorders linked to the leptin gene mutation.

Knockout mice can help us not only to determine gene functions but also to understand the genetic basis for inherited diseases. These model organisms are also important for testing new drugs and therapies.

BIOLOGY•SOURCE

Explore More

How are knockout mice and knockin mice developed?

Figure 6.31 Both of these mice have a defect in the *ob* gene. The mouse on the right was given leptin, which made up for its knocked-out gene.

Gene Therapy

BIOLOGY•SOURCE

Explore More

What are the challenges associated with therapy for cystic fibrosis?

BIOLOGY•SOURCE

Take It Further

Golden rice is a GM plant that contains increased amounts of beta-carotene. This nutrient is important for human health. Deficiencies in beta-carotene have been linked to medical problems such as infant blindness. Research and report on one other GM plant developed for human health or medicine.

For someone suffering from a disease caused by a missing or malfunctioning gene, one form of treatment might be to supplement or replace the affected gene with a healthy one. **Gene therapy** is the process of supplementing or replacing a gene in order to treat a medical condition. Gene therapy allows the body to make the protein that is not being made by the missing or malfunctioning gene.

A key part of gene therapy is delivering the functional, therapeutic gene to particular cells or affected areas of the body. One method uses viruses that are engineered to contain the therapeutic gene (Figure 6.32). The modified virus is administered to the patient in order to infect the person's cells. The virus inserts the therapeutic gene into the person's DNA, thereby correcting the missing or malfunctioning gene. Other possible delivery methods are cell or tissue transplants, microscopic injections, or aerosol inhalers.

Gene therapy is being studied for the treatment of Huntington's disease, skin cancer, and cystic fibrosis, among other conditions. Therapies are still in the early stages of development and considered to be high-risk experimental procedures. Two challenges are delivering a gene to the correct target and making sure the therapy works in the long term. Researchers are working out reliable ways to insert therapeutic genes, while ensuring that the DNA and delivery methods used do not harm patients.

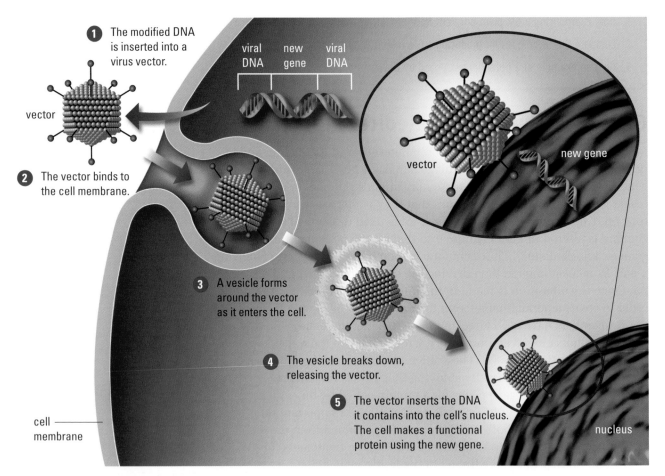

Figure 6.32 Gene therapy uses a functioning gene to supplement or replace a missing or malfunctioning gene.

©P

Clone a Mouse

Purpose

To study the nuclear transfer procedure

Activity Overview

The mouse is a favoured model organism for genetic research. In this activity, you will study the steps that would be taken in a nuclear transfer procedure to clone a mouse (Figure 6.33).

Your teacher will give you a copy of the full activity.

Prelab Questions

Consider the questions below before beginning this activity.

1. How many parents does a cloned mouse have?

2. Why might it be useful to clone a mouse?

3. Would a cloned mouse receive the donor's genetic material or the foster mother's genetic material?

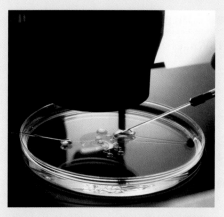

Figure 6.33 Tools for nuclear transfer. While looking through a microscope, the technician uses a pipette to hold cells in place and a needle to transfer nuclei.

REQUIRED SKILLS
- Evaluating research procedures
- Reporting results

Genetically Modified Foods

Issue

Are current Canadian regulations of genetically modified foods sufficient?

Activity Overview

The average Canadian kitchen contains many ingredients or foods that have been genetically modified. An estimated 30 000 different items on North American grocery store shelves contain products from GMOs (Figure 6.34). In this activity, you will investigate and report on whether or not current regulations for GM foods are sufficient to protect Canadian consumers.

Your teacher will give you a copy of the full activity.

Prelab Questions

Consider the questions below before beginning this activity.

1. What foods do you have at home that may contain ingredients from GMOs?

2. Suggest some reasons for producing GMOs for food.

3. Do you think GM food would taste different from non-GM food? Suggest why or why not.

4. What are three questions you have about GM food?

Figure 6.34 Many groups argue that GM food should be labelled as such, or even taken off store shelves.

Key Concept Review

1. What is a genetically modified organism?

2. List some benefits obtained from genetically modifying plants.

3. Describe a method for genetically modifying animals.

4. What is nuclear transplantation?

5. What is the name of the agency responsible for regulating the development and testing of genetically modified foods in Canada?

6. What is Bt toxin? Why have people engineered corn to carry the Bt toxin gene?

7. How is *Agrobacterium tumefaciens* used in genetic engineering?

Connect Your Understanding

8. What might a scientist examine to determine whether a person is a carrier for a genetic disorder?

9. The phrase "in vitro" means "in glass." Why is in vitro fertilization a suitable name for the technique?

10. Describe how to use genetic engineering to produce desired protein products from each of the following.
(a) bacteria
(b) plants
(c) mammals

11. How has genetic engineering increased genetic variation in some species?

12. How does gene therapy differ from taking medications such as pain killers?

13. What are some concerns related to the safety of genetically modified foods?

14. Draw a concept map to illustrate the relationships among biotechnology, genetic engineering, recombinant DNA, GMOs, transgenic organisms, and cloning.

15. Describe a way in which a GMO could be used to reduce chemical pollution of the environment.

16. What are some potential concerns about releasing transgenic species into the environment?

17. Why is it necessary to proceed with caution when conducting gene therapy experiments?

18. The frog in the photo was genetically engineered to be transparent. How might a transparent frog be useful in biology, especially to biology students?

Question 18

19. If transgenic glow-in-the-dark pets were available for sale at your local pet store, would you consider purchasing one? Why or why not?

20. Suggest why someone may choose not to learn if he or she carries an allele associated with a serious disease.

21. How does our genetic similarity to many model organisms make these species important in genetic research?

Reflection

22. How has your understanding of the term "clone" changed since reading this section?

23. Does our genetic similarity to many model organisms change the way you view their value? Explain.

For more questions, go to BIOLOGY•SOURCE

Molecular geneticist Dr. Steve Scherer runs one of the busiest research labs in Canada (Figure 6.35). A senior scientist with Toronto's Hospital for Sick Children and a professor with the University of Toronto, Dr. Scherer leads Canada's Autism Genome Project. Autism — a communication disorder with a spectrum of symptoms — is one of the most common childhood developmental disorders. Dr. Scherer's research team discovered that genetic variations in a region of chromosome 16 are a risk factor for developing autism.

The work on autism grew out of Dr. Scherer's co-discovery of copy number variation (CNV). About 12% of the human genome contains segments of DNA that are either deleted or repeated in varying amounts in different people. CNV can influence gene activity. CNV in chromosome 16 is important in autism, with deletions being linked to more severe cases.

Dr. Scherer also collaborated on the Human Genome Project, helping to analyze the sequence of chromosome 7, and has discovered several disease susceptibility genes.

Figure 6.35 Canadian geneticist Dr. Steve Scherer

Biology CAREERS   *Genetic Counsellor*

Genetic technologies allow for direct examination of an individual's DNA to check for chromosomal changes or gene mutations that may cause genetic disorders. However, genetic tests do not often yield results that are easy to decipher. A genetic counsellor not only coordinates genetic tests, but works with individuals or families to identify and interpret risks for genetic disorders on the basis of test results. The job requires a solid working knowledge of genetics and good communication skills (Figure 6.36).

Genetic testing can be an important part of diagnosis, treatment, or the prevention of disease. It also enables people who are thinking about having children to assess the risk of passing down genetic disorders to future generations. People undergoing testing may face a variety of social and emotional issues when they obtain genetic test results, and a genetic counsellor can help them work through these issues.

Figure 6.36 These students in the University of Toronto Master of Science (MSc) program at the Toronto Hospital for Sick Children are training to become genetic counsellors.

To find out more, visit BIOLOGY•SOURCE

Key Concept Review

1. What are restriction enzymes? **k**

2. What are two uses of gel electrophoresis? **k**

3. Define the term "genetically modified organism." **k**

4. What is meant by "gene cloning?" **k**

5. What is a knockout mouse? **k**

6. List three examples of GM plants or animals and the purpose of genetically modifying each one. **k**

7. Give two examples of useful products made by genetically engineered micro-organisms. **k**

8. (a) List the three main steps in DNA sequencing. **k**
   (b) Why might it be useful to determine the sequence of a DNA molecule? **k**

9. (a) Name a species with a genome over 2 billion base pairs in size. **k**
   (b) Name a species with a genome between 1 and 10 million base pairs in size. **k**
   (c) Name a species with more genes than humans have. **k**
   (d) Describe trends in genome size and numbers of genes for micro-organisms, plants, and animals. **t**

10. Describe one way that transfer of antibiotic resistance genes occurs in bacteria. **k**

11. Identify each of the following as an example of biotechnology, genetic engineering, or both.
    (a) using bacteria to make yogurt from milk **k**
    (b) using goats to produce pharmaceuticals in their milk **k**
    (c) using safflower plants to produce insulin **k**
    (d) creating a transgenic rat for medical studies **k**

12. How is gene therapy used to treat a genetic condition? **k**

13. Describe the main goals of the Human Genome Project. **k**

14. What is in vitro fertilization? **k**

Connect Your Understanding

15. How has the bacterium *E. coli* played a role in the development of biotechnology? **a**

16. Why are restriction enzymes needed for recombinant DNA technology? **t**

17. How can bacteria be used to make multiple copies of a particular gene? **t**

18. What is a plasmid? Describe one way in which biologists use plasmids as a tool in genetic engineering. **a**

19. Describe a method of DNA sequencing that uses fluorescent dye labels. **t**

20. During gel electrophoresis, do larger or smaller molecules move faster? Explain how the movement of molecules results in a pattern on the gel. **t**

21. Create a flow chart to show the sequence of steps involved in engineering a genetically modified plant. **c**

22. Contrast genetically modified bacteria with cloned bacteria. How are they made and why? **a**

23. Give two examples of model organisms. Explain why they are well suited for genetic research. **a**

24. Distinguish between two different cloning techniques discussed in this chapter. **t**

25. Explain how the use of knockout mice has led to a better understanding of childhood obesity. **a**

26. Soybeans and soy products are an important food for people around the world. In North America, some farmers grow GM soybean plants that are herbicide resistant. Farmers can therefore spray their fields with herbicides to kill weeds without killing the soybean plants. The soybean plants grow more plentifully as a result. Create a concept map about GM soybean plants, including proven and potential benefits, risks, and your concerns. **c**

Question 26

27. (a) Create a table showing the three primary components of the science of bioinformatics and specific fields of study. **c**
    (b) Which fields of study related to bioinformatics most interest you? Why? **a**

28. How much similarity would you expect to find between the DNA fingerprints of
    (a) a wife and husband?
    (b) a mother and daughter?
    Explain. **a**

29. Suggest a genetic test you could run to find out if someone carries a mutation associated with Parkinson's disease. **a**

30. Design an experiment to test a treatment for a genetic condition caused by a mutation in a single gene. **t**

31. Why might someone with food allergies be concerned about eating a GM food? **a**

32. Suppose you know the sequence for a neurotransmitter gene in rats. How could you use this information to help you locate a gene for a similar neurotransmitter in humans? **t**

33. (a) Describe two challenges in gene therapy technology. **t**
    (b) Do you think someone should be allowed to undergo gene therapy for a disease such as cystic fibrosis, even if the treatment is experimental? Explain. **a**

34. Do you think applications for genetic engineering need to have stricter regulations? Write a paragraph to express your opinion. **c**

35. A patent is a licence that declares someone's ownership of an invention or process. Some technology companies working on the Human Genome Project have applied for patents on the genetic information they obtain from their research. Many countries have denied all patent applications. Do you think companies should have the right to patent genetic information for a living organism? Justify your response. **a**

36. Speculate on how information from the Human Genome Project could affect health care in the future. Suggest two or more possible effects. **a**

37. The kittens in the following photo are clones. The genetic technology company that cloned Baba Ganoush (left) and Tabouli (right) used a process called chromatin transfer, developed especially to clone animals. If you could clone a favourite pet, would you? Justify your response. **a**

Question 37

38. Mammals can be genetically modified for biotechnology or for medical research. Do you view both reasons for genetically modifying mammals as equally valid? Justify your response. Consider benefits, risks, and ethical concerns related to both applications. **a**

39. What are some potential concerns with releasing transgenic bacteria into the environment? **a**

Reflection

40. Why is it important to you to know how genetic engineering can be used? **c**

41. What are three questions related to genomics that came to mind while you were completing this chapter? **c**

Unit Task Link

For your Unit Task, you will need an understanding of the treatment options and therapies currently available for common genetic conditions. To prepare for your Unit Task, create a new table of genetic conditions. Research treatments or therapies and any associated risks and record this information in your table.

For more questions, go to **BIOLOGY•SOURCE**

UNIT B SUMMARY

KEY CONCEPTS	CHAPTER SUMMARY

4 · The cell's genetic material determines inherited characteristics.

• DNA structure and packaging • The cell cycle • Mitosis and cell division • Meiosis and recombination of chromosomes • Non-disjunction and genetic conditions • Genetic screening	• The genetic information that is passed down from one generation of cells to another is composed of deoxyribonucleic acid (DNA). Genes are units of DNA that code for specific traits or functions. (4.1) • DNA is located in the nucleus of each cell and packaged into chromatin. Prior to cell division, chromatin condenses into structures called chromosomes. (4.1) • Over the course of a eukaryotic cell's life, it will go through an orderly sequence of events known as the cell cycle. (4.1) • Eukaryotic cells divide to repair damage and enable the body to grow. Each cell must duplicate its genetic information and distribute it to new cells through the process of mitosis. (4.2) • The stages of mitosis are prophase, metaphase, anaphase, and telophase. (4.2) • Meiosis, which occurs in sexual reproduction, distributes an assortment of chromosomes to the gametes. (4.2) • In meiosis I, homologous chromosomes exchange pieces of DNA. This produces unique chromosome combinations in the gametes following meiosis II. (4.2) • Occasionally, errors in meiosis lead to errors in chromosome number in the gametes. (4.3) • Duplication, deletion, inversion, and translocation are types of chromosomal damage. (4.3) • Genetic testing can be an important part of diagnosing, treating, or preventing particular genetic conditions. (4.3)

5 · Mendelian laws and chromosome theory help explain inheritance patterns.

• Alleles and genes • Dominant and recessive alleles • Probability • Punnett squares • Codominance and incomplete dominance • Polygenic traits • Environmental influence on phenotypes • Sex-linked genes	• Gregor Mendel's experiments of the 1800s helped explain basic inheritance patterns. (5.1) • Heritable factors known as alleles account for different inherited traits. (5.1) • A dominant allele is expressed in the traits of a heterozygous individual, while the recessive allele for the same gene is hidden. An individual must carry two copies of a recessive allele in order to express it as a trait. (5.1) • Punnett squares can be used to predict probabilities of offspring from genetic crosses. (5.1) • With incomplete dominance, one allele is partly expressed, and so heterozygous individuals have traits that fall between those of their parents. Codominant alleles are equally expressed in a heterozygous individual. (5.2) • Traits such as height or skin colour are influenced by many genes, each with two or more alleles. (5.2) • In many cases, the environment influences the expression of genes in an organism's phenotype. (5.2) • Genes are located at specific chromosome locations called loci. The proximity of the genes to each other on a chromosome influences how these genes are inherited. (5.3) • Some traits are linked to a particular sex chromosome and exhibit unique inheritance patterns. (5.3)

6 · Genetic and genomic research and technologies have social and ethical implications.

• DNA manipulation • The Human Genome Project • Bioinformatics and genomics • Model organisms • Recombinant DNA technology • Genetic engineering • Gene therapy	• Scientists can manipulate and sequence DNA using restriction enzymes and gel electrophoresis. (6.1) • The Human Genome Project completed the nucleotide sequence for the entire human genome. • *E. coli* bacteria, nematodes, yeast, fruit flies, and mice are common model organisms for genetic studies. (6.1) • Recombinant DNA technology can be used to modify an organism's genome. Desired genes can be cut and pasted into organisms to produce proteins used in industry or medicine or to produce transgenic species with desirable traits that would be difficult to achieve with conventional breeding. (6.2, 6.3) • Genetic engineering is used to genetically modify plants and animals to give them useful traits, such as improved nutritional content or pest resistance. Transgenic plants and animals are also used to make pharmaceuticals. (6.3) • Genetic technologies help us to investigate genetic conditions and develop gene therapies. (6.3)

UNIT **B** REVIEW

ACHIEVEMENT CHART CATEGORIES
k Knowledge and understanding   *t* Thinking and investigation
c Communication   *a* Application

Key Terms Review

1. Create a concept map that links all the terms in the list below. You may add more terms if you wish. Give examples, where applicable, of the various terms. *c*

   - allele
   - autosome
   - chromatin
   - chromosome
   - DNA
   - dominant
   - gene
   - genome
   - genotype
   - karyotype
   - meiosis
   - mitosis
   - non-disjunction
   - nucleotide
   - phenotype
   - sex chromosome
   - sister chromatids
   - recessive
   - trait
   - translocation

Key Concept Review

CHAPTER 4

2. Compare the meanings of "trait" and "inherited trait." *k*

3. Describe how chromosomes are packaged in a eukaryotic cell. *k*

4. What are the three parts that make up a nucleotide? *k*

5. What did X-ray crystallography reveal to Rosalind Franklin about the structure of DNA? *k*

6. Use a diagram to illustrate James Watson and Francis Crick's model of a DNA molecule. *k*

7. What is meant by "base pairing" when referring to a DNA double helix? *k*

8. Differentiate between somatic cells and sex cells. *k*

9. What is the cell cycle? *k*

10. What are the main events of the M phase of the cell cycle? *k*

11. Compare what happens to the chromosomes during meiosis I and meiosis II. *k*

12. Which type of chromosomal damage might affect more than one chromosome? Explain. *k*

CHAPTER 5

13. What is the term for an allele that is not expressed in the phenotype of a heterozygous individual? *k*

14. Define the term "probability." How is the concept of probability applied when examining genetic crosses? *k*

15. What is a hybrid (in the context of genetics)? Give an example. *k*

16. Give the genotype for each of the following organisms.
    (a) a mouse that is homozygous for the dominant black fur allele *k*
    (b) a pea plant that is heterozygous for the stem-length gene *k*
    (c) a fruit fly that is homozygous for the short wing length allele *k*

17. What is the term for a trait determined by more than one gene? *k*

18. List and briefly explain the four main points in Mendel's model of genetic inheritance. *k*

19. Differentiate between the law of independent assortment and the law of segregation. *k*

20. What does a gene map show? *k*

21. Do human ABO blood type alleles show incomplete dominance or codominance? Explain. *k*

22. Why are there more men than women with red-green colour blindness? *k*

23. What is the name for the initiative to determine the nucleotide sequence of all human chromosomes? **k**

24. What are some ways to identify genes in DNA sequences? **k**

25. How has the ability to label nucleotides with fluorescent dyes benefited genetic research? **k**

26. What are some features of plasmids that make them useful in genetic engineering? **k**

27. What is a DNA chip? **k**

28. Give one application for a transgenic plant and one for a transgenic animal. **k**

29. Give two reasons for determining the nucleotide sequence of a gene. **k**

30. Was Dolly the sheep a transgenic organism? Explain. **k**

31. List two difficulties with using somatic cells to clone animals. **k**

32. What is the main difference between taking a pharmaceutical, such as an antibiotic, and undergoing gene therapy? **k**

33. What is the term for a line of mice with a gene that has been altered so that it no longer functions? **k**

Connect Your Understanding

34. Why is it important for cells to have a control system that regulates cell division? Describe a possible consequence of a malfunction in cell cycle control. **a**

35. Why would undergoing meiosis be a problem for an organism that reproduces asexually? **t**

36. In which phase of the cell cycle would most of your somatic cells be at any particular time? Explain your reasoning. **t**

37. Predict what would happen if spindle fibres were disrupted during anaphase of mitosis. **t**

38. Describe how crossing over during meiosis recombines the genetic material of an individual organism's two parents. **t**

39. Explain how the assortment of chromosomes during meiosis contributes to variation in the gametes. **a**

40. Use diagrams to illustrate the four main types of large-scale mutations in chromosomes. **c**

41. Is it possible for a mutation to be beneficial to an organism? Explain. **a**

42. If DNA damage occurs in G1 phase, what might happen to the damaged region during S phase? **t**

43. Contrast the possible impacts of a chromosomal mutation that occurs in meiosis to one that occurs in mitosis in a somatic cell. **t**

44. How might a biologist use a karyotype to identify a species? **a**

45. Use the diagram below to answer the questions that follow.
    (a) On a separate piece of paper, draw the four gametes produced, including the number of chromosomes in each. Explain in what way each gamete is atypical. **c**
    (b) Note that the process shown is simplified, showing only two pairs of chromosomes at the start of meiosis I. In a human, how many pairs of chromosomes would there actually be at the start of meiosis I? **t**

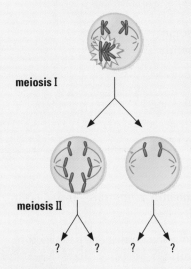

meiosis I

meiosis II

? ? ? ?

Question 45

46. Explain how a Punnett square can be used to predict the outcome of a genetic cross. **a**

47. Give three reasons that fruit flies are useful model organisms for genetic research. **t**

48. Use a diagram to illustrate the process of allele segregation. **c**

49. What evidence from Gregor Mendel's experiments showed that alleles assort randomly in meiosis? *t*

50. Sexually reproducing organisms use mitosis and meiosis, while asexual organisms use only mitosis. Which type of reproduction, asexual or sexual, results in offspring with a greater variation? Explain. *t*

51. Why would the blending of paint colours not be a good analogy to use to describe codominance or incomplete dominance? Suggest better analogies. *c*

52. The diagram below shows three gene loci on a pair of homologous chromosomes. Examine the diagram and answer the questions that follow.
(a) Of the three genes found on this pair of homologous chromosomes, which two are most likely to be separated from each other by a cross-over event? Explain. *t*
(b) If crossing over does not occur between any of the genes, list the possible combinations of alleles in this individual's gametes. *t*

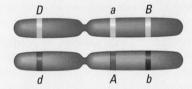

Question 52

53. Some genes for animal coat colour or feather colour are expressed differently depending on body temperature or season. How might this phenomenon benefit an animal in the wild? *a*

54. Why would it be important for an animal breeder to know the genotype of an animal and not only its phenotype? *a*

55. Is it likely that the human Y chromosome contains any genes necessary for survival? Explain. *t*

56. Create a concept map to compare and contrast selective breeding and genetic engineering. *c*

57. The effects of a particular mutation may not always be visible. How might a researcher determine if a mutation has occurred in a gene? *a*

58. Explain how a model organism could be used to help determine the effects of a mutation in a particular gene. *a*

59. Use a flowchart to outline the procedure for cloning a mammal from a somatic cell. *c*

60. What are three things that must occur in order for a gene therapy to be successful? *t*

61. Could a genetic counsellor use a karyotype to identify disease caused by a small DNA mutation? Explain. *a*

Skills Practice

62. Analyze the human karyotype below. Identify the name for this type of karyotype and the sex of the individual. Describe the effects of the condition associated with this karyotype. *t*

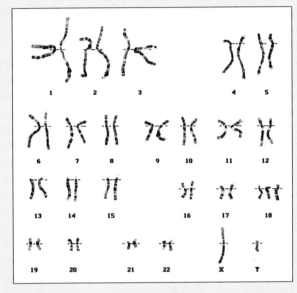

Question 62

63. List the four possible allele combinations in the gametes of a plant with genotype *PpWw*. *t*

64. Tim and Christine have freckles (a dominant trait that is not sex linked), but their son Michael does not.
(a) Use a Punnett square to show how this situation is possible. *c*
(b) Tim and Christine are expecting another baby. What is the probability of this child having freckles? *c*

65. In sheep, the allele for white wool (*W*) is dominant over the allele for black wool (*w*). Design a genetic cross that would determine the genotype of a white sheep. *t*

66. Draw a Punnett square to show how a white-eyed male fruit fly could have a red-eyed father. *c*

67. The range of heights in human populations can be explained by polygenic inheritance. Suppose that A, B, C, and D represent alleles that contribute to height, and a, b, c, and d represent alleles that do not. The table below shows the relationship between genotype and height.

Genotypes for Different Heights

Height	Number of Dominant Alleles	Example of Genotype
Above average	6–8	*AABBCCDD*
Average	4	*AaBbCcDd*
Below average	1–3	*aabbccdd*

Explain how two parents of average height may have a child of above-average height. 🅣

68. Suppose a chicken farmer wishes to produce a blue chicken from his flock of Andalusians. He has a black rooster and several black hens and white hens.
(a) Which birds should the farmer cross in order to produce a blue Andalusian chicken? 🅣
(b) Draw a Punnett square to illustrate the genetic cross. 🅒

69. In a hypothetical plant, tall (*T*) is dominant to short (*t*), and green leaves (*G*) are dominant to mottled leaves (*g*). Use a Punnett square to determine the genotypic and phenotypic ratios for a cross between two plants of genotype *TtGg*. 🅒

70. (a) Suppose one strand of a DNA fragment has the sequence CCGGGCTTAAGAA. What is the sequence of the complementary strand? 🅣
(b) Suppose you have access to a restriction enzyme that cuts DNA at the recognition sequence CTTAAG. Draw a diagram showing how the restriction enzyme could be used to produce sticky ends from the DNA fragment in (a). 🅒

Revisit the Big Ideas and Fundamental Concepts

71. Why is an understanding of meiosis helpful in explaining inheritance patterns? 🅣

72. How does chromosome structure support Mendel's ideas about pairs of inherited factors? 🅣

73. Create a concept map that shows the relationships among the following terms: DNA, chromosomes, gene, protein, genetic testing, genetic technology, gene therapy. 🅒

74. How has the information gained from the Human Genome Project helped to increase our understanding of genetic inheritance? 🅣

75. How does cellular information pass from one generation to another? 🅣

76. What are the major factors that determine biological characteristics? Give two or more specific examples to support your answer. 🅐

Science, Technology, Society, and the Environment

77. List three or more techniques used in health care that would not be possible without the Human Genome Project or related research. 🅐

78. When shopping at the grocery store, would you be able to distinguish the difference between a non-GM tomato and a GM tomato? What information do you feel consumers should have with regard to the origins, growth, and processing of produce? Give reasons to support your opinions. 🅐

Question 78

79. Select one form of biotechnology that you learned about in this unit. Evaluate the importance of this biotechnology by considering its impact on society. 🅐

80. Why is it so important to protect yourself from exposure to chemicals or radiation that could damage your DNA? How could such damage affect future generations? 🅐

81. Write a paragraph suggesting ways in which GM plants could improve the world's food supply. 🅒

82. How might studies of genetic linkage help in disease research? 🅐

83. The Human Genome Project includes an Ethical, Legal, and Social Implications Research Program to explore issues of genetic and genomic research affecting individuals, families, and communities. Which genetic technology do you feel has the most pressing social and ethical implications, both positive and negative? Write a paragraph that briefly describes this particular technology. Include a discussion of some of the social and ethical issues involved. *C*

84. Why are privacy issues an important consideration for people undergoing genetic testing? *a*

85. You have been asked to evaluate the adequacy of current Canadian regulations regarding biotechnology for a local paper. Write a brief article — the first of a series — describing your initial findings and recommendations. Also write a list of topics or questions that you could address in additional articles. *C*

86. Crop plants can be genetically engineered so that they can produce pharmaceuticals. Should land that would otherwise be used to grow crops for food be used to grow GM crops to make pharmaceuticals? Justify your response. *a*

87. Biologists may one day be able to alter a child's inherited traits. If this technology is developed, should it be permitted in certain circumstances? Write a persuasive paragraph expressing your opinion. *C*

Reflection

88. What genetic technology described in this unit did you find the most interesting? Why? *C*

89. How has your understanding of what is meant by "genetics" changed now that you have completed this unit? *C*

90. What ideas in this unit are you interested in learning more about? *C*

B17   Unit Task   *BIOLOGY SOURCE*

Be a Genetic Counsellor

Genetic disorders affect many people from all racial and cultural groups. As researchers learn more about the genes involved and the causes of these disorders, preventive approaches are being developed.

With some disorders a person can be a carrier with no symptoms, and with others the disorders can be late-onset, presenting symptoms in middle age or later. Unfortunately, with recessive disorders people may not know they are carriers unless they have an affected child. With late-onset disorders, individuals who are affected may have already had children before developing any symptoms. However, genetic testing is available for many situations (Figures 6.37 and 6.38).

Figure 6.37 This person is supplying a cell sample to be used for genetic analysis.

Question

How can genetic testing help people to assess their risk of having or passing down genetic disorders?

Task Overview

In this activity, you will play the role of a genetic counsellor and evaluate a given scenario. You will produce a risk assessment for the patient or family so that they can make an informed decision on whether or not to proceed with genetic testing.

Your teacher will give you a copy of the full activity.

Figure 6.38 A home gene-chip test

Evolution

Unit Contents

Unit Task

Different human activities can affect the evolution of species in negative and positive ways. In the Unit Task, you will research one conservation strategy that could potentially save a species from extinction. You will assess any political, economic, social, technological, and environmental issues associated with the conservation strategy and decide whether or not the strategy should be implemented. You will present your findings in a format of your choice.

DISCOVERING BIOLOGY

At first glance, this appears to be an image of colourful soft coral. However, if you look closely you will see a small crab. This soft-coral crab, *Hoplophrys oatesii*, is a superb example of camouflage. Its spines and colouration patterns make it virtually invisible against the soft coral it lives on. It will even bend parts of the coral over itself to further protect itself against predators. What has shaped this crab to blend in so perfectly with its environment?

The theory of evolution helps us understand the diversity of life.

Learning Expectations

By the end of this chapter, you will:

Relating Science to Technology, Society, and the Environment

- evaluate the possible impact of an environmental change on natural selection and on the vulnerability of species

Developing Skills of Investigation and Communication

- use appropriate terminology related to evolution

- research and report on the contributions of various scientists to the modern theories of evolution

Understanding Basic Concepts

- explain the fundamental theory of evolution, using the evolutionary mechanism of natural selection to illustrate the process of biological change over time

- explain the process of adaptation of individual organisms to their environment

Dinosaur skeletons such as this *Tyrannosaurus rex* are huge attractions at museums around the world (Figure 7.1). People marvel at their size. Dinosaurs were a diverse group of animals that roamed Earth for 100 million years, but most of them disappeared suddenly 65 million years ago. At about 13 m long, *T. rex* was one of the largest predators known to exist, while another dinosaur, *Compsognathus*, was the size of a turkey. The only proof of their existence are their fossils. **Fossils** are preserved remains or markings left by organisms. The presence of dinosaur fossils (and fossils of many other organisms) illustrates that life on Earth is constantly changing. However, even as life changes, it also remains the same in many ways. Dinosaurs no longer exist, but we can see that some of their structural features, such as an internal skeleton, are displayed in animals living today. Fossils help tell us the story of life. They tell us how life is united and has descended from organisms that appeared early in Earth's history.

Figure 7.1 Museum visitors look at the reconstructed fossilized skeleton of a *Tyrannosaurus rex*.

©P

7.1 Steps Leading Up to Charles Darwin's Theory

Section Summary

- The scientists Hutton, Lyell, and Lamarck challenged the prevailing ideas that Earth is young and that species do not change over time.

- In his role as a naturalist on the HMS *Beagle,* Charles Darwin made many observations in different locations around the world.

- Darwin observed the distribution of species around the world, fossils, and different geological phenomena.

Figure 7.2 Polar bears' fur is one of many characteristics that help them survive in the Arctic's cold, snowy climate.

A picture of the Arctic would not be complete without polar bears (Figure 7.2). Polar bears are one of the world's newest mammals. They first appeared about 100 000 years ago and are believed to have evolved from Alaskan brown bears. The polar bear's white fur helps it blend into the environment. By blending in, it can better ambush its prey. Its fur, however, is not really white. Each hair is transparent and hollow. The air in the hollow hair shafts provides insulation and also scatters and reflects visible light, making the bear appear white, like snow. Arctic animals, such as the polar bear, have characteristics that help them survive in the cold, harsh environment, while desert animals have characteristics that help them survive in the extreme heat. Around the world there is an enormous diversity of life, and each species has its own set of characteristics. A species is a group of organisms whose members can breed with one another and produce fertile young.

How can Earth's diversity and the similarities and differences within that diversity be explained in a scientific way? A **theory** is a set of statements that explains a group of facts or phenomena. These statements have been tested repeatedly and are supported by evidence. A theory can be used to make predictions about natural phenomena. In the 19th century, an Englishman named Charles Darwin developed a theory to explain the diversity of life on Earth and how all organisms are related to one another and to the environments in which they live.

Darwin's theory sought to explain evolution. **Evolution** is the idea that all species are descendants of ancient species that were different from modern-day species. Evolution is the biological history of life on Earth, from the earliest micro-organisms to the diversity of modern-day organisms.

The work of many scientists changed the shape of scientific thinking in the 19th century. In developing his theory, Darwin built on these scientists' ideas and added ideas of his own. Before Darwin's time, two main ideas about the natural world prevailed. One was that species were fixed, or permanent. In other words, they do not change over time. The other idea was that Earth is less than 10 000 years old and also relatively unchanging. However, the work of many different scientists challenged these ideas.

Changing Ideas About the Natural World

One of the first people to challenge the notion that Earth was young was James Hutton, a Scottish geologist. He proposed that rock formations are being continually formed. Molten material is forced up to Earth's surface to form rock, where it is then eroded away. The sediment from the erosion is washed into the sea and eventually compacts to form sedimentary rock. Hutton studied the rates of present-day erosion and sedimentation and the thickness of bands of sedimentary rock. He concluded that it must have taken millions of years, not thousands, to form the current landscape. His evidence supported the theory of **uniformitarianism,** which stated that Earth was formed entirely by slow-moving processes, such as erosion and sedimentation, and that these slow forces continue to shape the landscape.

In 1830, English geologist Charles Lyell popularized and expanded on Hutton's ideas of uniformitarianism in his book *Principles of Geology*. He found more evidence to support the idea that rock formations were formed by incredibly slow processes that are still at work today (Figure 7.3).

Just as the notion of a young Earth was being challenged, so was the concept that species are fixed. A French naturalist named Georges Cuvier compared the bones of modern-day elephants and fossilized mammoths (Figure 7.4). He concluded that the mammoth's skeleton was different enough from an elephant's that mammoths had to be considered a different species and that the mammoth had become extinct. An **extinct** organism is one that no longer exists. The discovery of dinosaur fossils, such as the *T. rex* in Figure 7.1, was also evidence that some organisms became extinct long ago.

Figure 7.3 In Lyell's view, processes such as erosion have formed many parts of the landscape and continue to change the landscape very slowly.

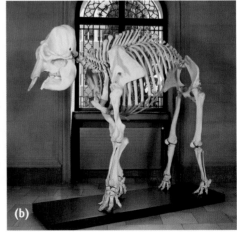

Figure 7.4 Even though the bones of (a) the mammoth and (b) the elephant are very similar, there are enough differences for a mammoth to be considered a distinct species.

In the early 1800s, another French naturalist named Jean-Baptiste Lamarck recognized that species are not permanent. He proposed that species evolve, or change, over time. He explained evolution as a process of adaptation. An **adaptation** is an inherited characteristic that improves an organism's ability to survive and reproduce in a particular environment. Also, he proposed a hypothesis to explain how changes in species happen. A **hypothesis** is a suggested explanation of observations, which can be tested by further research or experiments. Lamarck realized that organisms were adapted to their environments. Lamarck had three guiding ideas. First, he proposed that by using, or not using, certain body parts, an organism develops certain characteristics (Figure 7.5). For instance, giraffes needed to reach vegetation high up in the trees, and so they developed long necks. Second, Lamarck thought that these enhanced characteristics would be passed on to the offspring. Lamarck called this idea "inheritance of acquired characteristics." For example, the long necks that the giraffes developed during their lifetimes, were passed down to their offspring. Lamarck's last point was that all organisms have a "tendency towards perfection." Organisms continually change and acquire features in order to be more successful in their environments.

Although Lamarck's ideas seemed logical at the time, our knowledge of deoxyribonucleic acid (DNA) and its role in the inheritance of traits does not support Lamarck's hypotheses. An acquired characteristic would have to somehow change the DNA of specific genes in order to be inherited. There is no evidence that this happens (Figure 7.6). Regardless, Lamarck was important in analyzing the role of the environment and explaining evolution as a process of adaptation to the environment.

These ideas shaped Darwin's thinking about the natural world and would help him develop his theory.

Figure 7.5 Lamarck's Use and Disuse Theory: Giraffes developed long necks because they needed to and passed the feature down to their offspring.

BIOLOGY•SOURCE

Suggested Activity
• C1 Quick Lab Overview on page 193

Concept Check

1. (a) What is evolution?
   (b) Why is evolution referred to as a theory?

2. What was the significance of Lyell and Hutton's observations?

3. List Lamarck's guiding ideas.

Darwin's Observations

In 1831, the HMS *Beagle* set sail on a voyage around the world (Figure 7.7 on the next page). The main mission of the voyage was to chart poorly known stretches of the South American coastline. Charles Darwin was the ship's naturalist. Darwin's main interest was to study the geology, plants, and animals encountered on the voyage.

Darwin collected thousands of specimens of South American plants and animals from places as different as the Brazilian jungle, the grasslands of Argentina, and the frigid lands north of Antarctica. He also observed many different land forms and fossils. Throughout the voyage, Darwin maintained extensive journals of his observations, studies, and thoughts.

Figure 7.6 A bonsai tree is "trained" to grow as a dwarf by pruning and shaping the branches. But seeds from the tree would produce trees that grow to normal size. This shows that there is no inheritance of the characteristics acquired by pruning.

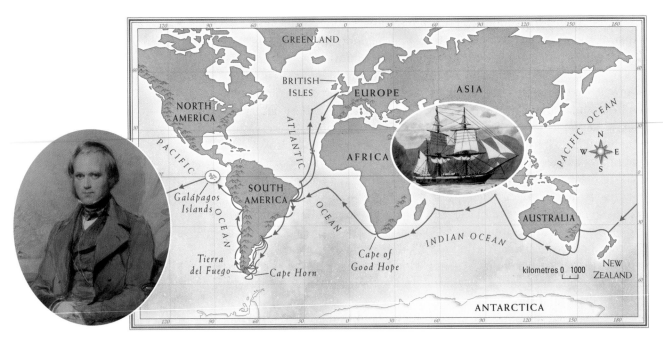

Figure 7.7 The route of Darwin's five-year journey on the HMS *Beagle*

Patterns in Diversity

Darwin was a keen observer of the species he encountered. He observed three patterns as he studied the biological diversity of the world and the fossils he found on his journey.

Species Vary Globally

The first pattern Darwin observed was that species vary globally in different ways. He noticed that distantly related species living in similar habitats in different parts of the world looked similar and acted in similar ways. For example, South America has rheas, Australia has emus, while Africa has ostriches (Figure 7.8). These three species of large, flightless birds live in grasslands on different continents.

Darwin also noticed that some areas had unique organisms not found anywhere else in the world. For example, kangaroos and other marsupials (pouched mammals) are found only in Australia.

Darwin noticed that the plants and animals of South America were quite distinct from species in Europe or Africa. The plants and animals throughout the continent all had a definite South American character. A tropical South American lizard, for example, was more like a South American desert lizard than like an African tropical lizard.

Figure 7.8 (a) Emus, (b) rheas, and (c) ostriches are unrelated flightless birds that have similar adaptations.

©P

Species Vary Locally

Darwin observed that species varied locally. He noticed that related animal species that occupied different habitats within a local environment had different features. This was most obvious on islands. Darwin was intrigued by life on islands such as the Galapagos Islands, 1000 km off the western coast of South America. Although the islands were relatively close to one another, the different islands had very different climates. Islands that rise farther above sea level, such as Isabela Island, have greater rainfall. The tortoises on Isabela island have adaptations that allow them to reach the abundant vegetation close to the ground (Figure 7.9). Española Island is hot, dry, and nearly barren. The Española Island tortoises have different adaptations to allow them to reach the high, sparse vegetation. They have longer necks as well as a notches in their shells to allow their necks to reach further upward.

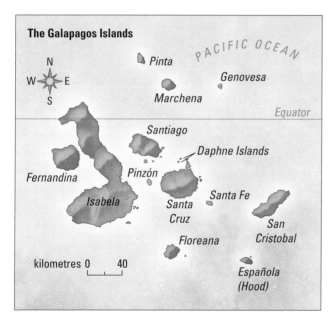

Figure 7.9 The shape of the tortoise's shell corresponds to different habitats on different islands in the Galapagos Island chain. (a) The Española Island tortoise has a shell that is curved and open to allow its long neck to reach the high, sparse vegetation on the island. (b) The tortoise from Isabela Island has a dome-shaped shell and a shorter neck, which reaches vegetation near the ground.

Similarly, Darwin also observed many different finch species. Initially, he thought these birds were from different bird families because they looked different from one another. But when he examined them more closely, he found they were all finches. Each species was adapted to feed on the particular food sources on its home island.

Darwin observed that the islands had many unique organisms. Most of these unique island species were similar to, but different from, the plants and animals of the nearest mainland. For example, Darwin noticed that all the Galapagos mockingbird species he found resembled a single species: the Ecuadorian long-tailed mockingbird. Darwin inferred from these observations that mainland species had changed after they colonized the islands and adapted to their various new environments.

Species Vary over Time

Another pattern Darwin observed was that species varied over time. This pattern emerged from his study of the fossils he found on his journey. Fossils had been discovered and studied by European naturalists for decades. However, the fossils that Darwin found were uniquely South American. Some of the fossils were gigantic versions of modern-day animals (Figure 7.10). His observations supported the idea that species living in South America today were descended from ancestral species on that continent. Other fossil remains, however, looked unlike any living creature. Darwin wondered what had caused the extinction of these species.

Figure 7.10 (a) The modern armadillo looks very similar to (b) the fossil remains of the extinct glypotodon. However, the modern armadillo is much smaller. It is only 0.5 m long, while the glyptodon was 3 m long.

Geological Change

During his voyage, Darwin read Lyell's book on geology. He observed some of the geological processes that Lyell had explored in his book. Darwin personally experienced an earthquake while doing field studies in the Andes Mountains of Chile. In a harbour, he observed a block of land that had been underwater move upward above the water level as a result of the quake. He also collected fossils of ocean organisms high in the Andes. Applying Lyell's ideas, Darwin reasoned that earthquakes had gradually lifted the rock containing those marine fossils from the sea floor. Darwin would eventually apply the idea of gradual change to the evolution of Earth's life forms.

Explore More

What conclusions did Darwin draw from his observations about the landforms he saw on his travels?

Suggested Activity
• C3 Quick Lab Overview on page 193

Take It Further

Various tools are used to analyze fossils. For example, scientists use radioactive decay of isotopes to determine the age of fossils. Research the different techniques used to analyze fossils. Create a brochure to educate your classmates on one of these techniques. Include any limitations to the technology.

Darwin Develops His Theory

After Darwin returned to England, he analyzed his collections of animals, plants, fossils, and rocks. He became convinced that Earth was ancient and that species can change, or evolve, through time. As Darwin thought about a mechanism for evolutionary change, he began to construct a scientific theory built on observations, inferences, and ideas from his own work and the work of others.

In 1838, as Darwin continued to think about the question of how species change, he read an essay on human population written a few decades earlier by Thomas Malthus. Malthus contended that much of human suffering was due to the human population's potential to grow. That is, populations can grow much faster than the rate at which supplies of food and other resources can be produced. Too many people and too few resources lead to war, disease, and famine. Darwin recognized that Malthus's ideas could be applied to all species. The production of more individuals than the environment can support leads to a struggle for existence. This concept helped Darwin to propose a mechanism of evolutionary change.

Investigating Scientists' Contributions

Purpose

To research certain scientists and explain how their ideas changed the way we interpret the world around us.

Activity Overview

In this Quick Lab, you will choose two scientists and research their contributions to scientific ideas about evolution. You will then create a report to summarize your research.

    Your teacher will give you a copy of the full activity.

Prelab Questions

Consider the questions below before beginning this activity.

1. What is evolution?

2. Brainstorm the types of observations of the natural world that would be needed to show evolution.

Figure 7.11 You will use computer search engines and library resources to do this activity.

Interpreting Graphs

Activity Overview

In this activity, you will analyze various graphs. You will describe the information depicted in each case.

    Your teacher will provide you with a copy of the full activity.

Exploring Population Growth

Purpose

To visually represent a population that doubles in size at regular intervals

Activity Overview

In this Quick Lab, you will model population growth by doubling the amount of small objects, such as beads, every 30 seconds. You will graph your results and explore factors that limit population growth.

    Your teacher will give you a copy of the full activity.

Prelab Questions

Consider the questions below before beginning the activity.

1. Do you think populations can continue growing forever?

2. Brainstorm factors that could limit population growth.

Figure 7.12 A student modelling population growth

Key Concept Review

1. What ideas from geology were important in developing the theory of evolution?

2. (a) How did Lamarck propose that species evolve?
   (b) What parts of Lamarck's hypotheses have been proved wrong?
   (c) What did Lamarck get right?

3. What was Malthus's view of population growth?

4. What three patterns did Darwin observe during his voyage on the HMS *Beagle*?

Connect Your Understanding

5. How would Lyell explain the formation of the Grand Canyon, shown in the photo below?

Question 5

6. Suggest how the ideas of a changing Earth and evolving life forms might be related.

7. Why are Lamarck's ideas called scientific hypotheses and not scientific theories?

8. (a) Write two examples of physical and behavioural traits that you have.
   (b) Identify which traits you believe you have inherited and which ones you have acquired.
   (c) Can any of your inherited traits be altered during your life? Explain.
   (d) Can any of your acquired traits be passed on to your offspring? How?

9. Suppose a chain of volcanic islands has just been discovered in the Atlantic ocean, 1000 km off the west coast of Africa. Each island has a different climate and terrain. Predict the kinds of organisms that you might find on the various islands. Justify your predictions.

10. A cave salamander is blind. (Its eyes are non-functional.)

Question 10

(a) How would Lamarck explain how this inability evolved from sighted ancestors?
(b) Can you think of an alternative explanation?

11. Suppose a young man works as a construction worker loading bags of cement onto trucks and he becomes very strong. If Lamarck's hypothesis of use and disuse were correct, would the man's offspring also be strong? Explain.

12. Why is studying islands, such as the Galapagos Islands, so important in our understanding of the diversity of life?

13. (a) In your own words, explain the difference between a theory and a hypothesis.
    (b) Describe two or three challenges scientists encounter while developing a scientific theory.

14. Paleontologists have discovered the fossilized remains of ancestors of whales in Pakistan. These remains were found far from any large body of water. What can you infer from this observation?

15. (a) Darwin observed unique species in some parts of the world. Do you think that modern travel has affected the distribution of species around the world? Justify your answer.
    (b) If an alien species visited Earth to examine its biodiversity, would they draw the same conclusions about species distribution as Darwin did? Justify your answer.

Reflection

16. Which of Darwin's observations from his voyage interests you the most? Explain why.

For more questions, go to *BIOLOGY•SOURCE*

Section Summary

- All of the species currently on Earth are a result of descent with modification from a common ancestral species, also known as evolution. The mechanism of evolution is natural selection.

- Evidence for evolution comes from the fossil record, geographic distribution of species, comparative anatomy, comparative development, and molecular biology.

- Evidence for natural selection comes from artificial selection and molecular biology, among other sources.

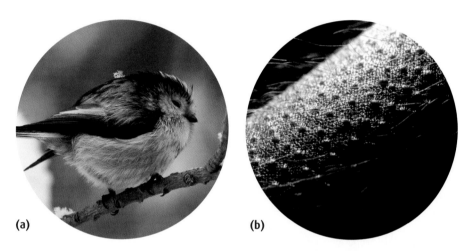

(a)　　　　(b)

Figure 7.13 (a) Raised feathers have a function in birds. (b) Raised hairs (goosebumps) have no function in humans.

When we look at our anatomy, we can see that we resemble other animals. For example, our arm looks similar to a cat's front leg, and it has a similar function. However, we have other features in common with other species that have no function for us, such as goosebumps. In birds and mammals, tiny muscles under the skin contract to raise their feathers or hairs. The raised feathers or hairs trap air close to the skin; this keeps them warm (Figure 7.13). When we feel cold, muscles under our skin contract to raise the hairs on our skin. The result is goosebumps. Our goosebumps, however, do not keep us warm because our skin hairs are so fine and sparse that little air is trapped. It is puzzling why we have this feature. The theory Darwin developed was able to explain why we have such functionless features, as well as explain the phenomena he observed on his voyage.

In 1844, Darwin wrote a 200-page essay that outlined his idea, but he didn't release it to the public. Instead, for the next several years he continued to accumulate more evidence to support his idea. He told only a few of his closest colleagues, who encouraged him to publish his work before someone else came to the same conclusions. In 1858, another British naturalist, Alfred Wallace, *did* come to the same conclusion. Darwin was shocked to receive a letter from Wallace that described the same basic mechanism for evolutionary change that Darwin had proposed. Within a month, some of Wallace's and Darwin's writings were jointly presented in public. Darwin published his book *The Origin of Species* about a year later.

BIOLOGY•SOURCE

Explore More

What were Wallace's ideas on evolutionary change?

In his book, Darwin made two main points.
- All species of organisms living on Earth today are descended from ancestral species. In other words, species evolve over time.
- The mechanism that causes species to change over time is natural selection.

Descent with Modification

Darwin proposed that the descendants of the earliest organisms spread into various habitats over millions of years. In these habitats, they accumulated different modifications, or adaptations, to diverse ways of life. Darwin called this process **descent with modification**. Darwin never actually used the term "evolution." "Evolution" came into use later and replaced "descent with modification."

Darwin saw descent with modification as an explanation for the diversity of life. For example, as hares spread into different environments in the distant past, some of them benefited by having various adaptations that allowed them to survive in these different environments (Figure 7.14). The jackrabbit benefits from fur that blends well in the desert and ears that help cool its body. White fur provides protective camouflage in the snowy northern regions of the snowshoe hare's range. According to Darwin's theory, both of these species descended from a common hare ancestor.

Figure 7.14 (a) The large ears of the jackrabbit are an adaptation to the animal's hot environment. Rich with blood vessels, the ears radiate heat, which helps cool the jackrabbit's body. (b) The white fur of the snowshoe hare camouflages the animal in its environment, and its short ears reduce heat loss.

Natural Selection: The Mechanism of Evolution

Darwin's second main point proposed a mechanism for evolution. Darwin based his theory on three key sets of observations: the struggle for existence, natural variations among members of a species, and the environment's role in evolution.

The Struggle for Existence

First, drawing from Malthus's ideas about humans, Darwin recognized that all species tend to produce excessive numbers of offspring (Figure 7.15). But in nature, resources are limited. The production of more individuals than the environment can support leads to a struggle for existence among the individuals of a population. The struggle for existence is direct competition among individuals of a species for limited resources. In most cases, only a small percentage of offspring will survive in each generation. Many eggs are laid, many young are born, and many seeds are spread, but only a tiny fraction complete their development and leave offspring of their own. The rest are starved, eaten, frozen, diseased, unmated, or unable to reproduce for other reasons.

Figure 7.15 A maple tree produces far more seeds than can possibly survive.

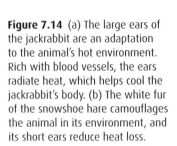

©P

Variation

Darwin's second set of observations was that there is variation among the individuals of a population (Figure 7.16). **Variation** refers to differences among members of the same species. For example, you need only look around your classroom to see how hair colour, skin tone, and facial features vary among even a small group of people. Just as no two people in a human population are alike, individual variation is widespread in all species. Much of this variation is **heritable,** meaning it passes from one generation to the next. For example, siblings usually share more traits with one another and with their parents than they do with unrelated members of the same population.

Darwin recognized that sometimes a certain variation was best suited to the local environment, and individuals with this heritable variation were more likely to leave the most offspring. When this process repeats over many generations, each new generation has a higher proportion of individuals with the advantageous traits.

Figure 7.16 These shells from individuals of the species *Amphidromus adamsii* show a wide variation in colours and patterns.

The Role of the Environment

Darwin's third observation outlined the role of the environment on evolution. Like Lamarck, Darwin observed that a key factor in the survival of an organism was how well it was suited to its environment. Lamarck thought that the environment makes individual organisms acquire characteristics throughout their lives that help them survive in their environment. Darwin explained that there were variations among members of a species. The environment selected those individuals with variations that were best suited for that environment. For example, Darwin would have said that in a population, some giraffes were born with short necks and some with long necks. The environment favoured the long-necked giraffes, so they survived and reproduced, passing along their characteristics to the next generation. Genetics supports Darwin's views. It does not support Lamarck's idea that giraffes grow longer necks during their lifetimes because they need to, and then they pass the acquired characteristic down to their offspring.

Synthesis of Observations

From these three observations, Darwin developed his theory of natural selection. **Natural selection** is the process by which individuals with inherited characteristics well suited to their environment leave more offspring on average than do individuals with adaptations less suited to the environment. The survivors' offspring also have those useful traits. In other words, the individuals that function best in the local environment tend to leave the most offspring. When this process repeats over many generations, each new generation has a higher proportion of individuals with the advantageous traits. Thus, this process can cause a population to change over time. Figure 7.17 on the next page summarizes natural selection working on a population of crickets.

① The Struggle for Existence: The cricket can lay more than 200 eggs at a time, but resources are limited. Only a small fraction of them will survive and reproduce. Therefore, there is competition among the offspring to survive.

② Variation and Adaptation: The cricket population has variations in colour (green and yellow). Some heritable variations improve an individual's chance of surviving and reproducing. These variations are adaptations. Green crickets, for example, blend into the green grass better than yellow ones, so they are less likely to be spotted by predators.

③ Survival of the Fittest: Since more green crickets survive and reproduce, they have greater reproductive success than yellow crickets.

Figure 7.17 The process of natural selection

④ Natural Selection: Green crickets become more common than yellow ones in the population with each generation because (1) more eggs are laid than can survive, (2) there is variation in colour, which is a heritable trait, and (3) the environment favours green crickets, so more survive and reproduce than yellow crickets.

Darwin called this theory "natural selection" because an organism's natural surroundings determine, or select, whether or not it will survive and reproduce. A species' natural surroundings include all aspects of its ecological niche. An **ecological niche** is the sum total of a species' use of the biotic and abiotic factors in its environment. Biotic factors, such as their predators and (in some cases) prey, as well as abiotic factors, such as water availability, can affect an organism's ability to survive and reproduce.

When biologists speak of Darwin's theory of evolution, they are referring to natural selection as the mechanism for evolution. The result of natural selection is adaptation. The process of natural selection is another way of defining evolution.

Survival of the Fittest

Darwin defined the **fitness** of an individual as its ability to survive and reproduce in its specific environment. Certain adaptations make individuals of a species better suited for an environment. Individuals with adaptations that increase their fitness survive and reproduce most successfully. The results of differences in rates of survival and reproduction is called **survival of the fittest**. In later editions of his book, Darwin used the term "survival of the fittest" as a synonym for natural selection.

Darwin also reasoned that natural selection could eventually cause isolated populations of the same species to become separate species as they adapted to their different environments.

Natural selection does not make organisms "better." Natural selection has no goal. Adaptations just enable an organism to pass on its genes to the next generation. There is no one ideal way of doing things, as demonstrated by Figure 7.18. An adaptation might work well in a certain environment, but if the environment changes, another adaptation might be favoured.

Suggested Activity
• C4 Case Study Overview on page 208

(a) (b)

Figure 7.18 There are many different styles of pollination. (a) Red maple tree flowers are pollinated by wind. (b) Apple tree flowers are pollinated by insects. Neither method is considered "better" than the other.

Concept Check

1. What were Darwin's two main points in *The Origin of Species?*

2. In your own words, describe the three main ideas in natural selection.

3. How did Darwin's explanation of the environment's role in evolution differ from Lamarck's?

Evidence for Evolution

Evolution, or descent with modification, leaves observable signs. Such clues to the past are essential to any historical science. Evolution has left marks on all aspects of life: in the fossil record; in the geographical distribution, anatomy, and development of species; and in molecular biology.

Explore More

How does the fossil *Archaeopteryx* link dinosaurs to modern birds?

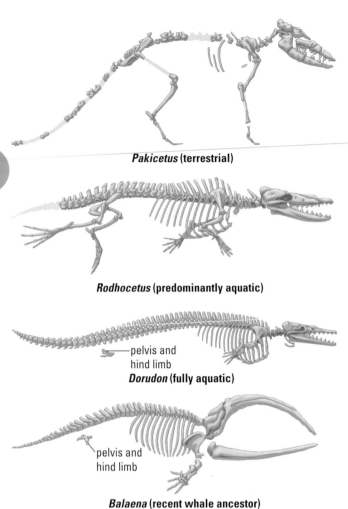

Pakicetus (terrestrial)

Rodhocetus (predominantly aquatic)

pelvis and hind limb
Dorudon (fully aquatic)

pelvis and hind limb
Balaena (recent whale ancestor)

Figure 7.19 The transition to life in the sea is evident in the fossil record. The hind limbs became progressively smaller as ancestral whale species became more aquatic.

The Fossil Record

Darwin used fossil evidence to support his theory. Most fossils are found in sedimentary rocks. Younger rock layers, or strata, are deposited on top of older ones. Thus, the positions of fossils in the rock strata can reveal their relative age. The deeper the layer in which the fossil is found, the older the age of the fossil. The **fossil record** is this chronological collection of life's remains in the rock layers, recorded during the passage of time. The oldest fossil evidence of life consists of chemical traces in rocks from Greenland that are 3.8 billion years old. Fossils of prokaryotes (bacteria and archaea) have been found in rocks about 3.5 billion years old.

Paleontologists are scientists who study fossils. They have discovered fossils of many ancestral life forms that link the past with the present. For example, fossil evidence supports the hypothesis that whales, which have no hind limbs, evolved from land-dwelling ancestors that had four limbs. Paleontologists digging in Egypt and Pakistan have identified ancient whales that had hind limb bones (Figure 7.19). *Pakicetus* was completely terrestrial, but *Rodhocetus* spent most of its life in water and its hind legs likely did not support much weight. The small hind limb bones of *Dorudon* more closely resemble the hind limb bones of modern whales.

The fossil record can also provide evidence of the extinction of some species. It shows that dinosaur-like animals first apppeared roughly 230 million years ago and their diversity increased over millions of years. Their sudden disappearance from the fossil record indicates most became extinct 65 million years ago.

There are limits to the fossil record in providing evidence for evolution. Species that do not possess hard tissue such as bones, shells, or exoskeletons rarely become fossilized. Thus, the fossil record is of little help in establishing the evolutionary history of these species.

Geographic Distribution

The differences and similarities between organisms in different parts of the world were some of the first observations that Darwin made on his voyage. These observations suggested to Darwin that today's organisms evolved from ancestral forms.

Closely Related but Different

Darwin's study of the finches of the Galapagos Islands revealed that the finches on the various islands were all descendents of a single ancestral species from the South American mainland. The finches became geographically isolated on the different islands and developed adaptations that were best suited for the local environment on each island. Today each finch species in the Galapagos has a beak shape adapted to eating a specific food (Figure 7.20). Similarly, all the tortoise species, however different they now look, are all descended from the same ancestral species.

(a)   (b)   (c)

Figure 7.20 Three of the 13 closely related finch species. (a) The medium ground finch eats seeds. (b) The woodpecker finch eats insects from under tree bark. (c) The warbler finch eats small insects.

Distantly Related but Similar

Sometimes similar habitats select for similar adaptations. Recall that Darwin observed similar ground-dwelling birds in the grasslands of South America, Australia, and Africa. They looked similar to each other, but their body structures indicated that they had descended from different types of birds. Similar selection pressures had caused these species to develop similar adaptations to survive in these environments. Figure 7.21 shows how quite distantly related rodents that live in similar environments have developed similar body types.

Many patterns in the geographic distribution of life forms make sense in an evolutionary context. There are two groups of mammals. In marsupials, the fetus leaves the uterus early and continues development in an external pouch. In placental mammals, the fetus is surrounded by a placenta and develops in the uterus. Darwin had wondered why Australia is home to so many kinds of marsupials, such as kangaroos and koalas, but very few placental mammals, such as deer and squirrels. It is *not* because placental mammals are unable to survive in Australia. (Humans have introduced rabbits, foxes, dogs, cats, and many other placental mammals to Australia, and they have all thrived.) The most widely accepted hypothesis suggests that Australia's diverse marsupial species evolved from marsupial ancestors on an island continent that was isolated from placental mammals in the distant past.

Figure 7.21 Darwin was puzzled by the existence of similar yet distantly related species. All of these animals are rodents, but they come from two distinct families. The environment they live in, however, has selected for similar body shapes.

Concept Check

1. Why are older fossils generally in deeper rock layers than younger fossils?

2. How can evolutionary theory explain why Australia is home to relatively few native placental mammals?

3. How can two species that look similar to each other be more distantly related than two species that look very different from each other?

Comparative Anatomy

Certain similarities in structure among species provide clues to evolutionary history. For example, the forelimbs of all mammals consist of the same skeletal parts. Human arms, cat forelegs, whale flippers, and bat wings all have the same basic combination of bones (Figure 7.22). These different types of limbs move each animal in a different way. For example, a whale's flipper helps it swim and a bat's wing helps it fly. Since the types of locomotion are completely different, you might expect that their structures would also be entirely different. Yet, that is not the case. Arms, forelegs, flippers, and wings of different mammals are variations on a common structural theme — one that has become adapted to different functions.

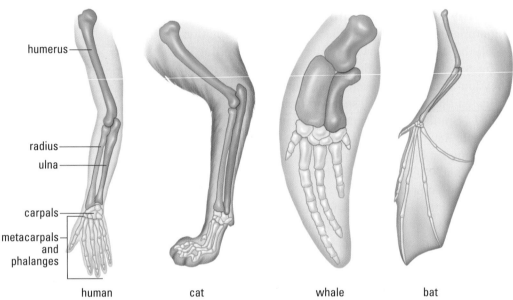

humerus

radius

ulna

carpals

metacarpals
and
phalanges

human   cat   whale   bat

Figure 7.22 The hypothesis that all mammals descended from a common ancestor predicts that their forelimbs would be variations of the structural form in that ancestor. The homologous bones are the same colour in each limb.

Homologous Structures

Similar structures in species that share a common ancestor are called **homologous structures**. Homologous structures support other evidence that evolution is a remodelling process. Structures that originally functioned one way in ancestral species become modified as they take on new functions. This idea is what Darwin meant by "descent with modification." The limitations of this remodelling are evident in structures that are less than perfect. For example, almost no person reaches old age without some form of knee or back problem. The human spine and knee joints were derived from ancestral structures that supported four-legged mammals — not two-legged mammals that walked upright.

Vestigial Structures

Some of the most interesting homologous structures are those that have a major function in one species but are not important in a related species. **Vestigial structures** are remnants of structures that may have had important functions in an ancestral species but have no clear function in some of the modern descendants. Often vestigial structures are reduced in size (Figure 7.23). The fossil record of whales (Figure 7.19 on page 200) shows how whales' hind limbs became vestigial. Modern whales lack hind limbs, but some have small vestigial hip bones probably derived from their four-footed ancestors described earlier. Lamarck's idea of inheritance of acquired characteristics could account for the reduced size of vestigial structures. If his idea were correct, then during an organism's life, its genes would have to change in some way in order to pass the change in its structure down to its offspring. There is no evidence that this happens. Natural selection provides a different explanation for vestigial structures. Natural selection would favour the survival and reproduction of individuals with genes that produced reduced versions of those structures.

Analogous Structures

Sometimes distantly related species develop structures that are anatomically different but perform the same function. These are called **analogous structures**. For example, the wing of a bee and the wing of a bird are analogous structures. Bees and birds are extremely distantly related. Their wings do not share any common structures. The evolutionary idea of common descent is based on common structures, not common functions.

Comparative Development

Other clues to evolutionary history come from comparing the development of various organisms. Embryos of closely related organisms often have similar stages in development (Figure 7.24). All vertebrates, for example, have an embryonic stage in which pharyngeal pouches appear on the sides of the throat. At this stage, the embryos of fishes, frogs, snakes, birds, and primates look relatively alike. As development progresses, these vertebrates take on more distinctive features. In fishes, for example, most of the pharyngeal pouches develop into gills. In land vertebrates, they are involved in the development of other structures, such as bones of the skull. Yet the similarity of these structures at early stages is further evidence that all vertebrates evolved from a common ancestor.

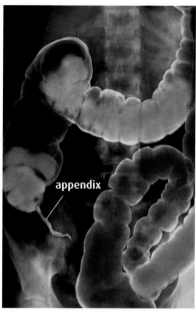

Figure 7.23 The human appendix is a vestigial structure. It has been reduced in size due to a change in the human diet. Humans have moved away from a predominantly vegetarian diet to an omnivorous one. There is some evidence that the appendix may have a secondary use in the immune system, but the organ is still considered vestigial because it has lost its original function: to aid in the digestion of food.

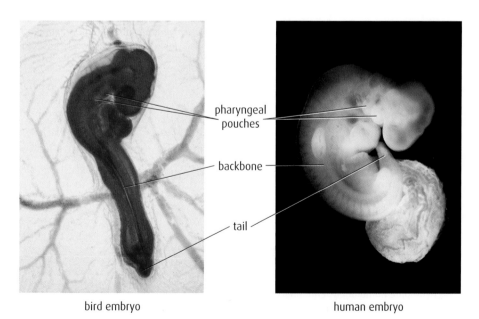

bird embryo   human embryo

Figure 7.24 Even at this early stage of development, there are similarities between vertebrate species. Notice the pharyngeal pouches and tails in both the bird embryo and the human embryo. In humans, the tail becomes a vestigial structure. (magnification 8× (left), 8× (right))

Molecular Biology

Today, some of the supportive evidence for evolution comes from the study of molecular biology. The ordered sequences of the components that make up DNA molecules are passed from parents to offspring. These information-rich molecules provide a record of an organism's ancestry (hereditary background). Among siblings, the DNA and protein sequences are very similar. Among unrelated individuals of the same species, however, these sequences show more differences.

This type of molecular comparison can also be made between species. If two species have genes and proteins with sequences that match closely, biologists conclude that the sequences must have been inherited from a relatively recent common ancestor. In contrast, the greater the number of differences in DNA and protein sequences between species, the less likely it is that they share a close common ancestry.

Figure 7.25 compares the amino acid sequence of human hemoglobin with those of other vertebrates. Hemoglobin is the protein that carries oxygen in blood. The data support the hypothesis that humans are more closely related to primates than to other vertebrates. Other evidence comes from DNA sequences in humans and chimpanzees. There is approximately a 5 percent difference in the total DNA between these two species.

BIOLOGY•SOURCE

Suggested Activity
• C5 Inquiry Activity Overview on page 208

species	human	gorilla	rhesus monkey	mouse	chicken	frog
number of amino acids that differ from a human hemoglobin chain*	0	1	8	27	45	67

*Total chain length = 146 amino acids

Figure 7.25 This table compares the amino acid sequences of hemoglobin in humans and other vertebrates. The data reveal the same pattern of evolutionary relationships that researchers find when they compare species using non-molecular methods.

BIOLOGY•SOURCE

Explore More

How have advancements in molecular biology improved our understanding of evolution?

Cytochrome C is another protein used to establish evolutionary relationships. Cytochrome C is found in all organisms that need oxygen to survive. It helps cells perform cellular respiration. There is very little variation in its structure among related species. Humans and chimpanzees have identical amino acid sequences, and the sequences in maseques and spider monkeys are very similar to the human sequence. These similarities imply that apes and monkeys diverged from a common ancestor very recently in evolutionary history.

Concept Check

1. Compare homologous and analogous structures. Give an example of each.

2. Why do vestigial structures provide evidence for evolution?

3. How can molecular evidence be used to establish evolutionary relationships?

©P

Evidence For Natural Selection

Darwin also found convincing evidence for his ideas in the results of artificial selection. Other evidence of natural selection has also been found since Darwin's time.

Artificial Selection

Artificial selection is the selective breeding of domesticated plants and animals to produce offspring with genetic traits that humans value (Figure 7.26). For example, a plant breeder might seek to improve traits such as grain production, disease resistance, or protein content. An animal breeder might select for growth rate or temperament. Darwin observed that breeders selected individuals with the desired traits as breeding stock. Breeders do what the environment does in natural selection: they allow only those plants or animals with useful traits to reproduce.

Figure 7.26 Artificial selection is commonly used to breed cats with certain desirable characteristics. Each cat pictured here is a different breed.

In fact, humans have been modifying species for thousands of years. You can see evidence of Darwin's point in the enormous diversity that dog breeders have produced within this single species in just the last 500 years.

Darwin observed that artificial selection could produce a great deal of change in a species in a short time. He reasoned that over thousands of generations, natural selection could also cause major change. Of course, there are important differences between artificial and natural selection. The traits that become more common in a population through artificial selection are those that humans choose. In contrast, natural selection favours traits that benefit the organisms in their particular environment — environmental conditions do the "selective breeding." The result is an evolutionary adaptation to the environment.

Changes in Beak Shape

Darwin thought that natural selection always works too slowly to actually be measured during a human lifetime. Since Darwin's time, natural selection and the evolution it causes can be observed. For 30 years, Peter and Rosemary Grant from Princeton University have been studying the finches of Daphne Major, an island in the Galapagos. With their data, they have been able to provide clear evidence for natural selection.

The Grants have shown conclusively how average beak and body size of the medium ground finch changes as El Niños come and go. El Niño is a warming of the ocean current that passes along the coasts of Peru and Equador and affects global weather patterns. This finch uses its strong beak to crush seeds. Given a choice of small or large seeds found on the island, the birds eat mostly small ones, which are easier to crush. During wet years, small seeds are so abundant that ground finches eat relatively few large seeds. However, in dry years, all seeds are in short supply, and the large seeds make up a greater part of the birds' diet. Those birds with larger beaks are more successful at cracking the large seeds. Dry years are difficult, and the finches that survive tend to be those with larger beaks that can crack the toughest seeds. This trend of larger beaks continues into the next generation of finches in the following year.

When wet years return to Daphne Major, the plants that produce small seeds recover. Small seeds are a more efficient food source for finches than large seeds. During wet years, birds with smaller beaks appear to forage for seeds more efficiently than the large-beaked birds. The average beak size in the population of birds changes again. The Grants have documented several such cycles of natural selection over their 30-year study (Figure 7.27).

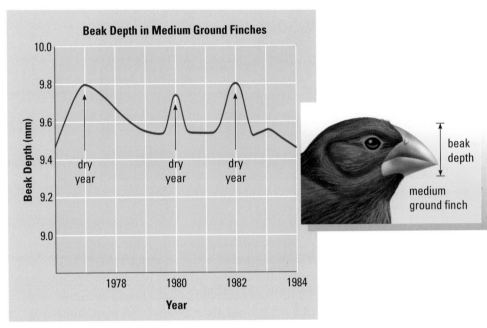

Figure 7.27 This graph shows changes in beak size among medium ground finches over an eight-year period of the Grants' study.

Antibiotic Resistance in Bacteria

Another example of natural selection in action can be found in the resurgence of tuberculosis. Tuberculosis (TB) is caused by a rod-shaped bacterium *Mycobacterium tuberculosis*. TB causes a severe bloody cough and chest pain (Figure 7.28). It can affect other organs and even cause death. TB affects all types of individuals and is very contagious. The majority of cases are in people between the ages of 15 and 54, who make up the primary working force; therefore, the economic impact of the disease is tremendous.

BIOLOGY•SOURCE

Explore More

Are humans evolving to be disease free?

©P

The drug Streptomycin was developed in the 1940s to treat tuberculosis. Streptomycin is in a class of drugs called antibiotics, which are drugs that kill infectious micro-organisms. By the 1970s, TB had been almost completely wiped out. However, in 2006 there was an outbreak of an extensively drug-resistant strain in KwaZulu-Natal in South Africa. By 2008, it had spread to 49 countries. In 2009 the World Health Organization (WHO) reported that one-third of the world's population has TB, and 5 percent of new cases do not respond to antibiotics. How did this resistance occur? Drug-resistant bacteria arose by means of natural selection.

Bacteria, like other organisms, have many variations. Some can be destroyed by antibiotics and others are resistant. The main therapy for TB is an intensive six- to nine-month course of four different antibiotics. This treatment has been effective in killing tuberculosis for many years. Patients, however, do not always take the full treatment. They may stop the treatment prematurely and not take all the antibiotics needed to kill all the bacteria. Some bacteria that are resistant to these antibiotics are then able to survive due to natural selection. The drug-resistant bacteria are able to reproduce and become more common (Figure 7.29). Scientists now struggle to find alternative antibiotics to kill these resistant strains.

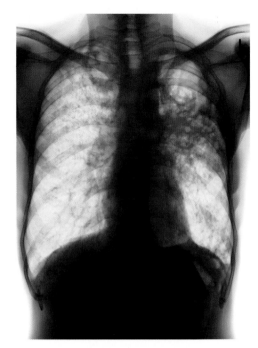

Figure 7.28 TB can cause severe lung infections, shown here in red, which may lead to death.

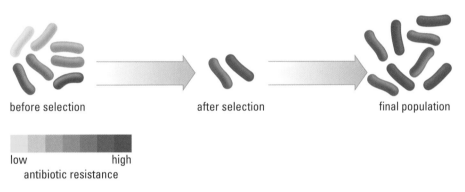

before selection   after selection   final population

low   high
antibiotic resistance

Figure 7.29 Natural selection works on the variations in the amount of resistance individual bacteria in the population have to antibiotics.

BIOLOGY•SOURCE

Take It Further

Areas with tropical climates tend to have greater species diversity and diversity within species than areas with cold, harsh climates. Recent DNA evidence indicates that mutation rates are higher in tropical climates than in cold climates. Research the role climate plays in natural selection and investigate the impact global warming may be having on the rate of evolution. Write a brief summary of your findings.

Staphylococcus aureus is another bacterium that has developed resistance to antibiotics, in this case, the antibiotic methicillin. *Staphylococcus aureus* is normally found on human skin, where it can cause minor skin infections such as pimples. However, if it enters the body through a break in the skin, such as a wound, it can cause life-threatening diseases, such as pneumonia. Unfortunately, methicillin-resistant *S. aureus* (MRSA) has now been found in a number of Ontario hospitals, which has led to an increase in MRSA infections in hospital patients. Protocols in hospitals, such as more thorough hand-washing and cleaning procedures, as well as quarantining infected individuals, are being explored to reduce the spread of MRSA and other antibiotic-resistant bacteria. Just as in antibiotic-resistant TB, the rise of MRSA is blamed on the misuse of antibiotics.

The Effects of Urbanization on Species

Issue

What effect does urbanization have on natural selection, and how does it affect the vulnerability of species?

Activity Overview

In this activity, you will analyze how urbanization has affected several different species. Then you will come up with a plan to manage the populations of these species.

Your teacher will give you a copy of the full activity.

Prelab Questions

1. List the wild animal species you can observe in your neighbourhood, or in a typical Canadian town or city.

2. Brainstorm possible reasons why these species can survive in an urban environment but not other species.

Figure 7.30 A raccoon scavenges for food in a residential garbage can.

Comparing Chromosomes

Question

What can the analysis of human and chimpanzee chromosomes tell us about their potential evolutionary relationship?

Activity Overview

In this activity, you will compare the similarities and differences between human and chimpanzee chromosomes. You will assess the DNA evidence to establish how closely related the two species are.

Your teacher will give you a copy of the full activity.

Prelab Questions

1. What is a chromosome? How many chromosomes do humans have?

2. Do all individuals of the same species have the same number of chromosomes? Explain.

3. What does DNA do?

Figure 7.31 Comparing chromosomes of chimpanzees and humans to establish evolutionary relationships

©P

Key Concept Review

1. Explain what Darwin meant by "descent with modification."

2. How did Darwin use Malthus's work to formulate his theory of natural selection?

3. (a) Explain in your own words "survival of the fittest."
   (b) What makes an organism more "fit" than others?

4. How does natural selection depend on variation?

5. Why do distantly related species in different places share similar traits?

6. Explain the difference between homologous and analogous structures. Which one is more important for evolution?

7. Hemoglobin is common to all animals with backbones. What does this tell us about the evolutionary history of animals with backbones?

8. For each of the following types of evidence, give an example and state what the evidence reveals about evolution.
   • fossil record
   • geographical distribution
   • comparative anatomy
   • embryology
   • molecular biology

Connect Your Understanding

9. For each of the following vestigial structures, hypothesize its ancient function and suggest a scenario that would have led to the loss of the function.
   (a) pelvic hip bones in some whales
   (b) webbed feet of the upland goose, which does not enter the water
   (c) muscles to make human ears move
   (d) goosebumps in humans

10. Explain in terms of natural selection why vestigial structures have not disappeared completely.

11. What type of animals do you think would be most represented in the fossil record? Explain.

12. Compare the two iguana species pictured below. Explain how natural selection can account for the differences between the two.

Question 12

13. Do you think that protecting endangered species is interfering with natural selection? Support your position.

14. Penguins and flying albatrosses might have a common ancestor.
    (a) How would Darwin use comparative anatomy and the fossil record to establish this evolutionary relationship?
    (b) What modern technological advancements might further support the evolutionary relationship?

15. Lamarck hypothesized that evolution moves species toward perfection. According to Darwin's theory, why is this statement incorrect?

16. Figure 7.17 on page 198 summarizes natural selection in a population of crickets. Suppose the climate changed and the grasses in the field tended to be a more golden brown colour. Apply the theory of natural selection to the population of crickets in these new environmental conditions.

Reflection

17. What piece of evidence do you find most convincing in understanding and supporting the theory of evolution? Explain.

For more questions, go to BIOLOGY•SOURCE

Key Concept Review

1. (a) What were two prevailing ideas about the natural world prior to the 1800s? **k**
   (b) What observations from geology and fossils caused people to question these ideas? **k**

2. Explain what is meant by the term "evolution," and give an example. **k**

3. (a) Explain Lamarck's hypothesis of "inheritance of acquired characteristics." **k**
   (b) What was the weakness of his hypothesis? **k**

4. How does natural selection lead to adaptation? **k**

5. Provide examples for each of the following observations Darwin made on his journey on the *Beagle*.
   (a) Species vary globally. **k**
   (b) Species vary locally. **k**
   (c) Species vary over time. **k**

6. Charles Darwin developed the theory of evolution.
   (a) What are the two major points of Darwin's theory? **k**
   (b) What evidence from his journey on the *Beagle* did he use to support these two points? **k**
   (c) What are two recent discoveries that support Darwin's theory? **k**

7. (a) What is meant by the term "variation"? **k**
   (b) List some variations in hares. **k**
   (c) Why are variations important in a species? **k**

8. Define "fitness." Give an example of how the environment can influence the fitness of individuals in a species. **k**

9. Compare natural selection to artificial selection. **k**

10. (a) How did Darwin explain the similarities between flightless birds on different continents? **k**
    (b) How did he explain the finch species he found on the different islands of the Galapagos? **k**

11. (a) What are vestigial structures? **k**
    (b) How do the vestigial structures in modern whales help us understand whales' evolutionary history? **k**

12. How can comparing amino-acid sequences between species help establish evolutionary relationships? **k**

Connect Your Understanding

13. How did the work of Hutton, Lyell, Cuvier and Malthus help Darwin form his theory of evolution? **k**

14. Use the diagram of sedimentary rock layers below to answer the questions.

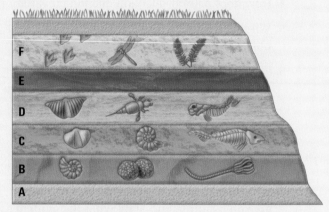

Question 14

(a) What major change in the environment occurred after layers D and E? Explain. **a**
(b) What inferences can you make about life forms at the time layer A was formed? **a**
(c) If radiometric dating identifies the rock in layer C as 425 million years old, what can you infer about the age of the fossils in layer C? In layers B and D? Explain. **a**

15. The peppered moth, *Biston betularia*, occurs in two forms: a grey mottled form, and a dark form. These moths like to rest on tree trunks. A biologist named H.D. Kettlewell observed that lighter grey forms suffered higher mortality in areas where there were more coal-burning factories.
    (a) How would Lamarck explain this observation? **a**
    (b) How would Darwin explain this observation? **a**

16. Does evolution make organisms "better"? Justify your answer. **c**

17. A population of snails that has striped and unstriped individuals has recently moved into a new region. Birds break the snails open by dropping them onto rocks. The birds eat the bodies of the snails and leave the shells. In one area, researchers counted both live snails and broken shells. The data are summarized below.

Numbers of Snail Shells

	Striped Shells	Unstriped Shells
Living snails	264	296
Broken snails	486	377

(a) Analyze the data. Which form of snail (striped or unstriped) is more likely to be caught by the birds for food? Explain. **t**

(b) Suggest a hypothesis to explain what is happening to the snails. **t**

(c) Predict how the frequencies of striped and unstriped individuals in the population might change over many generations. **t**

18. DDT is an insecticide that kills mosquitoes. Explain in terms of natural selection the trends exhibited in the graph. **t**

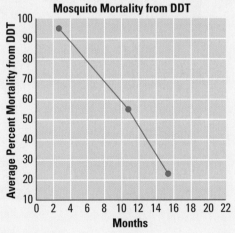

Mosquito Mortality from DDT

(Average Percent Mortality from DDT vs. Months)

Question 18

19. For each of the following adaptations, decide what aspect of the organism's environment played a role in the development of the adaptation and explain the process of natural selection that led to the adaptation.

(a) fat storage humps in camels **a**

(b) "white" fur in polar bears **a**

(c) a kangaroo's marsupial pouch **a**

(d) stripes on zebras **a**

20. Look at the drawing of a fossil of a *Maiacetus* found in Pakistan. It is believed to be an ancestor of modern whales. **a**

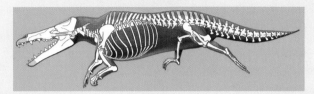

Question 20

(a) What features of this fossil are more suited for a terrestrial habitat?

(b) What features connect it to modern whales, which live in an aquatic habitat?

21. Form a hypothesis to explain the observation that animals and plants of India are almost completely different from the species found in nearby Southeast Asia. **t**

22. How do weather patterns affect the evolution of finches in the Galapagos Islands? **a**

23. (a) Compare the structural similarities between a bat's wing, a human's arm and a whale's flipper. **a**

(b) How is the limb in each of the cases above structurally modified to perform its function? **a**

24. For years, people have been artificially selecting certain traits in livestock. Do you think we should be interfering with "natural" evolutionary processes? Justify your opinion. **c**

Reflection

25. What can you explain about evolution that you were not able to before reading this chapter? **c**

Unit Task Link

In this chapter you learned about the process of natural selection. Using the theory of natural selection, explain how a species might become extinct.

For more questions, go to **BIOLOGY•SOURCE**

The mechanisms of evolution can lead to speciation or extinction.

This shocking-pink dragon millipede *Desmoxytes purpurosea* was first discovered in 2007 in the Greater Mekong region. This is an area that borders the Mekong River, which extends from China into Laos, Thailand, Cambodia, and Viet Nam (Figure 8.1). The bright colour might fascinate us, but it serves as a warning to predators that the animal is toxic. This millipede can shoot out a poisonous hydrogen cyanide solution that can kill its predators. It is among more than 1000 new species found in this area of the world in the last 10 years. Scientists compare these discoveries to Darwin's discoveries on the Galapagos Islands for the opportunity they offer to explore life's diversity. They believe this species-rich area should be conserved.

The great diversity in terrain has contributed to the region's biodiversity. This area is also home to the world's largest freshwater fish, the Mekong giant catfish; the saola, a newly discovered antelope; and the endangered Indo-Chinese tiger. Unfortunately, many species, including the newly discovered species, may soon become endangered or extinct. Deforestation, industrial development, and climate change are threatening the many ecosystems in the Greater Mekong region.

Figure 8.1 The shocking-pink dragon millipede was one of several species discovered in the Greater Mekong region. The region is named after the Mekong River, which flows through Southeast Asia.

©P

Section Summary

- Variation in the gene pool is due to mutation and sexual recombination.
- Microevolution occurs when allele frequencies in the gene pool change from generation to generation.
- Natural selection, sexual selection, artificial selection, genetic drift, and gene flow are mechanisms of microevolution.

Sickle-Cell Disease

The prevalance of sickle-cell disease in Canada is roughly one in 3800, but in some African populations, it affects about one in 25 individuals. The disease is named for the abnormal shape of red blood cells in individuals who inherit the disorder (Figure 8.2). People with the disease suffer a range of symptoms that include general weakening of the body, pain, damage to organs, and sometimes death. Sickle-cell disease is caused by a recessive allele. An allele is an alternative version of a gene. Each gene is composed of two alleles. If an individual has two alleles for a gene that are identical to each other, then the individual is homozygous. If an individual has two alleles for a gene that are different from each other, then the individual is heterozygous. With some exceptions, alleles are either dominant or recessive. A recessive allele is not expressed in a heterozygous individual. Physical effects result only if the individual has two recessive alleles. A dominant allele expresses itself physically both in homozygous and heterozygous individuals. Only individuals that are homozygous for recessive sickle-cell allele have sickle-cell disease. Heterozygous individuals — those with a single copy of the sickle-cell allele — do not have the disease. But they can pass the allele on to their children.

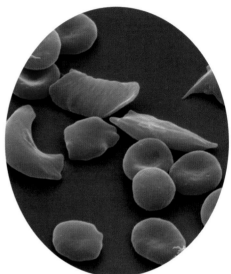

Figure 8.2 Sickle-cell disease produces red blood cells that resemble the crescent-shaped cutting tool called a sickle. Normal red blood cells have a rounded shape and pass through thin blood vessels more easily. (magnification 3000×)

Malaria Resistance

Why do many African populations have such high frequencies of an allele with the potential to shorten life (and thus reproductive success)? Evolutionary biology holds a possible answer. Although the sickle-cell allele has harmful effects, in the tropics it is also beneficial. Individuals with just one copy of the sickle-cell allele are resistant to the disease malaria. Malaria can cause fever, joint pain, anemia, vomiting, vision problems, and convulsions. It is widespread in tropical and subtropical regions, including sub-Saharan Africa. Resistance to malaria is an important advantage in environments where malaria is a major cause of death in infants.

The frequency of the sickle-cell allele in Africa is generally highest in areas where the malaria parasite is most common (Figure 8.3 on the next page). In some populations, as many as one in three people carry a single copy of the sickle-cell allele and are resistant to malaria. In populations with a high frequency of the sickle-cell allele, 4 percent of the population is homozygous and suffer from the disease. With malaria common in the environment, natural selection maintains a higher frequency of the sickle-cell allele than would be expected if the allele had only negative effects.

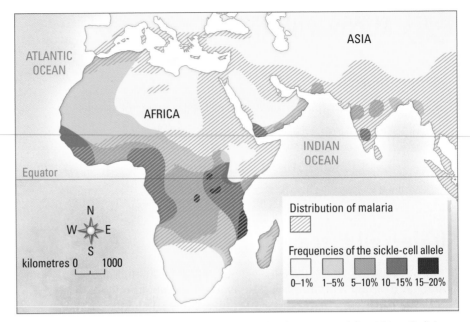

Figure 8.3 The distribution of malaria compared with the frequencies of the sickle-cell allele

Darwin could not explain how the variations that are the basis for natural selection pass from one generation to the next. Gregor Mendel might have been some help. Mendel solved the inheritance piece of the puzzle. But though they lived in the same era, Darwin knew nothing of Mendel's work. It wasn't until decades after both men were dead that biologists were able to apply Mendel's genetics to Darwin's ideas about natural selection. This union of genetics with evolutionary biology focusses on change within populations.

Gene Pools and Variation

A key concept in understanding the evolution of populations is the gene pool. The **gene pool** consists of all the alleles in all the individuals that make up a population. You can think of the gene pool as the reservoir from which the next generation draws its genes. As such, the population's gene pool is where genetic variation — the raw material of evolution — is stored. You can observe evidence of a gene pool's reservoir of variations in a population of wild mustangs (Figure 8.4). Each mustang has a unique combination of alleles. An individual organism's combination of alleles is its genotype. This uniqueness is reflected in individual variations such as the horses' colouring. Each mustang's alleles produce its phenotype. A **phenotype** is an organism's expressed traits. These include physical, physiological, and behavioural traits.

For some traits, there can be a range of phenotypes in the population, with some phenotypes appearing more frequently than others. Figure 8.5 shows the frequency of different heights in a population: the men and women in a U.S. marching band. The most frequent height in this population is 5 feet, 6 inches, which is equal to 167 cm. The least frequent height is 6 feet, 4 inches, which is equal to 193 cm.

Figure 8.4 The many different colours of the wild mustangs in this population are one reflection of the genetic variation in its gene pool.

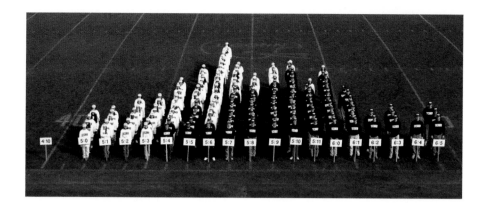

Figure 8.5 **Figure 8.5** People's heights vary in a population, in this case, a marching band. Women are in white and men are in blue.

Sources of Variation

The study of genetics can help us understand the sources of variation. There are two main sources within a population. One is mutation. A mutation is any change in a sequence of DNA. Mutations can arise as a result of mistakes in DNA replication or as a result of exposure to chemicals or radiation in the environment. Mutations do not always change an organism's phenotype, but some do (Figure 8.6). Some mutations, therefore, can have an effect on an organism's fitness in the environment.

Mutations are especially important as a source of variation in asexually reproducing organisms that clone themselves rapidly, such as bacteria. A new mutation that is favourable can rapidly increase in frequency in a bacteria population through natural selection.

The second source of variation comes from sexual reproduction. In sexually reproducing organisms with relatively long generation spans, most of the variation is not due to new mutations but to the scrambling of existing alleles, including those that originated as mutations in earlier generations. Differences among individuals are largely the result of sexual recombination. The processes of meiosis and fertilization shuffle the alleles and recombine them. Each offspring receives a new combination of alleles.

Figure 8.6 This peacock has a homozygous recessive mutation that causes lack of colouration. Its fitness is probably lower than individuals with colouration.

Changes to Gene Pools

Populations that do not undergo change to their gene pools are not currently evolving. This condition is known as the **Hardy-Weinberg equilibrium** (named for the two scientists who first described it). Such equilibrium of a gene pool means that the frequencies of alleles in that gene pool are constant over time. This frequency is usually expressed as a decimal or a percentage, as shown in Figure 8.7. The Hardy-Weinberg equilibrium will hold under five conditions: there must be random mating; there is a large population; there is no movement in or out of the population; there are no mutations; and there is no natural selection. In fact, populations rarely remain in Hardy-Weinberg equilibrium for long in nature, but the concept is useful because it provides a "no change" baseline that makes it possible to recognize when a gene pool *is* changing.

If the above conditions are not met, genetic equilibrium is disrupted, and the gene pool frequencies may change. A generation-to-generation change in the frequencies of alleles within a population is called **microevolution.** Microevolution is evolution on the smallest scale.

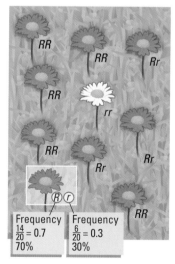

Frequency
$\frac{14}{20} = 0.7$
70%

Frequency
$\frac{6}{20} = 0.3$
30%

Figure 8.7 Each plant in this hypothetical population of wildflowers has 2 alleles for flower colour. In all, there are 14 red-flower alleles (R) and 6 white-flower alleles (r). The frequency of each allele is calculated as a ratio based on the total of 20.

Concept Check

1. Why is sickle-cell disease more common in Africa than in North America?
2. What is the Hardy-Weinberg equilibrium and under what conditions is it upheld?
3. When does microevolution occur?

Mechanisms of Microevolution

Several factors may disrupt Hardy-Weinberg equilibrium, or in other words, cause microevolution. These include natural selection, sexual selection, artificial selection, genetic drift, and gene flow.

Natural Selection

BIOLOGY•SOURCE

Explore More

How does malaria affect the genetic frequencies of sickle-cell disease?

Natural selection is one mechanism of microevolution. Natural selection is not a random process. The environment increases the frequency of alleles that provide a reproductive advantage to individuals and thus leads to the evolution of adaptations.

Different aspects of the environment, or selection pressures, can affect the relative fitness of phenotypes in the population. This, in turn, affects the relative frequencies of phenotypes in a population. Figure 8.8 shows what can happen to the frequencies of certain phenotypes under different selective pressures.

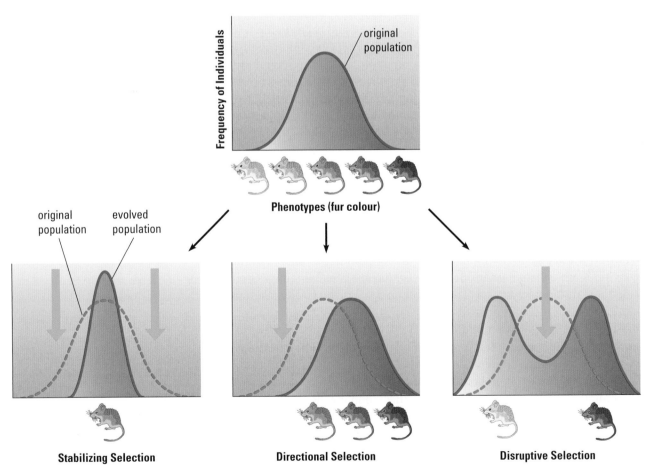

Figure 8.8 Different selection pressures are shown by blue arrows. The different selection pressures can cause stabilizing selection, directional selection, or disruptive selection.

Stabilizing selection occurs when individuals near the centre of the phenotype range have a higher fitness than individuals at either end of the range. In the case of the mice in Figure 8.8, the medium brown coloured mice were favoured. The masses of human babies at birth also display this pattern. Babies that are extremely underweight or overweight are less healthy and are less likely to survive and pass down their traits. **Directional selection** occurs when individuals at one end of the phenotype range, in this case, the darker-brown mice, have a higher fitness than individuals in the middle or at the other end of the range. As the light- and middle-brown individuals fail to survive and reproduce, the range of phenotypes shifts in one direction. **Disruptive selection** takes place when individuals at the upper and lower ends of the range of phenotypes have higher fitness than individuals near the middle. This type of selection is also called diversifying selection and may lead to the rise of two distinct phenotypes within a population.

Pesticide Resistance: Directional Selection in Action

An example of directional selection is the evolution of pesticide resistance in hundreds of insect species. Whenever a new type of pesticide is used to control agricultural pests, the outcome is predictable. Early results are encouraging. A relatively small amount of poison applied to a crop may kill 99 percent of the insects. But subsequent applications are less and less effective.

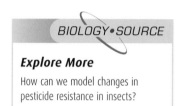

Explore More
How can we model changes in pesticide resistance in insects?

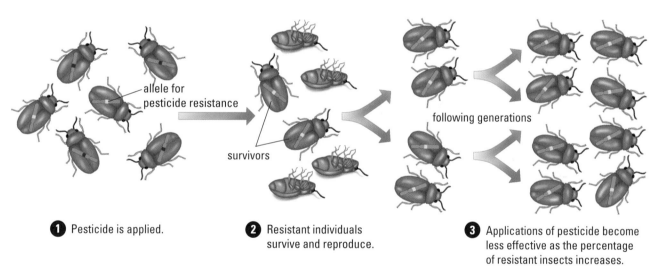

1 Pesticide is applied.

2 Resistant individuals survive and reproduce.

3 Applications of pesticide become less effective as the percentage of resistant insects increases.

Figure 8.9 By spraying crops with poisons to kill insect pests, humans have favoured the reproduction of insects with inherited resistance to the poisons over those with no resistance.

Figure 8.9 traces how pesticide resistance evolves. Most survivors of the first pesticide treatments were insects with genes that somehow enabled them to resist the chemical attack. Their offspring inherited the genes for pesticide resistance. In each generation, the percentage of pesticide-resistant individuals in the insect population increased. The population underwent directional selection. The alleles that produce higher pesticide resistance increase in the population (Figure 8.10).

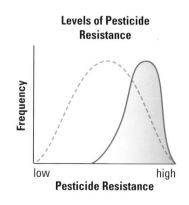

Figure 8.10 Over time, the mean level of resistance among individuals increases.

Sexual Selection

One of the conditions of Hardy-Weinberg equilibrium is that mating is random. However, mating is often not random: mates often choose each other based on certain criteria. Darwin originally proposed that secondary sexual characteristics in males, such as the elaborate tails of peacocks or the bright plumage in some male birds, evolved because females preferred to reproduce with males with such characteristics. **Sexual selection** is a form of natural selection in which individuals with certain inherited traits are more likely to obtain mates than other individuals. In sexual selection, other individuals of the same species screen the traits, but in natural selection it is the environment that screens the traits.

Widow Birds: Sexual Selection in Action

An interesting study of sexual selection was conducted on long-tailed widow birds. The females have short tails and are inconspicuous, but the males are black with red shoulders and have tails about 40 cm long. The male prominently displays his tail as he flies slowly over his territory (Figure 8.11). Four groups of birds were created for the experiment. The mating success of the birds in each group was measured by the number of nests with eggs or young birds in each male's territory, shown in Figure 8.12(a). Then some birds had their tails altered. Birds in group 1 had their tails shortened to 15 cm from the base, while birds in group 4 had their tails lengthened 25 cm by having feathers glued onto the ends of their tails. Birds in group 2 were left untouched, while birds in group 3 had their tails cut, but the feathers were glued back so that the tail was not noticeably shortened. Groups 2 and 3 were the control groups. The results of the experiment are shown in Figure 8.12(b). It is evident that before the alterations, each group had about the same reproductive success. But after the alterations, those with the extra-long tails were more successful at reproducing.

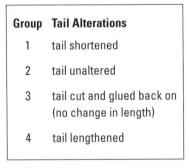

Figure 8.11 In long-tailed widow birds, the male secondary sexual characteristics are a long tail and red shoulder patches. They were named "widow birds" because they resembled widows, who dressed in black.

Group	Tail Alterations
1	tail shortened
2	tail unaltered
3	tail cut and glued back on (no change in length)
4	tail lengthened

Figure 8.12 The experiment shows sexual selection in long-tailed widow birds. Groups 2 and 3 were the controls.

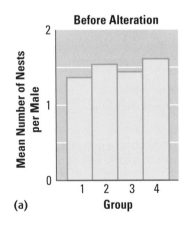

(a)

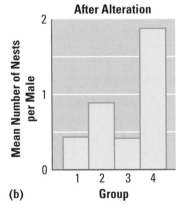

(b)

Artificial Selection

Recall from Chapter 7 that Darwin used artificial selection as evidence for natural selection. Artificial selection involves the intentional breeding of domestic plants and animals to produce certain traits. Like natural selection, it is a mechanism of microevolution. Instead of the environment selecting traits, human breeders select certain desired traits and breed only those individuals that exhibit the trait. For example, farmers may breed cows that excel in milk production. Crossing similar high-producing cows will increase the genetic frequency of these types of cows in future generations. This process is not random because breeders leave nothing to chance. In selective breeding, microevolution can occur at a very fast pace. However, because only high-producing cows are bred, this practice can reduce the genetic variability within the population.

BIOLOGY•SOURCE

Suggested Activity
• C6 Case Study Overview on page 222

Selective breeding can have unintended negative results. The American quarter horse is a breed of horse known for its speed. A world-champion quarter horse named Impressive was chosen for breeding stock in 1974 and currently has over 55 000 descendents (Figure 8.13). Nearly 30 of his descendants went on to become world champions as well. Unfortunately, many of his descendants have been found to have an inherited disorder called hyperkalemic periodic paralysis (HYPP). HYPP causes violent muscle twitching, muscle weakness, and paralysis. A horse can live through several attacks or may die after just one attack. Impressive never displayed symptoms of the disease. Horses from other blood lines do not exhibit HYPP. In this case, artificial selection increased the frequency of certain desired traits but, as a result, has increased the frequency of a harmful disorder as well.

Figure 8.13 Not all of Impressive's descendants have HYPP or carry the HYPP gene. There is now a genetic test to determine whether any of his descendants has the gene. Horses with the disease can be treated with special feeds and medications.

Genetic Drift

Unlike natural and artificial selection, genetic drift is a random process. **Genetic drift** is a change in the gene pool of a population due to chance. For example, the first generation of the small wildflower population illustrated in Figure 8.14 consists of nine plants with red flowers (*RR* and *Rr*) and one plant with white flowers (*rr*). It is partly chance that affects which plants reproduce. By the third generation, no plants carry the allele for white flowers. The result is a change in allele frequencies in this population.

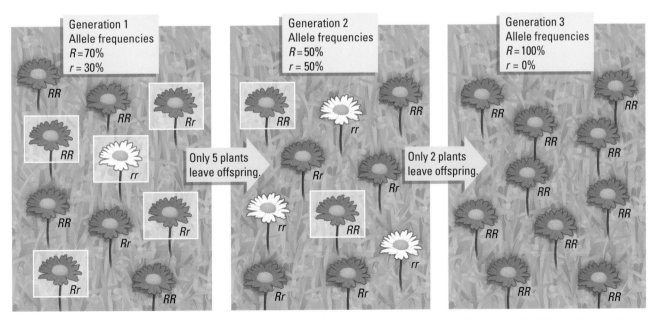

Generation 1
Allele frequencies
R = 70%
r = 30%

Only 5 plants leave offspring.

Generation 2
Allele frequencies
R = 50%
r = 50%

Only 2 plants leave offspring.

Generation 3
Allele frequencies
R = 100%
r = 0%

Figure 8.14 Only the alleles of organisms that successfully reproduce in one generation appear in the gene pool of the next generation.

All populations are subject to some genetic drift. However, the smaller the population, the more impact genetic drift has on it. That is why one condition for genetic equilibrium is that the population must be very large. A simple analogy is the erratic outcome from a small sample of coin tosses. Flip a coin 1000 times, and a result of 700 heads and 300 tails would make you very suspicious about that coin. But flip a coin ten times, and an outcome of seven heads and three tails would seem within reason. The smaller the sample, the greater the chance that the results will differ from an expected result — in this case, a roughly equal number of heads and tails. Similarly, in small populations the allele frequencies can vary erratically from generation to generation. As you will see in the following two situations, genetic drift can have major effects on a population.

The Bottleneck Effect

Disasters such as earthquakes, floods, droughts, and fires may drastically reduce the size of a population, which also reduces the size of its gene pool (Figure 8.15). By chance, certain alleles may then be represented more frequently than others among the survivors. Some alleles may be eliminated altogether. Such genetic drift, called the bottleneck effect, decreases genetic variation in a population.

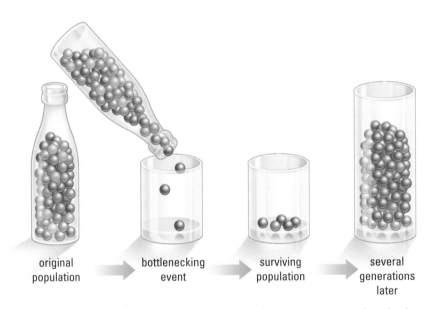

| original population | bottlenecking event | surviving population | several generations later |

Figure 8.15 Marbles falling through the narrow neck of a bottle serve as an analogy for the bottleneck effect. Compared to the original population (in the bottle) the new population has less variation.

Figure 8.16 Cheetah populations, like other endangered species, may have very little genetic variation.

The loss of variation due to a bottleneck effect could reduce the ability of a population to adapt to environmental change. For example, the cheetah — the fastest runner of all animals — may have suffered one or more bottleneck events (Figure 8.16). Like many African mammals, a sharp decrease in the cheetah population occurred during the last ice age about 10 000 years ago. In the 19th century, farmers hunted the animals to near extinction. Today only a few small populations of cheetahs exist in the wild. Some biologists who study cheetahs are concerned that with relatively little variation in their gene pools, the cheetah populations may not be able to resist disease or adapt to other environmental challenges to their survival.

The Founder Effect

Genetic drift is also likely when a few individuals colonize an isolated island, lake, or some other new habitat. The smaller the colony, the less its genetic makeup will represent the gene pool of the larger population from which the colonists came. Genetic drift in a new colony is known as the **founder effect** because the change in allele frequencies relates to the genetic makeup of the founders of the colony (Figure 8.17). The founder effect likely contributed to changes in the gene pools of the finches and other South American organisms that arrived as strays on the Galapagos Islands. Furthermore, the founder effect can be seen in the Afrikaner population in South Africa. Dutch immigrants from a few families that happened to have Huntington's disease — a neuromuscular disorder — established the Afrikaner population in South Africa. Therefore today we can see higher frequencies of Huntington's in Afrikaners than among the Dutch in Holland.

BIOLOGY•SOURCE

Explore More

In what ways do different mechanisms of microevolution affect the gene pool of a beetle population?

BIOLOGY•SOURCE

Suggested Activity
- C7 Inquiry Activity Overview on page 222

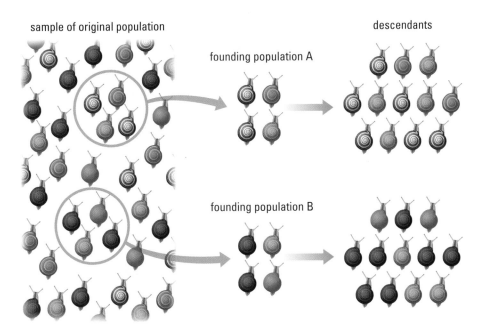

Figure 8.17 Two small groups from a large diverse population could produce new populations that are different from the original population.

Gene Flow

Like genetic drift, gene flow is a random process. **Gene flow** involves the exchange of genes with another population. Gene flow occurs when fertile individuals or their gametes (sex cells) migrate between populations. For example, suppose a population that neighbours the wildflowers pictured in Figure 8.14 on page 219 consists entirely of white-flowered individuals. A windstorm may blow pollen from these neighbours to the mostly red-flowered population. Interbreeding would increase the frequency of the white-flower allele in the original population. Thus the movement of genes in or out of the population disrupts genetic equilibrium. Gene flow tends to reduce genetic differences between populations. If it is extensive enough, gene flow can eventually mix neighbouring populations into a single population with a common gene pool.

BIOLOGY•SOURCE

Take It Further

Hardy-Weinberg equilibrium is used to investigate microevolution in populations. Learn how the Hardy-Weinberg equation is used to calculate genetic frequencies in a population.

Natural Selection versus Artificial Selection

Issue

Are the mechanisms of natural selection and artificial selection more similar to one another or more different from one another?

Activity Overview

In this activity, you will investigate an example of natural selection and artificial selection to find the similarities and differences between the two mechanisms.

Prelab Questions

1. How do you think spots on a guppy, a small freshwater fish, might benefit its survival?

2. How do you think crop varieties, such as cauliflower and broccoli, were developed?

Figure 8.18 You will investigate natural selection in guppies.

Birds on an Island

Question

Can natural selection change the frequency of traits in a population in only a few generations?

Activity Overview

In this activity, you will explore the role of natural selection on the microevolution of birds. You will use three different utensils to simulate the effectiveness of three bird beaks in obtaining food. You will then have an opportunity to design your own procedure to investigate another mechanism of microevolution.

Your teacher will give you a copy of the full activity.

Prelab Questions

1. Create a list of birds that have distinct beak shapes.

2. For each bird, how does its beak shape relate to its food source?

Figure 8.19 A bird's beak is designed to pick up certain types of food.

Key Concept Review

1. In genetic terms, what indicates that microevolution is occurring?

2. Define the terms "allele" and "gene pool."

3. What are two sources of genetic variation? Which source brings more diversity into a gene pool of a sexually reproducing species? Explain.

4. How are pesticide-resistant insects an example of natural selection?

5. (a) Describe three patterns of natural selection.
   (b) Which pattern is most likely to lead to two distinct phenotypes? Explain.

6. Under what circumstances is Hardy-Weinberg equilibrium disrupted?

7. Describe what can happen to a gene pool as a result of the bottleneck effect.

8. Explain the concept of sexual selection and provide an example.

9. Give an example of directional, disruptive, and stabilizing selection.

Connect Your Understanding

10. Suppose a recessive allele causes a disease that usually kills the animal before it can reproduce.
    (a) Predict what will happen to the frequency of that allele in the population.
    (b) What type of selection will occur? Explain.

11. For each of the following situations, predict whether the Hardy-Weinberg equilibrium would be maintained after several generations. Explain your reasoning.
    (a) A population of long-tailed widow birds is maintained at a local zoo.
    (b) A population of birds lives on an isolated island.
    (c) Climate change is melting the polar ice where polar bears live.
    (d) A rat population lives in the subway system in Toronto.

12. The female peacock is less colourful and has a shorter tail than the male, pictured below. Explain, in evolutionary terms, the advantage that the bright colouration and elaborate tail feathers give the male.

Question 12

13. Suppose a population of caribou leaves its herd and migrates to a new area where there are no natural predators. Hypothesize the effect this situation might have on the original population and on the founding population.

14. Many individuals with sickle-cell disease in North America are of African descent. Explain this phenomenon. Predict what should happen to the frequency of the sickle-cell allele in North America over time.

15. Which of the conditions that maintain Hardy-Weinberg equilibrium does each of the five mechanisms of microevolution upset?

16. Choose one mechanism of microevolution and explain how human activity has affected a particular species in this manner.

Reflection

17. Has your opinion about the use of pesticides changed as a result of reading this section? Explain why or why not.

18. What scientific terms do you understand better now than you did before you read this section?

For more questions, go to BIOLOGY•SOURCE

8.2 Speciation

Section Summary

- Reproductive barriers may lead to speciation.
- Adaptive radiation leads to the diversification of life.
- Punctuated equilibrium explains abrupt changes in the fossil record, as opposed to gradual changes in gradualism.
- Human activities can cause extinction of species but can also help species survive.

Figure 8.20 This is the first grizzly-polar bear hybrid ever found in the wild.

A **hybrid** is an offspring that results from the mating of individuals from two different species. Do hybrids between two different organisms actually exist? Hybrids do exist in the plant and animal kingdoms. For example, a mule is a cross between a donkey and a horse, and a tigon is a cross between a male tiger and a female lion. Mules and tigons, however, are not considered to be distinct species. Hybrids such as these are rare in nature. Species tend to mate only with their own kind. However, in 2006, a strange-looking polar bear was shot by hunters on Banks Island in Nunavut. DNA tests revealed that it was a naturally occurring hybrid between a grizzly bear and a polar bear (Figure 8.20).

What Is a Species?

Many biologists define a species using the **biological species concept,** which states that a species is a population or group of populations whose members have the ability to breed with one another in nature and produce fertile offspring. Fertile offspring are capable of mating and producing offspring. Members of one species cannot successfully interbreed with members of other species. This definition has limitations, however. For example, organisms that only reproduce asexually are not included. Fossils, of course, are no longer reproducing, so they cannot be evaluated by this definition, either. Even with these limitations, the biological species concept is useful.

From Microevolution to Macroevolution

Microevolution and adaptation explain how populations evolve. But if that were *all* that happened, Earth would be inhabited only by a highly adapted version of the first form of life.

Recall from section 8.1 that microevolution refers to change in the allele frequencies within a population. In contrast, the term macroevolution encompasses more dramatic biological changes, many of which are evident in the fossil record. These changes include the origin of different species, the extinction of species, and the evolution of major new features of living things, such as wings or flowers. The origin of new species is known as **speciation**. It is the main focus of the study of macroevolution, for with speciation comes diversity. Figure 8.21 is a simple example of how speciation leads to an increase in diversity.

Figure 8.21 If one species evolves into two or more surviving species, diversity increases.

©P

Reproductive Barriers Between Species

Clearly, a fly will not mate with a frog or a fern. But what about species that are not so different? The biological species concept relies on the inability of species to breed successfully with other species; therefore the formation of a new species depends on some form of reproductive isolation from similar species. **Reproductive isolation** refers to the inability of two organisms to reproduce due to some kind of physical or behavioural barrier. For example, the western spotted skunk and the eastern spotted skunk are so similar in appearance that only other spotted skunks and expert biologists can tell them apart. Where the skunks' ranges overlap in the North American prairies, however, individuals from these two species do not mate. These similar species have become reproductively isolated from each other. Many different mechanisms have led to reproductive isolation between similar species, including geographic and habitat isolation.

Geographic Isolation

Geologic processes constantly change and rearrange Earth's features. Such change can separate different populations of one species and lead to geographic isolation. For example, a mountain range may gradually emerge, slowly splitting a population of organisms that cannot cross it. In other cases, populations become separated when a small group disperses from the main population and colonizes an isolated location, such as an island.

How well a geographic barrier keeps populations apart and thus maintains reproductive isolation depends on the ability of organisms to move about. For example, biologists hypothesize that two species of antelope squirrels near the Grand Canyon in the southwest U.S. evolved from geographically separate populations (Figure 8.22). These species live on opposite rims of the canyon. Such small rodents may find a deep canyon or wide river too daunting to cross. In contrast, birds, mountain lions, and coyotes can navigate mountain ranges, rivers, and canyons. The windblown pollen of pine trees or the seeds of plants carried on animals also move back and forth.

Figure 8.22 The Grand Canyon forms a geographic barrier between Harris's antelope squirrel (left) and the white-tailed antelope squirrel (right).

The separation of a small "splinter" population from its main population is a crucial event in the origin of species. Once separate, the splinter population may follow its own evolutionary course. Changes in the allele frequencies caused by genetic drift and natural selection can accumulate in the splinter population, making it less and less like the main population.

For each small, isolated population that becomes a new species, many more simply die. Life in some environments is harsh, and most colonizing populations probably fail to survive in their new locations. Even if such populations survive and adapt to their local environments, they do not necessarily evolve into new species. Speciation has occurred only if one population can no longer breed with the other population, even if the two populations should come back into contact. Figure 8.23 shows two possible outcomes for populations that meet again after having been geographically separate.

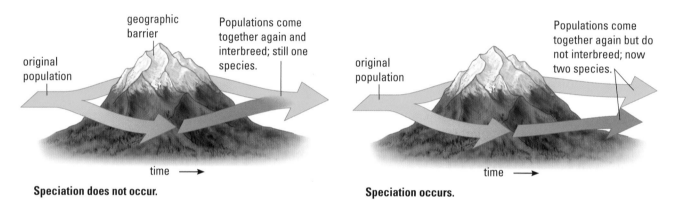

Figure 8.23 In this model, arrows symbolize populations that become geographically separated, then come together again at a later time.

Habitat Isolation

Some similar species have become reproductively isolated because they adapted to different habitats in the same general location. For example, certain lakes in British Columbia contain two different species of three-spined stickleback fish. One species is adapted to living along the lake bottom, feeding on small snails. Fish of the other species spend most of their lives in the open water, filtering plankton (small floating organisms). The two species' preferences for different habitats help maintain their isolation.

There are many other examples of habitat isolation. Two similar species of garter snake live in the same region, but one lives mainly in the water, while the other lives mainly on land. The two species rarely interact. Habitat isolation can also occur in plant species. For example, two similar species of oak tree live in the same area. However one grows in sandy soil but the other grows in loamy soil. Thus the two tree species remain separated.

Other Reproductive Barriers

Other reproductive barriers also prevent similar species from interbreeding. Table 8.1 below shows some of these barriers. Some similar species are able to physically mate. In these cases, there are other barriers that prevent the offspring from becoming fertile adults.

Table 8.1 Reproductive Barriers That Maintain Reproductive Isolation

Barrier	Example
Temporal Isolation: Species have different breeding seasons.	Western spotted skunks (left) breed in the fall, but the eastern species (right) breeds in the late winter.
Behavioural Isolation: Species have different courtship or mating behaviours.	Eastern meadowlarks (left) and western meadowlarks are almost identical in shape, colouring, and habitat. Both coexist in the central U.S. and Canada, yet they remain separate species because their courtship rituals differ, including the songs they use to attract mates.
Mechanical Isolation: Two seemingly similar species are unable to mate because their reproductive structures are physically incompatible.	Unlike snails from the same *Bradybaena* species (left), the genital openings of two different species of *Bradybaena* snails do not align (right) because their shells spiral in different directions. Thus mating cannot occur.
Gametic Isolation: Sperm and eggs of different species are unable to recognize each other by their molecular markers.	Sea urchins release their eggs and sperm into the surrounding water. The gametes of purple sea urchins (right) and red sea urchins (left) are unable to fuse because they have different proteins on their egg surfaces and sperm from the other species cannot bind to them.
Hybrid Inviability: Sometimes a hybrid dies early in development, or it lives to maturity but is not healthy and suffers an early death.	Some *Ensatina* salamander species may mate with each other, but most of the offspring do not live to adulthood, or if they do, they are weak.
Hybrid Infertility: The hybrid offspring mature into adults but are infertile.	A mule (right) is bred from a female horse (left) and a male donkey (centre). Mules are physically healthy but they are infertile.

Concept Check

1. Compare macroevolution to microevolution.

2. Why are horses and donkeys considered to be different species?

3. Give an example of a reproductive barrier that prevents mating and a reproductive barrier that happens after mating.

Adaptive Radiation

Since Darwin's time, oceanic islands have served as living laboratories for studying speciation. Islands often have species found nowhere else. The isolation and diverse habitats of some islands create conditions that seem to favour speciation. Only a few organisms manage to be the first to colonize new islands. Those that do enter a diverse, "empty" environment. The small populations of colonizing species may undergo evolutionary change. Some of these organisms may move on to other islands in the chain, where the process repeats itself. New and varying species may evolve through genetic drift and adaptation to the different habitats. Such evolution from a common ancestor that results in diverse species adapted to different environments is called **adaptive radiation**. It is also called divergent evolution.

Figure 8.24 is a simplified model of adaptive radiation of birds. In this example, one species is the common ancestor of several new species that arise on the islands. After migrating from the mainland, species A may have undergone significant change in its gene pool and become species B. Then, a few birds of species B may have migrated to a neighbouring island. This population could have evolved into species C. Some of these birds could later move back to the first island. They might coexist with species B if reproductive barriers have developed that keep the two species separate. Species C could also move to other islands, where the same evolutionary processes might continue. Geographic isolation is a key factor in this example because it prevents the splinter populations from breeding with the "parent" population on the mainland. Also, the different islands are far enough apart to keep the various island populations isolated.

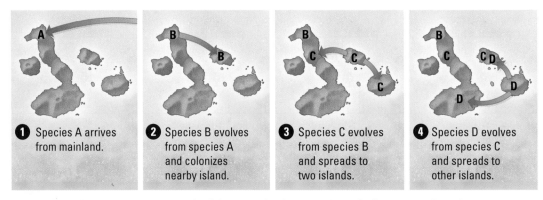

① Species A arrives from mainland.

② Species B evolves from species A and colonizes nearby island.

③ Species C evolves from species B and spreads to two islands.

④ Species D evolves from species C and spreads to other islands.

Figure 8.24 Adaptive radiation on an island chain may lead to several new bird species evolving from one founding population.

©P

The founder effect, natural selection, and reproductive isolating mechanisms such as geographic, habitat, and behavioural isolation have produced the diversity of species seen on island chains, such as the Galapagos Islands. This process of adaptive radiation explains why oceanic islands tend to have so many species that are found nowhere else in the world.

The Hawaiian Islands are one of the world's great showcases of evolution. The islands are about 4000 km from the nearest continent, and each island has several diverse environments. Originally, the islands were uninhabited. New lava flows continually increased the amount of vacant land (and still continue to do so). These conditions supported repeated instances of adaptive radiation. Most of the thousands of native species on the islands are found nowhere else in the world.

BIOLOGY•SOURCE

Explore More

What environmental conditions on the Hawaiian Islands enable plant species to undergo adaptive radiation?

Convergent Evolution

In **convergent evolution**, distantly-related species that live in similar environments develop similar adaptations. These traits were discussed in Chapter 7 as "analogous structures." For example, different mammals that eat ants tend to have long pointed noses and jaws and long, sticky tongues (Figure 8.25). Recall that rheas, emus, and ostriches have developed similar adaptations to similar environments, yet they are distantly related species.

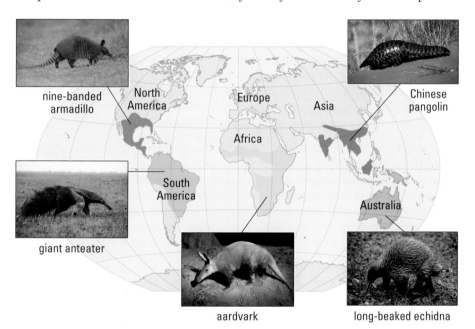

nine-banded armadillo

North America

Europe

Asia

Chinese pangolin

Africa

South America

Australia

giant anteater

aardvark

long-beaked echidna

Figure 8.25 Mammals that feed on ants and termites evolved independently five times. They all have similar features and are examples of convergent evolution.

The Rate of Speciation

Darwin understood that geological changes occurred very slowly and therefore believed that species also must evolve gradually over a long period of time. **Gradualism** is the evolution of a species by gradual accumulation of small genetic changes over a long period of time (Figure 8.26 on the next page).

However, on the time scale of the fossil record, species often seem to arise abruptly. A new fossil species may appear rather suddenly (in geological terms) in a layer of rock and persist for thousands or millions of years without noticeable change. Then it may disappear from the fossil record as suddenly as it appeared.

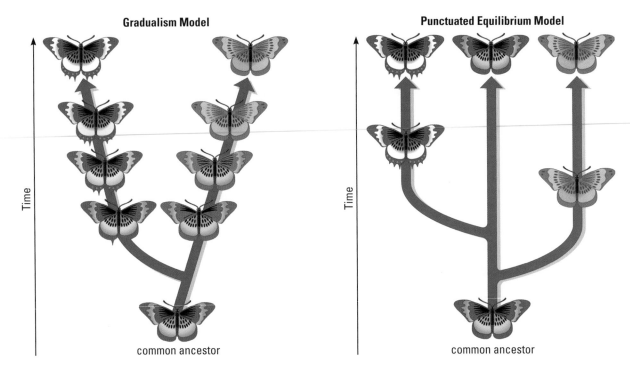

Gradualism Model

Punctuated Equilibrium Model

Time

common ancestor

Time

common ancestor

Figure 8.26 In contrast to gradualism, punctuated equilibrium suggests that a new species changes most as it buds from a parent species. There is little change for the rest of the time the species exists.

In 1972, paleontologists Niles Eldredge and Stephen Jay Gould developed a model to address these observations. Now known as **punctuated equilibrium**, the model suggests that species often diverge in spurts of relatively rapid evolutionary change. The term *punctuated equilibrium* comes from the idea that long periods of little evolutionary change (equilibrium) in a species are broken, or punctuated, by shorter times of rapid speciation.

Given a model of gradual adaptation through natural selection, how could species have sudden bursts of change? Speciation can sometimes be quite rapid. In just a few hundred to a few thousand generations, genetic drift and natural selection can cause significant change in a small population that is occupying a challenging new environment.

Keep in mind that punctuated equilibrium does not contradict or weaken Darwin's theory. The theory of natural selection can account for observations of punctuated equilibrium in the fossil record. Natural selection and adaptation still happen, but mostly during that time when a species is "young." By the time a new species grew in number and became widespread enough that it might leave a fossil record, its distinctive features would have already evolved. The addition of punctuated equilibrium to evolutionary biology demonstrates a refining of a scientific theory to reflect new evidence.

Human Activities Affect Diversity

It has taken billions of years for Earth's biodiversity to evolve, yet in a short amount of time, human activities have drastically reduced the variety of species. For example, oceanic islands have many species found nowhere else on the world. Island species are particularly vulnerable. Because islands often lack predators, the selection pressure for flight has been removed. As a result, over thousands of generations, many bird and insect species have lost the ability to fly.

BIOLOGY•SOURCE

Take It Further

Research cospeciation and create a poster that outlines the process and provides examples of species that have undergone cospeciation.

BIOLOGY•SOURCE

Suggested Activity

• C8 Inquiry Activity Overview on page 231

As humans explored the globe in the 18th and 19th centuries, they introduced predators such as rats and cats to these islands. These and other species have become invasive species on many islands. An invasive species is a non-native species that causes harm to the ecosystem into which it was introduced. Without the ability to fly from predators, these species were easy prey and many of them are now extinct, such as the dodo, or are endangered, such as the kakapo. The kakapo is a nocturnal flightless parrot native to New Zealand. As settlers introduced pets and livestock in the 19th century, the kakapo population was reduced almost to extinction (Figure 8.27).

Figure 8.27 Kakapo numbers have now risen from a handful to over 60 individuals.

Many other human activities affect the survival of endangered species, as shown by the plight of the leatherback turtle. This turtle is found off Canada's east coast. One reason for the decline in the number of leatherbacks is that they get tangled in abandoned commercial fishing gear and drown (Figure 8.28). Another reason is that the turtles mistake floating plastic bags for jellyfish, which are their main food source. They die either from intestinal blockage or malnutrition. Lastly, in their breeding grounds in Central and South America, humans harvest both their meat and their eggs for food.

The leatherback turtle is not an isolated example. Many other Canadian species face extinction due to a variety of human causes. However, various organizations are dedicated to saving endangered species from extinction. They use a variety of strategies, such as habitat protection and captive breeding programs. These have met with some success.

Figure 8.28 The leatherback turtle is now considered critically endangered.

REQUIRED SKILLS
- Measuring
- Drawing conclusions

Breeding Marmots

Question

Which of the male marmots in a captive population should be used for breeding?

Figure 8.29 Thanks to captive breeding programs, Vancouver Island marmot numbers are increasing.

Lab Overview

You will use chromatography to simulate gel electrophoresis in order to determine which individual animals should be used in a zoo's captive breeding program.

Your teacher will give you a copy of the full activity.

Prelab Questions

1. How would the solubility of a substance affect its ability to be absorbed by a paper filter?

2. What criteria do you think is important when selecting individual animals to breed in a breeding program?

Key Concept Review

1. What is the biological species concept?

2. Give an example of temporal isolation and an example of geographic isolation.

3. What types of reproductive barriers play a role in the adaptive radiation of the first bird species to arrive on oceanic islands? Explain.

4. Describe adaptive radiation in your own words.

5. (a) How does punctuated equilibrium account for the relatively few fossils that link newer species to older ones?
   (b) Does it contradict Darwin's theory? Explain.

Connect Your Understanding

6. Paleontologists examine fossils. Suggest some difficulties a fossil presents when paleontologists try to determine whether it is a distinct species.

7. Which reproductive isolating mechanism(s) might be operating in each situation? Explain.
   (a) Different species of songbirds inhabit the same forest yet do not interbreed.
   (b) Salmon and trout populations breed in the same streams in British Columbia.
   (c) A gardener has two closely related plant species. One blooms in the summer, while the other blooms in the spring.

8. (a) If the dots represent organisms, what does the diagram below represent?
   (b) What event happens at the time of the dashed line?

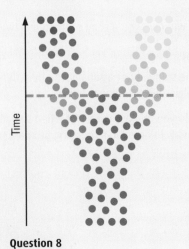

Question 8

9. How does comparative anatomy determine whether two species are an example of convergent evolution or adaptive radiation?

10. Suppose you find in neighbouring fields two populations of crickets that look very similar. How would you determine whether they were separate species?

11. The Panama Canal is a waterway that links the Atlantic and Pacific oceans. Predict the effect this canal might have on the speciation of terrestrial species.

12. (a) Describe the evolution in shell shape in the layers of sedimentary rock pictured below.
    (b) Which model best describes these fossils? Explain.

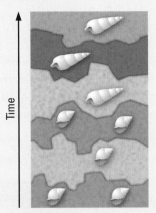

Question 12

13. The grey-headed albatross and the black-browed albatross both nest on the same island in the South Pacific ocean. The elaborate courtship dances that the two species do are different. Explain the advantage that having different courtship dances gives individuals of each species.

14. Zoos and animal conservation agencies work to protect endangered species. Some people think we should not interfere with "the natural order of evolution." Do you agree or disagree with this statement? Support your position.

Reflection

15. Which concept in this section did you find most interesting? Explain why.

For more questions, go to BIOLOGY·SOURCE

Section Summary

- In co-evolution, the evolution of one species affects the evolution of another species.
- Cumulative selection can give rise to complex structures.
- Adaptations to old structures can lead to new functions.

The diversity of life on Earth tells us that species have a unique ability to adapt to their environments. Sometimes two traits within a species develop that help individuals survive. For example, the skin of a poison-dart frog produces substances that are very toxic (Figure 8.30). Being toxic alone, however, does not necessarily save the frog from being eaten by predators. The frog's bright colour serves as a warning to predators that it is toxic. Therefore, the frog's poison and its brightly coloured skin both developed by means of natural selection. The frog's evolution affects the evolution of other organisms, too. For example, the frog's predators need to recognize what the frog's bright colours mean. Only those predators that avoid eating brightly coloured frogs end up surviving and reproducing. The evolution of one species' traits can be complex and has an impact on the evolution of other organisms as well.

Figure 8.30 This poison-dart frog's toxic substance coupled with its bright coloured skin helps ensure its survival.

Co-evolution

Co-evolution is the process in which one species evolves in response to the evolutionary changes in another species. The poison-dart frog's warning-coloration adaptation and the avoidance behaviour of its predators is an example of co-evolution. There are countless other examples of co-evolution between flowering plants and pollinating animals and between plants and herbivorous insects.

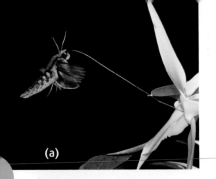

(a)

(b)

Figure 8.31 (a) The hawk moth and (b) Darwin's orchid co-evolved complementary nectar-gathering structures and nectar-producing structures.

Flowering Plants and Pollinators

Flowering plants have a mutualistic relationship with their pollinators. Mutualism is a symbiotic relationship in which both organisms benefit. The flowering plant's pollen is spread by sticking to the pollinator, while the pollinator receives food from the plant to maintain itself. Mutations that produce large, bright petals and a strong scent would attract more insect pollinators and therefore would be favoured over small, dull flowers with little scent. Similarly, pollinators that were more attracted to brighter flowers got more nectar and were more likely to survive. The shape of the flower can also co-evolve with a pollinator species. For example, in Madagascar, Darwin observed an orchid, *Angraecum sesquipedale*, that had a structure about 40 cm long called a spur. Inside the tip of the spur was a supply of nectar. Darwin predicted that a pollinator would have a 40-cm structure that could reach the orchid's nectar. It wasn't until 50 years later that researchers discovered a moth that supported Darwin's prediction (Figure 8.31).

Plants and Herbivorous Insects

Insects have been feeding on flowering plants ever since these two groups first emerged many millions of years ago. Over time, a number of plants have evolved toxic chemicals to prevent herbivorous (plant-eating) insects from feeding on them. However, once the plants began producing poisons, natural selection favoured any variation in insect populations that could alter, inactivate, or eliminate these poisons. Different insect species have developed adaptations to cope with the poisons. For example, milkweed plants produce toxic chemicals and so they are not eaten by most insects. However, the monarch caterpillar has not only managed to develop tolerance to the milkweed's toxin, but has found a way to store the toxin in its tissues to make itself poisonous to others.

Mimicry

Sometimes the evolution of one species can affect the evolution of another, but it does not work the other way round. This one-way influence is seen in mimicry. In **mimicry,** one species, the mimic, resembles another species, the model, in order to gain survival advantage. For example, a hoverfly looks like a wasp (Figure 8.32). The wasp has a poisonous sting, while the hoverfly does not. Predators associate the wasp's colouration with a painful poison, so they avoid wasps. Hoverflies that have a banding pattern similar to the wasp's also benefit from predators' avoidance behaviour. Some species mimic parts of very distantly related species. For example, katydids have adapted to resemble leaves of certain tree species (Figure 8.33). This form of mimicry makes the mimic invisible to predators and thus increases its chances of surviving and reproducing.

Figure 8.33 Each leaf-mimic katydid species mimics the leaves of a different tree species.

(a)   **(b)**

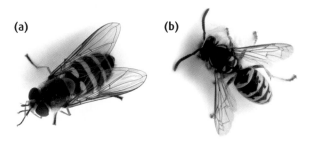

Figure 8.32 (a) The hoverfly has evolved markings that mimic the warning colouration of the (b) common wasp.

The Evolution of Complex Features

Most people think of evolution as involving more dramatic transformations, such as new body forms or the intricate structure of an eye. Darwin's theory of gradual change can account for such "breakthroughs" in form and function. In some cases, a complex structure has evolved from a simpler structure that has the same basic function by a process of refinement. For example, the camera-like eye of a mammal is an amazing structure with many interacting parts.

Among living molluscs (animals that include squids, octopuses, snails, and clams), you can find eyes ranging in complexity from clusters of light-sensitive cells to camera-like eyes with lenses (Figure 8.34). Some molluscs have very simple eyes. Other molluscs have structures called eyecups that have no lenses or other means of focussing images. However, all these animals can at least distinguish light from dark. Considering that many species with simple eyes have been around for many millions of years, simple eyes are obviously enough to meet these animals' needs. In those animals that do have complex eyes, the organs did not have to evolve from simpler ones in one giant evolutionary jump. Instead, complex eyes probably evolved by small steps of adaptation, refining organs that worked and benefitted their owners at each stage. Evidence of these small steps can be seen in other mollusc eyes. **Cumulative selection** is the evolution of a simple structure into a more complex structure through a series of small adaptations.

BIOLOGY•SOURCE

Suggested Activity
• C9 Quick Lab Overview on page 236

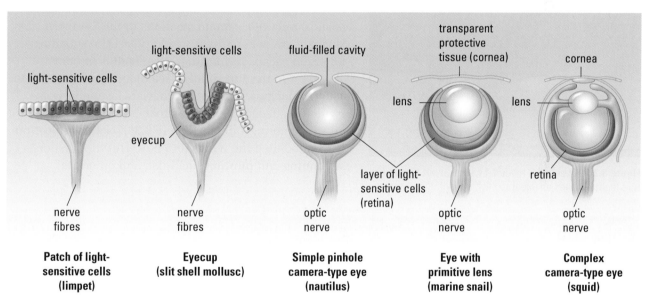

Figure 8.34 The range of complexity in the structure of eyes among molluscs shows us how complex features could have arisen from simple ones.

Concept Check

1. Explain how the bright colouration of the poison-dart frog is an example of co-evolution.

2. Explain the relationship between flowering plants and insect pollinators.

3. What is a mimic and what is a model?

Adaptation of Existing Structures to New Functions

BIOLOGY•SOURCE

Take It Further

Explore the different types of mimicry found in nature. Draw a poster that outlines these different types.

In the history of life, examples abound of materials or structures that evolved as adaptations for certain functions that later fulfilled different functions. Figure 8.35 shows the multiple functions of chitin, a main component of arthropod exoskeletons.

Figure 8.35 (a) The exoskeleton of a marine arthropod such as this reef lobster helps protect the animal from predators. (b) On land, the arthropod exoskeleton of this scorpion fulfills additional functions: resisting water loss and supporting its body on dry land. Chemical changes to this material made it even more watertight as the animals became adapted to living on land.

Figure 8.36 A penguin's modified wings do not function in true flight but they enable it to "fly" through the water.

The flippers of penguins are another example of how natural selection can modify existing structures for different functions. Penguins inhabit small, barren islands and other remote locations in the Southern Hemisphere, where flight would offer little advantage for either escape or hunting. Also, food is far more abundant in the surrounding sea than on the land or ice. Though penguins cannot fly, they are fast underwater swimmers. Their swimming stroke is unlike the strokes of other swimming animals (Figure 8.36). Natural selection has remodelled the wings into powerful flippers for swimming and hunting small fish and other prey.

C9 Quick Lab

BIOLOGY•SOURCE

Card Shuffle Race

Purpose

To model the development of a complex feature by chance or by cumulative selection.

Activity Overview

In this activity you will be divided into two teams. You will use cards to simulate the development of a complex feature by one of two means: random chance or cumulative selection. You will evaluate which method is more effective in producing a complex feature.

Your teacher will give you a copy of the full activity.

Prelab Questions

1. Brainstorm ways you could use a deck of cards to model cumulative selection.

2. What might each card represent?

Figure 8.37 Shuffling increases the randomness of the positions of cards in the deck.

Key Concept Review

1. How can evolution explain the range of complexity of eyes in modern organisms?

2. Give an example of evolutionary remodelling of an existing structure to perform a new function.

3. Define co-evolution and provide two examples.

Connect Your Understanding

4. The sunbird pollinates several species of flowers. Predict the shape of the flowers that the sunbird feeds on. Explain your reasoning.

Question 4

5. Analyze the advantages and disadvantages of remodelling an existing structure to perform a new function.

6. How do you think the advent of modern technology will influence the evolution of humans?

7. Describe the process that has led to the following situation. The old-world swallowtail caterpillar feeds on the fringed rue plant, despite the toxic oil contained in the plant's leaves.

Question 7

8. Examine the images of the less aggressive aardwolf (top) and the aggressive striped hyena (bottom).

Question 8

(a) Suggest a reason why some people believe that the aardwolf is a mimic.

(b) Are there any disadvantages to the model (the striped hyena) in having a mimic that is less aggressive?

(c) The striped hyena does not live in southern Africa but the aardwolf does. The aardwolf lives in the same areas in southern Africa as the brown hyena, which has a blotchy brown coat. Does this information contradict the idea that the aardwolf is a mimic? Explain.

(d) Propose an alternative explanation for the similar striped patterns in the two species.

9. Explain how you would provide evidence that the human hand evolved through cumulative selection.

10. Some people may assume cumulative selection makes some species "better" than others. Explain why this is not accurate.

Reflection

11. What part of this section did you find most interesting? Explain.

For more questions, go to *BIOLOGY•SOURCE*

Key Concept Review

1. Explain what variation within a species means. Explain how variations can arise in a sexually reproducing species. **k**

2. Explain what "allele frequency" means and provide an example. **k**

3. What is macroevolution? Give an example. **k**

4. Sketch a graph showing the typical range of frequencies of various phenotypes for a particular trait, such as height. **k**

5. What genotype for sickle cell disease is the most beneficial for individuals living in regions where malaria is common? Why? **k**

6. Create a Venn diagram to show the similarities and differences between sexual selection and artificial selection. **c**

7. (a) Explain the bottleneck and founder effects. (b) What are they examples of? **k**

8. Give an example of a reproductive barrier that prevents mating and a barrier that happens after mating has occurred. **k**

9. Under what conditions might adaptive radiation occur? **k**

10. What is the difference between punctuated equilibrium and gradualism? **k**

11. How is mimicry an example of co-evolution? **k**

12. In your own words, explain cumulative selection. **k**

13. How is a penguin's flipper a remodelled structure? **k**

Connect Your Understanding

14. What type of mutation has the potential to affect the evolution of a population: a mutation to an egg cell or a mutation to a body cell? Explain. **a**

15. Suppose taller people in a population are selected for.
    (a) What type of selection will occur? **k**
    (b) Graph the phenotype distribution before and after selection. **c**

16. Explain how fossil organisms, asexually reproducing species, and natural variation within a species make it hard for scientists to clearly define a species. **a**

17. Within a few weeks of administering the drug 3TC to a patient, the HIV population in his body consists entirely of 3TC-resistant viruses. How can you explain these results? **a**

18. The myrtle warbler and the Audubon's warbler were once considered to be two distinct species; but now, bird guides list them as eastern and western forms of a single species, the yellow-rumped warbler. What can explain this new classification? **k**

19. Explain why speciation would more likely occur on islands farther from a mainland, such as the Galapagos islands, than an island close to a mainland, such as P.E.I. **a**

20. In some zoos, one may see a tigon, but in the natural world this hybrid does not exist. Why? **a**

21. There is a range of coat colour in foxes. Which process might have produced the graph below? **a**

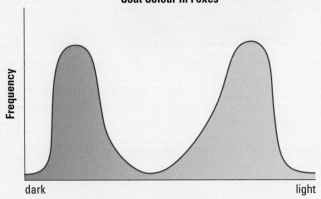

Coat Colour in Foxes

Question 21

22. Use the data table to answer the following questions.

Frequency of Coat Colour in Dogs

Year	Frequency of Black	Frequency of Yellow	Frequency of Red
1900	0.25	0.5	0.25
1920	0.20	0.65	0.15
1940	0.17	0.73	0.10
1960	0.12	0.80	0.08

(a) Describe the trend shown by the data. **t**

(b) What type of selection is occurring? **t**

(c) What might account for the trend shown in the data? **t**

23. Identify the type of barrier that led to speciation in each of the following cases.

   (a) Two closely related cichlid fish species live in Lake Victoria. One lives in shallow water near the shoreline, while the other is a bottom feeder in deep water. **a**

   (b) Female finches from the species *Geospiza difficilis* respond to the songs of males from the same island, but they ignore the songs of males from other islands. **a**

   (c) A botanist crosses two species of jimsonweed to produce a hybrid; however, the hybrid dies before it can reproduce. **a**

   (d) Mallard and pintail ducks mate at different times of the year. **a**

24. Two known species of violets grow in a field, but there are also several unknown violets growing there as well. These violets resemble the two known species but appear to be new species. Form a hypothesis to explain how the new species may have evolved. **t**

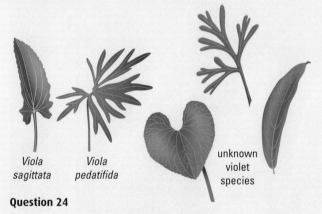

Viola sagittata *Viola pedatifida* unknown violet species

Question 24

25. Do you think it is ethical for humans to create hybrids of two species? Explain. **c**

26. Humans have a very complex brain structure. How would Darwin explain the evolution of such a trait? What evidence is there to support this claim? **a**

27. How do you think the genetic diversity of a population of northern pike in a small lake in northern Ontario compares to the population of northern pike in Lake Ontario? Justify your answer. **a**

28. The fossil record has helped us understand evolutionary process. On the other hand, it has its limitations. Describe two limitations in using the fossil record to understand the evolution of species. **a**

29. The dolphin and the shark are both species that live in the ocean and chase their prey. Propose an explanation for their similarities. **a**

Question 29

Reflection

30. In this chapter, we have learned about some Canadian species affected by human activity. Has your learning prompted you to become more involved in programs that promote the conservation of species? Explain why or why not. **c**

Unit Task Link

List some factors, both natural and human-caused, that could cause species to become endangered or extinct. Why is diversity within a species crucial?

For more questions, go to **BIOLOGY•SOURCE**

ACHIEVEMENT CHART CATEGORIES
k Knowledge and understanding   **t** Thinking and investigation
c Communication   **a** Application

Evolution has produced Earth's current biodiversity and influences modern medicine and agriculture.

Bananas are enjoyed by many people throughout the world, but they are vulnerable and may become endangered (Figure 9.1). How can a species that is so common in our markets be at risk? Despite there being 300 different varieties of bananas, most consumers prefer a single variety, the Cavendish. This makes bananas vulnerable to changing environmental conditions. After 15 000 years of artificial selection, Cavendish bananas, and other cultivated banana varieties, have very little genetic variation. Bananas grown on plantations are sterile. The banana fruit will not grow if planted. So new trees are produced by cuttings from existing trees. Therefore, there is very little genetic difference between a banana grown in Indonesia and a banana grown in South America. Because of this lack of variation, one disease could potentially wipe out our supply of Cavendish bananas.

This has happened before. In the 1960s, the preferred banana variety, the Gros Michel, was grown all over the world. A fungal disease called Panama disease spread quickly around the globe, infecting banana trees, and the world's supply was drastically reduced. The Cavendish, which was resistant to the disease, was planted in place of the Gros Michel. Today a new strain of Panama disease threatens the Cavendish. Evolution has taught us that genetic variation is key to survival of species.

Figure 9.1 The Cavendish banana is common in grocery stores, but their lack of genetic diversity threatens the variety.

©P

9.1 The Origins of Life on Earth

Section Summary

- In Earth's distant past, organic molecules, which are essential to life, could have arisen from simpler inorganic molecules.
- A series of steps led to the first organisms on Earth: prokaryotes.
- Prokaryotes evolved into multicellular eukaryotes.
- Continental drift and mass extinctions have influenced macroevolution.

Evidence indicates that Earth is about 4.6 billion years old. Think of a time scale that compresses Earth's entire history into one day (Figure 9.2). On this scale, Earth formed at midnight. The time you are living in right now is 11:59:59 P.M. When did life begin in this "day"?

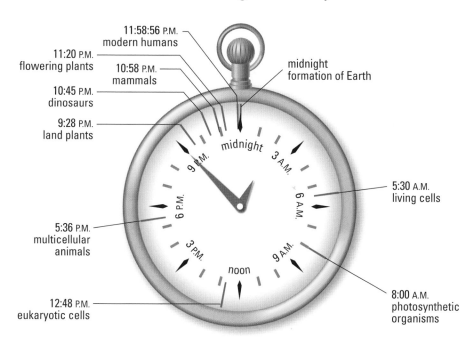

11:58:56 P.M. modern humans
11:20 P.M. flowering plants
10:58 P.M. mammals
10:45 P.M. dinosaurs
9:28 P.M. land plants
midnight formation of Earth
5:30 A.M. living cells
5:36 P.M. multicellular animals
8:00 A.M. photosynthetic organisms
12:48 P.M. eukaryotic cells

Figure 9.2 The red marks on the 24-hour clock indicate when certain organisms first appeared on Earth.

The Oldest Fossils

On this 24-hour time scale, Earth's crust began to cool and solidify about 400 million years after the planet formed. The oldest known fossils indicate that life existed by 8:00 A.M. (about 3.5 billion years ago). These ancient fossils are found in dome-shaped rock formations called stromatolites. **Stromatolites** are layered rocks that form when certain prokaryotes bind thin layers of sediment together (Figure 9.3). **Prokaryotes** are simple single-celled organisms that lack true nuclei and most organelles. The structure of fossilized stromatolites is very similar to the modern-day stromatolites that continue to be formed by colonies of photosynthetic prokaryotes living in salty marshes (Figure 9.4 on the next page). Fossils resembling photosynthetic prokaryotes have been found in stromatolites that scientists have measured to be about 3.5 billion years old.

Figure 9.3 A cross section of a fossilized stromatolite that shows the layers of sediment.

Figure 9.4 Modern-day colonies of photosynthetic prokaryotes. If one of these colonies were cut in half, it would look very similar to a cross section of a fossilized stromatolite.

BIOLOGY•SOURCE

Suggested Activity

• C10 Quick Lab Overview on page 249

Today, photosynthetic prokaryotes are among the simplest organisms that can produce their own food. However, photosynthesis is a complex process, and it is unlikely that photosynthetic bacteria were the first forms of life on Earth. The evidence that photosynthetic prokaryotes existed 3.5 billion years ago suggests that life in simpler forms began even earlier, perhaps around 5:30 A.M. (3.9 billion years ago), when Earth had cooled enough for liquid water to exist.

How Did Life Begin?

In the 1920s, Alexander Oparin and J.B.S. Haldane independently hypothesized the theory of **primary abiogenesis**, which states that the first living things on Earth arose from non-living material. They proposed that the first life forms must have arisen spontaneously once the first chemicals of life, organic molecules, were made. **Organic molecules** are molecules that contain the element carbon. Organic compounds include carbohydrates, lipids, proteins, and nucleic acids, which are the building blocks of DNA. The first organic compounds then arranged themselves into the first cell-like structures, isolating themselves from the outside environment.

Origin of Small Organic Molecules

One important question is how organic compounds first formed before there was life on early Earth. Geologic evidence suggests that the young Earth was a very different place from the planet today. The atmosphere contained carbon monoxide, carbon dioxide, nitrogen, methane (CH_3), hydrogen (H_2), ammonia (NH_4), and water vapour, but little or no oxygen. Oxygen is very reactive and it would have destroyed any organic compounds not protected within cells. Also, energy sources such as active volcanoes, lightning, and ultraviolet radiation from the sun were all more intense than they are today.

In 1953, Stanley Miller, a graduate student of Harold Urey at the University of Chicago, designed an experiment that simulated conditions on early Earth (Figure 9.5). Miller placed gases in a flask to represent Earth's ancient atmosphere. He used electric sparks to represent lightning as an energy source. The experiment produced a variety of small organic molecules that are essential to life, including amino acids — the building blocks of proteins.

Since the time of the Miller-Urey experiment, the types and amounts of gases in Earth's early atmosphere have been revised. The experiment has since been repeated using different gas combinations. These have produced an even wider variety of organic molecules. These results support the theory of primary abiogenesis.

water vapour (H_2O)
"atmosphere"
electrode
CH_4
NH_3
H_2
cold water
condenser
cooled water
"ocean"
water and simple organic molecules

Figure 9.5 Simulating Earth's ancient atmosphere, oceans, and sources of energy, the Miller-Urey experiment produced some of the organic compounds that are essential for life.

©P

Scientists have developed a hypothetical four-stage sequence for how life could have first arisen on Earth. First, small organic molecules, such as amino acids, formed from simpler molecules present in the environment. Second, these small molecules joined together into larger ones, such as proteins and nucleic acids. Third, molecules that could copy themselves provided a basis for the inheritance of molecular information. In the last stage, these various organic molecules became packaged within membranes and separated from their surroundings (Figure 9.6). In other words, they formed pre-cells.

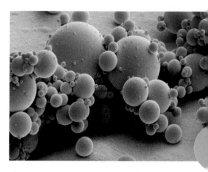

Figure 9.6 Simulating conditions on early Earth in laboratory experiments, scientists have been able to form structures that have some of the characteristics of cell membranes. (magnification 530×)

Where Did Life Begin?

One of the questions that scientists also continue to debate is *where* life might have originated. Until recently, most researchers thought that the most likely sites for the origin of life were shallow water or moist sediments such as clay. But during Earth's early history, the land surface may have been too hot and too extreme for complex organic molecules or pre-cells to "survive" for long. The discovery of deep-sea hydrothermal vents raised the possibility that similar environments might have supplied the energy and chemical raw materials for the origin of life (Figure 9.7). Today's deep-sea vents are populated with prokaryotic organisms that may resemble some of the earliest living cells.

Figure 9.7 Deep-sea hydrothermal vents like this one may resemble the environment where life first formed.

Concept Check

1. What do fossils found in stromatolites indicate about early life on Earth (3.5 billion years ago)?

2. What did the Miller-Urey experiment contribute to our understanding of how life began?

3. Describe an environment where life might have first appeared.

Free Oxygen Changes Earth

As mentioned earlier, stromatolites indicate that photosynthetic prokaryotes lived 3.5 billion years ago. However, it is believed that these organisms evolved from **chemoautotrophs**, organisms that synthesize their own organic molecules from simple inorganic materials (perhaps released from ocean-floor vents) without using light energy. The first photosynthetic prokaryotes evolved in the absence of oxygen. Over time, they became common and started to increase the oxygen concentration in the atmosphere, since oxygen is a byproduct of photosynthesis. Oxygen combined with iron, dissolved in oceans at the time, forming iron oxide. As the planet began to rust, the iron oxide fell to the ocean floor and changed the colour of oceans from brown to blue-green. Today these iron deposits are the source of most of the iron ore mined today.

The rise of highly reactive oxygen caused the first wave of extinctions of prokaryotes. They were not used to this atmosphere, and they survived only in a few environments that were free of oxygen. However, some prokaryotes evolved adaptations that allowed them to use the oxygen for cellular respiration. This was to be a crucial step in the development of more complex organisms. These prokaryotes were now **aerobic**, meaning they can function in the presence of oxygen.

Origin of Eukaryotic Cells

Prokaryotes ruled early Earth, but today many organisms, including protists, fungi, animals, and plants consist of eukaryotic cells. **Eukaryotes** contain membrane-bound organelles, such as nuclei, and have complex organelles, such as mitochondria. The development of eukaryotes from prokaryotes is one of the most important events in the history of life. On our 24-hour clock, eukaryotes appeared at 12:48 P.M.

Scientists have formed a hypothesis about the steps involved in the evolution of eukaryotes. Ancestral prokaryotes had cell walls (as modern prokaryotes do), but at some point, some of them had lost their cell walls. This allowed them to consume material more easily through their cell membranes. Some of the cell membrane began to fold inward and eventually became internalized (Figure 9.8). Some of these infolded membranes evolved into membrane-bound organelles such as the nucleus and Golgi apparatus. Membrane-bound organelles allowed the cell to carry out more complex chemical reactions in separate compartments. Because they had membrane-bound organelles, these cells were the ancestors of modern eukaryotic cells.

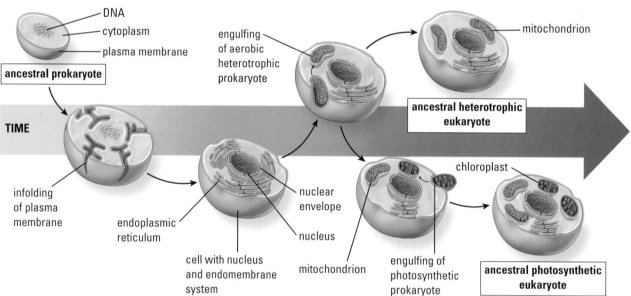

Figure 9.8 The transition from prokaryotes to eukaryotes involved two processes: infolding of the cell membrane and endosymbiosis.

The Endosymbiotic Theory

The ancestral eukaryotic cells lacked some organelles found in modern-day eukaryotic cells: mitochondria and chloroplasts. How did mitochondria and chloroplasts arise? According to the endosymbiotic theory, mitochondria evolved from small aerobic prokaryotes that lived inside larger eukaryotic cells. An ancestral eukaryote may have ingested some of these prokaryotes for food. Instead of being digested, these prokaryotes continued to live inside the larger eukaryote. Over time, they formed a symbiotic relationship with the host eukaryotic cell. Symbiosis is a relationship between organisms of two different species that live in close contact with each other. The ingested aerobic prokaryotes had the ability to use oxygen in cellular respiration to produce energy. These prokaryotes evolved into the mitochondria that provide energy in all eukaryotic cells today.

©P

Scientists theorize that chloroplasts evolved in a similar way. Some eukaryotes consumed prokaryotes that carried out photosynthesis. These developed a symbiotic relationship with their host eukaryotic cells and evolved into the chloroplasts found in modern plants and algae. Eventually, the photosynthetic eukaryotes developed a cell wall and became autotrophic, meaning they could make their own food.

The development of cell walls is another example of convergent evolution. The cell wall in prokaryotes is made out of a substance called peptidoglycan, and the cell wall in plant cells is made out of cellulose. Because they are made out of different substances, the cell walls must have evolved independently in the two different groups.

Evolution of Sexual Reproduction and Multicellular Life

Some time after eukaryotes evolved, around 5:36 P.M. on our 24-hour clock, some eukaryotic organisms began to reproduce sexually. This development allowed for greater genetic variation. Sexual reproduction, through meiosis and fertilization, allows for the shuffling of genes in each generation. Thus the offspring are never identical to their parents or their siblings, with the exception of identical twins. By increasing the number of genetic combinations, sexual reproduction allows for more genetic variation in the population. Variation is the raw material for natural selection. The environment selects those variations that allow individuals to survive and reproduce.

A few hundred million years later, the first multicellular organisms evolved from unicellular eukaryotes (protists). Multicellular eukaryotes diversified into multicellular protists, plants, animals, and fungi as a result of adaptive radiation.

The Fossil Record and Geologic Time Scale

The fossil record is a rich storehouse of information about macroevolution. In each layer of rock, the fossils found there are samples of the organisms that existed in that place at the time the sediment was deposited. Geologists have studied and compared sediments from sites around the world. The data collected provide a consistent and extensive record of Earth's history.

The **geologic time scale** organizes Earth's geological history into distinct blocks of time (Table 9.1 on the next page). These blocks of time, called **eras**, are the Paleozoic, Mesozoic, and Cenozoic eras. These eras are divided into shorter time spans called **periods**. Periods are divided into epochs. The boundaries between eras are marked in the fossil record by a major change in the forms of life. For example, the beginning of the Paleozoic era (the start of the Cambrian period) is marked by the appearance of a diversity of multicellular animals with hard parts. Fossils of these animals are absent in rocks of the precambrian time. The boundaries between eras and between some periods are also marked by widespread extinctions. For example, many of the animals that lived during the late Paleozoic era became extinct at the end of that era.

BIOLOGY•SOURCE

Explore More

Can radio-carbon dating be used to solve a fossil mystery?

Table 9.1 The Geologic Time Scale

Relative Duration of Eras	Era	Period	Epoch	Age (Millions of Years Ago)	Some Important Events in the History of Life
	Cenozoic	Neogene	Holocene		Historical time
				0.01	
			Pleistocene		Ice ages; humans appear
				1.8	
			Pliocene		Origin of genus *Homo*
				5.3	
			Miocene		Continued diversification of mammals and angiosperms; apelike ancestors of humans appear
				23	
		Paleogene	Oligocene		Origins of many primate groups, including apes
				33.9	
			Eocene		Angiosperm dominance increases; continued diversification of most present-day mammalian orders
				55.8	
			Paleocene		Major diversification of mammals, birds, and pollinating insects
				65.5	
	Mesozoic	Cretaceous			Flowering plants (angiosperms) appear; many groups of organisms, including most dinosaurs, become extinct at end of period
				145.5	
		Jurassic			Gymnosperms continue as dominant plants; dinosaurs abundant and diverse
				199.6	
		Triassic			Cone-bearing plants (gymnosperms) dominate landscape; origin and diversification of dinosaurs; origin of mammals
				251	
	Paleozoic	Permian			Diversification of reptiles; origin of most present-day groups of insects; extinction of many marine and terrestrial organisms at end of period
				299	
		Carboniferous			Extensive forests of vascular plants; first seed plants; origin of reptiles; amphibians dominant
				359.2	
		Devonian			Diversification of bony fishes; first tetrapods and insects
				416	
		Silurian			Diversification of early vascular plants
				443.7	
		Ordovician			Marine algae abundant; colonization of land by fungi, plants, and animals
				488.3	
		Cambrian			Sudden increase in diversity of many animal phyla (Cambrian explosion)
				542	
	precambrian time				Diverse algae and soft-bodied invertebrate animals
				635	
				2 100	Oldest fossils of eukaryotic cells
				2 500	
				2 700	Concentration of atmospheric oxygen begins to increase
				3 500	Oldest fossils of cells (prokaryotes)
				3 800	Oldest known rocks on Earth's surface
				approximately 4 600	Origin of Earth

Continental Drift and Macroevolution

Earth's continents are not locked in place. They move about the planet's surface on great plates of Earth's crust floating on the hot mantle. Land masses on different plates change position relative to each other. This movement is known as **continental drift**. North America and Europe, for example, are currently drifting apart at a rate of about 2 cm per year.

Continental drift is the solution to many biological puzzles. For example, paleontologists have discovered matching Mesozoic fossils in West Africa and Brazil. How could these two parts of the world, now separated by 3000 km of ocean, be home to the same organisms? The evidence makes sense if these two regions were part of one land mass in the early Mesozoic era. Similarly, continental drift explains why the plants and animals of Australia are so different from those in the rest of the world. After Australia became an isolated land mass, the organisms living there would have evolved independently of those living on other continents.

The Formation and Breakup of Pangaea

Two major events in the history of continental drift had an especially strong influence on life on Earth. The first occurred about 250 million years ago, near the end of the Paleozoic era (Figure 9.9). Plate movements brought all the land masses together into one supercontinent, named Pangaea (meaning "all land"). A variety of environmental changes followed. The amount of shoreline was reduced. Also, evidence suggests that sea levels dropped and shallow coastal seas were drained. Such changes would have destroyed the shallow water environments inhabited by many marine species. On land, continental interiors — which are drier and have more extreme climates than coastal areas — would have been affected as well. Species that had been evolving in isolation would have been brought together and forced to compete. All these changes likely caused the extinction of huge numbers of species.

The second major event in the history of continental drift occurred about 180 million years ago as Pangaea began to break up. As the continents drifted apart, each became an isolated and separate evolutionary arena. The species living on the different continents would have diverged in their evolution as they continued to adapt and diversify on the now separate continents.

This event helps explain the diversity of marsupial mammals in Australia. Both marsupial and placental mammals lived in Pangaea. The Australian land mass split off early in the break-up of Pangaea and remained isolated. The few placental mammals that lived there became extinct. But on the remaining parts of Pangaea, the reverse happened: most marsupials became extinct, and placental mammals dominated.

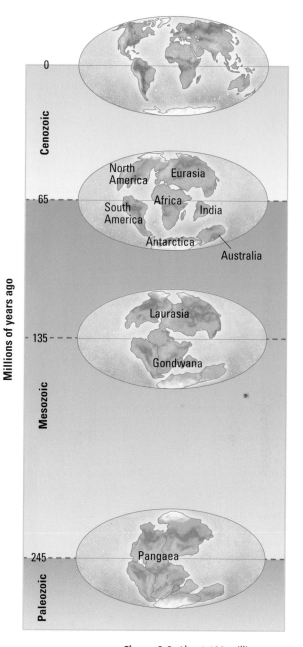

Figure 9.9 About 180 million years ago, Pangaea split into northern and southern landmasses that later separated into modern continents. India collided with Eurasia just 40 to 50 million years ago, forming the Himalayan mountain range. The continents continue to drift today.

Mass Extinctions

The fossil record reveals that Earth's history has long periods of relative stability, broken by comparatively brief episodes of great species loss known as **mass extinctions**. For example, at the end of the Cretaceous period, about 65 million years ago, the world lost an enormous number of species. Before then, dinosaurs had thrived on Earth for 150 million years. Less than 10 million years later — a brief period in geologic time — all the dinosaurs were gone, except those that evolved into birds. Scientists have been debating what happened for decades. The geologic record indicates a number of events that may have contributed to the extinction of the dinosaurs. The climate was cooling, and shallow seas were receding. But perhaps the final blow left its mark near the Yucatan Peninsula in Mexico (Figure 9.10). There, buried beneath sediment, lies a huge crater caused by the impact of a large meteor striking Earth. The timing of this impact corresponds with the last evidence of dinosaurs and many other species. Many scientists think that such a huge meteor strike would have polluted the sky with dusty debris for months. (Rock layers from that time period contain evidence of this debris.) By blocking sunlight, the dust would have reduced food production by photosynthesis.

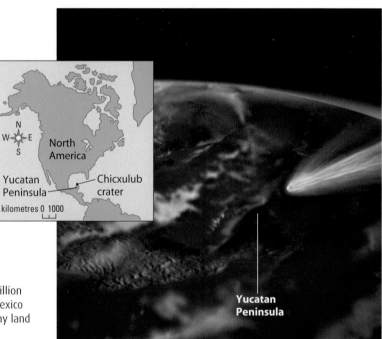

Figure 9.10 The impact of a meteor 65 million years ago near the Yucatan Peninsula in Mexico may be one cause of the extinction of many land plants and animals in North America.

Extinction is unavoidable in a changing world. While extinctions occur all the time, there have been five or six distinct periods of mass extinction over the last 600 million years. One example marks the end of the Permian period, when extinction claimed over 90 percent of the species of marine animals. Whatever their causes, mass extinctions greatly affect biodiversity. Yet there is a positive side to this story. Each massive loss of species has been followed by adaptive radiation of some survivors. In the aftermath of mass extinctions, biodiversity gradually increased again. Mass extinctions provided the surviving organisms with new opportunities. For example, just after the mass extinction marking the end of the Cretaceous period, fossil evidence suggests that mammals underwent widespread adaptive radiation. The rise of mammals probably resulted, in part, from the void left by the extinction of dinosaurs.

Comparing Atmospheres

Purpose

To explore the gases that probably made up Earth's early atmosphere

Activity Overview

In this Quick Lab, you will compare the gases found in Earth's atmosphere under normal conditions to the gases found near a volcanic eruption. The gases near a volcano are thought to be similar to the atmospheric gases of early Earth. By analyzing the differences in atmospheric composition, you will determine what life forms were most likely to have been present on early Earth.

Your teacher will give you a copy of the full activity.

Prelab Questions

Consider the questions below before beginning this activity.

1. What gases do you know are in our atmosphere?

2. What kind of gases do you think are released by a volcano?

3. What atmospheric gases are necessary for plants and animals to survive today?

Figure 9.11 Gases escaping from an active volcano

Changes in the Abundance of Marine Families

Purpose

To identify trends in the diversity of marine organisms

Activity Overview

In this Quick Lab, you will analyze a graph showing the number of marine fossils from different eras. You will identify any patterns and discuss their implications.

Your teacher will give you a copy of the full activity.

Prelab Questions

Consider the questions below before beginning this activity.

1. Do you think there is more or less marine biodiversity now than in earlier times in Earth's history?

2. According to what you have read in this section, which specific era do you think had the most biodiversity in marine animals?

Figure 9.12 Fossilized marine trilobites

Key Concept Review

1. (a) Summarize the Miller-Urey experiment.
  (b) Why was his experiment important to the primary abiogenesis theory?

2. Why is the creation of membrane-bound organelles beneficial to the cell?

3. Describe the endosymbiotic theory.

4. Why is sexual reproduction important for evolution?

5. (a) What are the three main geological eras in Earth's history?
  (b) What marks the change of eras in general?
  (c) Refer to Table 9.1 on page 246. What are the distinguishing features of each era?

6. What biological evidence is there that Pangaea once existed?

7. How did continental drift lead to macroevolution?

Connect Your Understanding

8. Below are three remote locations on Earth. Which location(s) might contain organisms that resemble the first living creatures on Earth? Explain.

Question 8

9. Draw a series of diagrams to represent the four-stage hypothesis on how life arose on Earth.

10. What evidence is there that mitochondria and chloroplasts evolved from self-sustaining prokaryotes?

11. Cyanobacteria, such as those shown below are believed to resemble some of the earlier autotrophs that existed on Earth. What cellular features do you think helped species succeed on early Earth? Explain why.

Question 11 (magnification 100×)

12. (a) Species evolve in response to environmental changes, but how did the evolution of species change the atmosphere? Give an example.
  (b) How do you think human activity today can affect the composition of gases in the atmosphere? Suggest how this will affect the evolution of species.

13. The endosymbiotic theory explains how eukaryotic cells may have evolved. Which do you think evolved first: autotrophic eukaryotes or heterotrophic eukaryotes? Explain your reasoning.

14. Madagascar is a large island off the east coast of Africa.
  (a) How can you explain the similarities in the fossil records from each location?
  (b) How can you explain the differences in species currently found in each location?

15. How can the mass extinction of one group of organisms, such as the dinosaurs, lead to diversification of other species?

Reflection

16. Identify two questions you have about how life arose on Earth.

For more questions, go to *BIOLOGY•SOURCE*

Section Summary

- Phylogeny establishes evolutionary relationships among species and groups of species.
- Cladograms can be produced by examining shared derived characteristics.
- Evidence of hominid evolution comes from the fossil record.

Imagine that you have a child. After a brief hospital stay, she becomes ill. Further testing reveals that she has HIV. Police inform you that many children staying at the hospital around the same time have tested positive for HIV. Police arrest a group of doctors and nurses and charge them with bioterrorism because they believe that these people intentionally infected the children with HIV.

Such a scenario may seem extreme, but it actually happened at El-Fatih Children's Hospital in the Libyan town of Benghazi (Figure 9.13). In 1998, six foreign medical workers (five Bulgarian nurses and one Palestinian medical intern) were accused of deliberately injecting 426 hospitalized children with HIV. They were accused of bioterrorism because authorities believed the six medics were being paid to do it by foreign governments in order to destabilize Libya. The six medics' trial in 2000 became highly political. It coincided with the trial of two Libyans accused of blowing up Pan Am flight 103 over Lockerbie, Scotland. The Libyan government felt that the trial of the Libyans was politically motivated and wanted to make the medics' trial political as well.

The medics were convicted. However, the workers maintained their innocence and said their confessions had been extracted under torture. When their story became known in Europe, a group of HIV experts examined the evidence and used evolution to try to convince the Libyan court that the medics were innocent. To understand the experts' conclusions, we must explore phylogeny.

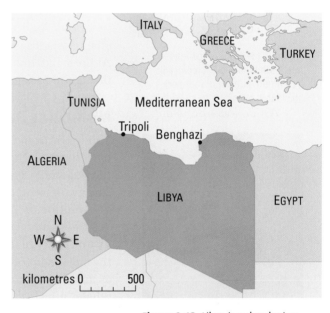

Figure 9.13 Libya is a developing nation on the southern shore of the Mediterranean Sea.

Phylogeny

Carolus Linnaeus developed a classification system for organisms based on similarities in their characteristics. Darwin, and biologists thereafter, strived to have classification represent the evolutionary development and relationships among species. **Phylogeny** is the evolutionary development and history of a species or group. A branching diagram that represents the evolutionary relationships among species or groups is called a **phylogenetic tree** (Figure 9.14 on the next page).

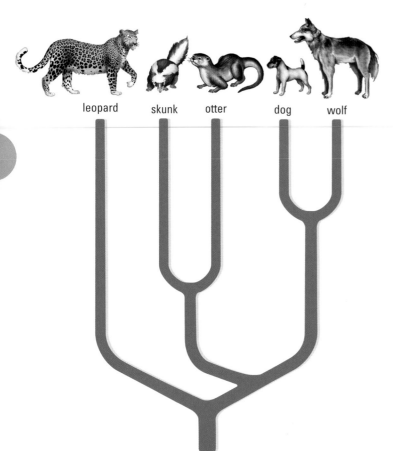

leopard   skunk   otter   dog   wolf

Figure 9.14 In a phylogenetic tree, each branch point represents a common ancestor of the species above that point.

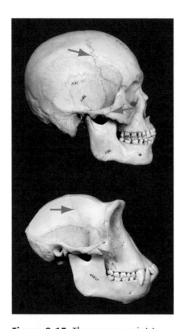

Figure 9.15 The arrows point to where some of the individual skull bones join together.

Homologous structures are one of the best clues to assess how closely organisms are related. Recall that homologous structures — such as a whale's flipper and a bat's wing — may look different and function very differently in different species. However, they will have basic underlying similarities if they both evolved from a single structure in a common ancestor. The greater the number of homologous structures two species have, the more closely the species are thought to be related. The skulls of chimpanzees and humans, for example, are not single bones. Rather, they are made of many bones fused together. And the two skulls match almost perfectly, bone for bone (Figure 9.15). It is highly unlikely that such complex structures that match in such detail could have separate origins. The bone patterns of these skulls were most likely inherited from a common ancestor.

Though only homologous structures should be used to classify organisms, this guideline is not always simple to apply. Adaptations can hide homologous characteristics, as they do in the wing of a bat and the flipper of a whale. At the same time, convergent evolution can produce analogous structures that could be mistaken for homologous ones.

Molecular Data As a Classification Tool

You know from Chapter 7 that the relatedness of species can be measured by comparing their genes and the proteins that genes code for. The more the sequences match up, the more closely the species are probably related. The availability of molecular data has led to a large increase in the study of evolutionary history.

These molecular data provide a new way to test hypotheses about evolutionary history. The strongest support for any such hypotheses is the agreement of molecular data with evidence from other sources, such as anatomy (body structure). For example, fossil data have indicated that whales are closely related to the group of mammals that includes hippos, cows, deer, and pigs. A comparison of molecular data from these animals has supported this hypothesis.

A Closer Look at Phylogenetic Trees

Taxonomy (the classification of organisms) entered a new age in the 1960s. An early breakthrough occurred when the molecular data described above became available for comparing species' DNA. At the same time, computer technology provided greater power to analyze information. These innovations coincided with new ways of building phylogenetic trees as hypotheses about evolutionary relationships.

Identifying Clades

Each evolutionary branch in a phylogenetic tree is called a **clade**. Clades, like taxonomic levels in classification, can nest within larger clades. In the phylogenetic tree in Figure 9.14, the dog group represents a clade within a larger clade that also includes the group that contains otters and skunks. Each item in a clade may be an individual species, a genus, a family, or some other taxonomic group. However, every clade consists of an ancestral species and all of its descendants. Look at the phylogenetic tree in Figure 9.16. Species B through H are members of a clade (yellow). So are species I through K (orange). But these two groups become part of a larger clade (blue) when you include species A. Species A is an ancestral species to all of the others in this larger clade.

Cladistics

The most common method used today to determine the sequence of branches in a phylogenetic tree is called **cladistics**. The key rule in cladistics is that all of the organisms of a particular clade must share homologous structures that do not occur outside the clade. These homologous structures that are common to all the organisms in a clade are called **derived characters**.

A phylogenetic diagram that specifies the derived characters of clades is called a **cladogram**. For example, compare the animals in the cladogram in Figure 9.17. The horse, wolf, leopard, and house cat all have hair. This derived character unites a clade that excludes the turtle. The turtle would be included in a broader clade of animals with backbones. Teeth adapted for eating meat is a derived character that unites the wolf, the leopard, and the house cat in a clade that excludes the plant-eating horse. Similarly, the ability to retract their claws unites the leopard and the house cat into a smaller clade that excludes the wolf.

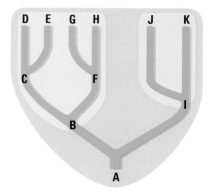

Figure 9.16 Each shaded area in the phylogenetic tree highlights one clade, such as the yellow area, including species B through H.

BIOLOGY·SOURCE

Explore More

How can cladograms provide insight into animal evolution?

BIOLOGY·SOURCE

Explore More

How does the discovery and study of fossils help scientists construct cladograms?

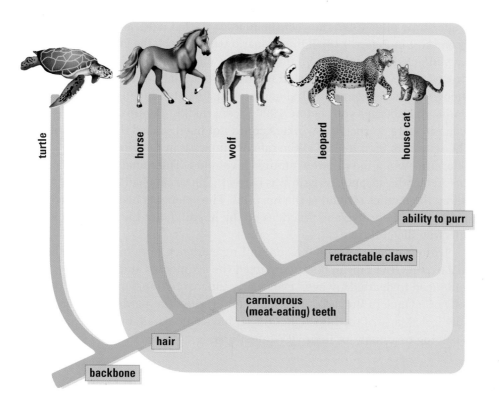

Figure 9.17 Each branch point on this cladogram represents the point at which two species diverged from a common ancestor. This cladogram shows how derived characters can be used to identify clades among certain vertebrates (animals with backbones). All the species shown here share a common ancestor that had a backbone. Each clade is actually defined by several derived characters, not just one.

Phylogeny and HIV Evolution

Let's revisit the Libyan bioterrorism case. Just as species evolve, so do viruses. HIV mutates at a fast pace, so new strains of the virus arise quickly. In fact, HIV can evolve into five new strains a year. Scientists examined the HIV viruses in the infected children and found that the viruses were very closely related to one another; therefore, it was likely that all children were infected from the same source. Before the scientists examined the evidence, they developed two possible scenarios (Figure 9.18).

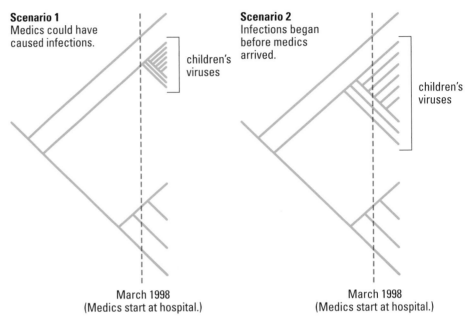

Figure 9.18 Genetic evidence supported scenario 2.

In the first scenario, the new strains would have developed from a single strain after 1998, the year the medics started work at the hospital (Scenario 1 in Figure 9.18). If this scenario were correct, the medics could have infected the children. In the second scenario, although the children's viruses were very closely related to one another, they were not similar enough to have a common viral ancestor that existed in 1998. In other words, the lineages split before 1998 (Scenario 2 in Figure 9.18). If this scenario were correct, the workers could not have caused the infection. The scientists then looked at the rate of mutation in the viruses to determine when the different strains developed. Their analysis revealed that in fact the second scenario was correct. The strains had been diverging before the medics arrived at the hospital. The scientists blamed tainted needles and poor hygiene practices by the hospital, not the medics, for infecting the children.

Unfortunately, despite the compelling evidence from international HIV experts, the Libyan court convicted the six medics and they were sentenced to death. However, eventually they were transferred back to Bulgaria. Once in Bulgaria, they received presidential pardons and are now free. Many of the infected children have since died, but most are receiving treatment for their HIV infections.

Concept Check

1. How are phylogenetic relationships established?

2. Why are analogous structures not useful for classifying species in an evolutionary context?

3. What does a branch point in a cladogram represent?

Phylogeny of Primates and Humans

Primates were one of the first placental mammals to have evolved about 65 million years ago. **Primates** are characterized by having grasping hands and feet with opposable first digits. They also have forward-facing eyes that provide depth perception. The ancestral primates diverged into two groups: prosimians and anthropoids (Figure 9.19). The prosimian lineage diverged several times and now includes modern lemurs, lorises, and tarsiers. The anthropoid lineage also diverged several times, starting about 25 to 30 million years ago. First, new-world monkeys and old-world monkeys diverged. Then hominoids and old-world monkeys diverged. **Hominoids** have relatively large brains, lack tails, and have swinging arms. Modern hominoids include gibbons, orangutans, gorillas, chimpanzees, and humans. Figure 9.20 shows the hominoid phylogenetic tree. Recent evidence shows that humans are more closely related to chimpanzees than to other hominoids, such as gorillas.

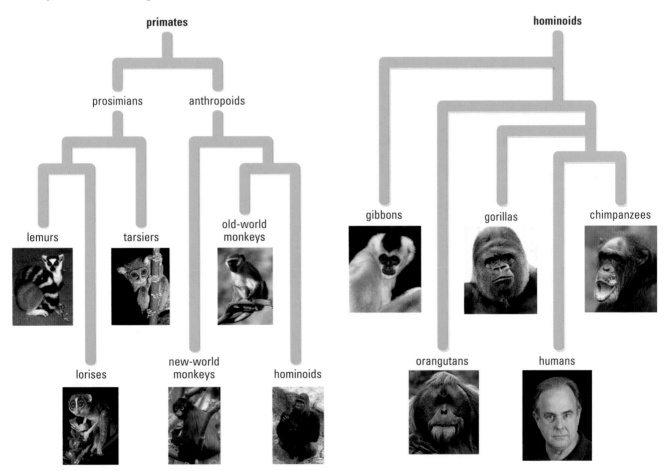

Figure 9.19 The primate phylogenetic tree. Anthropoids are different from prosimians in that they have a larger bodies, fused skulls, relatively larger brains, and binocular and colour vision.

Figure 9.20 Humans are more closely related to chimpanzees than to any other hominoid.

Explore More

What important discoveries have influenced our ideas about hominid evolution?

Suggested Activity

• C12 Quick Lab Overview on page 257

Take It Further

Mitochondrial DNA can tell us a lot about the possible migratory patterns of early humans. Research how genetic evidence helps us monitor the evolution of humans.

In Darwin's time no fossils of early humans had been discovered, and even today the fossil record is sparse. Every year new evidence appears, giving rise to new ideas about hominid evolution. **Hominids** are humans and all their ancestral species that arose after the split from ancestral chimpanzees. What distinguishes hominids from all other species is their large brain size and bipedalism. **Bipedalism** is the ability to walk on two feet.

Ardipethicus ramidus is one of the the oldest known bipedal species. It dates back 4.6 million years. The species was first discovered in 1992, but it took 15 years to fully understand its place in human evolution. Previously it was believed that the common ancestor, or "missing link," between humans and chimpanzees must have had features that were common to the two groups. *A. ramidus*, however, is more similar to early humans and ancestral apes than it is to chimpanzees. This shows that both humans and chimpanzees have evolved different features, and both species now look very different from their ancestors. For example, the habit of knuckle walking seen in chimpanzees and other apes may have evolved *after* the human and ape lineages diverged.

Figure 9.21 shows the hypothesized phylogenetic tree of hominids. The first members of the genus Homo are believed to have co-existed with some species of australopithecines. Members of the Homo genus differ from australopithecines by their larger brain size and the shape of their jaws and teeth. Although there is only one surviving species from the genus Homo, there were times when more than one Homo species co-existed. For example, *Homo neanderthalis* and *Homo sapiens* co-existed as recently as 130 000 years ago.

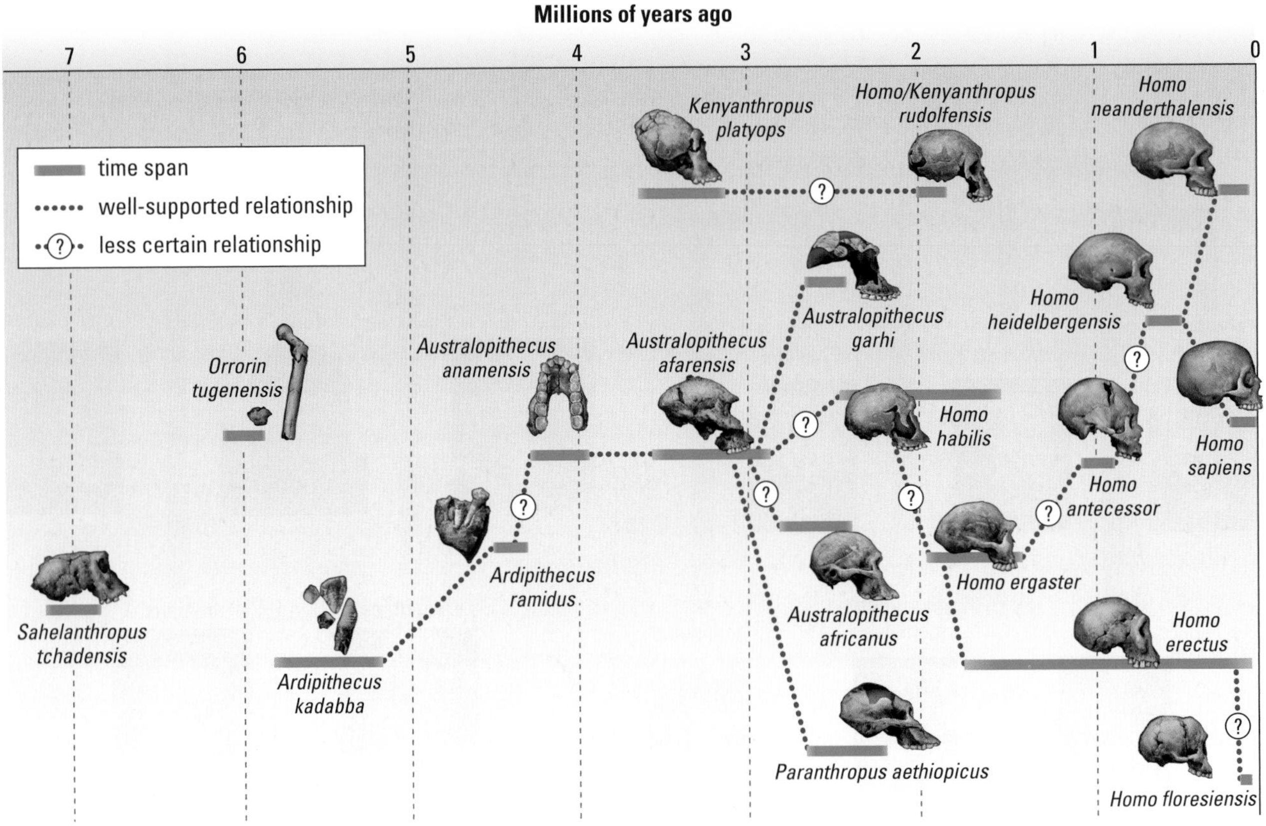

Figure 9.21 The evolutionary relationships among hominids are constantly being refined as more evidence is gathered.

The oldest *H. sapiens* fossils have been found in Ethiopia, which indicates that humans evolved in Africa. Recent DNA evidence supports this. Humans then migrated to other parts of the world (Figure 9.22). The first wave of migration was to Asia and the second wave was to Europe, Southeast Asia and Australia. Scientists are still debating the time of human migration to North America.

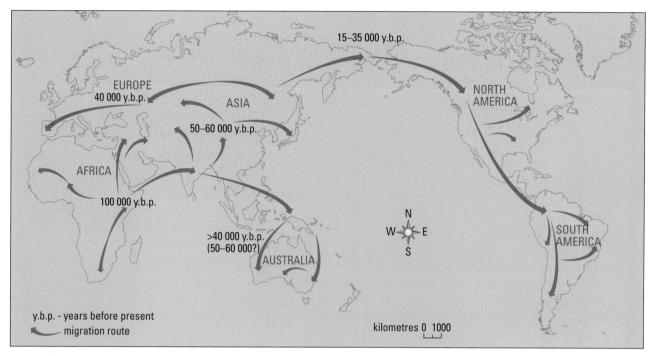

Figure 9.22 Early human fossils have been found on different continents; however, all modern humans have a common African ancestor.

BIOLOGY • SOURCE

Comparing Human, Australopithecine, and Chimpanzee Skeletons

Purpose

To identify the similarities and differences between humans, australopithecines, and chimpanzees

Activity Overview

In this Quick Lab, you will compare drawings of the skulls and skeletons of an australopithecine, a human, and a chimpanzee. You will determine which features in the australopithecine are more apelike and which features are more humanlike.

Your teacher will give you a copy of the full activity.

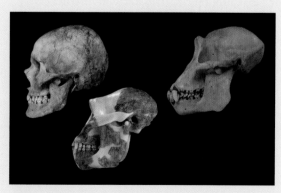

Figure 9.23 Human, australopithecine, and chimpanzee skulls

Prelab Questions

Consider the questions below before beginning this activity.

1. What do you think are the structural differences between humans and chimpanzees?

2. What features do you think make humans better adapted for bipedalism?

Key Concept Review

1. Explain how cladograms are constructed.

2. What are two subdivisions within the primate family?

3. What features are common to all hominoids?

4. What organisms are included in the hominid family?

5. How is the Homo genus different from australopithecines?

Connect Your Understanding

6. How has phylogeny been used to solve a crime?

7. Examine the cladogram below.
   (a) Which group are crocodiles most related to?
   (b) Some argue that birds belong in a separate clade from crocodiles. Why do you think they believe this?
   (c) What type of evidence do you think was used to create the cladogram?

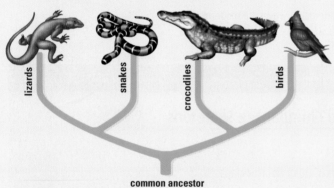

common ancestor

Question 7

8. The table below lists derived characters of certain organisms.
   (a) Using the information in the table, construct a cladogram.
   (b) Which trait most likely evolved first? Explain.

Derived Characters of Four Species

Organism	Backbone	Legs	Hair
Trout	✓	✗	✗
Earthworm	✗	✗	✗
Chimpanzee	✓	✓	✓
Salamander	✓	✓	✗

(c) What organism is most closely related to the chimpanzee?
(d) Where would a frog be inserted into your cladogram? Explain.

9. (a) Which do you think evolved first in human ancestors: bipedalism or large brain size?
   (b) What evidence is there that supports your answer to (a)?

10. What does the discovery of *Ardipethecus Ramidus* tell us about human evolution?

11. *Homo neanderthalis* and *Homo sapiens* lived at the same time but did not interbreed. If you were to find neanderthal DNA and compare it to modern human DNA, what would you expect to find if the above hypothesis were correct?

12. All modern humans are believed to have arisen from a common ancestor that lived in Africa. What evidence did scientists use to determine whether this is true?

13. Examine the hominoid skull. What would you have to do to decide how it fits into the human phylogenetic tree?

Question 13

14. Scientists use various animal species as "models" for humans in research studies. When scientists plan a study, they have to decide which species to use. How would these species' phylogenetic relationships to humans influence the scientists' choice of species to use and the conclusions they draw from their results?

Reflection

15. As you read through the information on human phylogeny, what did you learn that impressed you most about human origins?

For more questions, go to BIOLOGY•SOURCE

9.3 Evolution's Role in Medicine and Agriculture

> ### Section Summary
>
> - Studying the evolution of disease can help us understand and control disease frequencies.
> - Lack of variation can make crops and livestock vulnerable to evolutionary forces.

Medical Applications for Evolution

Microevolution happens from one generation to the next. Since micro-organisms can reproduce in as little as 20 minutes, microevolution can happen extremely fast. Scientists have to monitor disease-causing bacteria and viruses because of their ability to mutate quickly. Also, advances in genetics have allowed scientists to study the roles some alleles play in both causing and preventing diseases.

Monitoring Mutations in Pathogens

Monitoring the incidence of new mutations in pathogens and the rate at which they occur can help prevent outbreaks of disease. The people of the world have often suffered from influenza, an infection caused by the influenza virus. Influenza, also called the flu, causes thousands of deaths each year. Every year, scientists monitor mutations in influenza viruses and try to predict which strain will be most common and thus infect the most people. They then develop a vaccine against this strain to prevent infections. Because the virus mutates so quickly, every year new vaccines have to be created to protect against the new strains.

A disease outbreak over a large geographical area is called a pandemic. The 2009 outbreak of the H1N1 virus, a completely new strain of influenza, was considered a pandemic because it spread rapidly all around the world. Pandemics are not new. In the 1340s, Europe suffered from a pandemic of the bubonic plague, a disease caused by a bacterium. It killed about one-third of Europe's population. There were no antibiotics back then to fight the infection.

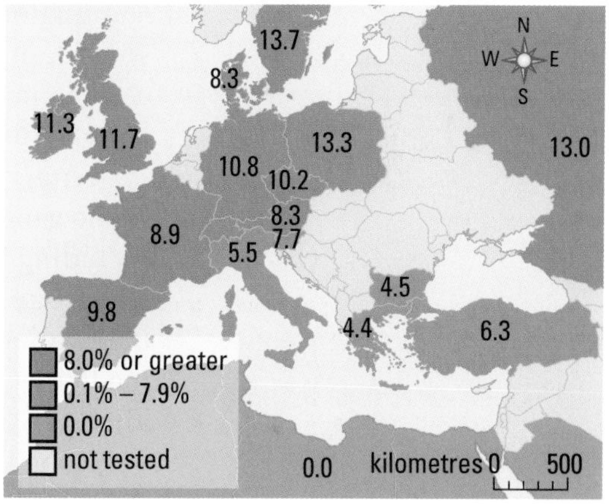

Figure 9.24 Northern Europeans are believed to have a higher frequency of the CCR5 D32 allele due to natural selection during the bubonic plague pandemic. This allele is associated with HIV resistance.

Alleles and Disease Resistance

As we have seen, bacteria and viruses can mutate and, through natural selection, become resistant to antibiotics and antiviral drugs. However, some humans are naturally resistant to certain infectious diseases. For example, 20 percent of Europeans and people of European descent have been found to carry at least one copy of the D32 allele of the CCR5 gene (Figure 9.24). Scientists think this allele allowed some people to resist plague infections in the past and they were more likely to survive. So individuals with the allele were selected for whenever there was an outbreak of the plague. Thus, the allele has remained in the gene pool.

In modern times, individuals with the D32 allele have been found to be resistant to infection by other pathogens, including HIV. The plagues of Europe in the past did not reach Africa and Asia, and these regions' gene pools do not contain the D32 allele. Therefore, Asian and African populations are more susceptible to HIV infections.

In Chapter 8, we saw how malaria in a region led to an increase in the allele for sickle-cell disease in the population. Similarly, one in 25 people of European descent carry an allele for cystic fibrosis. Individuals who inherit two copies of the allele develop this debilitating disease, which often leads to early death. Its effects include mucus build-up in the respiratory tract and tissue damage to the pancreas and lungs. Natural selection should have reduced the frequency of the allele for this disease, since those who carry it often do not live to reproduce. However, some evidence shows that heterozygous individuals may be resistant to several serious diseases caused by bacteria, including tuberculosis, typhoid fever, salmonella poisoning, and cholera (Figure 9.25). Cholera was once extremely common in Europe. Before the invention of antibiotics, those who got cholera had a 50 percent chance of dying from it. The survival benefits the cystic fibrosis allele gave its carriers allowed the allele to be maintained in the gene pool.

Figure 9.25 Cholera is caused by *Vibrio cholerae* bacteria pictured here in green. It is contracted through drinking contaminated water. The bacteria attack the lining of the small intestine, which causes severe diarrhea. (magnification 2050×)

Influencing Disease Frequencies

Sometimes, natural selection has no effect on the frequency of the disease-causing alleles in the gene pool. Natural selection usually weeds out traits that are not advantageous in a particular environment. Individuals that are selected against do not live to produce offspring. However, in adult-onset genetic diseases, symptoms may occur after reproduction has already taken place. Therefore, the disease-causing allele may have already been passed on to the offspring. For example, Huntington's disease causes a slow degeneration of brain tissue. People with Huntington's disease start to show symptoms of the disease in their early to mid forties. By this age, many of these people have reproduced and the disease-causing allele has already been passed on.

Modern medicine can affect the frequency of disease-causing alleles in the gene pool. Tests have been developed for many genetic diseases, including Huntington's. People who discover they have a disease-causing allele may choose not to reproduce. If they do not reproduce, the frequency of the allele in the gene pool will be reduced. On the other hand, modern medicine may indirectly increase the frequency of other disease-causing alleles in the gene pool. For example, better treatments have been developed for individuals with childhood diseases such as cystic fibrosis. As a result, people with the disease live longer and may be able to reproduce, passing down the disease-causing allele to their offspring.

Concept Check

1. Why are Europeans today thought to be more resistant to harmful pathogens such as H1N1?

2. Explain why so many Europeans are carriers of the cystic fibrosis gene.

3. How has modern medicine influenced the incidence of certain diseases?

Evolution in Agriculture

Humans have been breeding crops and livestock for as long as there has been agriculture. The goal of agricultural practices is to produce the most food possible. In order to protect crops, scientists are trying to fight the effects of directional selection in pest species. Some agricultural practices also reduce the genetic diversity of livestock and crop species, which can leave them vulnerable to evolutionary forces.

Slowing Pesticide Resistance

Chapter 8 explored the development of pesticide resistance in agricultural pests. Constantly developing new pesticides is costly and, as we have seen, only effective in the short term. New ways of using pesticides can help slow the development of pesticide resistance in insects. **Refugia** are any local environments that have not been affected by regional ecological change. In agriculture, refugia are blocks of land in fields that are not sprayed with pesticides. When pesticides are used on the field, only pesticide-resistant insects survive on the land sprayed. However, both pesticide-resistant and pesticide-sensitive insects survive in the refuge and they will interbreed. If the allele for pesticide resistance is recessive, only about a quarter of the offspring will be resistant. Thus, over several generations, the proportion of pesticide-resistant insects in the population will be significantly reduced (Figure 9.26). This technique does not eliminate pesticide-resistant insects, but it keeps their numbers low. It also reduces the need to develop new pesticides. A similar technique is used for slowing antibiotic resistance in bacteria.

Figure 9.26 The field without a refuge eventually has many pesticide-resistant insects compared to a field that has a refuge.

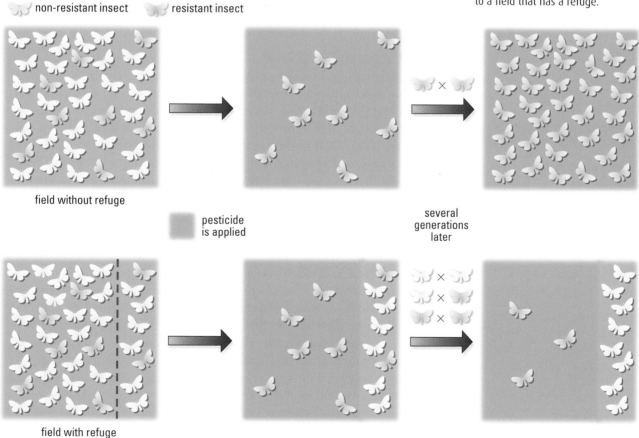

non-resistant insect   resistant insect

field without refuge

pesticide is applied

several generations later

field with refuge

Genetic Diversity in Crops

Crops are artificially selected to have certain traits. Once a crop variety has the desired traits, farmers plant as many of these plants as possible. However, this can lead to devastating outcomes. For example, in the 19th century, Ireland tried to feed its growing population using potatoes. They planted only the "lumper" variety. To create more plants, farmers planted cuttings from existing lumper plants, which grew into complete plants. This meant that all the plants were genetically identical, or clones. Low genetic variation makes a species more vulnerable to changing environmental conditions. In the 1840s, an organism called *Phytophthora infestans* spread through the lumper potato plants, causing a disease called potato blight. The entire crop was ruined. One out of eight people died of starvation in a three-year period following the infection. If genetic diversity had been maintained by growing several different potato varieties, the effect of potato blight probably would have been less severe (Figure 9.27).

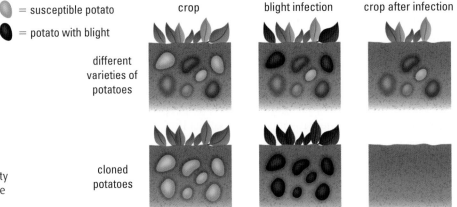

Figure 9.27 The lack of biodiversity makes the species more vulnerable to environmental changes.

Unfortunately, we have not learned our lesson. Growers still prefer to plant single varieties of crops. These varieties do not have a lot of genetic variation, making them vulnerable to evolutionary forces. For example, in 1970, the United States experienced massive corn-crop losses due to a fungal infection that spread through a widely planted corn variety. In the 1980s, a dependence on a single variety of grapevine in California led to the destruction of over 800 000 hectares of vineyards when a new insect pest, *Phyllorexia vitifoliae*, attacked the vines. As we have seen, our preference for the Cavendish banana has made bananas less diverse and vulnerable to extinction.

Genetic Diversity in Livestock

Artificial selection also affects genetic diversity in livestock. For centuries, farmers have bred farm animals to display particular traits. This has led to the creation of livestock breeds. As we have seen, selective breeding can reduce the amount of genetic variation quite quickly. For example, chicken breeds such as the white leghorn, the dominant breed used for egg production, are genetically uniform. For years they have been selectively bred for egg-laying ability (Figure 9.28). But selection for one trait comes at a cost. These chickens are susceptible to disease, and disease outbreaks can affect a farm's entire population. To increase the genetic diversity of the widely used commercial chicken breeds, the birds need to be interbred with birds from other breeds.

BIOLOGY•SOURCE

Suggested Activity
- C13 Decision-Making Analysis Overview on page 263

©P

Figure 9.28 The white leghorn is the breed most widely used for producing eggs. A single female can produce 280 eggs a year.

Today, modern reproductive technologies help increase the frequency of desired traits in breeds of cows, sheep, pigs, and turkeys. Artificial insemination is a technique by which semen is introduced into the reproductive tract of a female by means other than sexual intercourse. With artificial insemination, semen is extracted from males prized for their traits. The semen can be frozen and shipped to far-away locations and used to impregnate females also prized for their traits. Using this technique, a single prized male can produce far more offspring than he would have through conventional selective breeding. Though the desired traits are maintained in the population, the genetic diversity within the breed is reduced, since so many individuals have the same father.

REQUIRED SKILLS
- Gathering information
- Reporting results

DI Key Activity

C13 Decision-Making Analysis   *BIOLOGY•SOURCE*

Feeding a Growing Population versus Conserving Biodiversity

Issue

Do the benefits of relying on a few highly productive livestock breeds and crop varieties outweigh the risks of reducing genetic diversity by allowing less productive breeds to become extinct?

Figure 9.29 Holsteins are favoured in dairy production for their high milk yields.

Activity Overview

In this activity, you will research the techniques, crop varieties, and livestock breeds used in industrialized agriculture and compare them to those used in sustainable agriculture. You will then analyze the social, economic, and ethical issues to form an opinion on the issue.

Your teacher will give you a copy of the full activity.

Prelab Questions

1. Brainstorm what the terms "industrial agriculture" and "sustainable agriculture" might mean.

2. Are you familiar with any breeds of livestock or varieties of crops grown to produce the food you eat? Name as many as you have heard of.

3. Estimate how rapidly the global human population is growing.

Key Concept Review

1. Why are new flu vaccinations needed every year?

2. Why are Europeans more likely to be resistant to HIV than Asians or Africans?

3. Why do heritable adult-onset diseases such as Huntington's disease still occur in the population?

4. How does the occurrence of one disease affect the incidence of another? Provide an example.

5. How can refugia help reduce pesticide resistance?

6. Identify two alleles that cause disease yet have been favoured by natural selection. Explain why they were favoured.

7. Provide an example of how artificial insemination has affected livestock.

Connect Your Understanding

8. How have outbreaks of diseases such as cholera affected humans over time?

9. How have reproductive technologies such as genetic screening affected the evolution of diseases?

10. Suppose herbicide has been developed that attacks only purple loosestrife. Create a plan to slow herbicide resistance in these plants, which have invaded a large marsh.

11. How have modern agricultural practices made crops vulnerable to evolutionary forces?

12. Do you think a supermarket owner and his or her customers would support the introduction of new varieties of bananas? Justify your opinion.

13. Pregnant women often experience nausea, especially in the first three months of fetal development. The nausea is often triggered by certain types of food, including spices. Form a hypothesis about how this nausea might be an evolutionary adaptation.

14. Some people believe that because a new influenza vaccine is needed each year, there is no point in getting vaccinated.
    (a) Discuss some of the disadvantages in getting vaccinated each year.

    (b) Why should governments keep investing money to develop a new flu vaccine each year?

15. Some individuals who are infected with malaria develop anemia, which is a deficiency of red blood cells.
    (a) How could anemia benefit these individuals?
    (b) If these individuals then have children, will the children be anemic? Explain.

16. Examine the two images of pigs below.
    (a) Which population is more genetically diverse? Explain.
    (b) Which population is more vulnerable to disease? Explain.

Question 16

Reflection

17. What information in this section did you find the most interesting? Explain why.

For more questions, go to BIOLOGY•SOURCE

Dr. Bernatchez is one of the top molecular biologists in Canada and has won several awards for his work. Initially, he focussed on understanding the process of adaptation and speciation in whitefish, a group of freshwater fish species native to North America. During the last ice age, different groups within the same species were geographically isolated. When these species recolonized the same lake, Dr. Bernatchez found that they did not interbreed and they had established different ecological niches within the same lakes. Habitat isolation encouraged differences in the genomes within these groups. He is currently working on discovering exactly what genes are responsible for the ecological differences in the fish populations.

Dr. Bernatchez is also editor-in-chief of a new academic journal called *Evolutionary Applications*. It publishes papers on practical applications of evolution in areas such as health, agriculture, fisheries and wildlife management, climate change, and conservation biology.

Figure 9.30 Dr. Bernatchez is a professor of biology at the Université Laval, in Quebec City.

When you think of a paleontologist, you probably picture someone chipping away at the rock around a dinosaur bone in some remote location. While field work such as this can be part of the job, there are different areas in which paleontologists can work. They can be curators in museums, setting up displays and developing educational programs for the public. Others are employed by universities to teach and do research. Paleontologists need to be patient, be good at solving problems, have an imagination, and have a keen eye for detail. To become a paleontologist you need to take many high-school math and science courses. Most paleontologists have a bachelor's degree in evolution, zoology, earth science, or geology. They go on to get a master's or a PhD degree. One necessary pre-requisite is a passion for unveiling the mysteries of Earth's past.

Figure 9.31 A paleontologist in the process of excavating a mammoth fossil. Excavating work requires patience and attention to detail.

To find out more, visit   BIOLOGY•SOURCE

Key Concept Review

1. In the Miller-Urey experiment, what did each of the following represent?
   (a) electric sparks Ⓚ
   (b) mixture of gases: methane, ammonia, hydrogen Ⓚ
   (c) condenser Ⓚ

2. (a) What gas was missing in large quantities in Earth's first atmosphere? Ⓚ
   (b) What effect did the absence of this gas have on the type of life forms that could exist? Ⓚ
   (c) How did this gas then accumulate in the atmosphere? Ⓚ

3. Describe how eukaryotes evolved from prokaryotes. Ⓚ

4. What marks the divisions on the geologic time scale? Ⓚ

5. Why was continental drift important for adaptive radiation? Ⓚ

6. What are derived characters, and how are they used in cladograms? Ⓚ

7. How are hominids different from other hominoids? Ⓚ

8. How can the resistance to one disease help fight another? Give an example. Ⓚ

9. Describe the purpose of refugia. Ⓚ

10. Describe two different methods used in the artificial selection of livestock and crops. Ⓚ

11. Describe two ways modern medicine has affected the evolution of diseases. Ⓚ

Connect Your Understanding

12. How did cells that ingested the ancestors of modern mitochondria and chloroplasts benefit from having them remain in their cytoplasm? Ⓚ

13. Use the geologic time scale (Table 9.1 on page 246) to answer the following questions.
    (a) Estimate the length of time that prokaryotes existed before eukaryotes evolved. Ⓚ
    (b) What event occurred at the end of the Paleozoic era? What was the significance of this event? Ⓚ
    (c) When did the diversification of mammals occur and in what period? Ⓚ

14. Use the diagram below to answer the questions that follow.

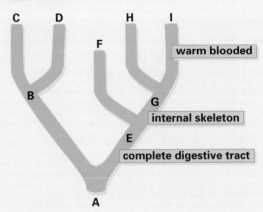

Question 14

(a) Which species is the common ancestor of C and D? Ⓚ
(b) Which species have internal skeletons? Ⓚ
(c) What are the traits in the boxes called? Ⓚ
(d) How many clades are contained in the diagram? List the species in each clade. Ⓚ

15. Use the information in the table to answer the questions below.

Derived Characters for Selected Organisms

Organism	Flowers	Multicellular Embryo	Vascular Tissue	Seeds
Fern	✗	✓	✓	✗
Maple tree	✓	✓	✓	✓
Kelp	✗	✗	✗	✗
Liverwort	✗	✓	✗	✗
Pine tree	✗	✓	✓	✓

(a) Create a cladogram that includes all the organisms listed. Ⓒ
(b) Which organism is the most dissimilar to the rest? Explain. Ⓣ
(c) Which organism is relatively the "youngest"? Ⓣ
(d) Flowering plants, such as maple trees, have a network of vein-like structures in their leaves, while other plants, such as palm trees, have vein-like structures in their leaves that run parallel to one another. Modify the cladogram to include a palm tree. Ⓒ

©P

16. How can cladistics be used in real-life situations? ⓐ

17. What type of evidence do scientists prefer to use to establish phylogenetic relationships? Explain. ⓐ

18. In 1974, an *Australopithecus afarensis* fossil, nicknamed "Lucy," was discovered. Below is an anatomical comparison between Lucy, a human, and a chimpanzee.
    (a) What features does Lucy have in common with chimpanzees? ⓣ
    (b) What features does Lucy have in common with humans? ⓣ
    (c) Make a hypothesis about whether or not Lucy was bipedal. Support your opinion. ⓣ

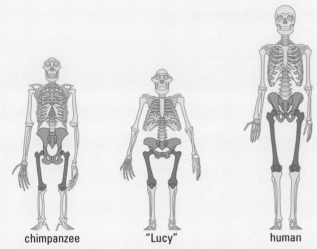

chimpanzee   "Lucy"   human

Question 18

19. *Homo erectus* (the word "erectus" means walking upright) was discovered in Indonesia in 1891 before any of the other early hominid fossils (including australopithecines) were discovered in Africa in the 1950s.
    (a) In 1891, what inferences do you think scientists made about where hominids originated? ⓐ
    (b) Hominids that lived before *Homo erectus* also walked upright. Due to these more recent finds, do you think the name "*Homo erectus*" is misleading? Justify your answer. ⓐ

20. Fossils of *Homo neanderthalis* and *Homo sapiens* were sometimes found in groups or with objects around them such as tools. What can you infer about the behaviour of these humans?

21. Complete fossils of one organism are rarely found. Paleontologists usually reconstruct a species by combining the fossilized remains of many individuals. For example, they might use a skull from one individual and a femur from another.
    (a) What are the advantages and disadvantages of this process? ⓐ
    (b) What clues can scientists use to make sure that the organisms do in fact belong to the same species? ⓐ

22. Suppose the CCR5 gene has been artificially inserted into the DNA of a strain of bacteria that can be infected by HIV. Some of the bacteria have the D32 allele and some do not. Design an experiment to test whether the D32 allele for the CCR5 gene provides resistance to HIV in the bacteria. Include what your control will be and what you will measure. ⓣ

23. Compare traditional selective breeding practices with modern techniques such as artificial insemination. Which method is more likely to result in a quicker loss of genetic diversity? ⓐ

24. Do you think artificial selection practices by farmers should be restricted? Justify your opinion. ⓐ

25. Suppose a farmer is trying to convince all the neighbouring farmers to use the same pesticide on their crops as he uses. Describe one advantage and one disadvantage to his neighbours doing this. ⓐ

26. Write a short story that depicts Earth 3.8 billion years ago. ⓒ

Reflection

27. What information from this chapter can you relate to the most? Explain why. ⓒ

Unit Task Link

In the Unit Task, you will be assessing conservation strategies. What role do you think artificial selection might have in conserving endangered species?

For more questions, go to BIOLOGY•SOURCE

SUMMARY

KEY CONCEPTS	CHAPTER SUMMARY

7 The theory of evolution helps us understand the diversity of life.

- Evolution
- Adaptation
- Lamarck's inheritance of acquired characteristics hypothesis
- Natural selection
- Survival of the fittest
- Evidence for evolution
- Homologous, analogous, and vestigial structures
- Antibiotic resistance

- The work of 18th- and 19th-century thinkers challenged the notion that Earth was young and that species did not change over time. (7.1)
- Darwin used the work of Hutton, Lyell, Cuvier, and Malthus to build his theory of evolution. (7.1)
- Evolution is the change in species over time. Natural selection is the mechanism behind evolution. (7.2)
- In natural selection, more young are produced than can survive, and those individuals that have variations that help them survive live to reproduce and pass down their traits to their offspring. (7.2)
- Evidence for evolution and natural selection comes from the study of fossils, geographic distribution of species, comparative anatomy, comparative development, artificial selection, and molecular biology. (7.2)
- Genetics disproves Lamarck's hypothesis of inheritance of acquired characteristics and supports Darwin's theory of natural selection. (7.2)
- Natural selection can explain the rise of antibiotic-resistant bacteria. (7.2)

8 The mechanisms of evolution can lead to speciation or extinction.

- Microevolution
- Directional, disruptive, and stabilizing selection
- Artificial selection and sexual selection
- Genetic drift and gene flow
- Macroevolution and speciation
- Reproductive and post-reproductive barriers
- Adaptive radiation and convergent evolution
- Punctuated equilibrium and gradualism
- Co-evolution

- Microevolution occurs when allele frequencies in the gene pool change from generation to generation. (8.1)
- Natural selection, sexual selection, artificial selection, genetic drift, and gene flow are the mechanisms of microevolution. (8.1)
- Directional, disruptive, and stabilizing selection affect allele frequencies in a population in different ways. (8.1)
- Macroevolution includes the formation of new species, the extinction of species, and the rise of major structures such as a backbone. (8.2)
- There are barriers to reproduction that may lead to speciation. (8.2)
- In adaptive radiation, an ancestral species diverges into various species with different traits as a result of changes in its environment. (8.2)
- In convergent evolution, distantly related species evolve similar traits as a result of living in similar environments. (8.2)
- Punctuated equilibrium explains the sudden appearance of new species in the fossil record. (8.2)
- Some human activities can cause extinction, but others can help preserve the diversity of life. (8.2)
- In co-evolution, one species evolves in response to evolutionary changes in another species. (8.3)
- Cumulative selection can result in complex features. (8.3)
- Ongoing natural selection can adapt existing structures to perform new functions. (8.3)

9 Evolution has produced Earth's current biodiversity and influences modern medicine and agriculture.

- Miller-Urey experiment
- Endosymbiotic theory
- Oxygen's influence on life
- Phylogeny and cladistics
- Primates, hominoids, hominids
- Applications of evolution

- Organic molecules, which are the building blocks of life, could have arisen from simpler molecules found in the environment. (9.1)
- Endosymbiotic theory explains the origins of mitochondria and chloroplasts in eukaryotes. (9.1)
- Phylogeny and cladistics establish evolutionary relationships among species. (9.2)
- The human phylogenic tree includes *Australopithecus* and *Homo* species, which were all bipedal. (9.2)
- The study of evolution can help us control disease frequencies. (9.3)
- The lack of diversity can make crops and livestock vulnerable to evolutionary forces. (9.3)

©P

UNIT C REVIEW

ACHIEVEMENT CHART CATEGORIES
k Knowledge and understanding   t Thinking and investigation
c Communication   a Application

Key Terms Review

1. Create a concept map that links all the terms in the list below. Give examples, where applicable, of the various terms. You may then add additional terms from the unit that you find helpful.

   - sexual selection
   - inheritance of acquired characteristics
   - directional selection
   - refugia
   - phylogeny
   - mutation
   - disruptive selection
   - genetic drift
   - gene flow
   - adaptation
   - artificial selection
   - speciation
   - reproductive isolation
   - natural selection
   - microevolution
   - stabilizing selection
   - macroevolution
   - shared derived characters
   - adaptive radiation
   - co-evolution

Key Concept Review

CHAPTER 7

2. Explain the work of the following individuals and how Darwin used their work to construct his theory of evolution.
   (a) Hutton k
   (b) Cuvier k
   (c) Malthus k

3. What other scientist had ideas similar to Darwin's theory of natural selection? k

4. (a) How did Darwin's visit to the Galapagos Islands affect his thoughts on evolution? k
   (b) Describe three different observations Darwin made on his voyage to other parts of the world. k

5. (a) Explain Darwin's theory of natural selection. k
   (b) Explain Lamarck's two ideas: principle of use and disuse, and the inheritance of acquired traits. k
   (c) How were Darwin's and Lamarck's ideas similar? k
   (d) How were Darwin's and Lamarck's ideas different? k
   (e) Why were Lamarck's hypotheses rejected? k

6. (a) What is variation? k
   (b) List two sources of variation. k
   (c) Why is variation within a species important? k

7. How are homologous structures used as evidence for evolution? Give an example. k

8. What are vestigial structures? Provide an example. k

9. How are similarities in embryos of different species evidence for evolution? k

10. How did Darwin use the geographical distribution of various organisms as evidence for evolution? Provide at least two examples. k

11. Explain how Rosemary and Peter Grant's work supported Darwin's theory of evolution. k

CHAPTER 8

12. Compare the similarities and differences between microevolution and macroevolution. Provide an example of each. k

13. (a) What is meant by Hardy-Weinberg equilibrium? k
    (b) Under what circumstances is it disrupted? k

14. How can you determine if two squirrels belong to the same species? k

15. Identify the similarities and differences between each of the following pairs of terms.
    (a) natural selection and genetic drift k
    (b) disruptive and stabilizing selection k
    (c) hybrid inviability and hybrid infertility k
    (d) temporal isolation and geographical isolation k

16. What is cumulative selection? Give an example. **ⓚ**

17. How does a penguin's flipper show that a penguin is more closely related to flying birds than to a shark? **ⓚ**

18. How is mimicry an example of co-evolution? **ⓚ**

19. Explain the following terms and provide an example of each, where possible.
    (a) adaptive radiation **ⓚ**
    (b) co-evolution **ⓚ**
    (c) punctuated equilibrium **ⓚ**

CHAPTER 9

20. Provide two examples of how molecular biology has been used to establish phylogenetic relationships. **ⓚ**

21. (a) What is the primary abiogenesis theory? **ⓚ**
    (b) Using the diagram, explain what each part of the Miller-Urey experimental set-up represented and explain the significance of this experiment to the primary abiogenesis theory. **ⓚ**

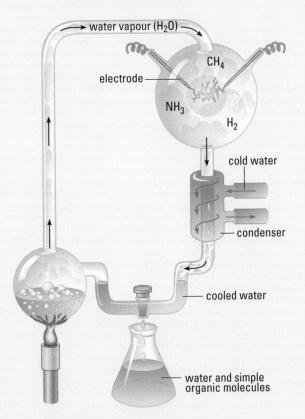

Question 21

22. Explain the significance of adding oxygen to Earth's atmosphere. **ⓚ**

23. What is the geological time scale? **ⓚ**

24. (a) How are homologous structures evidence for divergent evolution? **ⓚ**
    (b) How are analogous structures evidence for convergent evolution? **ⓚ**

25. What role does the environment play in convergent evolution? **ⓚ**

26. What do stromatolites tell us about evolution? **ⓚ**

27. What do cladograms show? **ⓚ**

28. Evolution is more likely to occur when a small population has been separated from the main population. Explain this phenomenon. **ⓚ**

29. Place the following items in order of occurrence: oxygen in the atmosphere, multicellular organisms, heterotrophic eukaryotes, prokaryotes, autotrophic eukaryotes. **ⓚ**

30. Why is the development of sexual reproduction so important in the history of life? **ⓚ**

31. What are the roles of homologous structures and molecular data in phylogeny? **ⓚ**

Connect Your Understanding

32. Examine the two images below.
    (a) How would Darwin explain the change in the population? **ⓐ**
    (b) How would Lamarck explain the change in the population? **ⓐ**

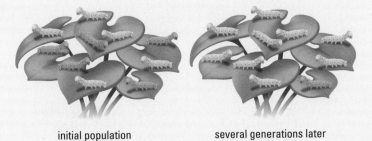

initial population   several generations later

Question 32

33. A mutation occurs in an individual in a population. What events must take place for the trait the mutation produces to become established in the population? **ⓐ**

34. Birds build nests. How might this behaviour contribute to fitness? **ⓐ**

35. Identify the similarities and differences between each of the following pairs of concepts.
    (a) fitness and adaptation **ⓚ**
    (b) artificial selection and natural selection **ⓚ**

©P

36. How do each of the following provide evidence for evolution?
  (a) A girl gets frequent strep throat infections. Over time the antibiotic she is given no longer cures the infection. ⓐ
  (b) In order to increase milk yield of his herd, a farmer selectively breeds only those cows that produce the most milk. ⓐ
  (c) The embryos of primates, birds, and fish all have pharyngeal pouches. ⓐ

37. Looking at the images below, identify:
  (a) the pairs of animals that have homologous structures. ⓐ
  (b) the pairs of animals that have analogous structures. ⓐ

Question 37

38. Explain each of the following human traits in terms of the theory of natural selection.
  (a) high variation of hair types ⓐ
  (b) low variation in the hemoglobin gene ⓐ
  (c) high variation in alleles for a noncoding gene (a gene that does not code for a protein) ⓐ
  (d) low variation in alleles for a coding gene (a gene that codes for a protein) ⓐ

39. Some mobile molluscs, such as octopuses, developed a centralized brain and head. Other molluscs that do not move, such as clams, did not develop a centralized brain and head. Form a hypothesis to explain this observation. ⓐ

40. Suppose that, in the laboratory, you were able to mate two organisms successfully and the hybrid produced viable offspring. Does this mean that the two populations belong to the same species? Justify your answer. ⓐ

41. How can the study of evolution help us understand the following.
  (a) pesticide resistance in insects ⓐ
  (b) high frequencies of Huntington's disease among Afrikaners ⓐ
  (c) diversity of tortoise species on the Galapagos Islands ⓐ

42. Examine the fossils below.
  (a) Which features in each fossil are adaptations for a particular type of movement? Explain why. ⓐ
  (b) Identify the homologous structures in the two fossils. ⓐ

Question 42

43. Many diseases, such as sickle-cell disease, are caused by recessive alleles. Give two reasons why natural selection has not eliminated these diseases completely from the population. ⓐ

44. A bridge is being constructed to cross a canyon. Predict how this might affect the evolution of species on each side of the canyon. ⓐ

45. Suggest reasons why genetic drift is not as big a factor in present-day human evolution as it was 20 000 or more years ago. ⓐ

46. Explain how the two species shown in the photograph have co-evolved. ⓐ

Question 46

47. A species of grass that was eaten by many species of herbivores develops a mutation that makes its leaves toxic to the animals that eat it. Predict what might happen to the herbivores that eat the plant.

48. Why are geological changes often accompanied by mass extinctions? **Ⓚ**

49. Form two hypotheses to account for the sudden appearance of species in the fossil record. **Ⓐ**

50. Compare the similarities and differences of the extinction of species through natural selection and mass extinction. **Ⓐ**

51. Why is it sometimes difficult to establish whether two fossils are of the same species or belong to similar yet different species, using fossil evidence alone? **Ⓐ**

52. *Homo sapiens* do not have tails, are bipedal, have a relatively large brain, and do not walk on their knuckles. Chimpanzees do not have tails, are not bipedal, have a relatively small brain, and walk on their knuckles. Fossil evidence suggests *Ardipithecus ramidus* had no tail, was bipedal, had a relatively small brain, and did not walk on its knuckles.
 (a) What characteristic do all three species have in common? **Ⓐ**
 (b) What feature did chimpanzees develop after the point at which ancestral chimpanzees and hominids diverged? **Ⓐ**
 (c) What feature did *Homo sapiens* develop after ancestral chimpanzees and hominids diverged? **Ⓐ**

53. A common misconception is that the human baby toe no longer has a function and so it is becoming progressively smaller and will eventually disappear. Explain why this is not true. **Ⓐ**

Skills Practice

54. (a) Use the data in the table to graph the changes in phenotypes over time. **Ⓒ**

Phenotypic Frequencies of Rabbit Coat Colours

Year	White (percent)	Light Brown (percent)	Dark Brown (percent)
1900	25	50	25
1920	20	40	40
1950	10	30	60

 (b) Analyze the graph to decide which type of selection is occurring. **ⓣ**
 (c) Is this an example of microevolution or macroevolution? Explain. **Ⓐ**
 (d) Provide a possible hypothesis to explain the change in phenotype. **ⓣ**

55. Examine the graph below depicting the approximate amount of oxygen in the atmosphere over time.

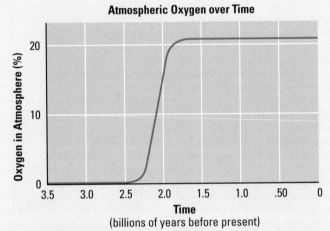

Atmospheric Oxygen over Time

Question 55

 (a) What event took place between 2.5 and 2.0 billion years ago? **ⓣ**
 (b) Form a hypothesis to explain why the oxygen content levelled off 2.0 billion years ago. **ⓣ**

56. Analyze the following cladogram to answer the questions below. **ⓣ**

Question 56

 (a) Which groups have amniotic eggs? **ⓣ**
 (b) What derived character is only shared by primates and rodents? **ⓣ**
 (c) Which organism shares the fewest derived characters? **ⓣ**

57. (a) Use the information in the table to construct a cladogram. **C**

Derived Characters for Selected Organisms

Organism	Specialized Shearing Teeth	Amniotic Egg	Hair	Retractable Claws
Dog	✓	✓	✓	X
Lizard	X	✓	X	X
Cat	✓	✓	✓	✓
Frog	X	X	X	X
Kangaroo	X	✓	✓	X

(b) What derived character was shared by all organisms but one? **a**

(c) What can you infer about the evolution of retractable claws as compared to the evolution of an amniotic egg? **a**

(d) A kangaroo is a marsupial. What derived character, not shown in the table, evolved after the branch split off from the main group? **a**

Revisit the Big Ideas and Fundamental Concepts

58. Outline the process of natural selection. **K**

59. Explain why today evolutionary biologists depend on both comparative anatomy and DNA evidence to establish evolutionary relationships. Why is DNA evidence alone insufficient? **a**

60. What are the advantages and disadvantages to using artificial insemination in agriculture? **a**

Science, Technology, Society, and the Environment

61. (a) Explain, using natural selection, how pesticide resistance develops. **K**

(b) Explain how refugia can reduce pesticide resistance. **K**

62. Some people dispute the effectiveness of the flu shot since you have to get a new one every year.

(a) Explain in evolutionary terms why a new flu shot every year is required. **K**

(b) Would you get the annual flu shot? Use a plus-minus-interesting chart to help you form an opinion. **C**

63. Choose one method you have learned about in this unit by which humans have interfered with natural evolutionary mechanisms. Evaluate whether or not we should interfere with nature in this way. **t**

Reflection

64. What activities in your life do you think might affect the evolution of other species? Explain. **C**

65. What aspects of this unit confirmed your prior knowledge of evolution? Explain. **C**

66. Did anything you learned in this unit contradict your prior knowledge of evolution? Explain. **C**

C14 **Unit Task**

BIOLOGY SOURCE

Assessing Conservation Strategies

Question

How effective is a particular conservation strategy in protecting an endangered species from extinction?

Task Overview

You will choose one of several different conservation strategies to research. You will analyze any political, economic, social, technological, and environmental issues surrounding your conservation strategy. You will then decide whether or not your conservation strategy is a feasible option for protecting a particular endangered species. You will present your findings in a format of your choice.

Figure 9.32 One conservation strategy involves storing frozen cells from endangered species for future use.

UNIT D

Animals: Structure and Function

Unit Contents

Unit Task

In this unit, you will learn about the structures and functions of the digestive, circulatory, and respiratory systems and how they interact with each other. In the Unit Task, you will assume the role of a health reporter who investigates the nature of a disorder of one of the systems. You will report on how the disorder affects both the individual and Canadian society as a whole.

DISCOVERING BIOLOGY

These may look like models of human bodies that have been designed and built by scientists, but they are real human bodies that have been preserved by a process called Plastination. In Plastination, a plastic, rubber-like material replaces fluids in the body and halts the body's decomposition. Once the body has been preserved this way, scientists can study cells, slices of tissue, organs, systems, and the interrelationships between all these components of the body. What other technologies have allowed us a glimpse into the relationships between body systems?

Animals obtain and process nutrients for energy and growth from the food they eat.

Scientists have wondered why some humans have a "sweet tooth." Recent research has investigated connections between the food we choose to eat, the DNA or genetic information in our cells, and the structures found in our digestive systems. There are also studies of the DNA of animals with different diets, such as lions and red pandas. The results showed that some meat-eating animals, such as lions, do not have genetic information or structures needed to sense or taste sweet foods. However, other animals, such as red pandas, have genetic information and structures for tasting sweetness (Figure 10.1). Interestingly, the red panda also showed a preference for artificially sweetened foods.

Scientists have hypothesized that the way each individual tastes food is unique and is related to the structures involved in tasting. Research about the genetic information and structures needed for tasting could lead to a better understanding of how humans make food choices and may ultimately be used to improve nutritional health.

Figure 10.1 The red panda eats mostly plants and has a preference for sweet foods.

10.1 Nutrition and Digestion

Section Summary

- Food contains the nutrients that we need for energy and growth.
- A balanced diet provides fuel and building materials and promotes good health.
- You must process food in your digestive system in order to use the nutrients effectively.
- Food processing occurs in four stages.

You use chemicals from the food you eat to provide building blocks to build molecules, to generate energy for your body's activities, and to assemble essential nutrients that your body cannot produce.

It All Starts with a Healthy Diet

Think about taking a big bite of a tasty sandwich (Figure 10.2). You take a bite, chew, and swallow. You probably are not saying to yourself, "There, I am providing my cells with the chemicals they need to live and grow." However, that is exactly what you are doing.

Your body is made from the raw materials in the food you eat. In addition to supplying building materials for your body, food provides energy for all the work done by your cells and supplies over 40 substances that your body needs but cannot produce itself. **Nutrients** are the chemicals in the food you eat that help your body perform all its functions.

There are six types of nutrients in food: carbohydrates, proteins, fats, vitamins, minerals, and water. Carbohydrates, proteins, fats, and water are sometimes called *macronutrients*, because your body needs so much of them on a daily basis. Most vitamins and minerals are classed as *micronutrients*, because you need far less of them on a daily basis. When you eat a healthy diet, you provide your body with the variety of nutrients it needs and you help prevent health problems from occurring.

Figure 10.2 When you eat a variety of healthy foods, you provide your body with all six types of nutrients.

Processing Molecules

The food you eat usually contains large, complex molecules. These large molecules are too big to pass through your cell membranes into your cells. In addition, these larger molecules are not exactly the same as the smaller molecules that are found in your body. Your digestive system must disassemble the food you eat into smaller molecules. Your cells can then use these molecules as a source of energy or assemble them into more complex molecules and use them to build and maintain cell structure and function.

Suppose you were eating a cheese sandwich. The cheese is partly made of proteins. However, the proteins in the cheese are large molecules that your cells cannot use in their present state. Your digestive system disassembles the proteins into their basic "building block" molecules. Your cells can then use the building blocks to assemble your own proteins. All organisms use the same components to make their molecules. For example, lions, pandas, humans, and trees all make their proteins from the same 20 kinds of building block molecules.

Figure 10.3 Food is a part of many social activities.

Nutrients

Most of us eat because we enjoy our food. Meals are often a social time and are frequently a key part of celebrations (Figure 10.3). However, in reality, we eat food because our bodies need the nutrients in the food. When we eat the right types of foods in the right amounts, we are eating for health.

Carbohydrates

Carbohydrates are compounds made up of carbon, hydrogen, and oxygen atoms and are the major source of energy for your body. You can use carbohydrates as an energy source just minutes after a meal or you can store them for later use.

Foods that contain simple carbohydrates include sugars, such as from fruit, honey, and milk. Sugar molecules, particularly the type of sugar called **glucose**, are the main fuel supply for the work done by your cells. Your cells break down glucose molecules and extract their stored energy. Your cells also use the carbon chains of simple sugars as raw material to manufacture other kinds of molecules. Glucose molecules that your cells do not use immediately are incorporated into larger carbohydrates, or are used to make fat molecules.

Starches, such as from whole-grain cereals and bread, rice, and potatoes, are complex carbohydrates. Complex carbohydrates are broken down by your digestive system into simple sugars. The simple sugars are absorbed into the blood and carried to cells in the body. Excess blood sugar is converted into **glycogen**, which is a chain of many glucose molecules. In humans, most glycogen is stored in the liver and in muscle and fat cells. When the body needs energy, it breaks down glycogen, releasing glucose.

Fibre from Plant Foods

Many fruits and vegetables, whole-grain breads, bran, and wheat germ contain cellulose. Cellulose is a complex carbohydrate that is often called **fibre** (Figure 10.4). Although the human digestive system cannot break down cellulose, you need to include it in your diet. Fibre supplies bulk to help your muscles move food and wastes though your digestive system. Fibre may also have other benefits, such as reducing the risk of heart disease.

Figure 10.4 Many fruits and vegetables are a source of fibre for your diet.

Concept Check

1. What are the six types of nutrients?
2. What are the two types of carbohydrates?
3. Why do you need fibre in your diet?

Proteins

A **protein** is a complex molecule that is constructed from 20 kinds of smaller molecules called **amino acids**. Proteins contribute to almost all your day-to-day functions. For example, proteins form hair and muscles, and they provide long-term nutrient storage. Some proteins circulate in the blood and defend the body from harmful micro-organisms.

©P

Other proteins convey messages from one cell to another. There are also proteins that work with enzymes to control the chemical reactions in a cell. **Enzymes** are proteins that speed up specific chemical reactions without being consumed in the reaction.

There are eight amino acids, called essential amino acids, that your cells cannot make from other molecules. If you lack even one essential amino acid, you cannot make protein properly. Animal products such as meat, milk, eggs, and cheese provide all eight essential amino acids (Figure 10.5). People who do not eat animal products must eat combinations of plant foods to obtain all the essential amino acids. Some vegetarian combinations of complete protein include corn and beans, rice and lentils, and hummus (chickpeas and sesame seed paste) with pita bread.

Figure 10.5 Your body cannot store excess amino acids, so you need to eat protein every day.

Fats

Fats, also called lipids, are molecules formed from fatty acids and glycerol. Fats store energy in your body and help your body absorb fat-soluble vitamins. Fatty tissues cushion your organs and provide your body with insulation. There are several types of fats:

- *Saturated fats* Some fats have only single bonds between carbon atoms in the fatty acids. Each of these carbon atoms has the maximum number of hydrogen atoms, so the fat is called "saturated." Most animal fats, such as lard and butter, are saturated fats. Diets rich in saturated fats may promote the build-up of fat deposits within the walls of blood vessels, which can reduce blood flow and contribute to heart disease. Only a small percentage of your daily intake of fats should come from saturated fats.

- *Unsaturated fats* Fats in fruits, vegetables, nuts, seeds, and fish have at least one double bond in a fatty acid chain, so we say the fat is "unsaturated." Unsaturated fats, such as olive oil and sunflower seed oil, are usually liquids at room temperature. Small amounts of unsaturated fats are an important part of a healthy diet (Figure 10.6).

- *Trans fats* Some unsaturated fats have been partially hydrogenated, which means they have been processed to accept more hydrogen atoms. Hydrogenated fats, also called "trans fats," are solid at room temperature and have a longer shelf life than other unsaturated fats. For example, margarine that is solid at room temperature is a trans fat. Trans fats are often used in frying fast foods. You should avoid consuming trans fats as they contribute to heart disease and other health problems.

Figure 10.6 Examples of unsaturated vegetable oils (from left to right): canola, olive, soy, and sunflower seed oil

BIOLOGY·SOURCE

Suggested Activity
- D1 Quick Lab Overview on page 284

Vitamins and Minerals

Vitamins are organic nutrients that you need in small amounts to regulate your body processes and perform chemical reactions. Organic nutrients are nutrients that contain carbon. If you picture carbohydrates, proteins, and fats as the building blocks, then vitamins are the tools to help put them together.

There are two types of vitamins: water-soluble and fat-soluble. Water-soluble vitamins, such as vitamin C and the B vitamins, cannot be stored in your body and should be included in your diet every day. Small amounts of fat-soluble vitamins, such as vitamins A, D, E, and K, can be stored in the fatty tissue of your body for future use.

Minerals are inorganic nutrients and do not contain carbon. You need a variety of minerals in your diet, such as calcium, iron, phosphorus, copper, sodium, and zinc, to perform many different tasks. For example, you use calcium to make bones and teeth. You need to consume foods rich in minerals each day to replace the minerals you lose in sweat, urine, and digestive wastes.

Vitamins and minerals are found naturally in many foods such as meat, eggs, dairy products, whole-grain products, tofu, green leafy vegetables, and some fruits. People who are not able to eat enough of a variety of foods from the basic groups sometimes take vitamin and mineral supplements. However, large doses of vitamin and mineral supplements may be harmful, so it is important to read the recommended dose on the labels carefully and consult your health practitioner.

Water

Water is the most important nutrient and you need to drink it regularly (Figure 10.7). Every one of your cells needs water to complete its processes. Many of the body's chemical reactions take place in water. Water makes up the bulk of blood, extra-cellular fluid, and other bodily fluids. Many guidelines suggest drinking at least 1 L of water each day. You need even more water when you are physically active and in hot weather. If you do not take in enough water to replace what you lose through sweat, urine, and respiration, you can suffer from dehydration, which leads to problems with many body systems.

Table 10.1 summarizes a few of the many functions of nutrients in your body.

Figure 10.7 Make a habit of drinking plain, pure water to satisfy your thirst.

Table 10.1 Some Functions of Nutrients

Nutrient	Some Functions
Carbohydrates	Provide carbon chains for building other molecules; used as primary fuel source
Proteins	Provide raw materials for growth and repair, and to make enzymes and other proteins; help transport oxygen; may be used as a fuel
Fats	Provide raw materials for building cellular membranes, nerve cells, and certain hormones; used as fuel
Vitamins	Help growth of skin cells; improve night vision and blood clotting; metabolize energy; prevent cellular damage; increase absorption of other nutrients; assist enzymes
Minerals	Help form and maintain bones and teeth; maintain acid-base balance; metabolize energy; improve muscle function
Water	Makes up the bulk of blood and other bodily fluids

Concept Check

1. What are the building blocks of proteins called?
2. What are enzymes?
3. What are three types of fats?

Food as Fuel

During the process of cellular respiration, molecules such as glucose make cellular energy by reacting with oxygen. Your cells convert about 40 percent of the energy from food into energy for performing cell functions. The other 60 percent of the energy is converted to thermal energy, which radiates from your body in the form of heat.

The heat generated by cellular respiration is not wasted. Retaining some of this heat enables your body to maintain a constant temperature, even when the surrounding air is cold. When you are sitting still in class, you radiate about as much heat as a 100-W light bulb. When you exercise, your cells increase the rate of cellular respiration. This is why you feel warm after exercising. Your body loses excess heat through sweating and other cooling methods.

Calories

You have probably heard the term "calorie" used to refer to food or exercise. A **calorie** is the amount of energy required to raise the temperature of 1 g of water by 1°C. The calories you will learn about in this unit are actually "dietary calories," which are often written with an uppercase C. One dietary calorie is equal to 1000 calories.

Cells can use carbohydrates, proteins, or fats to generate energy through cellular respiration. Fats are especially rich in energy, containing more than twice the energy of carbohydrates per gram. Fat contains about 9 calories per gram, while carbohydrates and proteins contain about 4 calories per gram. Why the difference? The carbon atoms in fats generally have more carbon-to-hydrogen bonds than the carbon atoms in carbohydrates or proteins. Breaking these bonds releases a great deal of energy, so a gram of fat releases more energy than a gram of protein or carbohydrate.

You must consume a minimum number of calories every day just to maintain the metabolic processes that sustain life. For this basic maintenance, plus energy needed for an active lifestyle, female teenagers require about 2200 calories each day and male teenagers require about 2500 calories. Most of the calories you consume each day should come from carbohydrates as shown in Table 10.2.

We need to have a balance between calories consumed in food and calories spent in daily activities and exercise. Daily physical activity of at least 30 minutes helps to burn any excess calories and maintain a healthful weight. Physical activity also strengthens the heart, bones, and muscles (Figure 10.8).

Figure 10.8 Being active every day helps you achieve and maintain a healthy weight.

Table 10.2 Recommended Daily Intake of Nutrients

Nutrient	Percent of Total Daily Calories
Carbohydrates	45–65
Proteins	10–30
Fats	25–35

Nutrition Facts		
Per 125 mL (87 g)		
Amount		**% Daily Value**
Calories 80		
Fat 0.5 g		1 %
Saturated 0 g + Trans 0 g		0 %
Cholesterol 0 mg		
Sodium 0 mg		0 %
Carbohydrate 18 g		6 %
Fibre 2 g		8 %
Sugars 2 g		
Protein 3 g		
Vitamin A	2 %	Vitamin C 10 %
Calcium	0 %	Iron 2 %

Figure 10.9 Canada's standardized nutritional labels help Canadians to make informed food choices.

BIOLOGY•SOURCE

Explore More

What other information can you find about food labels to help you make healthy choices?

Figure 10.10 Omega fatty acids are unsaturated fats that have been shown to have health benefits.

Figure 10.11 You may have noticed the label "probiotic" on some foods.

Read Before You Eat

The science of nutrition is the study of food and its effects on the body. Nutritionists have developed many tools to help people plan healthful diets. One of these tools is the nutrition label found on packaged foods.

In order to help consumers identify the nutritional value of foods, Health Canada requires that nutritional information be placed in a standardized manner on all packaged foods. These nutrition labels show the nutrient contents and nutritional claims in a format that is easy to read and understand. Figure 10.9 shows a typical nutritional label.

Reading food labels can help you track if you are meeting your daily requirement for important nutrients, such as dietary fibre, protein, vitamins, and healthy fats. The labels also identify ingredients such as unhealthy fats, sugars, and sodium that may contribute to heart disease, high blood pressure, and stroke. By reading the labels on foods, you can make informed choices about what you eat.

Foods that May Fight Disease

Although everyone can benefit from understanding general guidelines for healthy eating, individuals vary in their nutritional needs. Food industries are aggressively developing foods designed to meet the needs of individual consumers. A new branch of the food industry called "functional foods" or "nutraceuticals" is based on the idea that foods can be disease-fighters. A **nutraceutical** is a substance that is purified from foods and taken like a medicine to provide health benefits including disease prevention. An example of a nutraceutical is an omega-3 fish oil pill that is taken as a supplement (Figure 10.10).

Although a relatively new term, a **functional food** is a food that has health benefits, including disease prevention, that are beyond the normal nutritional benefit of the food. Fruits and vegetables that contain vitamins such as A, C, E and beta-carotene have been identified as some good candidates. You may have noticed orange juice enriched with calcium, eggs enriched with omega-3, and milk enriched with vitamin D. A study conducted by the National Cancer Institute in the United States has selected foods such as garlic, cabbage, carrots, licorice, soy, and ginger as possible cancer-fighters. Consuming wheat bran can reduce the risk of colon cancer and breast cancer. Canada currently has hundreds of companies involved in the functional food industry and is becoming a world leader in the supply of such foods.

Probiotics

One of the fastest-growing areas of dietary products is **probiotics**, which are foods that contain substances that support health and that may help to strengthen the body's natural defence against disease.

You may know that bacteria are numerous and are found in our environment and on our skin. However, you may not realize that bacteria live inside your digestive system and that some of these bacteria actually make you healthier. There has been extensive research into the positive health benefits of these intestinal bacteria. Antibiotics kill bacteria in the body, including some of these helpful intestinal bacteria. Probiotic products, such as probiotic yogurt, help to add beneficial bacteria back into the large intestine (Figure 10.11).

Industry experts expect that there will be continued growth in the "designer" food business. As consumers become more knowledgeable about the health benefits of foods and as the costs of health care rise, there will be a continued demand for foods that fight disease. In addition, these new markets offer financial opportunities for food producers and grocers in Canada.

Canada's Food Guide

To eat in a healthy way, you need to eat the right foods and the right amount of different foods. One way to get the information you need to make healthy choices is to use Canada's Food Guide to Healthy Eating. In Canada's Food Guide, shown in Figure 10.12, you can see the recommended types of foods and the number of servings of those foods that you should consume each day in order to have a healthy diet.

A sample one serving size of vegetables and fruit is a medium fruit or 125 mL vegetables. A sample grain product serving is half a bagel or a small waffle. Sample milk and alternatives servings include 200 mL milk or 200 mL yogurt. Sample meat and alternatives servings include 30 mL peanut butter or 75 g chicken.

Canada's Food Guide also provides the guidelines shown in Table 10.3.

	Recommended Number of Food Guide Servings per day			
	Children 2–3 years old	Children 4–13 years old	Teens and Adults (Females)	Teens and Adults (Males)
Vegetables and Fruit Fresh, frozen and canned.	4	5–6	7–8	7–10
Grain Products	3	4–6	6–7	7–8
Milk and Alternatives	2	2–4	Teens 3–4 / Adults (19–50 years) 2 / Adults (51+ years) 3	Teens 3–4 / Adults (19–50 years) 2 / Adults (51+ years) 3
Meat and Alternatives	1	1–2	2	3

Figure 10.12 Canada's Food Guide recommended daily servings

Table 10.3 Healthy Eating Guidelines

Food Groups	Guidelines
Vegetables and fruits	Eat at least one dark green and one orange vegetable each day. Choose vegetables and fruit prepared with little or no added fat, sugar, and salt. Have vegetables and fruit more often than juice.
Grain products	Make at least half of your grain products whole grain each day. Choose grain products that are lower in fat, sugar, or salt.
Milk and alternatives	Drink skim, 1%, or 2% milk each day. Select lower-fat milk alternatives.
Meat and alternatives	Have meat alternatives such as beans, lentils, and tofu often. Eat at least two Food Guide servings of fish each week. Select lean meat and alternatives prepared with little or no added fats and salt.
Other	Include a small amount of unsaturated fat each day. Satisfy your thirst with water. Limit foods and beverages high in calories, fat, sugar, and salt. Be active each day.

BIOLOGY•SOURCE

Suggested Activity
- D2 Quick Lab Overview on page 284

BIOLOGY•SOURCE

Take It Further

One example of a healthy eating plan comes from the diet of people in countries that border the Mediterranean Sea. The Mediterranean diet emphasizes whole grains, fruits, vegetables, and healthy fats. This diet may reduce heart disease and cancer. Create a sample week's menu of foods you like to eat based on the Mediterranean diet.

Concept Check

1. What is a calorie?

2. What information can you find on a food label?

3. What information can you find in Canada's Food Guide?

Nutritional Disorders Damage Health

Purpose

To explore the important roles that vitamins play in maintaining a healthy body

Activity Overview

Your body needs vitamins to aid in essential chemical reactions. In this activity, you will read cases and examine clues to help you discover which vitamins may be missing in the subjects' diets.

Your teacher will give you a full copy of this activity.

Prelab Questions

Consider the questions below before beginning this activity.

1. What roles do vitamins play in keeping your body healthy?

2. What might happen if your diet is lacking in one or more vitamins?

Figure 10.13 A diet rich in a variety of foods helps provide the vitamins you need to be healthy.

You Are What You Eat

Purpose

To interpret a food label, understand the relationship between calorie intake and energy needs, and plan for healthy eating

Activity Overview

One of the ways that you can maintain good health is to eat a nutritious diet on a regular basis. By consuming foods from a variety of food groups, you ensure that you are obtaining necessary nutrients and also limiting your exposure to harmful substances. Diets that are high in fats, sugars, and salt may increase your risk of heart disease, cancer, and other diseases.

One of your tasks in this activity is to interpret a basic food label (Figure 10.14). Your teacher will give you a copy of the full activity.

Prelab Questions

Consider the questions below before beginning this activity.

1. Why does a person require a minimum number of calories per day?

2. Why would a diet high in fats, sugars, and salt increase your risk of certain diseases?

3. List three types of information that can be found on a food label.

Figure 10.14 Reading food labels can help you decide which foods to eat.

Key Concept Review

1. What are three main functions of food in your body?

2. (a) What are six nutrients that may be found in food?
   (b) Give an example of a source of each nutrient.

3. Which three nutrients may be used as a source of fuel for your body?

4. (a) Name the two main types of carbohydrates.
   (b) State their functions in your diet.

5. What is the difference between glucose and glycogen?

6. Describe three functions of proteins.

7. Why is water considered to be the most important nutrient?

8. (a) What is a calorie a measure of?
   (b) Approximately how many calories do you need to consume each day?

9. What information is contained in a nutritional label?

10. How are nutritional labels helpful to consumers?

11. Explain why some products are called "probiotic."

12. What is the purpose of Canada's Food Guide?

Connect Your Understanding

13. Explain why your body must process food in order for you to use it.

14. Why do you need to eat a variety of foods each day?

15. Which do you think contains more fibre, whole-grain products or products made from processed grains? Explain.

16. Create a Venn diagram to show how saturated fats and unsaturated fats are similar and different.

17. Why is it important to ensure that your diet has the right amount of vitamins and minerals?

18. Name two sources of information that can assist you in eating in a healthy way.

19. (a) What is the difference between antibiotics and probiotics?
    (b) Why might a pharmacist advise you to eat yogurt while you are taking prescription antibiotics?

20. Create your own healthy menu for a typical school day. Use Canada's Food Guide to Healthy Eating to help you plan your menu.

21. (a) Explain the meaning of the term "functional food."
    (b) What is an example of a functional food that you consume on a regular basis?

22. Refer to the table below.
    (a) Why does jogging burn more calories per minute than walking?
    (b) How long would each activity take to burn off an entire eight-piece pizza?

Calories Used by a 68-kg Person During Different Activities

	Jogging	Swimming	Walking
Calories burned per min	11.7	8.9	2.6
Time to burn calories in one slice of cheese pizza	26 min	34 min	1 h 55 min

Reflection

23. Have you changed your eating habits based on diets and nutritional claims presented in the media? Why or why not?

For more questions, go to BIOLOGY•SOURCE

10.2 Structure and Function of the Digestive System

Section Summary

- Food is processed as it moves through a tube called the alimentary canal.
- The digestive system consists of six major digestive organs and several accessory organs and glands.
- Some digestive disorders include ulcers, inflammatory bowel disease, constipation, and diarrhea.

Figure 10.15 Spallanzani's subjects included both birds and humans.

The famous scientist Isaac Newton is thought to have said, "If I have seen further, it is because I have stood on the shoulders of giants." Like Newton's discoveries, our modern technologies are due in part to the science of previous centuries. For instance, the search to understand how our bodies digest food actually began hundreds of years ago. In the 1700s, a professor of natural history, Lazzaro Spallanzani, devised a simple experiment to find out how food was broken down. He had his subjects swallow a small sponge attached to a thread (Figure 10.15). After a time, he pulled the sponge out and examined it. Spallanzani observed that the juice that filled the sponge could break down meat. He concluded that an area in the body produced special juice that could digest food.

Spallanzani's theory overturned the previous theory, which was that food was "cooked" in the heat of the stomach. His investigation used little of what we call "technology," but still demonstrated the process of inquiry. The scientists who today use computers, lasers, and biotechnology to study digestion are, in fact, "standing on the shoulders" of curious thinkers like Spallanzani who lived hundreds of years ago.

Four Stages of Food Processing

Investigations into the digestive systems of many animals have shown that there are four steps in processing nutrients from food: ingestion, digestion, absorption, and elimination (Figure 10.16 below and Figures 10.17 and 10.18 on the next page).

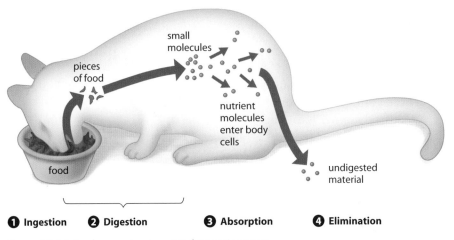

❶ **Ingestion**   ❷ **Digestion**   ❸ **Absorption**   ❹ **Elimination**

Figure 10.16 Food processing occurs in four main stages.

❶   **Ingestion**
                    Ingestion is the act of eating or drinking.

❷   **Digestion**
Digestion is the process of breaking food down into molecules that are small
enough for the body to absorb.
- **Mechanical digestion**, such as chewing, chops and grinds food into
  smaller pieces, increasing its surface area.
- **Chemical digestion** breaks the chemical bonds within the large
  molecules of carbohydrates, fats, and proteins and produces smaller
  molecules during hydrolysis. **Hydrolysis** is a process that breaks bonds
  in food molecules by adding water to them in the presence of specific
  enzymes. (Figure 10.17).

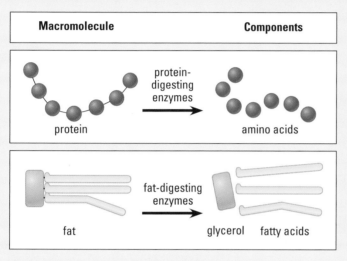

Figure 10.17 Examples of chemical digestion

❸   **Absorption**
Absorption occurs in the small intestine, where the cells absorb small
molecules, such as amino acids and simple sugars. From the small intestine,
the molecules enter the circulatory system. The molecules are transported in
the blood to body cells, where they join to make bigger molecules or are
broken down to provide energy. If there are more molecules than are needed
immediately, they are converted to fat for storage.

❹   **Elimination**
Elimination is the process of removing from the digestive tract any
undigested materials. These materials travel through the large intestine and
are eliminated as feces.

Figure 10.18 A food-processing flowchart

BIOLOGY•SOURCE

Explore More

How does hydrolysis help you digest
a pizza?

Digestion Occurs in a Tube

Some animals, such as the sea anemone in Figure 10.19(a), process nutrients in a digestive sac. In a digestive sac, food enters and wastes exit through the same opening.

In more complex animals, such as the microscopic nematode shown in Figure 10.19(b), digestion occurs in a tube called an alimentary canal. An **alimentary canal** is a digestive tract with two openings, a mouth and an anus. Food enters through the mouth at one end of the alimentary canal and is churned and mixed as it travels along the tube. Further along the tube, nutrients are absorbed from the digested food and then the wastes are disposed of through the anus. An alimentary canal is a more efficient than a digestive sac for obtaining nutrients from food because an alimentary canal has more specialized regions for processing food.

Another name for the alimentary canal is the gastrointestinal tract or GI tract. The combining form *gastr-* means "stomach" in Greek, and "intestinal" refers to intestines.

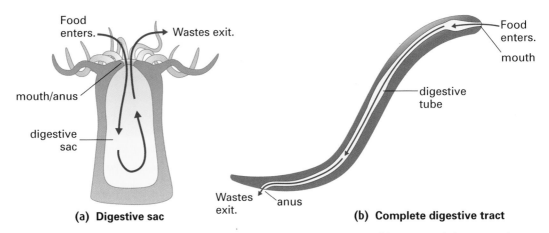

Food enters.   Wastes exit.

mouth/anus

digestive sac

(a) Digestive sac

Food enters.

mouth

digestive tube

Wastes exit.   anus

(b) Complete digestive tract

Figure 10.19 (a) A sea anemone has a simple digestive sac. (b) A nematode has a complete digestive tract.

Alimentary Canal Length

The length of an animal's alimentary canal is often correlated with diet. In general, herbivores and omnivores have longer alimentary canals, relative to their body size, than carnivores. Vegetation is more difficult to digest than meat because it contains cell walls. A longer alimentary canal provides more time for digestion and more surface area for absorption of nutrients.

In humans and many other animals, the alimentary canal is much longer than the distance between the mouth and anus. A person 1.8 m tall can have a 9-m alimentary canal. The tube fits inside the body because portions wind and loop back and forth.

Concept Check

1. What are the four stages of food processing?
2. What is hydrolysis?
3. What are two advantages of a longer alimentary canal?

Specialized Organs

Your body is made from nutrients such as carbohydrates, proteins, and fats. These are the same types of nutrients that your digestive system breaks down during digestion. So you might wonder how you can digest food without digesting your own cells and tissues. Most animal species process food in specialized organs — an adaptation that avoids the risk of self-digestion.

In humans, six main organs make up the alimentary canal: the mouth, pharynx, esophagus, stomach, small intestine, and large intestine (Figure 10.20). Accessory glands and organs include the salivary glands, pancreas, liver, and gallbladder, which secrete digestive juices into the alimentary canal.

Mouth

Your mouth functions both in ingestion and in the beginning of digestion (Figure 10.21). Your teeth and tongue work together to accomplish mechanical digestion. For example, your tongue moves food around so that it comes in contact with your teeth. Your incisors, cuspids, and bicuspids cut into and tear at food. Then your molars grind and crush food into a fine paste that can be swallowed. This makes the food easier to swallow and exposes more surface area so that chemical digestion can occur more easily.

As your teeth cut and grind the food, your salivary glands secrete saliva. **Saliva** is a watery liquid that contains digestive enzymes, mucus, and other chemicals to help chemically digest your food.

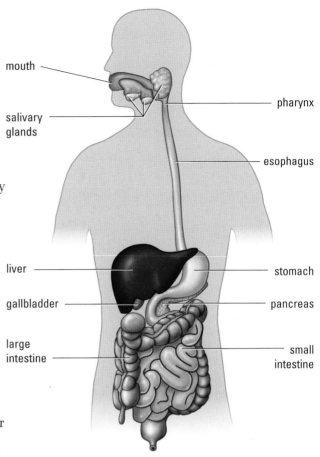

Figure 10.20 The human digestive system

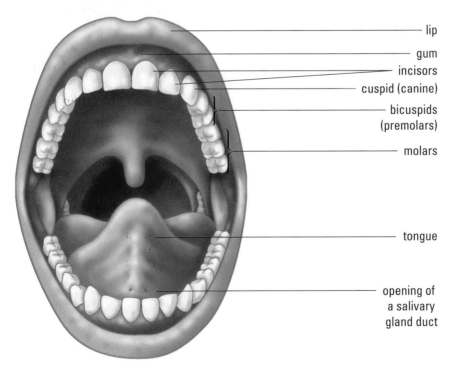

Figure 10.21 The mouth functions in both ingestion and digestion. The different shapes of your teeth are specialized for cutting and grinding food.

Saliva

Digestive enzymes in saliva include amylase, which breaks the chemical bonds in starches, such as pasta and bread, to form sugars. This is why if you chew on a starchy food long enough it will begin to taste sweet. Another enzyme, lysozyme, helps fight infection by digesting the cell walls of bacteria that may enter the mouth along with food.

Saliva contains **mucus**, a sticky substance that coats and lubricates the food so that it can slide down the tube without harming the tissues that line the tube. Chemicals in saliva neutralize certain acids in foods, protecting your teeth from decay. Saliva also helps to moisten the food and make it easier to chew. In a typical day, salivary glands in your mouth secrete more than 1 L of saliva.

Pharynx

The tongue pushes each chewed clump of food, called a **bolus**, down the throat. The upper portion of the throat, called the **pharynx**, is a short tube that is shared by the digestive system and respiratory system. When you swallow, a cartilage flap called the **epiglottis** temporarily seals off the airway and prevents food from moving into the air passageway as it passes through the pharynx and into the esophagus.

Esophagus

The bolus enters a long, muscle-encased tube called the **esophagus**, which connects the pharynx to the stomach. Although the esophagus is oriented vertically in your body, gravity is not the reason that food moves toward your stomach. Instead, food is pushed through the esophagus by a series of muscle contractions called **peristalsis**. During peristalsis the muscles contract in a wave-like motion that forces the bolus of food toward the stomach (Figure 10.22).

After the food passes into the stomach, a muscular valve called a **sphincter** closes the esophagus and prevents the contents of the stomach from flowing back into the esophagus. If the muscle opens at an inappropriate time, such as caused by overeating, acid from the stomach can flow backward into the esophagus, creating a burning sensation called heartburn. Despite its name, heartburn is not related to the heart.

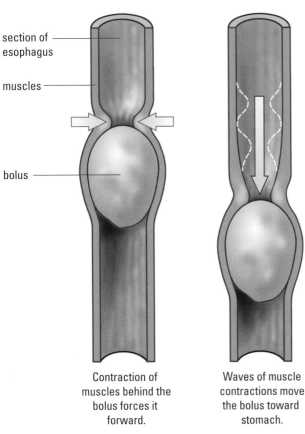

section of esophagus

muscles

bolus

Contraction of muscles behind the bolus forces it forward.

Waves of muscle contractions move the bolus toward stomach.

Figure 10.22 A wave of muscular contractions called peristalsis pushes food through your esophagus.

Stomach

The stomach is an elastic, muscular sac that continues the chemical and mechanical digestion of food. With its accordion-like folds and highly elastic wall, your stomach can stretch to hold up to 2 L of food and drink, enough to satisfy your body's needs for many hours.

Chemical Digestion in the Stomach

After the bolus enters the stomach, it is bathed in a liquid called **gastric juice**, which is a mixture of hydrochloric acid, enzymes, and mucus secreted by glands in the stomach lining (Figure 10.23). Hydrochloric acid breaks apart the cells in food and kills many of the bacteria swallowed with food. One of the gastric enzymes, pepsin, assists in breaking large protein molecules into smaller molecules. Mucus lubricates and protects the stomach wall from the hydrochloric acid and prevents the stomach from digesting itself. Even with the protection of mucus, the cells of the stomach lining are constantly eroded. Every three days, enough new cells are generated to completely replace the stomach lining.

The cells in the gastric glands do not secrete gastric juice constantly. When you see, smell, or taste food, a signal from your brain to your stomach stimulates your gastric glands to secrete gastric juice. Your gastric glands secrete as much as 3 L litres of gastric juice each day.

Figure 10.23 Pits in the lining of the stomach secrete gastric juice. (magnification 700×)

Mechanical Digestion in the Stomach

About every 20 seconds, the stomach contents are mixed by the churning action of muscles in the stomach wall (Figure 10.24). This form of mechanical digestion turns the bolus into an acidic, nutrient-rich liquid called **chyme**. The stomach muscles contract, creating a churning motion that stirs the chyme and eventually forces it into the small intestine. A sphincter regulates the flow of chyme into the small intestine. It typically takes two to six hours after a meal for the stomach to empty.

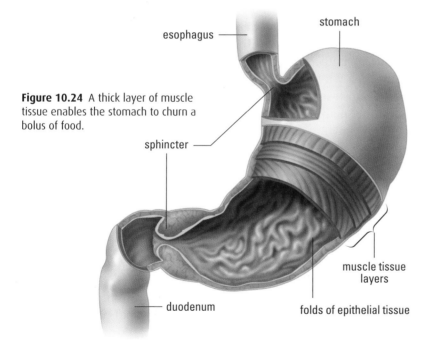

Figure 10.24 A thick layer of muscle tissue enables the stomach to churn a bolus of food.

esophagus

stomach

sphincter

muscle tissue layers

duodenum

folds of epithelial tissue

Concept Check

1. What six organs make up the digestive system?
2. By what process does food move from the pharynx to the stomach?
3. How does a bolus turn into chyme?

Small Intestine

From the stomach, chyme passes into the small intestine (Figure 10.25). The small intestine is a long (6 m), narrow (2.5 cm) tube where digestion is completed and absorption of most nutrients takes place. Digestion mostly occurs in the first portion of the small intestine, while absorption occurs along the rest of its length. Peristalsis moves chyme along the small intestine, a journey that takes about three to five hours.

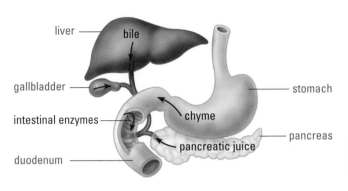

liver
bile
gallbladder
intestinal enzymes
chyme
stomach
pancreatic juice
pancreas
duodenum

Figure 10.25 The passage of chyme into the small intestine

BIOLOGY•SOURCE

Suggested Activity

• D3 Inquiry Activity Overview on page 296

The first section of the small intestine is called the **duodenum**. Fats remain undigested until they reach the duodenum because they are insoluble in water. So how do fats undergo hydrolysis? As chyme enters the duodenum, it mixes with several digestive juices. One of these digestive juices is a liquid called bile. **Bile** is a yellow or greenish alkaline liquid produced outside of the small intestine by the body's largest internal organ, the liver. Bile is stored in a sac-like structure called the gallbladder until it is secreted into the duodenum. Although bile contains no enzymes, it has substances that help prepare fats for hydrolysis. Fats tend to clump together, making it difficult for enzymes to reach the molecules. Bile separates small fat droplets, which enables digestive enzymes to break down the fats more efficiently.

The pancreas also secretes digestive juice. **Pancreatic juice** is a clear alkaline liquid that neutralizes the acidic chyme and contains enzymes that further break down carbohydrates, proteins, and fats. Pancreatic enzymes, along with enzymes secreted by the lining of the small intestine, complete the chemical digestion of food.

Completing Digestion

As an end result of digestion, carbohydrates are broken down to form sugars, which provide your cells with a source of energy. These sugars are also a source of chains of carbon atoms that your body can use to construct other molecules containing carbon. The complete digestion of proteins results in amino acids that your cells use to build proteins. The complete digestion of fats results in molecules of fatty acids and glycerol. Your cells use these molecules to build fats.

Absorbing Nutrients

The small intestine is highly specialized for absorbing nutrients (Figure 10.26). The wall of the small intestine is folded into many small, finger-like projections called **villi** (singular, *villus*). The cells lining each villus have microscopic projections called microvilli. The total surface area of all the villi in the small intestine is about equal to that of a tennis court!

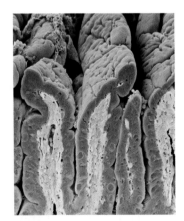

Figure 10.26 A coloured scanning electron micrograph of the surface of the small intestine (magnification 49×)

At its core, each villus has a network of microscopic blood vessels and a small lymph vessel. **Lymph vessels** are structures that carry fluid away from cells. After fatty acids and glycerol are absorbed by intestinal cells, these building blocks are recombined into fats that are then transported into the lymph vessel. Sugars and amino acids are absorbed into the bloodstream through the blood vessels in each villus (Figure 10.27).

The nutrient-laden blood from the small intestine then travels to the liver where many of the nutrients are converted into new substances, such as proteins. The liver also modifies and detoxifies substances absorbed by the digestive tract before the blood carries these materials to the heart for distribution to the rest of the body.

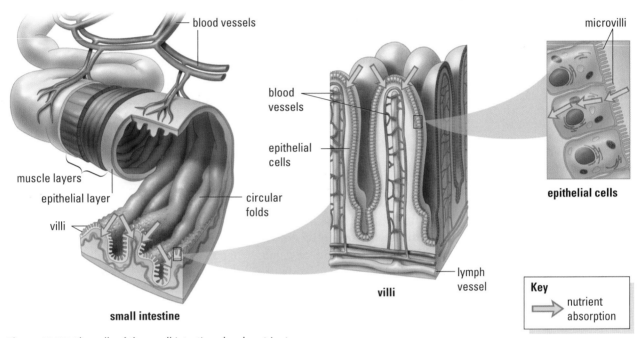

Figure 10.27 The cells of the small intestine absorb nutrients.

Large Intestine

By the time food reaches the end of the small intestine, all the nutrients have been broken down and absorbed. Undigested material passes through a sphincter from the small intestine into the large intestine (Figure 10.28 and Figure 10.29 on the next page). The large intestine, also called the colon, is a short (1.5 m) wide (5 cm) tube. As the material enters the large intestine, it passes by a small sac-like organ called the appendix. In some mammals, the appendix processes cellulose and other materials. In humans, the appendix contains white blood cells and plays a role in immunity.

Saliva, gastric juice, and other digestive juices all contain large amounts of water. Altogether about 7 L of fluid are secreted into the alimentary canal each day. Some of that water is absorbed along with nutrients in the small intestine. The large intestine finishes the job by absorbing most of the remaining water. Together, the small intestine and large intestine reclaim 90 percent of the water that enters the alimentary canal.

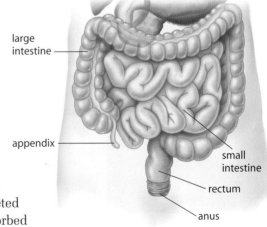

Figure 10.28 The small and large intestines are named for their diameters, not their lengths.

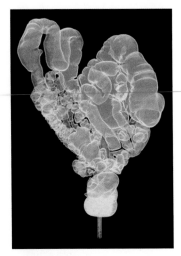

Figure 10.29 This CT scan of the large intestine was made using an X-ray beam to scan "slices" from different angles of the body. The slices were then reconstructed and coloured by medical imaging software. Some parts of the small intestine are visible in the centre of the scan.

BIOLOGY•SOURCE

Suggested Activity

• D4 Inquiry Activity Overview on page 296

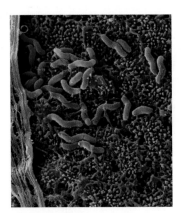

Figure 10.30 A coloured scanning electron micrograph of *Helicobacter pylori* bacteria on the surface of the human intestine (magnification 5560×)

As the water is absorbed, the remains of the digested food become more solid. The wastes move along the colon by peristalsis, a journey that takes about 12 to 24 hours to complete. Undigested food material and other waste products are called **feces**. Feces are stored in the final portion of the colon, the **rectum**, until they can be eliminated. Two rectal sphincters, one voluntary and the other involuntary, regulate the opening of the anus.

Bacteria in the colon produce important vitamins, including Vitamin K and some B vitamins. These vitamins are absorbed into the bloodstream from the colon.

Concept Check

1. What is the first section of the small intestine called?
2. What are the names of two different digestive juices that are added to the small intestine?
3. What is another name for the large intestine?

Diagnosing Digestive Disorders

From time to time, you may experience some discomfort in your digestive system, caused by eating too much, eating too quickly, or eating an inappropriate combination of foods. You may also notice gas in the digestive system, which is a result of swallowed air or the breakdown of undigested food in the colon. Gas is made of odourless carbon dioxide, oxygen, hydrogen, and nitrogen. When gas is passed through the rectum it also includes small amounts of sulphur produced by bacteria there and so may smell unpleasant.

Experiences of mild discomfort in the digestive system are common, but if they persist or intensify, you should discuss them with your doctor. Sometimes discomfort is caused by inflammation, infection, malabsorption, or another disorder.

Diagnostic Tools

Recent technological advances have provided useful tools for diagnosing problems within the digestive tract. In **endoscopy**, a narrow tube is inserted into the throat and passed into the esophagus, stomach, and upper intestine. A small camera in the narrow tube enables the doctor to see the internal structures and to identify abnormalities. Sometimes, the tube has tiny scissors that are used to cut a small piece of tissue for viewing under a microscope. This cutting procedure is called a **biopsy**. A biopsy is used to determine if the cells are normal and can also identify the presence of the *Helicobacter pylori* bacteria, which burrow into the stomach wall and cause inflammation (Figure 10.30).

In order to diagnose intestinal disorders, the doctor may want to see inside further along the intestines. During a **colonoscopy**, a thin, lighted tube with an attached camera is inserted through the rectum (Figure 10.31 on the next page). If an unusual growth is detected, the doctor may choose to perform a biopsy. If the biopsy indicates that the cells are abnormal or cancerous, it is sometimes possible to surgically remove those cells during the diagnostic procedure.

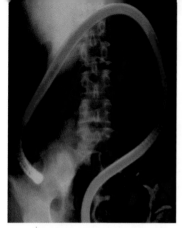

Figure 10.31 Coloured X-ray of a patient's abdomen showing an endoscope winding through the colon

Figure 10.32 A capsule endoscope or "pill cam" is swallowed like a pill.

A less invasive procedure requires the patient to swallow a pill that contains a camera (Figure 10.32). As the pill proceeds through the intestines, it takes pictures of the structures. The pill is later eliminated in the feces.

Table 10.4 summarizes some digestive disorders and diagnoses.

Table 10.4 Examples of Digestive Disorders

Condition	Description	Diagnosis and Treatment
Gastroesophageal reflux disease (GERD)	Gastroesophageal reflux disease occurs when acid from the stomach spills back up into the esophagus so frequently that it harms the lining of the esophagus.	Since smoking, drinking alcohol, and excess eating seem to make this condition worse, doctors suggest that they be avoided. Antacids are prescribed to neutralize the stomach acid. Sometimes surgery is needed to strengthen the muscle that sits at the junction between the esophagus and the stomach.
Ulcer	If the stomach lining is broken down it becomes irritated by gastric acid. The gastric acid can also spill into other parts of the digestive system and irritate the tissues of nearby organs. Sores found in the stomach lining, esophagus or the upper small intestine are called peptic ulcers.	In order to properly diagnose an ulcer, a doctor may order a number of diagnostic tests including a blood test, feces or stool test, barium X-ray, and endoscopy. Barium is a white metallic liquid that coats the digestive system and makes the ulcer more visible in the radiograph produced by the X-ray. The blood and stool tests are used to identify the presence of *H. pylori* bacteria, the cause of most ulcers.
Inflammatory bowel disease (IBD)	In inflammatory bowel disease, the intestines become irritated and inflamed and develop many ulcers, causing abdominal pain and diarrhea. Two common inflammatory bowel diseases are ulcerative colitis and Crohn's disease. Ulcerative colitis is found in continuous sections of the intestine and rectum. Crohn's disease may occur anywhere in the digestive tract.	The exact cause of inflammatory bowel disease is still being researched. It is thought that the presence of foreign substances in the intestines may cause the body to attack itself in order to rid itself of the foreign invaders. This allergic type of reaction causes inflammation, which results in the development of ulcers.
Constipation	Constipation occurs when peristalsis moves the feces along too slowly or when the colon absorbs too much water and the feces become too compacted. Constipation is usually a temporary condition resulting from a diet that does not include enough plant fibre. Constipation sometimes results from surgery, medication, air travel, and pregnancy.	To prevent constipation: • Eat a healthy diet that contains a lot of fibre, such as fruit, vegetables, and grains. Fibre adds softness and bulk to the waste in the colon. As a result, the waste can pass through the colon more easily. • Get plenty of exercise. • Drink at least 1 L of water every day.
Diarrhea	If the lining of the colon is irritated — by a viral or bacterial infection, for instance — the colon is less effective in reclaiming water, and diarrhea may result. Severe diarrhea can cause dehydration and become life-threatening without treatment.	A healthy patient usually recovers from diarrhea within several days, given enough clean water and nutritious food. However, diarrhea can also be a symptom of more serious disease, such as inflammatory bowel disease.

Considering the Need for Chemical Digestion

Question

How does the size of a particle affect its movement across the cell membrane?

Activity Overview

Nutrients are chemicals in foods that help your body perform all of its functions (Figure 10.33). However, some of these molecules are so large and complex that they cannot pass through cell membranes and into cells. These large molecules must be chemically digested in order to form smaller, simpler molecules that can enter cells. In this activity, you will observe how the size of molecules affects the movement across a simulated cell membrane.

    Your teacher will give you a copy of the full activity.

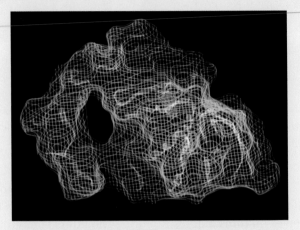

Figure 10.33 This picture shows a molecular computer graphics representation of amylase. Amylase is an enzyme that breaks down starch into the sugars glucose and maltose.

Prelab Questions

Consider the questions below before beginning this activity.

1. What is the difference between a simple carbohydrate and a complex carbohydrate?

2. Why do your cells need glucose?

Testing Simulated Urine for Protein and Sugar

Question

How does the detection of sugar or protein in the urine aid in the diagnosis of certain conditions?

Activity Overview

Sugars, such as glucose, and protein are not normally present in the urine. However, if a patient is suffering from a disorder, such as diabetes or high blood pressure, nutrients may not be completely used by the body and may exit the body in the urine. In this activity, you will take on the role of a medical technologist as you test simulated urine samples from three "patients" to detect the presence of sugar and protein. You will compare test results with results from solutions containing known amounts of sugar or protein.

    Your teacher will give you a copy of the full activity.

Prelab Questions

Consider the questions below before beginning this activity.

1. What does your body use glucose for?

2. What does your body use protein for?

Figure 10.34 A Biuret test indicates whether there are proteins in a solution.

Key Concept Review

1. Describe what occurs at each of the following stages of food processing:
   (a) ingestion
   (b) digestion
   (c) absorption
   (d) elimination

2. Write the labels A-K in your notebook and identify each organ or gland.

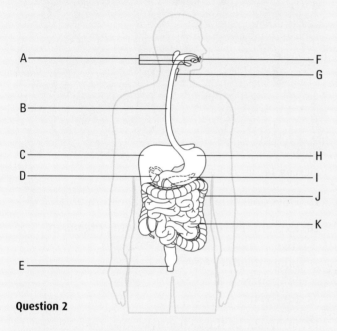

Question 2

3. Explain the statement "Digestion occurs in a tube."

4. Compare and contrast the terms "mechanical digestion" and "chemical digestion":
   (a) in the mouth
   (b) in the stomach

5. (a) What is a bolus?
   (b) How is a bolus formed?

6. What happens during hydrolysis?

7. (a) Define peristalsis.
   (b) Describe its role in the digestive system.

8. What is chyme?

9. (a) What is bile?
   (b) What is the role of bile in digestion?

10. Explain the process of chemical digestion in the duodenum.

11. (a) State four locations where sphincters are found in the digestive system.
    (b) What is the role of a sphincter?

12. Fill in the blanks in the following statements by recording the answers in your notebook. As the end result of digestion:
    (a) Carbohydrates are broken down to form ___, which provide your cells with ___.
    (b) Proteins are broken down to form ___ that your cells use to ___.
    (c) Fats are broken down to produce molecules of ___ and ___ that your cells use to build ___.

13. How do the villi and microvilli maximize the ability of the intestine to absorb nutrients?

14. What is a major function of the large intestine?

15. (a) What is a colonoscopy?
    (b) Why is it important?

16. What does the abbreviation "GERD" stand for?

17. (a) What is an ulcer?
    (b) What causes an ulcer?

Connect Your Understanding

18. Make a flowchart that shows the route food takes through the digestive system.

19. Create a graphic organizer that shows the relationships between the following terms: small intestine, gallbladder, liver, and pancreas.

20. Use your knowledge of the digestive system to explain why saliva is a very important bodily fluid.

21. Why might an individual with gallbladder disease have difficulty digesting ice cream?

Reflection

22. Describe three things that you understand now about the digestive system that you did not know before reading this section.

For more questions, go to **BIOLOGY•SOURCE**

Key Concept Review

1. What is the meaning of the word "nutrient"? **k**

2. Identify the nutrients that perform each of the following functions.
   (a) provide the body with raw materials for growth and repair **k**
   (b) help to build cell membranes and store energy **k**
   (c) are major source of energy for the body **k**
   (d) make up the bulk of most bodily fluids **k**
   (e) are inorganic nutrients that help form bones and teeth **k**
   (f) are organic molecules needed to help metabolize energy **k**

3. What is the difference between simple carbohydrates and complex carbohydrates? **k**

4. Why is fibre so important in your diet? **k**

5. Why must vegetarians combine different protein sources or eat some eggs or milk products? **k**

6. Describe one possible effect of a diet lacking in protein. **k**

7. (a) What is the chemical difference between a saturated fat and an unsaturated fat? **k**
   (b) State an example of each type of fat. **k**

8. (a) Name one mineral that is an important part of your diet. **k**
   (b) State its function. **k**

9. (a) Define the term "nutraceutical." **k**
   (b) Give an example that illustrates its meaning. **k**

10. Describe the relationship between the amount of food consumed and the physical activity level in a healthy individual. **k**

11. Why is it important to chew your food thoroughly? **k**

12. (a) Define saliva. **k**
    (b) Explain its role in digestion. **k**

13. Explain how the stomach accomplishes both mechanical and chemical digestion. **k**

14. (a) Identify the structures shown below. **k**
    (b) Explain how these structures enable the absorption of nutrients in your body. **k**

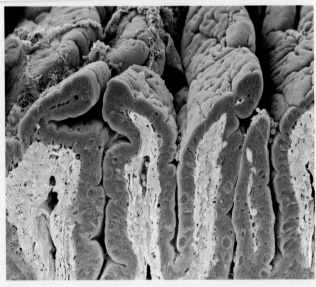

Question 14 (magnification 49×)

15. How does bile help in the digestion of fats? **k**

16. Explain the role of the following organs in digestion.
    (a) gallbladder **k**
    (b) pancreas **k**
    (c) liver **k**

17. (a) Describe three digestive disorders. **k**
    (b) Explain the cause of each disorder. **k**

Connect Your Understanding

18. The transformation of nutrients in your body can be summarized in a flow chart:

    Food → bolus → chyme → feces

    Copy this flow chart into your notebook and expand it to show what happens to the nutrients at each stage. **c**

19. (a) Which animal would have a longer alimentary canal for its size, a wolf or a sheep? **a**
    (b) Explain why. **a**

20. How is digestion in the small intestine different from digestion in the large intestine? **t**

21. The diagram below shows a simplified view of the digestive system as a tube. Copy the labels A–H into your notebook. Identify each organ. **c**

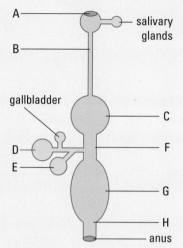

A —

B —

salivary glands

gallbladder

D —
E —

C

F

G

H

anus

Question 21

22. People who have had part or all of their stomachs removed can survive if they eat predigested food. Could a person survive without a small intestine? Explain. **t**

23. Why would an excess of fat-soluble vitamins be more dangerous than an excess of water-soluble vitamins? **a**

24. A kindergarten teacher has asked you to write a story for his class that describes the travels of a sandwich through the digestive system. Write an outline of your story, including information about what happens to the different nutrients in each part of the digestive system. **c**

25. "Nutrient-dense food" is food that contains many nutrients. Food that contains many calories but few nutrients is said to have "empty calories."

(a) Use the knowledge you gained in this section to explain why it might be helpful to consume nutrient-dense food. **a**

(b) What is an example of nutrient-dense food? **a**

(c) What do you think the phrase "empty calories" means? **a**

(d) What is an example of an empty-calories food? **a**

(e) One common piece of dieting advice is to replace calorie-dense food with nutrient-dense food. What does this mean? **a**

(f) Explain why you think this is or is not good advice. **a**

26. Fad diets that claim to produce rapid weight loss often involve eating a very limited variety of foods, such as eating only protein or eating only fruit. Are these diets a healthy way to lose weight? Explain why they are or are not. **a**

27. Using the knowledge you gained in this chapter, identify three changes that you can make to improve the functioning of your digestive system. **a**

28. Undernourishment is a condition resulting from a diet that does not provide enough calories. Malnourishment is a condition resulting from a diet that does not provide all the essential nutrients.

(a) Which of these conditions do you think is more common in human populations in developing countries? **a**

(b) Why? **a**

(c) Which of these conditions do you think is more common in human populations in developed countries? **a**

(d) Why? **a**

Reflection

29. Has the knowledge you have gained in this chapter changed the way you eat? If so, explain the changes you have made. If not, explain why not. **c**

Unit Task Link

Review your notes about the digestive system and select one of the disorders. Create a graphic organizer that summarizes the following information.

• What are the symptoms of the disorder?
• What are the causes of the disorder?
• How is the disorder diagnosed?
• How can this disorder be prevented?
• How is the disorder treated?

For more questions, go to **BIOLOGY•SOURCE**

The circulatory system transports materials through the body.

The old saying "laughter is the best medicine" might be more than just a quaint expression. Your emotions may have a significant effect on the health of your body.

The leading cause of death for Canadian adult men and women is cardiovascular disease. **Cardiovascular disease** is any disease that affects the heart and blood vessels. Research has shown that certain cardiovascular diseases cause changes to the lining of arteries, reducing the rate of blood flow (Figure 11.1). When the flow of blood in arteries is restricted, the cells cannot always obtain necessary nutrients efficiently and cell function is reduced or ceases. Stressful experiences can decrease the diameter of the arteries.

What kinds of experiences can *increase* the diameter of the arteries? Scientists have investigated changes in the rate of blood flow in arteries before and after exposure to laughing. They have also investigated the effects of exposure to joyful music. In both types of experiments, results showed an increase in arterial diameter. The conclusion? Including positive and joyful experiences in our daily lives could indeed be good medicine.

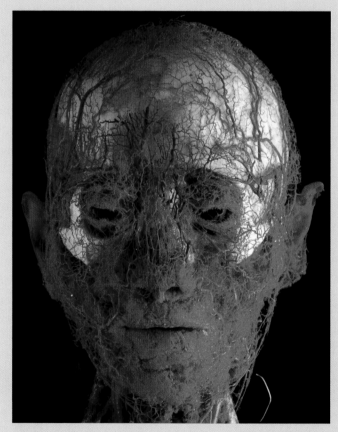

Figure 11.1 Networks of blood vessels must continually supply nutrients to cells in the brain. If the arteries become clogged, blood flow is reduced.

©P

Structure and Function of Blood and Blood Vessels

Your cells need a constant supply of nutrients and oxygen. After you have ingested food, and your body has digested and absorbed the nutrients, the next step is to distribute the building-block molecules to all the cells in your body. Fortunately, your body has an efficient distribution system — your circulatory system.

Circulatory Systems

All the cells in an animal need to gain nutrients, exchange gases, and remove waste products. Some aquatic animals with bodies only a few cells thick transport materials across their cell membranes to and from their environment. Larger animals use an internal transport system to bring resources close enough to all the cells for exchange of materials to occur. Most animals have a circulatory system that transports oxygen and carbon dioxide, distributes nutrients to body cells, and removes cellular wastes.

The three primary components of the circulatory system are the blood, the heart, and the blood vessels. Blood, a type of connective tissue made up of cells and fluids, carries both nutrients and wastes. Blood is pumped through the body by the heart, a multi-chambered, muscular organ. Blood flows in blood vessels, which are tubes that form a pipeline within the body.

Open Circulatory Systems

Many invertebrates have an open circulatory system in which blood is not entirely contained within blood vessels. In an open circulatory system, such as in the grasshopper in Figure 11.2, a tubular heart pumps blood through vessels that open into spongy chambers called sinuses. From the sinuses, the blood bathes the body tissues, then collects in another set of sinuses and makes its way back to the heart.

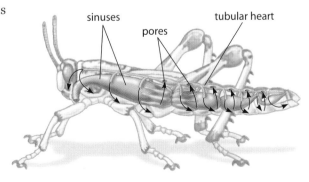

sinuses   pores   tubular heart

Figure 11.2 In an open circulatory system, the blood vessels open into sinuses where the organs are bathed directly in blood.

Closed Circulatory Systems

Earthworms, squids, octopuses, and vertebrates all have closed circulatory systems (Figure 11.3). In a closed circulatory system, blood remains contained entirely within blood vessels that extend throughout the body. Nutrients, oxygen, and wastes move in and out through the thin walls of the smallest blood vessels.

Blood is circulated more efficiently in a closed circulatory system than an open circulatory system. The increased efficiency is because blood that is completely contained within blood vessels can be pumped under higher pressure than blood in open-ended vessels.

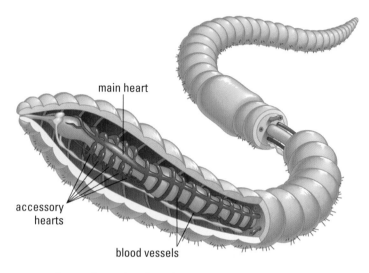

Figure 11.3 An earthworm has a closed circulatory system. Blood stays within the vessels of a closed circulatory system.

Human Circulatory System

The closed circulatory system in humans and other vertebrates is sometimes called the **cardiovascular system** (from the Greek *kardia,* heart, and Latin *vas,* vessel). Your cardiovascular system includes a network of about 100 000 km of blood vessels (Figure 11.4). Laid end to end, your blood vessels would encircle Earth two and a half times! This network of vessels supplies the trillion cells in your body with nutrients and oxygen, and removes carbon dioxide and other waste products.

A healthy cardiovascular system is amazingly efficient in its function. Under normal activity, it takes about one minute for blood to make a complete circuit through your body. Increased activity, such as running or dancing, causes your blood to circulate more quickly, keeping your cells supplied with oxygen and nutrients.

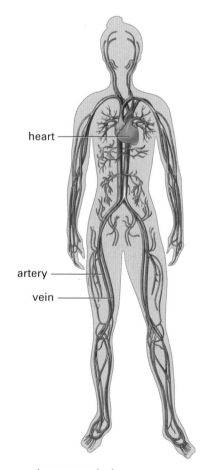

Figure 11.4 The human cardiovascular system is an internal transport system and consists of the blood, blood vessels, and the heart. Only a few major blood vessels are shown here.

Concept Check

1. What is the function of a circulatory system?
2. What are two types of circulatory systems?
3. What is another name for the circulatory system in humans?

©P

Blood

Blood is a highly specialized connective tissue — part fluid and part cellular. Your body contains about 4 to 6 L of blood.

Your blood has several functions that are essential to good health. Blood transports oxygen, water, nutrients, and other chemicals to your cells. Blood also removes waste products from the tissues and delivers them to the areas where they can be removed from your body. In addition to its transport functions, blood also helps to regulate body temperature, fight infection, and heal wounds.

Blood is made of plasma, red blood cells, white blood cells, and platelets (Figure 11.5).

Plasma

Fifty-five percent of the volume of blood is a straw-coloured solution called **plasma**. Plasma is about 90 percent water, which helps to control body temperature. The remaining 10 percent is made of proteins, dissolved nutrients, and wastes, such as carbon dioxide. Plasma proteins transport fatty acids and vitamins, and fight viral and bacterial infections.

Red Blood Cells

The remaining 45 percent of blood volume consists mostly of red blood cells. **Red blood cells** are cells that carry oxygen from the lungs to all the tissues of the body. One cubic millimetre of blood (approximately one drop) contains about five million red blood cells.

Each red blood cell contains about 250 million molecules of **hemoglobin**, which is a protein that binds oxygen in the lungs and releases it throughout the body. Once oxygen is released, the red blood cells transport carbon dioxide to the lungs. Oxygen molecules bind to the iron portion of the hemoglobin molecule, which gives red blood cells their crimson colour.

Red blood cells are produced in bone marrow at the rate of two million per second in a healthy adult. As red blood cells mature, they lose their nuclei and mitochondria. The loss of these structures helps give red blood cells their distinctive shape, like a flat disk that curves inward in the middle on both the top and bottom (Figure 11.6). This structure provides increased surface area for oxygen transfer compared to a spherical shape with the same volume. The shape of red blood cells also gives them flexibility so that they can pass through blood vessels of different shapes and sizes.

Since a mature red blood cell has no nucleus, it cannot replace proteins, grow, or divide. The typical lifespan of a red blood cell is between 100 and 120 days. As red blood cells age, they become fragile and are eventually broken down. The iron from broken-down red blood cells is recycled in the bone marrow where it becomes part of new red blood cells.

Plasma (55%)
- water
- dissolved salts
- plasma proteins
- transported substances:
  - nutrients
  - metabolic wastes
  - oxygen
  - carbon dioxide
  - hormones

Cellular components (45%)
- red blood cells
- white blood cells
- platelets

Figure 11.5 Blood consists of both solid and fluid components.

BIOLOGY•SOURCE

Explore More

What might happen if the water content of a person's blood were too high or too low?

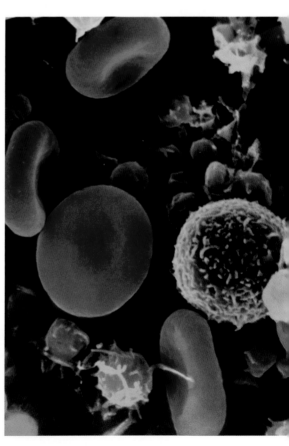

Figure 11.6 This micrograph shows red blood cells (red discs), a white blood cell (large green orb), and platelets (small green fragments). (magnification 13 860×)

White Blood Cells

White blood cells are cells that guard against infection, fight parasites, and attack bacteria. White blood cells do not have to stay within the blood vessels. They can move through the vessel walls when they are needed to attack foreign organisms. Normally, there are between 4000 and 11 000 white blood cells in one cubic millimetre of blood. However, when infection invades your body, the number of white blood cells dramatically increases. For example, if you get a cut, white blood cells gather at the cut to fight bacteria. Sometimes, you may notice pus forming at the site of a cut. Pus is a combination of white blood cells and dead bacteria.

Like red blood cells, white blood cells are produced in the bone marrow. Unlike red blood cells, white blood cells keep their nuclei and can live for years.

Platelets

When you get a small cut or scrape, your blood clots, stopping the bleeding and sealing the wound. The clotting process depends on plasma proteins and cell fragments called platelets. **Platelets** are cell fragments that originate when the cytoplasm of certain bone marrow cells divides. The fragments, each enclosed in a cell membrane, break off and enter the blood. Each cubic millimetre of blood contains between 250 000 and 500 000 platelets.

The blood-clotting process begins when platelets stick to the site where the blood vessel is damaged (Figure 11.7). The platelets break apart and release substances called clotting factors. The clotting factors make other nearby platelets sticky and activate a series of reactions among other clotting factors in the plasma. These reactions result in the formation of a strand-like protein called **fibrin**. Fibrin threads trap red blood cells and platelets. Within a few minutes of injury, this network of threads and cells builds up, eventually forming a patch that stretches over the torn tissue. This patch dries into a scab. The scab protects the area while new tissue grows.

Some people have a condition called hemophilia, in which they do not have the necessary protein to form blood clots. Their wounds bleed for longer than normal periods and they may need medical assistance to stop the flow of blood.

BIOLOGY•SOURCE

Suggested Activities
- D5 Quick Lab Overview on page 308
- D6 Case Study Overview on page 308

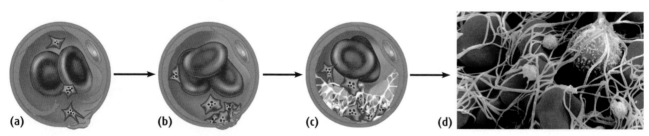

(a) (b) (c) (d)

Figure 11.7 (a) A capillary wall breaks. (b) Platelets gather at the break and release clotting factors. (c) A clot forms. (d) The clot seals the break and prevents further loss of blood. (magnification 2100×)

Concept Check

1. What is the fluid part of blood?
2. (a) What are the three solid parts of blood?
   (b) Identify the main function of each part.

Blood Vessels

As blood flows through the circulatory system, it moves through three types of blood vessels — arteries, capillaries, and veins (Figure 11.8). A blood vessel's walls consist of smooth muscle tissue that regulates the diameter of the blood vessel, and connective tissue that enables the blood vessel to expand and contract as blood flows through it. Epithelial tissue lines the walls of all blood vessels.

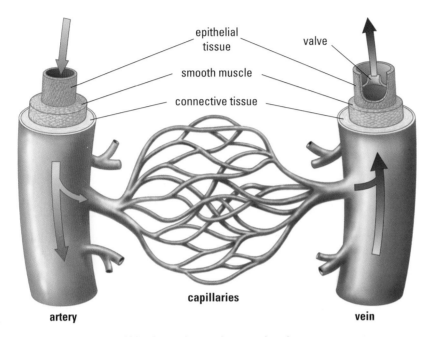

Figure 11.8 The structure of blood vessels contributes to their functions.

Arteries

Arteries are large blood vessels that carry blood from the heart to the tissues. The walls of arteries are made of epithelial tissue wrapped in layers of smooth muscle and connective tissue. The blood in arteries is under pressure due to the heart's pumping action. This pressure helps to ensure that blood flows only in one direction — toward the tissues. Further from the heart, the arteries branch into smaller and smaller vessels. The narrowest arteries, called arterioles, flow into capillaries.

Capillaries

To distribute nutrients and oxygen effectively, the circulatory system must have close contact with all the cells of the body. This close contact is accomplished by millions of capillaries. **Capillaries** are microscopic blood vessels with a high surface area resembling a network of tiny tubes. Some capillaries are so narrow that blood cells must travel through them only a few at a time (Figure 11.9).

The walls of capillaries consist of a very thin layer of epithelial tissue encased in a moist membrane. This structure enables the nutrients and oxygen to pass out of the blood, and waste products to pass into the blood.

Figure 11.9 Red blood cells inside a capillary (magnification 1000×)

Veins

Blood returns from the capillaries to the heart through blood vessels called **veins.** The walls of veins also consist of epithelial tissue surrounded by smooth muscle and connective tissue. But the muscle layer in veins is thinner than that in arteries. The blood in veins is under very little pressure. The main force that pushes blood through the veins comes from the skeletal muscle tissue in which many veins are located. Contracting these muscles squeezes the veins and forces blood through them. Most veins contain flaps of tissue called valves that allow blood to flow only toward the heart. Small veins merge together into larger veins.

Concept Check

1. What is the function of arteries?
2. What is the function of capillaries?
3. What is the function of veins?

Nutrient Exchange Between Blood and Cells

How do the nutrients pass from the blood vessels into the individual cells of your body? In the process of **diffusion**, molecules move across a membrane from an area of higher concentration to an area of lower concentration (Figure 11.10). The **diffusion gradient** is the gradual change in the concentration of solutes in a solution as a function of the distance through a solution. In other words, if the blood in a capillary contains a higher concentration of oxygen than does the fluid next to it, the oxygen moves spontaneously into the fluid by diffusion.

The process of molecules diffusing out of the blood and into the cells occurs in the capillaries. Capillaries are in close contact with the cells of your body. In fact, most cells in your body are no farther than 10μm (micrometres) from a capillary and the blood inside it. This capillary network and the structure of the individual capillaries are critical to accomplishing the main functions of the circulatory system — the distribution of oxygen and nutrients, and the removal of waste products.

Cells in body tissues are surrounded by fluid. The molecules in capillaries cannot enter cells directly but must first enter the fluid, and then enter the cells. The exchange of molecules between blood and the fluid occurs in several ways. Some small molecules, such as oxygen and carbon dioxide, diffuse across membranes or pass through gaps between the epithelial cells of the capillary wall. For example, oxygen moves by diffusion from the blood into the fluid, and carbon dioxide moves by diffusion from the fluid into the blood. Larger molecules move across the membranes using other transport processes. The force that blood exerts against the artery walls is called **blood pressure.** This force drives blood through the arteries, into the capillaries, and through the capillary walls (Figure 11.11 on the next page).

Once in the fluid, the molecules that are needed by the cells move into the cells by diffusion. Cellular wastes move out of the cells into the fluid and eventually enter the blood. Wastes are carried by the blood to sites where they can be excreted from the body.

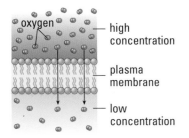

Figure 11.10 Oxygen molecules are small enough to diffuse across a plasma membrane.

oxygen — high concentration

plasma membrane

— low concentration

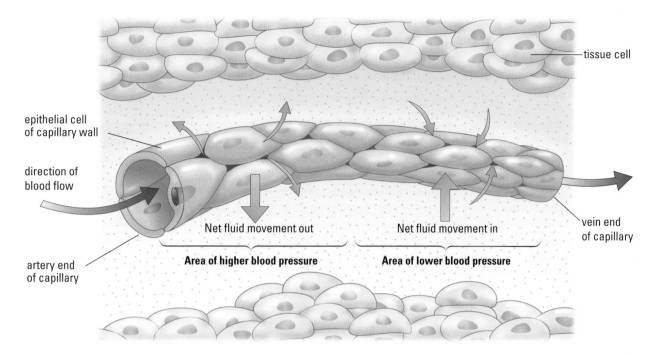

Figure 11.11 Blood pressure is higher at the artery end of a capillary, and it forces fluid out of the capillary. Blood pressure is lower at the vein end, and it allows fluid to enter the capillary.

labels in figure:
tissue cell
epithelial cell of capillary wall
direction of blood flow
Net fluid movement out
Net fluid movement in
vein end of capillary
artery end of capillary
Area of higher blood pressure
Area of lower blood pressure

The Lymphatic System

As blood passes through capillaries, some of its components move through capillary walls and into the fluid between cells. Each day, about 3 or 4 L of fluid leave the blood to surround your cells. The **lymphatic system** is a network of vessels, nodes (connecting points), and organs that collects the fluid that leaves capillaries, "screens" it for micro-organisms, and returns it to the circulatory system (Figure 11.12). Once inside the lymphatic vessels, this collected fluid is called lymph. **Lymph** is a clear, watery fluid made up of protein molecules, salt, glucose, and other substances. If the lymphatic system did not drain lymph from the tissues, the lymph would accumulate, causing swelling called edema.

Lymph collects in a system of lymph vessels, which have valves that prevent lymph from flowing back toward the capillaries. The combination of muscle contractions squeezing the vessels and the one-way valves helps fluid move through the lymphatic system. Eventually, lymph drains into the circulatory system near the heart.

In the upper left part of the abdomen under the ribcage is a part of the lymphatic system called the spleen. The spleen is an organ that helps remove old or damaged blood cells, stores platelets, and helps control the amount of blood and blood cells that circulate through the body. Some lymph vessels run alongside the small intestine to pick up fats and fat-soluble vitamins from the digestive tract and transport them into the bloodstream.

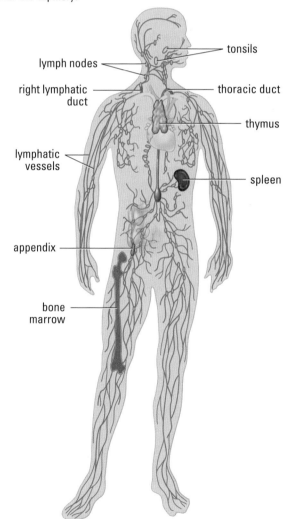

Figure 11.12 The lymphatic system is a network of vessels, nodes, and organs that recycles fluids from tissues.

labels in figure:
tonsils
lymph nodes
right lymphatic duct
thoracic duct
thymus
lymphatic vessels
spleen
appendix
bone marrow

Take It Further

Anemia is a condition that occurs when the blood does not contain enough red blood cells or when blood lacks sufficient hemoglobin. Find out more about iron deficiency anemia, vitamin B-12 anemia, or folic acid anemia by researching the causes, symptoms, and treatments. Present your findings in the form of a table and share with your classmates.

The lymphatic system also helps provide immunity. White blood cells mature in an organ called the thymus. Hundreds of lymph nodes, which are small, bean-shaped enlargements, are scattered along lymph vessels throughout the body. The lymph nodes filter out harmful micro-organisms and abnormal cells.

Concept Check

1. What is diffusion?
2. What must the molecules in a capillary enter before they can enter a cell?
3. What are three main functions of the lymphatic system?

D5 Quick Lab

Blood Components

Purpose

To analyze a sample of blood (Figure 11.13)

Activity Overview

In this activity, you will examine the composition of blood, and analyze the blood sample of a patient with some troubling symptoms.

Your teacher will give you a copy of the full activity.

Prelab Questions

Consider the questions below before beginning this activity.

1. What substances make up the fluid part of blood?
2. What three types of cells make up the solid part of blood?

Figure 11.13 Red blood cells (magnification 1635×)

D6 Case Study

REQUIRED SKILLS
- Stating a conclusion
- Reporting results

Blood Doping

Issue

Athletes sometimes attempt to improve their performance by increasing the number of red blood cells in their bloodstream.

Activity Overview

Red blood cells carry oxygen from the lungs to the muscles. More red blood cells carry more oxygen, which can boost athletic endurance. Athletes sometimes harvest their own red blood cells weeks before a competition, store the blood cells, and then inject them shortly before the event. There are many risks associated with the practice. In this activity, you will consider the pros and cons of the practice of blood doping.

Your teacher will give you a copy of the full activity.

Prelab Questions

Consider the questions below before beginning this activity.

1. Do you consider it wrong for an athlete to use his or her own blood to boost performance?
2. How can a ban on blood doping be enforced?

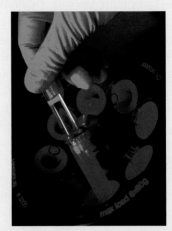

Figure 11.14 When blood is spun at high speeds in a centrifuge, it settles into its components. If more than 50 percent of the volume is red blood cells, then blood doping may have been involved.

©P

Key Concept Review

1. What are three main components of the circulatory system?

2. (a) What is an open circulatory system?
   (b) What is an example of an animal that has an open circulatory system?

3. (a) What is a closed circulatory system?
   (b) What is an example of an animal that has a closed circulatory system?

4. What are five main functions of blood?

5. About how long does it take for blood to make a complete circuit through the human body?

6. About how much blood is found in an average human body?

7. List the four main components of blood.

8. Describe the characteristics of plasma.

9. (a) What is the main function of red blood cells?
   (b) What is the average life span of a red blood cell?

10. (a) What is the main function of white blood cells?
    (b) What is the average life span of a white blood cell?

11. What is the main function of platelets?

12. Where are blood cells made?

13. (a) What is the function of an artery?
    (b) What is the function of a vein?
    (c) What is the function of the valves in veins?

14. Explain what is happening at A, B, C, and D in the diagram below.

15. What is the role of fibrin in blood clotting?

16. (a) What is lymph?
    (b) What is the main function of lymph?

17. What happens if lymph accumulates?

18. How does lymph move through the lymphatic system?

19. What are three functions of the spleen?

Connect Your Understanding

20. How does having a closed circulatory system benefit a large, active animal?

21. Draw a pie chart or graph showing the approximate ratios of the different components of blood.

22. Make a flowchart that describes the blood-clotting process.

23. (a) Define the term "diffusion."
    (b) Explain the role of diffusion in the transport of nutrients from the source to the cell.

24. How does the lymphatic system assist the circulatory system?

25. Use a Venn diagram to show how the functions of veins and lymphatic vessels are similar and different.

Reflection

26. (a) What is one thing that you learned in this section that you would like to find out more about?
    (b) Why?

For more questions, go to  BIOLOGY•SOURCE

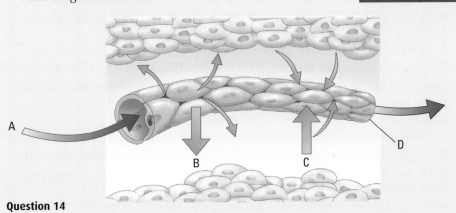

Question 14

Section Summary

- The heart pumps blood through the circulatory system.
- The rhythm of the heartbeat is controlled by the actions of nerves and hormones.
- The pumping action of the heart creates a pressure in the blood that can be measured.

Figure 11.15(a) The word stethoscope comes from two Greek words that mean "chest" and "explore."

Figure 11.15(b) A stethoscope transmits vibrations from the patient through the chest piece, which is a diaphragm or hollow cup. The sounds then vibrate through hollow tubes to the listener's ears. The diaphragm transmits higher-frequency vibrations and the hollow cup transmits lower-frequency vibrations.

In 1816, a French doctor named René Laënnec wanted to better diagnose his patients by listening to their heartbeat and other sounds in the chest. He was frustrated at being able to hear very little when he pressed his ear against a patient's chest. Laënnec recalled that if you place your ear against a piece of wood, you could clearly hear the scratch of a pin at the other end of the wood. His conclusion was that wood amplified the sound. Since paper was made from wood, he predicted it would have the same effect. He rolled a piece of paper into a tube and place one end next to his ear and the other on his patient's chest. As he predicted, the heart sounds were much clearer.

Laënnec invented the first stethoscope, which was later refined to become the important instrument it is today (Figure 11.15). However, Laënnec's initial prediction was not actually correct. The reason his paper tube worked was not that it was made from wood, but that the hollow tube focussed and reflected the sounds.

The invention of the stethoscope allowed doctors to better understand the body and disease, because it allowed them to more accurately determine what was happening inside the body. Since Laënnec's time, many new tools have been developed that enable doctors to view and interact with the body's circulatory system and other internal systems.

Anatomy of the Heart

Your heart, which is about the size of a clenched fist, is a hollow organ located between your lungs and made almost entirely of muscle. The structure of your heart enables it to pump oxygen-poor blood to your lungs and oxygen-rich blood to your entire body. As your heart contracts, blood is pumped out. When your heart relaxes, blood enters the heart. For an average person at rest, the entire process of pumping and filling the heart, known as the cardiac cycle, takes approximately 0.8 seconds.

A protective sac called the pericardium encloses the heart. The pericardium is filled with fluid that lubricates the surfaces of the heart and the roots of the major blood vessels. The human heart, like the hearts of other mammals, has four chambers: the right atrium, the right ventricle, the left atrium, and the left ventricle (Figure 11.16).

- The two upper chambers, which receive blood returning to the heart, are called **atria** (singular, *atrium*). The atria, which pump blood a short distance into the ventricles, have fairly thin walls.
- The two lower chambers, which pump blood out of the heart to the body, are called **ventricles**, Ventricles have thicker muscular walls that enable them to pump blood throughout the body.

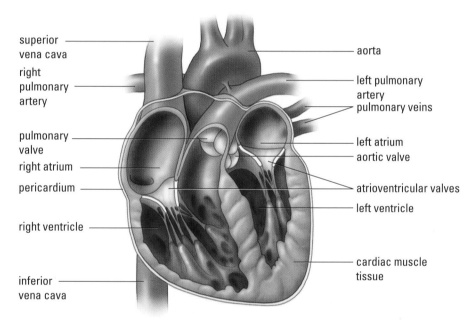

Figure 11.16 The left and right sides of the heart refer to the person's left and right sides, causing them to appear reversed in this face-on view.

Valves in the heart prevent blood from flowing backward. The valves that are located between the atria and ventricles are called **atrioventricular valves**. The **pulmonary valve** is between the right ventricle and the pulmonary artery. The word "pulmonary" comes from the Latin word meaning "lung." The **aortic valve** is between the left ventricle and the aorta. The word "aortic" comes from a Greek word meaning "to lift."

With each heartbeat, the valves open, allowing blood to flow through. Then the valves close, preventing blood from flowing back. When the valves close, they cause the familiar heart sound of "lub dub." The "lub" sound is the atrioventricular valves closing, while the "dub" sound happens when the pulmonary and aortic valves close.

BIOLOGY•SOURCE

Suggested Activity
- D8 Inquiry Activity Overview on page 316

Two Circuits of Blood Flow

Although it is one organ, the heart functions as two pumps. One pump pushes blood to the lungs, while the other pump pushes blood to the rest of the body. This double pathway ensures that oxygen-rich blood is constantly delivered to cells. The two pathways or circuits of blood through the body are called the pulmonary circuit and the systemic circuit (Figure 11.17).

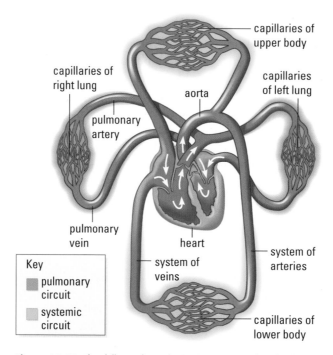

Figure 11.17 Blood flows through circuits composed of the heart and blood vessels.

Pulmonary Circuit

In the **pulmonary circuit**, blood travels from the right side of your heart through the pulmonary arteries to your lungs. In the lungs, blood picks up oxygen and releases carbon dioxide, which you then exhale. The pulmonary veins return the oxygen-rich blood to the left side of the heart.

Most arteries in your body carry oxygen-rich blood and most veins carry oxygen-depleted blood. However, the blood vessels in the pulmonary circuit do the exact opposite. Pulmonary arteries carry oxygen-depleted blood to the lungs. Pulmonary veins carry oxygen-rich blood from the lungs to the heart.

Systemic Circuit

In the **systemic circuit,** oxygen-rich blood from the lungs gathers in the left atrium and is then pumped to the left ventricle. From there, blood is pumped through the **aorta**, which is the artery that supplies oxygen-rich blood to all of the systems of the body. From the aorta, oxygen-rich blood flows through the branching arteries to the capillaries. In the capillaries, oxygen and other necessary nutrients diffuse out of the blood, and carbon dioxide and other wastes diffuse in.

The blood is now said to be oxygen-depleted and returns to the right atrium of the heart through the vena cava veins. "Vena" is Latin for vein and "cava" is Latin for cave or hollow. The vein entering the heart from the upper body is called the **superior vena cava**. The vein entering the heart from the lower body is called the **inferior vena cava**. Blood is pumped into the right ventricle, which pumps it to the lungs through pulmonary arteries. After being replenished with oxygen in the lungs, blood once again returns to the heart through pulmonary veins and gathers in the left atrium.

Blood Supply for the Heart

The heart receives very little oxygen and nutrients for its own cells from the blood it pumps through its chambers. Instead, a pair of arteries called coronary arteries branch from the aorta. In Latin, the word "coronary" means crowned. The **coronary arteries** cover the surface of the heart like a crown and supply the heart muscle with the necessary nutrients.

Regulation of the Heartbeat

The heart of a teenager or adult beats over 100 000 times every day, on average between 60 and 100 times per minute. The rate at which your heart pumps and the amount of blood that it pumps are affected by factors such as your age, fitness, and emotions. For example, an athlete might have a heart rate lower than 60. Children and babies tend to have heart rates over 100. When you run up a flight of stairs or are startled by a sudden noise, your heart is likely to beat faster than it does when you are at rest. A specific region of your heart muscle, known as the **pacemaker**, sets the rate at which your heart contracts (Figure 11.18).

BIOLOGY•SOURCE

Explore More

What are the stages of electrical activity in one complete heartbeat?

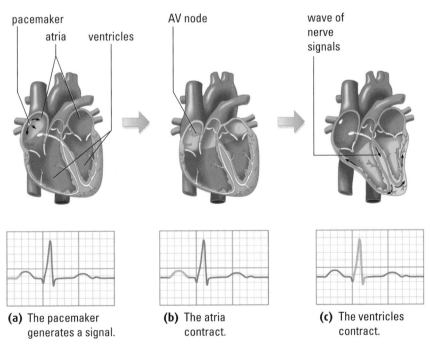

(a) The pacemaker generates a signal.

(b) The atria contract.

(c) The ventricles contract.

Figure 11.18 The signals from a pacemaker generate electrical changes that can be measured as an electrocardiogram (ECG). The yellow colour in the ECG indicates the different stages of the heartbeat.

The pacemaker is located in the wall of the right atrium. It generates electrical impulses that spread rapidly over the walls of both atria, making them contract. The impulses then spread to a region of the heart called the atrioventricular (AV) node. From there, the electrical impulses spread to the ventricles, causing them to contract. The contracting ventricles send blood to the rest of the body.

The pacemaker ensures that the heart beats in a rhythmic cycle. First the atria contract, and blood is forced into the ventricles, which are relaxed. Then the ventricles contract, pumping blood into arteries, while the atria are relaxed. This cycle repeats about every second when you are resting.

The pacemaker is controlled by both the nervous system and the endocrine system, which produces chemicals called **hormones**. Two sets of opposing nerves control the pacemaker by speeding it up and by slowing it down. Hormones, which are secreted into the blood, also control the pacemaker. For example, the hormone epinephrine, also called adrenaline, increases the heart rate when the body is under stress.

Concept Check

1. What are the names of the two circuits that blood flows in?
2. What is the function of the coronary arteries?
3. What is the function of the pacemaker?

Measuring Blood Pressure

Suggested Activity
• D9 Quick Lab Overview on page 316

Blood pressure can be measured using a pressure cuff called a **sphygmomanometer** (Figure 11.19). A measurement of blood pressure is made in millimetres of mercury (mm Hg), a standard unit of liquid pressure. The measurement is represented by two numbers separated by a slash, such as 120/70. The first number is referred to as **systolic pressure**, the highest recorded pressure in an artery when the ventricles contract. **Diastolic pressure**, the second number, is the lowest recorded pressure in an artery during the relaxation phase of the heartbeat.

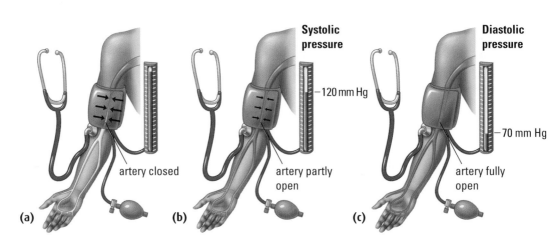

Figure 11.19 (a) An inflatable cuff of a sphygmomanometer is wrapped around a person's arm. (b) As air is pumped in, the cuff squeezes the arm and closes a large artery. (c) As air is slowly released from the cuff, a stethoscope is used to detect the sounds of blood flowing through the artery.

Blood pressure depends on two factors. The first factor, cardiac output, is the amount of blood that is pumped by the heart each minute. For example, if the volume of blood pumped through an artery increases, you would expect that the pressure of the blood would also increase.

The second factor that affects blood pressure is the resistance of the arteries. Arterial resistance is related to the elasticity in the arteries. For example, if the arteries do not expand easily and instead resist the flow of blood, the pressure of the blood on the arterial walls increases.

Blood pressure varies according to an individual's height, weight, and fitness level, as well as by time of day, physical activity, hydration, and other factors. As a person ages, blood pressure may increase. Smoking or a diet high in fats can contribute to an increase in blood pressure by causing arteries to become less elastic. Blood pressure in a healthy young adult might vary between about 110 and 130 over 70 to 90, with an average of about 120/80. A blood pressure consistently above 140/90 is considered high.

BIOLOGY•SOURCE

Take It Further

Fighter pilots and astronauts are subjected to extreme forces during acceleration that can make their blood pool in their feet and cause loss of consciousness. In 1941, a Canadian team led by Dr. Wilbur R. Franks developed the first workable antigravity suit that boosted blood pressure and prevented gravity-induced loss of consciousness. Find out how modern antigravity suits are designed and draw a labelled diagram.

Concept Check

1. What machine is used to measure blood pressure?

2. What is the difference between systolic and diastolic pressure?

3. On what two factors does blood pressure depend?

D7 Skill Builder Activity

Dissecting

Activity Overview

Important terms used in dissection include the following.

- dorsal: facing the top or the backside of the body
- ventral: facing the underside or the stomach side of the body
- cranial (anterior): the head end of the body
- caudal (posterior): the tail end of the body
- lateral: the side of the body
- median: the centre of the body
- anatomical right and left: the animal's right and left
- proximal: closer to an area
- distal: farther from an area
- superficial: closer to the body surface
- deep: under or below

In this activity, you will use these terms while dissecting a vegetable. Your teacher will give you a copy of the full activity.

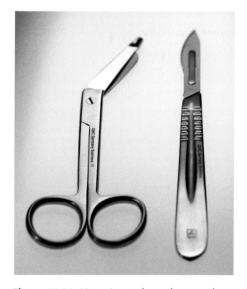

Figure 11.20 Dissection tools can be very sharp. Take care in handling blades and scissors.

Dissecting a Heart

Question

How does the structure of the heart support its function?

Activity Overview

Blood is connective tissue that is transported through the entire body of a living organism. Blood transports dissolved gases, wastes, hormones, enzymes, and nutrients. The heart acts as the pump in the system in most complex animals. In this activity, you will look at a heart to understand blood transport (Figure 11.21).

Your teacher will give you a copy of the full activity.

Prelab Questions

Consider the questions below before beginning this activity.

1. What are the four main chambers of the heart?

2. Why is the mammalian heart sometimes called a "double pump?"

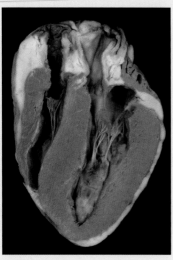

Figure 11.21 A sheep heart

Getting to Know Your Circulatory System

Purpose

To listen to your heart sounds, measure your blood pressure, and find your pulse

Activity Overview

In this activity, you will learn to take your pulse (Figure 11.22). You will use a stethoscope to listen to sounds of your heart beating and to measure blood pressure (Figure 11.23).

Your teacher will give you a copy of the full activity.

Prelab Questions

Consider the questions below before beginning this activity.

1. What do your heart valves sound like when they close?

2. How does your heart rate change with exercise?

3. Where can you measure your pulse?

Figure 11.22 The pulse found at the radial artery or carotid artery is a measure of the rate at which the heart is beating.

Figure 11.23 Measuring blood pressure

Key Concept Review

1. How does a stethoscope work?

2. (a) What happens when the heart muscle contracts?
   (b) What happens when the heart muscle relaxes?

3. Copy the labels A to M into your notebook. Identify each structure shown below.

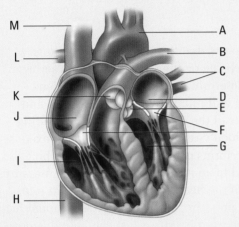

Question 3

4. What is the function of valves in the heart?

5. What makes the "lub dub" sound of your heart beating?

6. Copy the labels A to G into your notebook. Identify each structure shown below.

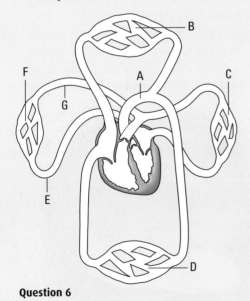

Question 6

7. State one way in which the function of the pulmonary artery is different from the function of other arteries in the body.

8. What is the difference between the superior vena cava and the inferior vena cava?

9. How are the cells of the heart supplied with necessary oxygen and nutrients?

10. Where in the heart would you find the area known as the pacemaker?

11. About how many times does a heart beat per minute?

12. What is a sphygmomanometer?

13. Define the following terms:
    (a) diastolic pressure
    (b) systolic pressure

14. What two factors does blood pressure depend on?

15. What is an average blood pressure reading for a healthy adult?

Connect Your Understanding

16. Create a flowchart that names each structure that blood encounters from when it enters the heart deprived of oxygen to when it exits the heart full of oxygen.

17. Write a brief story describing the path of a blood cell as it travels though the pulmonary system and the systemic system.

18. Explain why the heart is called a "double pump."

19. Suppose you listened with a stethoscope below a sphygmomanometer and heard sounds beginning at 140 mm Hg and stopping at 95 mm Hg.
    (a) What is the systolic blood pressure reading?
    (b) What is the diastolic blood pressure reading?
    (c) What is this person's blood pressure?
    (d) Is this a healthy blood pressure? Explain.

Reflection

20. What are three questions you have about your heart and circulatory system after reading this section?

For more questions, go to *BIOLOGY•SOURCE*

Promoting a Healthy Circulatory System

Section Summary

- Disorders in the structure and function of the circulatory system pose a significant risk to health.

- Diagnosis and treatment of cardiovascular disorders involve a variety of technologies.

- Strategies to promote the health of the circulatory system include eating a healthy diet, maintaining a healthy weight, leading an active lifestyle, refraining from smoking, and having regular medical assessments.

When a physician suspects that the circulatory system is not functioning properly, he or she can administer a series of diagnostic tests to determine the cause of the problem. In most cases, the tests will monitor both the structure and function of components of the circulatory system including the heart, blood, and blood vessels. For example, in an exercise stress test, a patient performs exercise on a stationary bike or treadmill while hooked to an electrocardiograph that measures the electrical activity of the heart (Figure 11.24). Heart rate, respiratory rate, blood pressure, and how tired the patient feels are also monitored. The exercise stress test can help diagnose coronary artery disease, determine a safe level of exercise, and predict the risk of dangerous conditions such as heart attack.

Plaque

If you could look into the arteries of a newborn baby, you would probably see fairly smooth surfaces. If you could inspect the arteries of an older person, however, you might find a patchwork of cholesterol, calcium, and fat deposits, called **plaque**, sticking to the interior walls (Figure 11.25). Plaque builds up throughout a person's life. Significant buildup of plaque can ultimately lead to cardiovascular disease.

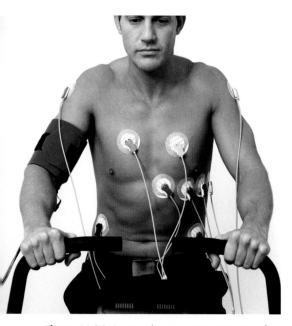

Figure 11.24 An exercise stress test measures the changes in electrical activity in the heart as the body responds to increased need for oxygen.

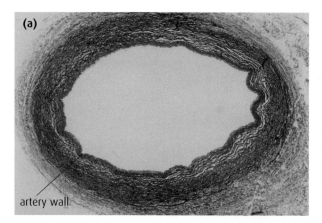

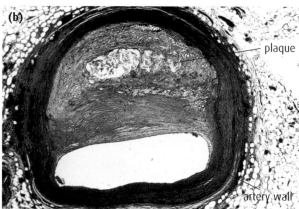

Figure 11.25 (a) A healthy artery (magnification 8×) and (b) a clogged artery (magnification 6×)

©P

Dangers of Plaque Buildup

Atherosclerosis is a narrowing of the arteries resulting from plaque building up inside the artery wall. As the pathway narrows, blood pressure increases. Sometimes the narrowing completely blocks the flow of blood. If such a blockage occurs in one of the coronary arteries, the heart becomes deprived of oxygen and other nutrients. In mild cases with partial blockage, the person may feel occasional chest pains, called angina pectoris. Treatment may include angioplasty, in which a small metal mesh tube is placed into the artery, where it expands to prevent the artery from closing up (Figure 11.26). In cases of severe blockage, a blood clot could close up the artery, leading to a heart attack.

BIOLOGY•SOURCE

Explore More

Are atherosclerosis and heart disease a concern for teenagers?

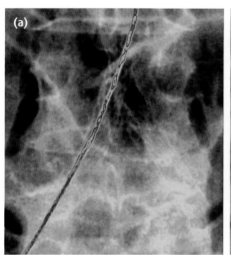
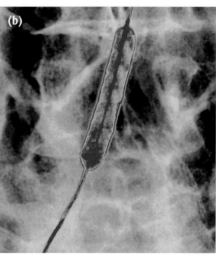

Figure 11.26 (a) In angioplasty, an expandable tube is placed in a clogged artery. (b) The tube is expanded to allow blood to flow through the artery.

BIOLOGY•SOURCE

Explore More

What is a heart murmur and is it dangerous?

A **heart attack** occurs when the blood supply to heart tissue is slowed or stopped. In the majority of cases, the cause of heart attack is the narrowing of coronary arteries due to atherosclerosis. During a heart attack, the heart usually does not stop beating. Symptoms of a heart attack include pain in the chest and upper body that may be accompanied by shortness of breath and nausea. If treatment is not started quickly, some of the heart muscle will die and be replaced by scar tissue. Heart attacks are very rare in teenagers.

Arteriosclerosis is an advanced stage of plaque buildup, which occurs when the deposits on the artery wall harden. Arteries are flexible and can expand and contract, which helps to control blood pressure. With arteriosclerosis, the arteries lose their ability to stretch. This disease increases blood pressure and the chance for blood clots to form within the blood vessels. Treatment may include heart bypass surgery in which a surgeon may take a vein or artery from another part of the body and use it to makes a detour around the blocked part of the coronary artery.

Sudden cardiac arrest occurs when a heart suddenly stops functioning, as from drowning, electrocution, trauma, or choking. The most common cause of cardiac arrest is coronary heart disease. In this case, the arteries that supply the heart tissues with nutrients become blocked. Coronary blockages cause the heart to beat irregularly so that blood is not pumped efficiently and in a regular rhythm. If the heart rhythm is not reset immediately, such as by a cardiac defibrillator, death can occur within minutes (Figure 11.27).

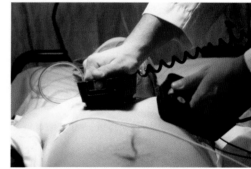

Figure 11.27 When a patient's heart stops beating, paddle-like appliances called defibrillators are applied to the patient's chest. The paddles produce a strong electrical current that can cause the person's heart to resume beating.

Some Cardiovascular Disorders

Arrhythmia is a condition in which the heart beats irregularly, too quickly, or too slowly. Most arrhythmia arises from problems with the electrical activity of the heart. Symptoms of arrhythmia include dizziness, chest pain, and shortness of breath. Treatment to restore a normal heartbeat may include implanting an artificial pacemaker or a small defibrillator under the skin in the chest or abdomen (Figure 11.28).

Hypertension, or high blood pressure, is a condition where a person's blood pressure is 140/90 or higher for an extended period of time. Prolonged hypertension damages the heart and blood vessels. The heart must work harder to pump blood throughout the body, and over time the heart muscles expand. If these muscles expand too much, they become weakened and can no longer push blood throughout the body. Hypertension also exerts greater than normal pressure on the walls of the arteries, which can cause small tears. These tears can speed up atherosclerosis, which further increases blood pressure. Teenagers can have high blood pressure caused by genetic factors, excess body weight, diet, or lack of exercise.

Heart failure is a condition in which the heart cannot pump blood efficiently because it cannot fill with enough blood or cannot send the blood to the rest of body with enough force. Heart failure is a common condition, affecting both children and adults. If it is diagnosed early, people with heart failure can live longer and lead more active lives by improving their lifestyle and following treatment plans. In the most severe forms, it may be necessary to receive a heart transplant (Figure 11.29).

An **aneurysm** is a bulge in the wall of an artery (Figure 11.30). Aneurysms can be caused by injuries, genetic conditions, or disease. As blood rushes through the artery, it further weakens the bulging wall and may burst through, causing serious internal bleeding. An aneurysm can occur in any artery in the body, but most often occurs in branches of the aorta. Aneurysms can be detected using magnetic resonance imaging (MRI), a non-invasive imaging technology that produces three-dimensional views of organs and tissues.

A **stroke** occurs if a blood clot forms in an artery going to the brain. Tissue downstream from the blockage can die from lack of oxygen. Some effects of stroke are partial paralysis, loss of speech, memory loss, and sometimes death. These effects depend in part on where in the brain the blockage occurs.

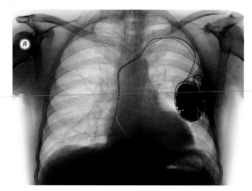

Figure 11.28 An artificial pacemaker delivers electrical impulses to make the heart beat in a more regular manner.

Figure 11.29 A human heart

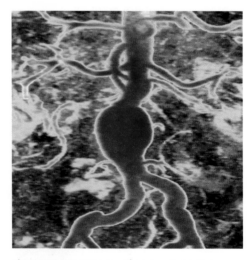

Figure 11.30 MRI scan of an aneurysm in an abdominal artery

BIOLOGY•SOURCE

Suggested Activities

- D10 Quick Lab Overview on page 322
- D11 Decision-Making Analysis Overview on page 322

Concept Check

1. Why is plaque buildup dangerous?
2. What are three causes of hypertension in teenagers?
3. What is an aneurysm?

Choices that Promote Cardiovascular Health

Although some risk for cardiovascular disease is genetic, there are many controllable factors that play a role. For example, low-fat diets, plenty of exercise, and not smoking all decrease the risk of cardiovascular disease.

- *Eat a Healthy Diet* Imagine you are walking into a food court to buy lunch. How do you decide which food is the healthiest for you to eat? Good choices for your heart include foods that are high in fibre and low in salt and cholesterol.

    Cholesterol is a fat that is part of your cell membranes and is used to synthesize hormones, bile, and vitamin D. Your liver manufactures cholesterol, which your blood carries to the tissues. Cholesterol is transported by two types of lipoproteins, which are carriers made of fat and protein. High-density lipoprotein (HDL) is sometimes called "good cholesterol" as it helps remove excess cholesterol from the tissues and arteries. Low-density lipoprotein (LDL) is sometimes called "bad cholesterol" because it becomes part of the plaque in the arteries. LDL is found in foods that are high in saturated or trans fats, such as beef, butter, cheese, ice cream, deep-fried fast foods, bakery products, margarines, and packaged snack foods. Read the label of packaged food to determine the types of fats in the product.

    In the food court, you might consider choosing a falafel instead of a burger, a baked potato or fruit salad instead of French fries, or a whole-grain sandwich instead of a pizza. You could also encourage your school administrators to replace high-fat, high-sugar choices in the cafeteria and vending machines with high-quality, healthy foods that are competitively priced.

- *Maintain a Healthy Weight* If you are concerned about your weight, consult your health practitioner for a long-term plan that will help you achieve and maintain a healthy weight. Avoid fad diets. If you feel that stress affects the way that you eat, try to learn new ways to deal with it. A counsellor or health-care practitioner can help recommend some coping strategies.

- *Exercise Regularly* Regular exercise reduces your chances of developing conditions that may strain your heart, such as high blood pressure, high cholesterol, and diabetes. Find ways to be more active by including simple activities such as walking the dog, taking the stairs instead of the elevator, or riding your bike for errands instead of taking the bus or driving. Aim for 40-60 minutes of moderately intense activity most days of the week.

- *Avoid Smoking and Second-hand Smoke* Tobacco smoke contains thousands of chemicals that can damage the tissues of your heart and blood vessels. Nicotine, a chemical found in tobacco smoke, narrows your blood vessels and increases your heart rate and blood pressure. The carbon monoxide in cigarette smoke replaces some of the oxygen in your blood, which forces your heart to work harder to supply enough oxygen.

- *Get Regular Health Checkups* Your health practitioner can check your blood pressure, heart sounds, pulse rate, weight, and other indicators of your health and track them from year to year.

    It is much easier to prevent cardiovascular disease than to cure it. Prevention starts now, while you are young. You can lessen your risk by making healthy choices throughout your life.

Figure 11.31 Choosing to eat lots of fresh fruits, vegetables, and whole-grain foods ensures that you are getting the necessary nutrients and lots of fibre. Fibre may help reduce cholesterol levels.

BIOLOGY•SOURCE

Take It Further

In Ontario alone, approximately 7000 cardiac arrests occur each year. The Heart and Stroke Foundation and other agencies have placed emergency defibrillators in public places like subway stations, airports, and sporting arenas. Find out more about public access defibrillation (PAD) programs. Create a graphic organizer that answers "Who," "What," "When," "Where," and "Why" questions about PAD in your community.

Track the Clogging of an Artery

Purpose

To explore how atherosclerosis can lead to a heart attack

Activity Overview

Like all your body cells, heart muscle cells require oxygen and nutrient-rich blood to survive. If one or more of the heart's coronary arteries become blocked, heart muscles cells will quickly die. Such an event is called a heart attack. In this activity, you will observe a virtual heart attack.

Your teacher will give you a copy of the full activity.

Prelab Questions

Consider the questions below before beginning this activity.

1. What factors can increase your risk of a heart attack?

2. How can you reduce risk of heart disease?

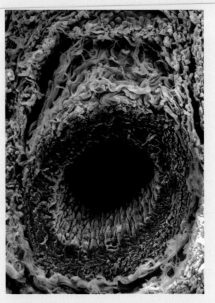

Figure 11.32 A healthy artery (magnification 440×)

Top Canadian Technological Innovations

Issue

The value that you place on technological development is sometimes related to your own knowledge about technology or how you feel it meets a need in your life or in the lives of people you know.

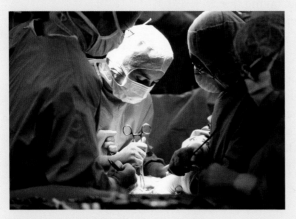

Figure 11.33 Canadian doctors have helped pioneer both open- and closed-chest heart surgery.

Activity Overview

In this activity, you will increase your level of awareness by surveying Canadian technological developments that meet societal needs and are related to the circulatory system.

Your teacher will give you a copy of the full activity.

Prelab Questions

Consider the questions below before beginning this activity.

1. Which technologies related to the cardiovascular system do you think are the most important?

2. How would you determine who gets access to these technologies?

Key Concept Review

1. (a) What is plaque?
   (b) How is it formed?
   (c) Why is plaque dangerous to the health of the circulatory system?

2. What is the difference between arteriosclerosis and atherosclerosis?

3. What is the difference between a heart attack and cardiac arrest?

4. (a) Where does an aneurysm occur?
   (b) What are three causes of aneurysms?

5. (a) What is hypertension?
   (b) What are three factors that can cause hypertension in teenagers?

6. List five things that you can choose to do in order to promote good cardiovascular health.

7. What is cholesterol?

8. Define lipoprotein.

9. (a) What is HDL?
   (b) What is LDL?

10. Why should you aim for having at least 40 minutes of moderately intense physical activity most days?

11. (a) What does the nicotine in cigarette smoke do to your arteries?
    (b) What does the carbon monoxide in cigarette smoke do to your blood?

Connect Your Understanding

12. Why is it important for teenagers to monitor their intake of foods that are high in cholesterol?

13. How does maintaining a healthy weight help your cardiovascular system work more efficiently?

14. How is a stroke related to an aneurysm?

15. Make a chart that compares controllable risk factors and uncontrollable risk factors for cardiovascular disease.

16. Poutine is a combination of French fries (carbohydrates), cheese (protein), and gravy (fat). Even though poutine includes three major nutrients, it is not a good choice of food for your heart. Explain why.

17. An angiography is a non-invasive diagnostic test in which a patient is injected with an iodine-based dye. Multiple X-rays are taken of the heart, which a computer uses to form three-dimensional images (see below).
    (a) What does non-invasive mean?
    (b) Why is it important to have non-invasive methods of diagnosing cardiovascular disease?
    (c) What are several conditions that this test might help diagnose?

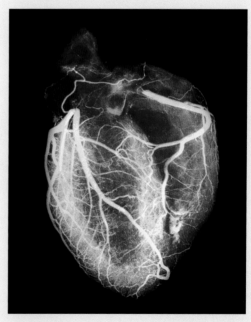

Question 17

18. Most cardiovascular disease affects adults. Why should you care now about your diet and daily exercise?

Reflection

19. What information in this section did you find especially interesting? Explain why.

For more questions, go to BIOLOGY•SOURCE

Key Concept Review

1. What is the function of the circulatory system? Ⓚ

2. (a) List the three main components of the circulatory system. Ⓚ
   (b) Describe the function of each component. Ⓚ

3. What role does hemoglobin play in your blood? Ⓚ

4. Why must red blood cells continually be replaced? Ⓚ

5. What is the role of platelets? Ⓚ

6. Describe the process of blood clotting. Ⓚ

7. Copy and complete the following chart in your notebook. Ⓚ

	Structure	Function
Arteries		
Veins		
Capillaries		

8. What two types of blood vessels does an arteriole connect? Ⓚ

9. Explain how a nutrient gets from your blood into your cells. Ⓚ

10. Define the term "lymph." Ⓚ

11. How does the lymphatic system return fluid to the circulatory system? Ⓚ

12. What is the usual range of the heart rate for an average adult? Ⓚ

13. Distinguish between the atria and ventricles in regards to their:
    (a) structure Ⓚ
    (b) function Ⓚ

14. What is the function of a heart valve? Ⓚ

15. What causes the sounds of the heart beating? Ⓚ

16. Define the following terms:
    (a) pulmonary circuit Ⓚ
    (b) systemic circuit Ⓚ

17. Explain how the pacemaker regulates contractions. Ⓚ

18. What is the difference in meaning between the terms systole and diastole? Ⓚ

19. What two factors determine blood pressure? Ⓚ

20. What is a normal blood pressure reading for a young adult? Ⓚ

21. What is the difference between atherosclerosis and arteriosclerosis? Ⓚ

22. What causes a stroke? Ⓚ

23. How much moderately intense physical activity should you aim for each day? Ⓚ

24. How does smoking affect the circulatory system? Ⓚ

Connect Your Understanding

25. (a) Sketch a diagram of the heart. Ⓚ
    (b) Add labels to identify the four chambers, pacemaker area, and heart valves. Ⓚ
    (c) Use a coloured arrow to show the flow of blood through the heart. Ⓚ

26. The diagram below shows a sample of blood that has been separated into its components.
    (a) In which part of the test tube would you expect to find the greatest concentration of hemoglobin? Ⓣ
    (b) Explain your reasoning for your answer in (a). Ⓣ
    (c) What are four substances you might find dissolved in the part labelled x? Ⓚ
    (d) Considering what you have read about the materials that make up blood, why do you think the materials in part x rise to the top? Ⓣ

Question 26

27. (a) Why is HDL called "good" cholesterol? Ⓚ
    (b) Why is LDL called "bad" cholesterol? Ⓚ

28. (a) Why do some large veins have valves? **k**
(b) Why do arteries not need valves? **a**

29. A person with a low red blood cell count may often feel tired. Why? **a**

30. The graph below shows blood pressure in different parts of the cardiovascular system. For the area of the graph labelled *x*, state the person's
(a) systolic pressure **a**
(b) diastolic pressure **a**

31. (a) According to the graph, in which type of blood vessels is the blood pressure the highest? **a**
(b) In which type of blood vessels is the blood pressure the lowest? **a**

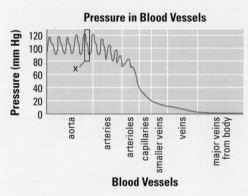

Pressure in Blood Vessels

Questions 30 and 31

32. Why could a very high systolic pressure be dangerous? **t**

33. (a) What is the name of the major artery that leads out of the heart? **k**
(b) Describe physical characteristics that you would expect to find in this blood vessel. **a**

34. How does your blood move back to your heart even though the pressure in your veins is low? **t**

35. Your friend is on her way to the gym. She tells you that she is planning to start with 30 minutes of "cardio." What does she mean? **a**

36. Explain the error in the following statement. "All arteries carry oxygenated blood away from the heart." **t**

37. Explain why the loss of regular heart rhythm could result in serious illness or even death. **a**

38. An individual's blood pressure was measured several times over the course of a day, and the reading was 145/90.
(a) Explain why a doctor may have reason to be concerned with this blood pressure measurement. **k**
(b) Explain why the blood pressure was measured at different times of the day. **a**

39. Why might you infer that the left ventricle would be more muscular than the right ventricle? **a**

40. Write a paragraph that describes lifestyle choices that can promote cardiovascular health. **c**

41. Sometimes we use expressions that have a biological basis to express everyday concepts. If someone said that you were the "lifeblood" of the team, use your understanding from this section to explain what is being said about you. **c**

42. More than 50 percent of Canadian teenagers are less active than the equivalent of walking at least one hour per day.
(a) How much physical activity do you average daily? **a**
(b) How could you increase your amount of physical activity? **a**

Reflection

43. How has the information that you have learned in this unit affected your thinking about the importance of your own cardiovascular health? Explain. **c**

Unit Task Link

Review your notes about the circulatory system and select one of the disorders. Create a graphic organizer that summarizes the following information.
• What are the symptoms of the disorder?
• What are the causes of the disorder?
• How is the disorder diagnosed?
• How can this disorder be prevented?
• How is the disorder treated?

For more questions, go to BIOLOGY•SOURCE

The respiratory system exchanges gases between blood and air.

Lung cancer is currently the leading cause of cancer deaths worldwide. Traditional means of detecting cancer involve the use of X-rays or CT scans, but these technologies detect cancer only after the cancer is well-developed. It is difficult to detect cancer in its early stages using these technologies.

Is it possible to "sniff out" cancer in its early stages? A team of researchers conducted studies to answer this question. Over a period of three weeks, they trained dogs to recognize the presence of cancer by exposing the dogs to the breath of cancer patients. The breath of healthy patients was used as an experimental control. With a level of accuracy between 88 and 97 percent, the dogs could identify patients who had cancer, simply by sniffing their breath.

What was it about the patients' breath that revealed the presence of cancer? Scientists found that the cells of lung cancer patients produced unique chemicals. These chemicals formed gases that were then expelled from the patient's body in the breath. The dogs probably were able to sniff these cancer chemicals in the patient's breath.

Although it is unlikely that dogs will be used in routine screening for cancer, this research could lead to the development of a simple and effective way to screen for the presence of lung cancer using the exhaled breath of an individual.

Figure 12.1 Dogs can detect the presence of chemicals in the air that they breathe. "Sniffer dogs" may be used to detect land mines, drugs, and even the presence of cancer.

12.1 Structure and Function of the Respiratory System

Section Summary

- All cells need a regular supply of oxygen in order to produce energy.
- The transfer of gases occurs in three phases: breathing, transport of gases, and gas exchange.
- Respiratory surfaces are thin, moist, selectively permeable membranes with a large surface area.
- Hemoglobin transports oxygen through the body.
- The level of carbon dioxide in the blood controls the breathing rate.

Organisms survive by exchanging materials with their environment. If you were stranded on a desert island, you would be able to survive for days without fresh water and for weeks without food. However, you can live for only a few minutes without oxygen. All of your cells require oxygen to obtain energy from molecules of carbohydrates, fats, and proteins during the process of cellular respiration.

Transferring Gases to and from the Cells

Cellular respiration is a process that produces the energy needed to fuel all cell activities. This process occurs in the mitochondria in cells. Cells must have a constant supply of O_2 and must constantly dispose of CO_2. If there is not enough oxygen available to the cells, energy is not produced efficiently, and cells are harmed. Typically, about 21 percent of a sample of air is oxygen. So in order for cells to obtain enough oxygen for energy production, a large enough volume of air must enter the body.

In animals with lungs, including humans, the transfer of gases from the environment into the body and to the cells occurs in three phases: breathing, transport of gases, and exchange of gases in cells (Figure 12.2).

Respiratory Surface in Animals

In multicellular organisms, gas exchange usually occurs along a special membrane called the **respiratory surface**. Although animals live in a wide variety of environments, the process of diffusion governs the function of their respiratory surfaces.

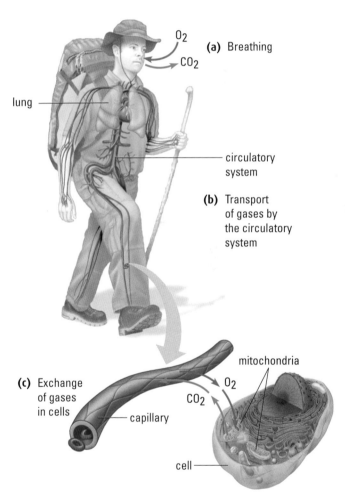

(a) Breathing

O_2

CO_2

lung

circulatory system

(b) Transport of gases by the circulatory system

(c) Exchange of gases in cells

capillary

mitochondria

O_2

CO_2

cell

Figure 12.2 (a) Breathing moves gases between the environment and the body. (b) The circulatory system transports gases to and from the cells. (c) The cells take up O_2 from the blood and release CO_2.

A respiratory surface has certain characteristics to ensure that diffusion occurs efficiently.

- A respiratory surface is a very thin and moist membrane that is permeable to the gases being diffused.
- The surface area of the membrane is large so as to maximize diffusion.
- A diffusion gradient must be maintained since diffusion moves gases from higher concentration to lower concentration. In other words, there needs to be a difference in the relative concentration of oxygen and carbon dioxide on either side of the membrane surface. In most organisms, the circulatory system serves to transport gases to and from the membrane so that appropriate gas concentrations can be maintained.

Some animals, such as the earthworm in Figure 12.3, use their entire body surface as a respiratory surface. Animals that breathe through their skin are generally small or have flat bodies that provide a high ratio of respiratory surface to body volume. Earthworms and other animals that breathe through their skin live in damp places or in water to keep their entire body surface moist.

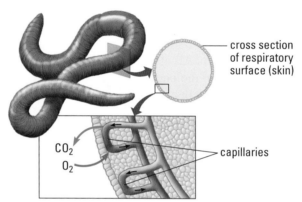

Figure 12.3 An earthworm's entire skin is its respiratory surface.

Gas Exchange in Aquatic Animals

Aquatic animals live in water, so their respiratory surface is always moist. However, because the source of useful gas is dissolved in water, an appropriate volume of water must come into close contact with the thin respiratory membranes and yet not damage the membranes. Most aquatic animals have gills. **Gills** are folds in the body surface that are specialized for gas exchange. The design of the fish gill enables water to flow so that gases can diffuse from the water and across the respiratory membranes (Figure 12.4). Oxygen diffuses directly into the capillaries and CO_2 diffuses out of the capillaries and into the environment. The capillaries transport the gases to and from the gills to the cells of the body.

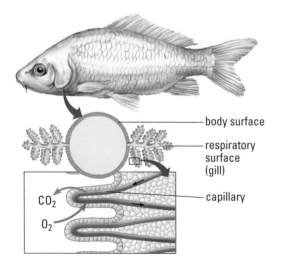

Figure 12.4 The gills on a fish are extensions of its body surface. Gills exchange gases directly with surrounding water.

Concept Check

1. What are the three phases of gas exchange?
2. What occurs along the respiratory surface?
3. What are gills?

Gas Exchange in Terrestrial Animals

Terrestrial animals that exchange gases by breathing air have two advantages over aquatic animals that exchange gases in water. There is a higher concentration of oxygen in air than in water. Also, air is both lighter and easier to move than water. This means that terrestrial animals need to spend less energy than aquatic animals in exchanging gases across their respiratory surface. However, one disadvantage that terrestrial animals face is the loss of moisture to their environment. Most terrestrial animals have evolved internal respiratory surfaces, such as tracheal systems and lungs, to help minimize the loss of moisture.

BIOLOGY·SOURCE

Explore More

What adaptations do aquatic mammals have in their respiratory and circulatory systems that allow them to stay under water for long periods of time?

Tracheal System

Many insects have a **tracheal system**, which is a system of tubes that extend through their bodies (Figure 12.5). Air enters and leaves the system through openings in the body surface. The larger tubes, called tracheae, branch into smaller and smaller tubes called tracheoles, which extend to nearly every cell in the insect's body. Gas exchange occurs along the moist membrane at the tips of the tracheoles.

Insects do not need a circulatory system to exchange gases. Smaller insects can receive enough O_2 and get rid of enough CO_2 through diffusion across their membranes. Larger insects sometimes pump in more air through rhythmic body movements that compress and expand the air. Insects consume much more oxygen when they fly than when they are at rest. Their flight muscles help to rapidly pump air through their tracheal systems.

Lungs

Many terrestrial organisms primarily use internal respiratory structures that are surrounded by fluids or by moist tissues and blood vessels. For reptiles, birds, mammals, and some amphibians, gas exchange occurs in **lungs**, which are internal, thin-walled sacs with a large surface area (Figure 12.6). Inside the lungs, oxygen gas diffuses into the blood and is transported through blood vessels to the cells of the body. Carbon dioxide diffuses out of the blood, enters the lungs, and is moved out of the body by the mechanical movements of breathing. Aquatic reptiles and aquatic mammals such as whales breathe with lungs and must hold their breath under water.

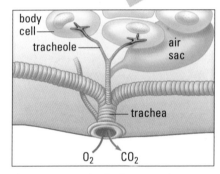

Figure 12.5 Tracheal tubes extend throughout a grasshopper's body.

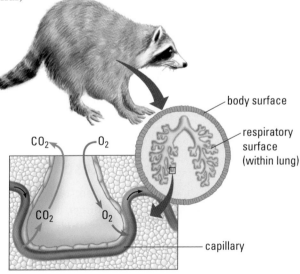

Figure 12.6 Lungs are internal organs of respiration that are lined with moist membranes.

Concept Check

1. What are two advantages of breathing air over exchanging gases in water?

2. What is a tracheal system?

3. What are lungs?

Human Respiratory System

The structures of the human respiratory system, including the mouth, nose, pharynx, larynx, trachea, and lungs, work together to move gases in and out of the body (Figure 12.7).

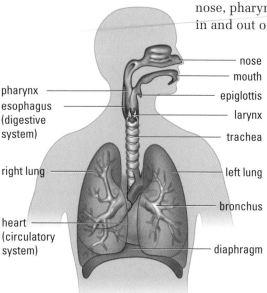

pharynx
esophagus (digestive system)

right lung

heart (circulatory system)

nose
mouth
epiglottis
larynx
trachea
left lung
bronchus
diaphragm

Figure 12.7 The human respiratory system

As you inhale, air enters the respiratory system. Many of the impurities in air, such as dirt and bacteria, are filtered by hair and mucus in your nose. Air is warmed and moisture is added.

Air passes into the pharynx where the passageways for air and food cross. The air pathway in the pharynx is always open, except when you swallow. When you swallow, the epiglottis covers the air pathway to prevent food from entering the trachea, instead of the esophagus.

From the pharynx, air passes through your voice box or **larynx**. Vocal cords in your larynx vibrate, producing sounds. Air next passes into the **trachea**, or windpipe. C-shaped rings of cartilage maintain the tubular shape of the trachea. The trachea forks into two **bronchi** (singular, *bronchus*), which are air tubes that connect the trachea to the lungs.

Within each lung, the bronchus branches repeatedly into finer and finer tubes called **bronchioles** (Figure 12.8). The bronchi and bronchioles are surrounded by smooth muscles. As the muscles contract or relax, they control the size of the airways.

Each bronchiole ends in grapelike clusters of tiny air sacs called **alveoli** (singular, *alveolus*). Your lungs contain millions of these tiny air sacs, which provide a very large surface area for gas exchange.

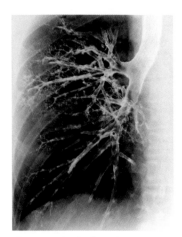

Figure 12.8 The branching pattern of bronchioles is sometimes called "the respiratory tree" because it looks somewhat like an upside-down tree.

Figure 12.9 Cilia (yellow), mucus-producing cells (orange, round), mucus drops (pale pink), and dust particle (green) (magnification 670×)

Respiratory System Lining

Your respiratory system, from your nose and mouth all the way to your lungs, is lined with moist epithelial tissue. In the trachea and bronchi, the epithelial cells are covered with cilia and a fine layer of mucus. **Cilia** are short, hair-like structures protruding from a cell that move fluid and particles over the cell's surface (Figure 12.9). The mucus traps foreign particles and removes them from the air. The cilia then sweep the mucus-trapped particles up toward the pharynx where they can be expelled or swallowed.

Breathing

The structures of the respiratory system work together so that air can be exchanged with the environment. If this system is functioning well, an appropriate volume of air is obtained from the environment, is warmed and purified, and then is passed through a series of airways into the lungs.

Breathing, also called ventilation, is the process of moving air into and out of your lungs (Figure 12.10). Although you may not have noticed it, you probably took a breath of air and released it while you were reading this sentence. On average, you breathe about 15 times per minute, or more than 21 000 breaths each day.

Each of your lungs is about the size of a football, and together your lungs have a total capacity of about 6 L. However, you use only about 0.6 L of that volume in a normal breath. When you are exercising vigorously, you can use up to about 20 times the amount of oxygen you use at rest.

The Role of the Diaphragm

The process of ventilation is largely a passive process. This means that the process works without your attention and without using extra energy. The chest cavity is like a sealed container that has a volume and is subject to air pressure. In the process of breathing, structures of the respiratory system can increase or decrease the volume and thereby change the air pressure. Two key structures involved in this process are the diaphragm and the rib muscles. The **diaphragm** is a large dome-shaped sheet of muscle that forms the bottom wall of your chest cavity (Figure 12.11).

- When your diaphragm and rib muscles contract, you inhale. Your inhalation expands your chest cavity, which increases the volume of your lungs, resulting in reduced air pressure within the alveoli. Since air tends to move from an area of higher pressure to an area of lower pressure, air rushes in through your nose or mouth and fills the alveoli.
- When your diaphragm and rib muscles relax, your lung volume decreases, causing higher air pressure in the alveoli. Air rushes from your lungs out through your nose or mouth as you exhale.

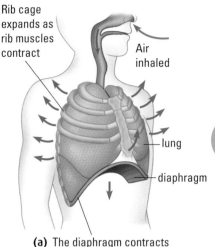

Rib cage expands as rib muscles contract

Air inhaled

lung

diaphragm

(a) The diaphragm contracts (moves down).

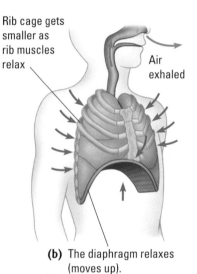

Rib cage gets smaller as rib muscles relax

Air exhaled

(b) The diaphragm relaxes (moves up).

Figure 12.10 (a) Inhalation and (b) exhalation. You increase and decrease the volume of your lungs when you inhale and exhale.

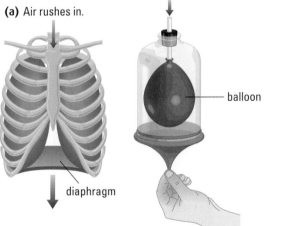

(a) Air rushes in.

balloon

diaphragm

Figure 12.11(a) When the bottom of the bell jar moves down, the volume of the jar increases, the air pressure decreases, and the air rushes into the balloon. Likewise, when the diaphragm contracts and moves down, the air pressure decreases, and the air rushes into the lungs.

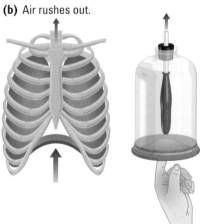

(b) Air rushes out.

Figure 12.11(b) When the bottom of the bell jar moves up, the volume of the jar decreases, the air pressure increases, and the air rushes out of the balloon. Likewise, when the diaphragm relaxes and moves up, the air pressure increases, and the air rushes out of the lungs.

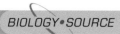
Concept Check

1. What is the function of the alveoli?

2. What are cilia?

3. What happens when your diaphragm and rib muscles contract?

From Your Lungs to All Your Body Cells

The process of breathing accomplishes the important task of moving gas into your lungs. Once air is in your lungs, the task of exchanging oxygen for carbon dioxide begins in the alveoli in the lungs.

Gas Exchange

The inner surface of each alveolus is lined with a layer of moist epithelial cells. Oxygen in the air you inhale dissolves in the film of moisture on these epithelial cells. The oxygen then diffuses into a web of capillaries surrounding each alveolus and enters red blood cells, binding to hemoglobin (Figure 12.12).

Hemoglobin increases the efficiency of gas exchange by creating a diffusion gradient. In other words, when the hemoglobin in a red blood cell binds to the oxygen, it removes the oxygen from the plasma. Oxygen then keeps on diffusing from the alveolus into the plasma because the oxygen is at a lower concentration in the plasma than in the alveolus. By binding oxygen, the hemoglobin actually increases the blood's ability to transport oxygen by about 60 times.

Figure 12.12 As shown in this model, hemoglobin molecules have several sites to which oxygen molecules can bind.

Transport

Your cells access the oxygen they need from nearby blood vessels. As cellular respiration produces energy, carbon dioxide is produced as a by-product of that process. Carbon dioxide diffuses the opposite way to oxygen, from the capillaries across the epithelial cells and into the alveoli (Figure 12.13). The carbon dioxide is carried away from the cells and deposited in the lungs. Then the carbon dioxide is expelled back up the trachea, through the nose or mouth, and into the environment.

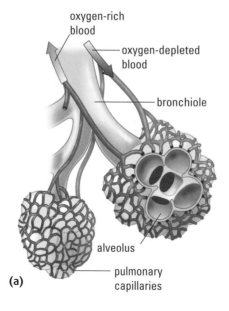

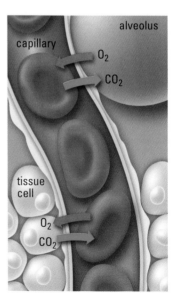

Figure 12.13 (a) Gas exchange occurs in tiny air sacs in your lungs called alveoli. (b) Carbon dioxide and oxygen diffuse across capillary and alveolus walls.

Regulation of Breathing

In order to supply cells with adequate energy, both the mechanical process of ventilation and the process of gas exchange must be working effectively. Enough air must flow in and out of the organism and also must contact the respiratory membranes.

Breathing is usually an involuntary process that you seldom realize is occurring. However, you can temporarily exert conscious control over breathing, such as when you hold your breath under water. Most of the time, breathing is controlled by the medulla oblongata, a part of the brain located near the top of the spinal cord. The medulla oblongata sends nerve signals to the diaphragm and rib muscles, causing them to contract and relax.

You might think that the level of oxygen in the body controls the rate of breathing. But, surprisingly, it is usually the level of carbon dioxide that controls breathing rate (Figure 12.14). When carbon dioxide dissolves in a solution containing water, it forms carbonic acid (H_2CO_3). As carbon dioxide diffuses through a capillary wall, most of it dissolves in the plasma, the watery portion of blood.

BIOLOGY•SOURCE

Explore More

What happens during hyperventilation, when air is inhaled too quickly?

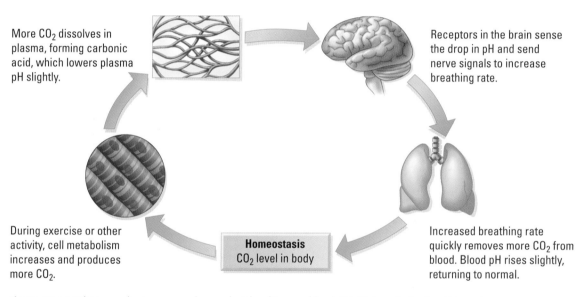

More CO_2 dissolves in plasma, forming carbonic acid, which lowers plasma pH slightly.

Receptors in the brain sense the drop in pH and send nerve signals to increase breathing rate.

During exercise or other activity, cell metabolism increases and produces more CO_2.

Homeostasis
CO_2 level in body

Increased breathing rate quickly removes more CO_2 from blood. Blood pH rises slightly, returning to normal.

Figure 12.14 When your brain senses a lowered pH level in your blood, it initiates a faster breathing rate.

If, for example, you exercise heavily, cell metabolism increases carbon dioxide output. This causes more carbon dioxide to dissolve in the plasma. The increased carbon dioxide dissolved in the plasma slightly lowers the pH of the plasma. A drop in pH level causes the brain to send nerve impulses that increase breathing rate. As a result, more carbon dioxide is exhaled, and the pH returns to normal, a state called homeostasis. **Homeostasis** is the state of internal stability maintained by the body.

BIOLOGY•SOURCE

Take It Further

Sometimes, an allergic reaction to foods such as peanuts causes changes in the respiratory system that can restrict or prevent airflow. In these cases, an EpiPen® is administered so that air can begin to flow again. Find out more about how peanut allergies can affect the respiratory system and how an EpiPen® can save a life. Participate in a class discussion about your findings.

Concept Check

1. What does oxygen bind to in the blood?

2. What part of the brain controls breathing?

3. What is homeostasis?

Fetal Pig Dissection

Question

How do the respiratory, circulatory, and digestive systems of a mammal work together?

Figure 12.15 An X-ray of a fetal pig

Activity Overview

Dissecting a representative mammal can help you to understand your own body and how its organ systems work together. In this activity, you will observe the relative positions and sizes of organs in the digestive, circulatory, and respiratory systems of a fetal pig (Figure 12.15). You will also be able to observe some of the interrelations betweens organs and organ systems.

Your teacher will give you a copy of the full activity.

Prelab Questions

Consider the questions below before beginning this activity.

1. What are the major organs of the digestive system?

2. What are the major organs of the circulatory system?

3. What are the major organs of the respiratory system?

Lung Capacity and the Body's Response to Exercise

Purpose

To determine the vital capacity of your lungs and how your circulatory and respiratory systems respond to moderate exercise

Activity Overview

Health experts suggest that regular exercise helps to strengthen the muscles in our bodies and promotes good cardiovascular health. When you exercise, your body needs more oxygen. It attempts to meet this increased oxygen demand by taking in more oxygen and by pumping blood faster so that the oxygen reaches your tissues faster. Research has shown that regular exercise actually increases your lung volume and your body's ability to use oxygen efficiently (Figure 12.16).

Your teacher will give you a copy of the full activity.

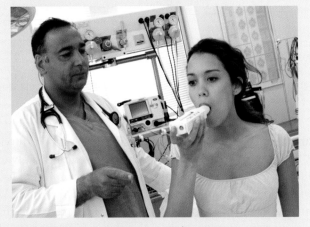

Figure 12.16 You can measure your lung capacity using a respirometer.

Prelab Questions

Consider the questions below before beginning this activity.

1. What happens to your breathing rate during exercise?

2. What happens to your heart rate during exercise?

Key Concept Review

1. Why do your cells need oxygen?

2. What is cellular respiration?

3. Approximately what percentage of air is oxygen?

4. What are the three phases of transferring gases between the environment and the cells?

5. Define "respiratory surface."

6. What process governs the function of the respiratory surface?

7. Describe three characteristics of the structure of a respiratory surface that ensure efficient diffusion.

8. Why do earthworms need to live in damp places?

9. (a) What are gills?
   (b) How does the design of gills enable their function?

10. (a) In terms of exchange of gases, what two advantages do terrestrial animals have over aquatic animals?
    (b) In terms of the respiratory surface, what is one advantage that aquatic animals have over terrestrial animals?

11. Where does gas exchange occur in most insects?

12. How do larger insects and flying insects receive enough O_2 to support their functions?

13. Where does gas exchange occur in reptiles, birds, mammals, and some amphibians?

14. What are six main structures of the human respiratory system?

15. What is another name for the following?
    (a) windpipe
    (b) voice box

16. What is the difference between the bronchi and the bronchioles?

17. Why does air rush in through the nose or mouth to fill the alveoli during inhalation?

18. What is the role of hemoglobin in the blood?

19. (a) What is the medulla oblongata?
    (b) What is its role in the breathing process?

20. Describe the role of carbon dioxide in controlling breathing.

Connect Your Understanding

21. Copy and complete the following table in your notebook.

	Inhalation	Exhalation
Volume in the lungs		
Pressure in the lungs		
Position of rib cage		
Position of diaphragm		

22. How is the respiratory system of a fish similar to that of a mammal?

23. Use a labelled diagram to explain how gas exchange is accomplished in the alveoli.

24. How do cilia and mucus help your respiratory system to function efficiently?

25. Explain how the movements of the diaphragm and rib muscles can increase the volume of the chest cavity during inhalation.

26. Breathing is an involuntary process, meaning that even if we do not think about it, breathing occurs.
    (a) Describe a time when you experienced difficulty in breathing or observed someone with a breathing problem.
    (b) How was the breathing problem solved?

Reflection

27. (a) What information did you find the most interesting in this section?
    (b) What are two questions that you have about the structures of your respiratory system?
    (c) What are two questions that you have about how your respiratory system functions?

For more questions, go to BIOLOGY•SOURCE

Section Summary

- Some respiratory disorders include asthma, bronchitis, cystic fibrosis, emphysema, and lung cancer.
- Your internal body systems interact to maintain the health of your body.
- Smoking and second-hand smoke cause serious problems for the respiratory system and other body systems.
- A sedentary lifestyle can influence the development of serious diseases such as diabetes.

Figure 12.17 For the health of your respiratory system and all your other internal systems, make a point of enjoying physical activity every day.

Regular exercise is one of the best things you can do for your respiratory health (Figure 12.17). Exercise helps to strengthen all the muscles of your body, including your heart and your diaphragm. Vigorous activities such as swimming and skiing increase your lung capacity and help your body to use oxygen more effectively. However, inactivity and a sedentary lifestyle decrease your ability to exchange oxygen for carbon dioxide. A sedentary lifestyle is one that lacks enough vigorous physical activity.

Common Disorders of the Respiratory System

The structure and function of the respiratory system can be altered by disease or exposure to viruses or environmental pollutants. For example, environmental pollutants can trigger respiratory allergies, such as hay fever, and can cause the tissues in the airways to swell.

The common cold is a group of symptoms such as coughing, sneezing, and a sore throat. A cold can be caused by a number of different viruses that pass through the protective lining of the nose and throat. The common cold is sometimes accompanied by sinusitis. **Sinusitis** is a condition caused by viruses or bacteria in which the sinuses become swollen and irritated. The sinuses are moist air spaces around the nose. When they become inflamed, you may notice a change in how your voice sounds. Sinusitis often includes a stuffy or runny nose, pain or swelling around the eyes and cheekbones, and a feeling of pressure in the head. Dry air, lack of sleep, allergies, stress, second-hand smoke, and not eating properly all lower your resistance to being infected with a cold and sinusitis.

Like the common cold, **influenza**, also called the flu, is a common viral infection of the upper respiratory system. The flu is spread by airborne droplets and contact with contaminated objects. Influenza viruses can cause more serious respiratory illnesses, especially in the elderly, infants, and people with heart and lung disease. For example, the flu can develop into **pneumonia**, which is a serious infection of the lungs. In pneumonia, the alveoli in the lungs fill with fluid, which prevents oxygen from reaching the blood. Pneumonia can be caused by a variety of viruses, bacteria, fungi, and parasites.

Other Disorders of the Respiratory System

Damage to structures of the respiratory system can affect the function of the whole system, including the processes of ventilation and gas exchange.

Asthma

Asthma is a chronic disorder of the respiratory system in which airways become narrowed. Smooth muscles surround the bronchi and bronchioles. When these muscles contract, they narrow the airway, making breathing very difficult. As a result, this condition can be life-threatening. Asthma may be caused by exposure to airborne pollutants, cold air, cigarette smoke, some drugs, and respiratory infections. While there is no real cure for asthma, attempts can be made to control the condition. Often, a doctor may prescribe the use of a "puffer" in order to improve the breathing (Figure 12.18). A puffer administers a regulated amount of a drug called a **bronchodilator** that causes the narrowed airways to expand.

Figure 12.18 A puffer administers a specific dosage of a bronchodilator.

Bronchitis

When the bronchioles or the airways that connect the alveoli and the trachea become irritated or infected, they swell and produce excess mucus, a condition called **bronchitis**. The excess mucus causes frequent coughing and difficulty breathing. Bronchitis may become chronic, or long-lasting, when individuals are exposed to cigarette smoke or other harmful air pollutants. In this case, the swollen airways and presence of mucus may last for months or years. The heart must work harder to transport an adequate amount of oxygen through the body.

Emphysema

The word "emphysema" is from a Greek word meaning to puff up. **Emphysema** means "over-inflated lungs." Emphysema occurs when the cilia lining the airways have become damaged. Since the cilia no longer filter and channel particles, the bronchioles become clogged and less air reaches the alveoli. Air pressure builds up, causing the lungs to appear inflated. The pressure eventually tears the walls of the alveoli and some cells become deprived of oxygen, which causes the breath rate and heart rate to increase. The body becomes stressed and fatigued from spending more and more energy breathing. Causes of emphysema include smoking and longtime exposure to workplace chemical hazards, such as working in underground mines.

BIOLOGY • SOURCE

Explore More

What technologies do miners need to protect their respiratory health?

Chronic Obstructive Pulmonary Disease (COPD)

Chronic obstructive pulmonary disease (COPD) is a serious condition that occurs when chronic bronchitis and emphysema are found together. People suffering from chronic pulmonary obstructive disease may need an external source of oxygen in the form of a canister connected to the nostrils (Figure 12.19). Medications such as bronchodilators may be used to reduce inflammation and improve the airflow. If left untreated, this disease could lead to respiratory failure.

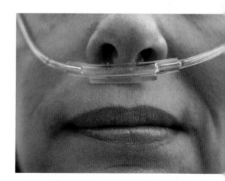

Figure 12.19 A portable air delivery system including an oxygen tank and breathing tube provides oxygen-enriched air for a person who has difficulties breathing.

Cystic Fibrosis

Cystic fibrosis is a fatal genetic disease in which abnormally thick mucus blocks the airways. This thick mucus traps bacteria in the lungs and leads to infection that damages the lung tissue. The mucus is very difficult to dislodge, so breathing becomes very difficult. Patients must participate in daily physical therapy to ease the flow of air. Cystic fibrosis affects several organ systems including the respiratory and digestive system. A recent estimate suggests that 1 in 3600 Canadian children are born with the disease. In 1989, Lap-Chee Tsui, a geneticist working at the University of Toronto, identified a gene that was responsible for cystic fibrosis. Research into a cure for cystic fibrosis is still ongoing.

Severe Acute Respiratory Syndrome (SARS)

Severe acute respiratory syndrome (SARS) is a serious pneumonia-like respiratory disease that is caused by a type of virus called a coronavirus (Figure 12.20). The virus is spread through coughing or sneezing. This illness causes an unusual inflammation of the lungs, fever, and cough. Breathing becomes extremely difficult and hospitalization may become necessary. In some cases, this disease is fatal. The first case of SARS appeared in November 2002 in China, and by the time it had run its course in July 2003, it had affected people in 37 countries and caused approximately 800 deaths worldwide. All the cases in Canada were limited to Ontario, where Drs. Sheela Basrur, Colin D'Cunha, James Young, and others helped to install infection-control procedures. In April 2003, scientists working in Vancouver and Winnipeg mapped the genetic sequence of the virus linked to SARS, an important step toward fighting the disease. The spread of SARS has been fully contained, but the disease may still be present in animal populations and so could return to the human population in the future.

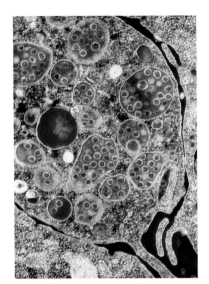

Figure 12.20 The surface proteins on the coronavirus (red) attach to host cells (blue and green). Once inside a host cell, the coronavirus uses the cell to make copies of itself. (magnification 19 000×)

Lung Cancer

Lung cancer is a disease that starts when cells in the lungs begin to behave abnormally by growing too fast and grouping together in abnormal ways (Figure 12.21). Groups of cancer cells are called **tumours**. Lung cancer victims may develop recurring lung infections, chronic coughs, or difficulty breathing. There are two main types of lung cancer and the treatments of these cancers differ. In some cases, surgery is used to remove tumours from the lung. The amount of lung tissue that is removed can vary from a small wedge to an entire lung. Drugs or different types of radiation may also be used in an attempt to destroy the cancer cells. Eighty-five percent of lung cancers are linked to smoking.

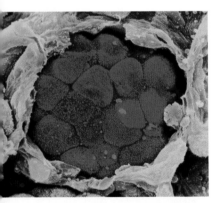

Figure 12.21 Cancer cells (red) in an alveolus (magnification 1500×)

Concept Check

1. What is the function of a bronchodilator?
2. What two diseases make up chronic obstructive pulmonary disease?
3. What is the most common cause of lung cancer?

Technologies Used to Diagnose and Treat Respiratory Disorders

When an individual is suffering from a respiratory disorder, the doctor may investigate the structure and function of the respiratory system using some of the technologies shown in Figures 12.22–12.27.

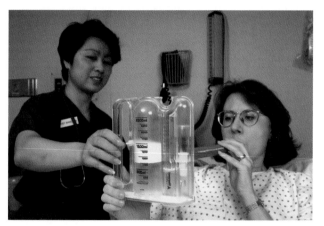

Figure 12.22 A doctor uses a respirometer to measure a patient's breathing movements and lung capacity. Samples of blood and mucus are observed so that the presence of abnormalities can be identified.

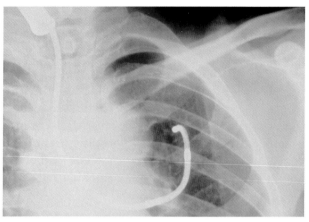

Figure 12.23 An endoscope can remove obstructions in the nasal passages. If the source of the problem appears to be in the trachea and lungs, an endoscope called a bronchoscope may be inserted through the nose or throat and passed into the lungs.

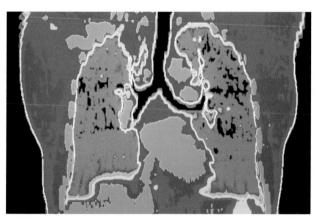

Figure 12.24 After observing your nose and throat, a doctor may order an ultrasound, X-ray, CT scan or MRI scan. These imaging technologies can reveal the size and shape of airways and the presence of abnormalities such as tumours.

Figure 12.25 Sometimes, the information gained through imaging technologies results in a decision for surgery to remove or repair structures. Lasers can be used during surgery to destroy obstructions.

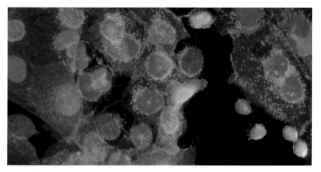

Figure 12.26 Through the use of fluorescent dyes and a two-photon imaging microscope, researchers can investigate the molecular structure of individual cells of the respiratory system, such as these lung cancer cells. (magnification 125×)

Figure 12.27 A lung transplant may be considered when other treatment options have failed. Where damage to lungs is severe, as in the case of cystic fibrosis, a double lung transplant may be recommended.

BIOLOGY•SOURCE

Suggested Activity

• D14 Inquiry Activity Overview on page 343

Disorders Affect Other Systems

Your respiratory, circulatory, and digestive systems are closely connected in their structures and in their functions. A problem in any one of these systems affects the functioning of other systems and your overall health. For example, tuberculosis is a bacterial infection that is spread when an infected person coughs or sneezes, releasing the bacteria into the environment. The bacteria usually target the lungs. However, once in the lungs, the bacteria sometimes cross through the alveoli into the bloodstream. The blood then transports the bacteria to other tissues and organs, infecting them as well.

Another example of the interconnectedness of systems is heart failure, which is primarily a problem of the circulatory system. Heart failure can result in reduced transportation of nutrients to cells, which affects the digestive system. Heart failure can also result in leakage of fluid from capillaries in the lungs to the alveoli, causing problems in the respiratory system. Two other examples of conditions that affect all three systems are smoking and diabetes.

BIOLOGY•SOURCE

Explore More

How does smoking damage the body and shorten life?

Smoking

Cigarette smoke basically consists of microscopic particles of carbon that are coated with toxic chemicals (Figure 12.28). The toxic substances in tobacco smoke irritate the cells lining the bronchi and destroy the cilia. Without cilia, these cells lose the ability to move particles out of the respiratory system. The smoker must cough frequently to try to clear the mucus that is no longer moved by the cilia. Once they lose the ability to remove these harmful particles from their lungs, smokers are at a greater risk for diseases caused by these particles. In addition to the toxins from cigarette smoke, damage to the respiratory system also increases the risk of damage from air pollution, dust, and airborne bacteria.

(a)

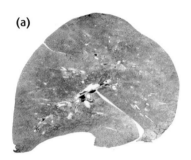

(b)

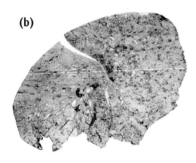

Figure 12.28 (a) A healthy lung. (b) The lung linings of a smoker are black from the long-term buildup of smoke particles

Chemicals found in cigarette smoke cause cancer. Smokers account for 85 percent of all lung cancer cases. Smokers also have increased risk for cancer of the gallbladder, pancreas, mouth, and throat. Women who smoke during pregnancy are more likely to have babies born prematurely and/or with a lower birth weight.

After cancer, cardiovascular disease causes the second highest number of deaths among smokers. Smoking raises blood pressure, and increases cholesterol levels in the blood. The damage from smoking to the respiratory system requires the heart to work harder to deliver enough oxygen to the cells. As a result, smokers have a higher rate of heart attack and stroke than non-smokers.

Some of the toxins from cigarette smoke are in even greater concentration in second-hand smoke, which is the cigarette smoke of others. Second-hand smoke can also cause cancer. Children of smokers are at a higher risk for developing colds, asthma, and allergies, and have more frequent hospitalizations for bronchitis and pneumonia.

Fortunately, there are huge health benefits from stopping smoking, no matter how old the smoker is or how long he or she has been smoking. After 10 to 15 years of not smoking, the chances of getting lung cancer and heart disease return to normal levels. If you avoid smoking and second-hand smoke, you will help to keep your respiratory system healthy.

BIOLOGY•SOURCE

Suggested Activity

• D15 Decision-Making Analysis Overview on page 343

Concept Check

1. What are four examples of imaging technologies?
2. What is tuberculosis?
3. What is second-hand smoke?

Diabetes

As knowledge of biology has increased, there has been a greater recognition of the need to view health problems in a holistic way that considers the connections between body systems. Rather than viewing a problem as if it affected only one organ or organ system, doctors consider the health problem in the context of interacting systems of the body. This approach to the diagnosis and treatment of health problems has led to the development of many new products and technologies. An example of the need to view a condition and its treatment holistically is diabetes.

Diabetes is a group of diseases in which high levels of blood glucose result from a problem with insulin secretion, insulin action, or both. **Insulin** is a chemical produced by the pancreas that controls the level of blood glucose (Figure 12.29). Insulin was discovered by two Canadians, Frederick Banting and Charles Best, in 1921.

If insulin is not present or not functioning correctly, glucose builds up in the blood and cannot be used by cells for energy. Patients with diabetes may suffer from fatigue because the sugar that is usually used to make energy by cellular respiration is not available to cells but remains in the blood. Over time, high blood glucose can result in serious health problems including blindness, kidney problems, and heart disease. High blood glucose can damage coronary arteries by increasing plaque in the arteries. The presence of these deposits can lead to atherosclerosis, which can increase blood pressure.

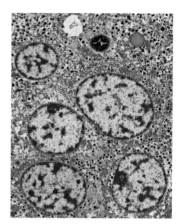

Figure 12.29 A human pancreas cell. The orange-coloured granules secrete insulin into the blood, which helps to control blood-sugar levels. (magnification 30 000×)

Type 1 Diabetes

In Type 1 diabetes, the cells of the pancreas are damaged so that they cannot produce insulin. The exact cause of this disease is not fully understood. Although there are several genes associated with the onset of this disease, it appears that the cellular environment also plays a role in its development. At present, Type 1 diabetes cannot be prevented, but the effects can be controlled.

Type 2 Diabetes

In Type 2 diabetes, the body cells do not respond to insulin appropriately. The incidence of Type 2 diabetes is increasing at a dramatic rate. Reasons for this increase include rising rates of obesity and the increasingly sedentary lifestyle of Canadians. Recent research has found that 29 percent of Canadians watch television for 15 or more hours per week. Fifteen percent of Canadians report using the computer for 11 or more hours per week for leisure activities. This sedentary lifestyle contributes to the accumulation of extra weight. Excess body fat seems to interfere with the body's ability to use insulin effectively.

BIOLOGY•SOURCE

Take It Further

Regular exercise improves your cardiovascular health, improves your lung capacity and efficiency, and helps you achieve and maintain an ideal body weight. Find out about different types of exercise that could improve your overall health. Design an exercise program you could follow to help keep your body strong and healthy.

Treatment of Diabetes

Individuals with diabetes must have their insulin replaced, and usually this occurs through daily injections (Figure 12.30). In order to administer the correct amount of insulin, diabetics test their blood sugar through blood tests (Figure 12.31). Physical activity, nutrition, and emotional state can all affect the levels of blood sugar, and so insulin must be administered accurately. Diabetics need to make careful choices of appropriate physical activities and foods to help control levels of blood glucose. The planning and timing of meals are important considerations in maintaining consistent levels of blood glucose.

Research and Innovations

Much research has occurred into how to acquire and release insulin appropriately. Genetic technologies have enabled doctors to identify genes that seem to control the body's response to diabetic medication. With this knowledge, a more personalized approach to medication can occur. An experimental treatment for Type 1 diabetes includes transplanting cells from a donor pancreas into a patient's pancreas to produce insulin for the patient. In addition, it may be possible to deliver the insulin gene into cells that line the small intestine using very small particles called nanoparticles. By adding the gene to intestinal cells, the cells could be re-programmed to produce the insulin needed by the body.

Technological innovations have offered some help to diabetics. Imaging technologies such as MRI and CT scans enable doctors to view internal organs in a three-dimensional manner. In recent years, NASA imaging technologies used to view landforms from space have been used to analyze images of the pancreas. Although the sophistication of the imaging technologies has increased, the availability of these technologies to citizens outside urban centres remains a challenge.

Reducing the Risk of Type 2 Diabetes

Research has shown that a healthy and active lifestyle can reduce the risk of Type 2 diabetes by 50 percent. It also appears that the negative effects of sedentary behaviours such as sitting at a computer may be reduced somewhat by taking frequent and active breaks during the day. This research has implications for students who spend long periods of time sitting at desks and computers during the school day. Exercise can improve your overall level of health by increasing blood flow to cells, normalizing blood pressure, and reducing blood glucose levels. Health Canada recommends the following in order to limit your risk of Type 2 diabetes:

- Do not smoke.
- Achieve a healthy weight and maintain it.
- Be physically active.
- Limit your intake of fat and sugar.
- Eat regular, balanced meals that include the four food groups from Canada's Food Guide to Healthy Eating.
- Keep your cholesterol and other blood fats within the target level.
- Maintain a normal blood pressure.

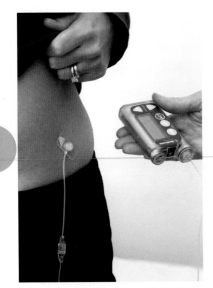

Figure 12.30 In recent years, the insulin pump has provided a convenient and reliable alternative to injections. This pump administers a reliable dosage of insulin through a tube that is connected to the blood stream. The pump and tubing are worn under the clothes.

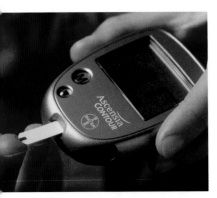

Figure 12.31 A drop of blood is placed on a test strip in a glucometer, which measures blood glucose level.

©P

Concept Check

1. What is diabetes?

2. What is the role of insulin in the body?

3. Why do diabetics need to be careful making choices about food and activity?

Comparing Taste, Nutritional Value, and Cost of Bread Spreads

Question

How do different bread spreads compare in sensory appeal, nutritional value, and cost per serving?

Figure 12.32 A saturated fat, such as butter, is a solid at room temperature.

Activity Overview

In this activity, you will evaluate common bread spreads, such as butter, margarine, and olive oil. You will assign a score from 1 to 10 for each spread based on its sensory appeal, nutritional value, and cost per serving. You will then calculate the average score for each spread to determine which is the best overall choice.

Your teacher will give you a copy of the full activity.

Prelab Questions

Consider the questions below before beginning this activity.

1. What is a saturated fat?

2. How does the hydrogenation process change vegetable oils?

Reducing Smoking Rates in Teens

Issue

Because of the serious risks associated with smoking, it is important to find strategies to reduce smoking rates.

Activity Overview

Smoking has been called the number one cause of preventable death in the world. It is linked to 30 percent of all cancers and to 85 percent of all lung cancers. Exposure to second–hand smoke is considered to be a public health risk for both youth and adults (Figure 12.33).

Your teacher will give you a copy of the full activity.

Prelab Questions

Consider the questions below before beginning this activity.

1. Why do people start smoking?

2. Why do people stop smoking?

Figure 12.33 Second-hand smoke increases your risk for cardiovascular and respiratory disease.

Key Concept Review

1. What are three ways in which exercise helps improve your respiratory system?

2. What are two common viral infections of the upper respiratory system?

3. What causes the common cold?

4. What is sinusitis?

5. What are five factors that can increase your chance of catching a cold or sinusitis?

6. How are the alveoli affected in pneumonia?

7. Draw a flowchart showing how asthma develops. Begin with "exposure to airborne particles."

8. Explain why individuals with asthma may need to use puffers in order to breathe effectively.

9. What happens in the condition called bronchitis?

10. Why does a person with bronchitis need to cough frequently?

11. (a) In the photograph below, the lung on the right is the normal size. The lung on the left is enlarged. What disease is this patient likely suffering from?
    (b) Explain your reasoning.

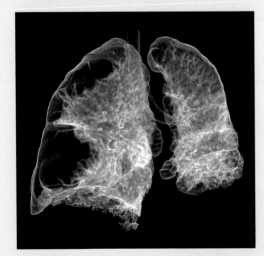

Question 11

12. Draw a flow chart showing how cystic fibrosis develops.

13. SARS has now been fully contained. Does that mean that the disease is finished? Explain why or why not.

14. What are three ways of treating lung cancer?

15. Explain two different technologies that can be used in the diagnosis of a respiratory disease.

16. How does smoking disable the normal cleaning and protective processes of the respiratory system?

17. (a) What is insulin?
    (b) What is its role in the body?

18. Explain three ways by which diabetics maintain appropriate levels of blood sugar

Connect Your Understanding

19. Use a Venn diagram to compare and contrast bronchitis and emphysema.

20. Use a Venn diagram to compare and contrast Type 1 diabetes and Type 2 diabetes.

21. The incidence of Type 2 diabetes is increasing dramatically in Canada and other western countries. Why do you think it is increasing?

22. What are some ways to reduce your risk of Type 2 diabetes?

23. Explain why physical exercise is both a form of treatment and means of prevention for Type 2 diabetes.

24. Teenage girls represent the fastest-growing population of smokers. What facts could you share with a friend to help convince her not to smoke?

25. A medical ventilator is a machine that can move air into and out of the lungs. In some cases, people whose respiratory system has failed can be kept alive by a ventilator. What factors do you think should be considered in deciding whether to sustain life on a ventilator?

Reflection

26. What are three things you learned in this section that you did not know before?

For more questions, go to BIOLOGY•SOURCE

When you get a cut or scrape, your blood clots, stopping the bleeding and sealing the wound. You might apply a bandage to protect the site. However, as you may have experienced, it is sometimes very difficult to change bandages on a larger wound because the process of bandage removal can hurt and even harm the tissue below the bandage.

Dr. Robert Burrell of the University of Alberta thought that he could provide a different method of wound healing. Since 1991, he has researched the use of an ancient remedy — silver particles — to speed the healing process and prevent scarring from wounds. He chose silver because of its antimicrobial properties. However, he knew that the chloride ions in the skin could cause the silver to become inactive. In order to solve this problem, Dr. Burrell used very small silver particles (about 20 atoms in size) as a coating on the bandage surface. The silver nanoparticles may prevent this chemical reaction because the silver is released into the skin slowly.

The bandage, known as Acticoat, has been used in over 30 countries around the world, enabling a higher quality of medical care for wound patients. Dr. Robert Burrell has been credited with the invention of a revolutionary bandage, which may be the world's first commercial medical application of nanotechnology.

Figure 12.34 Dr. Robert Burrell and his silver nanoparticle bandage

Regular exercise helps keep your inner body systems healthy and strong. However, many people are unsure of how to get the most out of their fitness activities. To help them plan and undertake an effective program, they can consult a fitness trainer. A fitness trainer or consultant may work with individuals or groups of all ages to research, plan, implement, and manage the delivery of fitness routines.

The career of a fitness trainer can follow several different paths. Generally, the individual has some post-secondary training in physical and health education or kinesiology. Knowledge of the structure (anatomy) and function (physiology) of the human body, as well as leadership and coaching skills, are important aspects of educational preparation. Personal traits such as the ability to solve problems creatively and to be a team player are also of great value.

Fitness consultants need to be able to provide directions and to communicate clearly with clients. In some situations, consultants may also need to have skills in sales and marketing of fitness products or services.

Figure 12.35 Fitness trainers offer classes at recreation centres and businesses as well as one-on-one consultations.

A fitness consultant can use knowledge and skills in a variety of job situations including government and institutional settings, recreational and professional sport settings, and private industry.

To find out more, visit **BIOLOGY•SOURCE**

Key Concept Review

1. Describe how diffusion is involved in the respiratory systems of
   (a) earthworms Ⓚ
   (b) grasshoppers Ⓚ

2. Explain why most terrestrial organisms need to have respiratory systems that are found inside rather than outside the organism. Ⓚ

3. Make a flowchart showing the pathway of air beginning with the intake of air and ending at the alveoli. Ⓚ

4. What are two ways in which the air is changed as it passes through the nose? Ⓚ

5. What is the function of the epiglottis? Ⓚ

6. What is the function of the diaphragm? Ⓚ

7. Describe the process of the diffusion of oxygen and carbon dioxide in the lungs. Ⓚ

8. Describe how breathing is controlled in the brain. Ⓚ

9. Why is the process of ventilation described as a passive process? Ⓚ

10. Write a paragraph that defines and distinguishes between the terms bronchi, bronchioles, and alveoli. Ⓚ

11. Write a paragraph that explains how the movements of the ribs, chest and diaphragm are involved in the process of breathing. Ⓚ

12. In your own words, explain what is happening at A, B, C, and D of the diagram below. Ⓚ

13. Define "homeostasis." Ⓚ

14. What is sinusitis? Ⓚ

15. (a) Define the term "asthma." Ⓚ
    (b) Explain how asthma may affect the function of the respiratory system. Ⓚ

16. Describe the condition called bronchitis. Ⓚ

17. What happens in the lungs of a person with emphysema? Ⓚ

18. (a) What does COPD stand for? Ⓚ
    (b) When is this condition found? Ⓚ

19. Why do patients with cystic fibrosis need daily physical therapy? Ⓚ

20. (a) What does SARS stand for? Ⓚ
    (b) What type of virus causes SARS? Ⓚ

21. What are groups of cancer cells called? Ⓚ

22. What does a respirometer measure? Ⓚ

23. How does smoking affect the respiratory system? Ⓚ

24. (a) What is an insulin pump? Ⓚ
    (b) Why is it used? Ⓚ

25. How does diabetes show the interconnectedness of body systems? Ⓚ

26. How is Type 2 diabetes different from Type 1 diabetes? Ⓚ

27. (a) What is a sedentary lifestyle? Ⓚ
    (b) What is the relationship between a sedentary lifestyle and Type 2 diabetes? Ⓚ

28. What are seven ways you can reduce your risk of developing Type 2 diabetes? Ⓚ

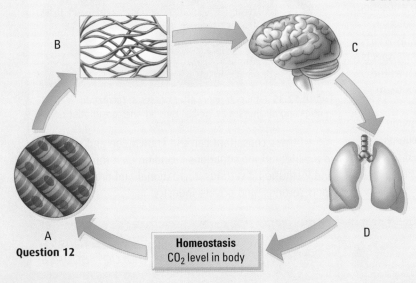

B

C

A

Question 12

Homeostasis
CO_2 level in body

D

Connect Your Understanding

29. Draw a labelled diagram of an alveolus surrounded by capillaries. Show on your diagram where oxygen and carbon dioxide levels are higher or lower after an inhalation. **ⓒ**

30. (a) Why is it a good idea to wear a breathing mask, shown in the photograph below when doing carpentry or working in a dusty area? **ⓐ**

    (b) What are two other situations in which it would be a good idea to wear a breathing mask? **ⓐ**

Question 30

31. What is the relationship between the availability of oxygen gas and energy production in an organism? **ⓣ**

32. Use a Venn diagram to compare and contrast inhalation and exhalation. **ⓣ**

33. Why is it important for a respiratory surface to have a large surface area? **ⓣ**

34. Continued exposure to airborne pollutants found in cigarette smoke can cause the destruction of cilia that line the respiratory passages. Explain how this change to the structure of the respiratory passages can affect breathing function. **ⓐ**

35. Explain why the analogy of a "respiratory tree" fits the structure and function of the bronchioles. **ⓣ**

36. Explain how technology can be used to improve the life of individuals who have diabetes. **ⓐ**

37. Bromothymol blue solution is a chemical indicator that changes colour from blue to yellow or green when in the presence of carbon dioxide. Predict how the bromothymol blue solution would change if a student blows through a straw into the indicator solution. **ⓐ**

38. An individual was exposed to a poison that was known to paralyze muscles. Explain why the individual stopped breathing soon after contacting the poison. **ⓐ**

39. Your lifestyle choices affect your chances of having serious diseases like diabetes or emphysema. How can you reduce your risk for these diseases? **ⓐ**

40. Carbon monoxide is an odourless, colourless gas found in cigarette smoke and car exhaust. When inhaled, carbon monoxide is more than 200 times more efficient at binding to hemoglobin than oxygen is. Explain why it is very dangerous for the respiratory system to breathe in carbon monoxide. **ⓐ**

41. Explain how you can maintain the health of your respiratory structures. **ⓐ**

Reflection

42. What are three questions you have about your respiratory system that you would like to find out more about? **ⓒ**

Unit Task Link

Review your notes about the respiratory system and select one of the disorders. Create a graphic organizer that summarizes the following information.

- What are the symptoms of the disorder?
- What are the causes of the disorder?
- How is the disorder diagnosed?
- How can this disorder be prevented?
- How is the disorder treated?

For more questions, go to 

KEY CONCEPTS	CHAPTER SUMMARY
10 Animals obtain and process nutrients for energy and growth from the food they eat.	
• Nutrients • Processing nutrients • Digestive system • Technologies to diagnose digestive disorders	• We need nutrients from food for energy and growth. (10.1) • Nutrients include carbohydrates, proteins, fats, vitamins, minerals, and water. (10.1) • Advances in technology have increased our understanding of the structure and function of the digestive system and have led to the development of helpful dietary products. (10.1) • We can use food labels and Canada's Food Guide to Healthy Eating to make informed choices about the food we eat. (10.1) • We process food through our digestive system in order to use nutrients from the food effectively. (10.2) • Food processing occurs in four stages: ingestion, digestion, absorption, and elimination. (10.2) • In mammals, food is processed as it moves through the alimentary canal. (10.2) • The digestive system consists of six specialized digestive organs and several accessory organs and glands. (10.2) • Diagnostic tools, such as endoscopy, are used to diagnose digestive disorders, such as ulcers. (10.2)
11 The circulatory system transports materials through the body.	
• Blood • Blood vessels • Heart • Cardiovascular disorders • Promoting cardiovascular health	• Animals may have an open or a closed circulatory system. (11.1) • The human cardiovascular system includes a heart, blood, and a network of blood vessels that delivers nutrients to cells and removes cellular wastes. (11.1) • Blood is made of plasma, red blood cells, and white blood cells. (11.1) • Blood vessels include arteries, veins, and capillaries. (11.1) • Substances are exchanged between the blood and other tissues. (11.1) • The lymphatic system is a transport system that recycles fluids needed in the circulatory system. (11.1) • The heart pumps blood through the circulatory system. (11.2) • The rhythm of the heartbeat is controlled by the actions of nerves and hormones. (11.2) • The pumping action of the heart creates a pressure in the blood that can be measured. (11.2) • Disorders of the structures and functions of the circulatory system pose a significant risk to health. (11.3) • Diagnosis and treatment of cardiovascular disorders involve an array of technologies. (11.3) • Strategies to promote the health of the circulatory system include eating a healthy diet, maintaining active lifestyle, not smoking, and having regular medical assessments. (11.3)
12 The respiratory system exchanges gases between blood and air.	
• Gas exchange in aquatic and terrestrial animals • Structures of the human respiratory system • Breathing • Disorders of the respiratory system • Interconnected systems	• All cells need a regular supply of oxygen in order to obtain energy. (12.1) • Gas exchange occurs by diffusion along the respiratory surfaces, which are thin, moist, selectively permeable membranes with a large surface area. (12.1) • Structures of the respiratory system allow air to flow from the environment into the body. (12.1) • The process of breathing moves air in and out of the body. (12.1) • A blood protein called hemoglobin transports oxygen through the body. (12.1) • Breathing rate is controlled by the level of carbon dioxide in the blood. (12.1) • Some respiratory disorders include asthma, bronchitis, cystic fibrosis, emphysema, and lung cancer. (12.2) • Internal systems of the body interact together to maintain the health of the body. (12.2) • An active lifestyle can reduce the risk of serious diseases such as diabetes. (12.2)

Key Terms Review

1. Create a concept map with the main idea "Nutrient Transport" at the centre that links all of the terms in the list below. Use additional words to clarify your understanding. Ⓒ

   - diffusion
   - oxygen
   - carbon dioxide
   - glucose
   - cellular respiration
   - hemoglobin
   - artery
   - vein
   - capillary
   - lung
   - alveoli
   - mechanical digestion
   - chemical digestion
   - enzymes
   - villus
   - protein
   - fat
   - water
   - vitamins
   - minerals

Key Concept Review

CHAPTER 10

2. Copy and complete the following table in your notebook. For each nutrient, list two sources and two functions. Ⓚ

Nutrient	Two Sources	Two Functions

3. (a) Name three categories of fats. Ⓚ
   (b) Explain the difference between them. Ⓚ

4. (a) Describe the relationship between protein and amino acids. Ⓚ
   (b) Why must your diet include essential amino acids? Ⓚ

5. Explain why it is dangerous to ingest high quantities of fat-soluble vitamins. Ⓚ

6. (a) What is a calorie? Ⓚ
   (b) Approximately how many calories per day do you need for an active lifestyle? Ⓚ

7. Which nutrient should make up half or more of your daily intake of nutrients? Ⓚ

8. What term describes a substance that is purified from foods and taken like a medicine? Ⓚ

9. What term describes a food that has health benefits beyond the normal nutritional benefit of the food? Ⓚ

10. What are five of the guidelines provided by Canada's Food Guide to Healthy Eating? Ⓚ

11. Copy the labels A-D in your notebook. Identify the stage of food processing that takes place at each label. Ⓚ

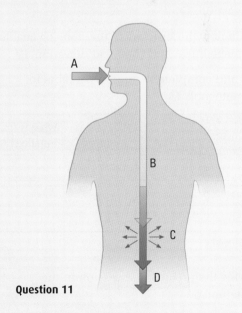

Question 11

12. What is the difference between a digestive sac and an alimentary canal? **k**

13. Why would a herbivore have a longer alimentary canal than a carnivore? **k**

14. Explain how the structures of the mouth prepare the food for processing in the rest of the digestive system. **k**

15. List the labels A–G in your notebook. Identify each labeled part of the digestive system. **k**

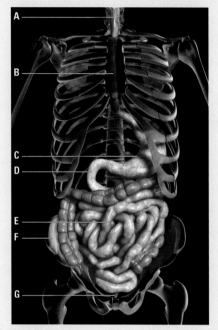

Question 15

16. (a) Define the term "peristalsis." **k**
    (b) Explain the function of peristalsis in digestion. **k**

17. Explain how the structure of the stomach enables both mechanical and chemical digestion. **k**

18. Copy and complete the following table in your notebook. **k**

	What is it?	Where is it produced?	What is its function?
Saliva			
Gastric juice			
Bile			
Pancreatic juice			

19. Describe the process of digestion in the duodenum. **k**

20. Use an example to explain the role of enzymes in digestion. **k**

21. Explain how the structure of the villus enables absorption of nutrients. **k**

22. Describe the relationship between the liver and the gallbladder. **k**

23. Describe the relationship between the pancreas and the duodenum. **k**

24. What are the functions of the large intestine? **k**

25. What is the relationship between fibre and constipation? **k**

CHAPTER 11

26. Name the three primary components of the circulatory system. **k**

27. (a) Use a Venn diagram to compare and contrast an open circulatory system and a closed circulatory system. **k**
    (b) Explain how blood is circulated more efficiently in a closed circulatory system than in an open circulatory system. **k**

28. Copy and complete the following chart in your notebook. **k**

	Structure	Function
Plasma		
Red blood cells		
White blood cells		
Platelets		

29. How does the structure of each of the following enable its function?
    (a) artery **k**
    (b) vein **k**
    (c) capillary **k**

30. (a) What is diffusion? **k**
    (b) What is a diffusion gradient? **k**

31. Describe how materials such as oxygen move from the blood into a cell. **k**

32. What function does the lymphatic system perform for the circulatory system? **k**

33. What is the difference between the pulmonary circuit and the systemic circuit? **k**

©P

34. Describe the flow of blood through the heart, starting with the right atrium. *(k)*

35. The heart is an organ that contains muscle tissue. Explain how the function of the heart is related to the function of muscle tissue. *(k)*

36. (a) What is a valve? *(k)*
(b) Describe the location and function of a valve in your heart. *(k)*

37. What is the role of the pacemaker in your heart?

38. Explain the relationship between cholesterol, plaque, and cardiovascular disease. *(k)*

CHAPTER 12

39. Define and distinguish between the terms "breathing," "cellular respiration," and "gas exchange." *(k)*

40. Why must a respiratory membrane have a high surface area? *(k)*

41. Explain how gas exchange can occur in aquatic organisms such as fish. *(k)*

42. Explain how insects exchange gases with their environment. *(k)*

43. What two gases exchange in your lungs?

44. Draw labelled diagrams to show how diffusion is involved in the respiratory systems of two animals. *(k)*

45. Describe the pathway of air from the nose or mouth to the lungs. *(k)*

46. Explain how the structure of the lungs enables the function of gas exchange. *(k)*

47. How does hemoglobin increase the efficiency of gas exchange? *(k)*

48. Describe the role that pressure plays in inhaling and exhaling. *(k)*

49. How is breathing controlled in humans? *(k)*

50. What is homeostasis? *(k)*

51. How does pneumonia interfere with gas exchange? *(k)*

52. Describe asthma, including its cause and treatment. *(k)*

53. Describe several methods by which a diabetic individual may obtain necessary insulin. *(k)*

Connect Your Understanding

54. It is your turn to plan and prepare dinner, and you want to make sure it is nutritious.
(a) What nutritional factors do you need to consider in deciding what foods to prepare? *(a)*
(b) How can you use the information on a food label to make informed choices about what to serve? *(a)*

55. Explain the relationship between exercise and cardiovascular health. *(a)*

56. Why is it important to breathe deeply when exercising? *(a)*

57. How is the structure and function of villi similar to the structure and function of alveoli? *(t)*

58. Explain how smoking can contribute to the development of diseases like emphysema or lung cancer. *(a)*

59. Explain why the level of oxygen in blood in the aorta differs from the level of oxygen in the pulmonary arteries. *(t)*

60. Explain how the structure of the capillary is critical in accomplishing the task of distributing oxygen and nutrients to cells and removing waste products from cells. *(t)*

61. Write a paragraph that explains the meaning of these terms and shows their connections: inhalation, exhalation, diaphragm, ribs, muscles, air pressure, volume, chest cavity, breathing. *(k)*

62. Write a paragraph that explains the meaning of these terms and shows their connections: hemoglobin, diffusion gradient, oxygen, carbon dioxide, capillaries. *(k)*

63. Under normal activity, blood takes about one minute to make a complete circuit through your body.
(a) Explain how the rate of blood flow changes during increased activity such as running or dancing. *(k)*
(b) Explain why blood flow must change during increased activity in order to maintain the health of the tissue of the body. *(a)*

64. The world's first lung transplant surgery occurred in Toronto in 1983. In the late 1980s, the practice of double lung transplantation was developed and practised in Toronto. Describe a condition in which it may be necessary to have a double lung transplant. *a*

Skills Practice

65. (a) Which of the subjects in the chart below is most likely a smoker? *t*
(b) Explain your reasoning for your choice in part (a). *t*
(c) Which of the subjects in the chart below is most likely an athlete? *t*
(d) Explain your reasoning for your choice in part (c). *t*

Subject	O₂ Content of Blood (mL/100 mL)	Breaths per min	Resting Heart Rate	Blood Pressure
A	8	23	84	145/95
B	16	16	62	135/85
C	24	10	50	110/70
D	18	14	70	125/80

66. Use the figure shown below to describe how blood pressure changes as blood flows through an artery, vein, and capillary. *t*

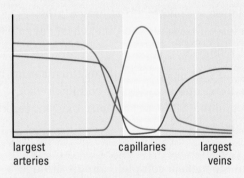

largest arteries   capillaries   largest veins

—— Blood pressure (mm Hg)
—— Velocity (cm/sec)
—— Total area (cm²)

Question 66

Revisit the Big Ideas and Fundamental Concepts

67. Explain why during your annual physical the doctor records your weight, analyzes a sample of your blood, and may ask about your diet and level of physical activity as part of an assessment of your level of overall health. *a*

68. A patient visits a doctor and is diagnosed with a mild case of atherosclerosis.
(a) What is atherosclerosis? *k*
(b) How is it caused? *k*
(c) Explain why the doctor told the patient she could be in danger of having a heart attack in the future. *a*
(d) Explain why the doctor would suggest that the patient's blood pressure and blood levels of cholesterol must be carefully monitored. *a*

69. Create a three-circle Venn diagram to show how the digestive, circulatory, and respiratory systems are interconnected. *c*

70. A person with diabetes may suffer from fatigue and weight loss if the blood sugar is not managed through medication. Use your knowledge of the functions of the digestive system, respiratory system, and circulatory system to explain the relationship between the symptoms of fatigue and weight loss and the presence of high blood sugar. *a*

71. It is widely known that smoking and second-hand smoke negatively affect the digestive, circulatory, and respiratory systems. What evidence supports this line of thinking? *a*

Science, Technology, Society, and the Environment

72. A student complains of abdominal pain and frequent diarrhea. How might a doctor obtain the information needed to diagnose the student's complaints? *a*

73. (a) How has imaging technology greatly assisted in understanding the internal systems of the body? Use some examples as part of your answer. *a*
(b) Give an example to show the relationship between imaging technology, costs, availability, equity of access, and presence of qualified personnel in providing doctors with valuable information about internal body systems. *t*

74. Between 2003 and 2004, there was a campaign in Canada to increase physical activity of all Canadians. To accomplish this task, a simple form of technology called the pedometer was distributed through cereal boxes or through purchase from a website. The pedometer records the number of steps taken by an individual. The idea was that as Canadians became aware of the number of steps taken each day, they would be more likely to make changes to increase their activity levels and be healthier as a result. Results from the study showed that by making simple technology like the pedometer accessible to the public and by providing motivational messages in the media, behaviour changes were possible. What media messages would motivate you to increase your own level of activity? **C**

75. Explain how society's need for healthy foods leads to the development of dietary products such as probiotics and nutraceuticals. **a**

76. Health officials are concerned about the increasing incidence of diabetes. Explain why this disease is of such great concern to public health officials. **t**

Reflection

77. In this unit, you have learned how the internal systems of your body can interact to maintain the health of your body. You have learned that lifestyle choices can affect your overall health. Use an example to show how a lifestyle choice that you have made this year can maintain or improve upon your level of health. **C**

The Health Show

Question

How does a digestive, circulatory, or respiratory disorder affect the individual and Canadian society as a whole?

Task Overview

In this unit, you have learned about the structures and functions of the digestive, circulatory, and respiratory systems and how these systems can interact with each other and with their environments in healthy ways. In addition, you have considered how structural and functional disorders related to these systems can negatively affect the quality and length of your life.

In this task, you will assume the role of a health reporter who investigates the nature of a disorder of the digestive, circulatory, or respiratory systems and its effects on individuals and on Canadian society as a whole. You will share the results of your investigation in the form of a video, oral presentation, or blog, or other format approved by your teacher. Your teacher will give you a copy of the full activity.

Figure 12.36 You may want to use visual aids as part of your presentation.

UNIT
E

Plants: Anatomy, Growth, and Function

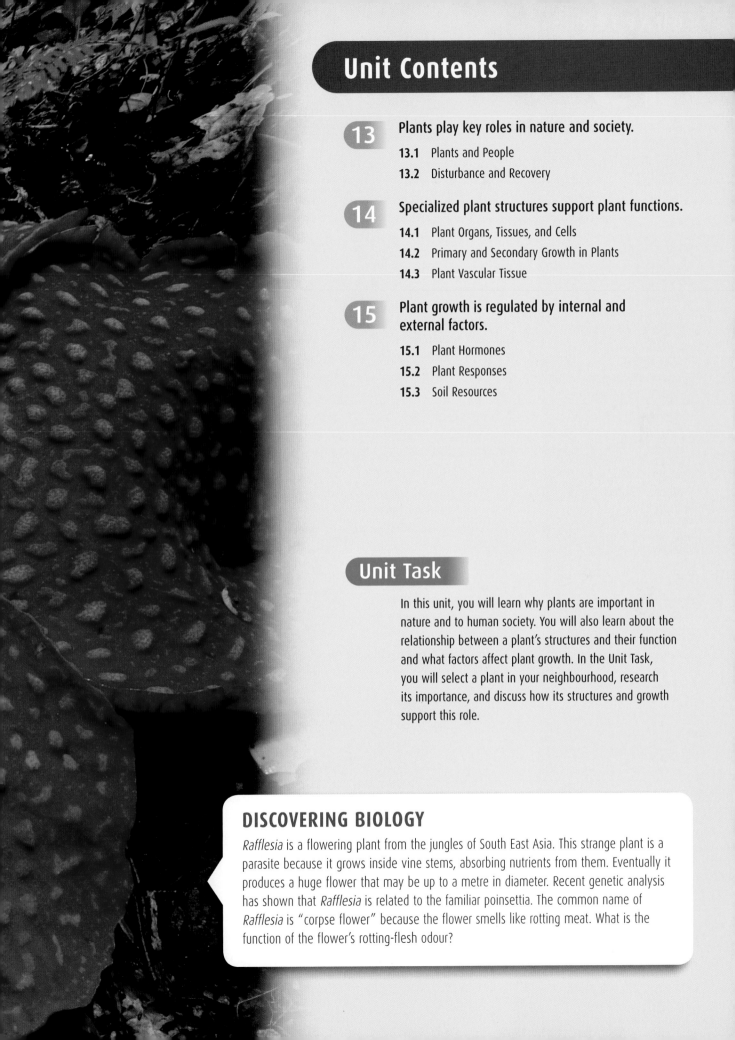

Unit Contents

Unit Task

In this unit, you will learn why plants are important in nature and to human society. You will also learn about the relationship between a plant's structures and their function and what factors affect plant growth. In the Unit Task, you will select a plant in your neighbourhood, research its importance, and discuss how its structures and growth support this role.

DISCOVERING BIOLOGY

Rafflesia is a flowering plant from the jungles of South East Asia. This strange plant is a parasite because it grows inside vine stems, absorbing nutrients from them. Eventually it produces a huge flower that may be up to a metre in diameter. Recent genetic analysis has shown that *Rafflesia* is related to the familiar poinsettia. The common name of *Rafflesia* is "corpse flower" because the flower smells like rotting meat. What is the function of the flower's rotting-flesh odour?

Plants play key roles in nature and society.

Learning Expectations

By the end of this chapter, you will:

Relating Science to Technology, Society, and the Environment

- evaluate, on the basis of research, the importance of plants to the growth and development of Canadian society

- evaluate, on the basis of research, ways in which different societies or cultures have used plants to sustain human populations while supporting environmental sustainability

Developing Skills of Investigation and Communication

- use appropriate terminology related to plants

Understanding Basic Concepts

- explain the process of ecological succession, including the role of plants in maintaining biodiversity and the survival of organisms after a disturbance to an ecosystem

Many foods were in short supply in Canada during World War II, especially foods with military uses. Oil was needed to lubricate machinery, and there was little oil available for cooking. Phyllis Turner, commissioner of the Wartime Prices and Trade Board, decided that Canada should develop its own oilseed crop. Sunflowers, cherries, peaches, apricots, and linseed were all considered and rejected as unsuitable. In 1942, Canada purchased 20 kg of rapeseed from Argentina and by 1948, 32 000 ha of rapeseed plants were growing in the Prairies. But there was a problem: rapeseed oil did not taste very good. It contained two compounds that give mustard and radishes their sharp flavour. Canadian scientists used traditional plant-breeding techniques to improve the taste of rapeseed oil by reducing levels of both compounds. The new form of rapeseed was renamed "canola." Canola comes from Canada plus *oleum*, which is Latin for oil.

Canola, the world's only "made in Canada" plant, is now grown on five million hectares across Ontario and the Prairies (Figure 13.1). It competes with wheat as Canada's top farm export. Canola is one of the healthiest edible oils, with about half the level of saturated fats found in olive or soy oil. Once the oil is extracted, the remaining meal is a high-protein feed for farm animals and aquaculture. Canola oil can also be made into biodiesel, a renewable fuel that replaces diesel made from fossil fuels.

In the 1990s, canola was genetically modified (GM) with the insertion of foreign genes that are associated with herbicide resistance. GM canola can be treated with the herbicide glyphosate, which kills a great variety of weeds, while leaving GM canola unharmed. About 80 percent of the canola grown in Canada is GM. Most of the remaining 20 percent is conventionally grown, with the application of herbicides that kill fewer weed species. Only 0.07 percent of Canada's canola crop is organically grown, without any application of herbicides and pesticides.

Figure 13.1 Canola is a "made in Canada" plant.

©P

Plants and People

Section Summary

- Plants have many key roles in human society, providing food, medicines, building materials, and energy.

- The human food supply is based on the cultivation of relatively few species of plants.

- The use of biofuels has environmental, economic, and social costs and benefits.

- Plants provide a number of ecosystem services.

- Sustainable development meets the needs of the present without compromising the ability of future generations to meet their own needs.

Imagine a world without plants. You may immediately think about edible plants: the fruits, vegetables, and grains you eat every day. But you wouldn't have meat, if farm animals didn't have plants to eat. In addition, many of the building materials in the room around you were made from plant products. Some of them are obvious: wooden benches and cedar shingles, for example. Other plant products, such as glues, resins, and paints, are less easy to spot. Textiles, packaging, and medicines also come from plants. Even the oxygen you are breathing is produced by plants as a waste product of photosynthesis.

BIOLOGY·SOURCE

Suggested Activity

- E1 Quick Lab Overview on page 365

Canada's Food Crops

Early humans collected wild seeds and fruits for food. Agriculture developed as humans began sowing seeds and cultivating plants in order to have a more dependable food supply. Later, humans began to breed plants to improve food quantity and quality. Over human history, people became more and more dependent on domesticated crops as a source of food. Today, almost all the human food supply is based on the cultivation of only 14 species of plants. Canada's main crops, in order of income generated, are wheat, canola, barley, corn, soybeans, potatoes, flax, and oats (Figure 13.2).

Figure 13.2 Wheat is one of Canada's main crops.

All fruit and almost all vegetable crops come from flowering plants, which are the angiosperms. Corn, rice, wheat, and other cereal grains are the fruits of grass species. In addition to feeding humans, cereal grains are the main food source for domesticated animals such as cows and chickens. Other foods, such as avocados, lentils, and okra, come from broad-leaf plants.

The most important crops in the world are cereal grains and legumes, members of the pea and bean family. Half of the protein consumed by people worldwide comes from cereal grains. Rice is the most important cereal grain throughout Asia. Wheat is the most common grain in North American and European diets. Another 15 percent of human dietary protein comes from the dried fruits of legumes.

Figure 13.3 Cocoa pods are 15–25 cm long and often grow directly from the tree trunk. Cocoa is made from the seeds inside the cocoa pod.

Food comes from all plant parts. Lettuce, spinach, and tea are leaves; celery, potatoes, sugar cane, and bamboo shoots are stems; carrots, sweet potatoes, and beets are roots; coffee and cocoa are seeds (Figure 13.3). Edible fruits include bananas, apples, strawberries, and oranges. Spices are strongly flavoured plant parts. Cinnamon is from bark; vanilla and black pepper are fruits; cardamom is a seed; and cloves are a flower. Tasty herbs such as basil, thyme, and mint are the leaves of aromatic plants. One of the world's most expensive herbs, saffron, is the male floral parts of a crocus flower, collected laboriously by hand.

Many of the foods we eat contain hidden processed plant products, such as sugars from corn or beets and oil from canola or sunflowers. We use thickeners, such as guar gum and corn starch, and soy protein is often added to increase protein and improve texture.

Although Canada is a major food-producing country, many edible plants such as coffee, tea, cocoa, and bananas cannot be grown in our temperate climate and must be imported. Ontario alone spends almost $16 billion on imported food and food products each year.

Plants as a Source of Pharmaceuticals

Plants have long been used as a source of traditional medicine. In 400 B.C.E., Hippocrates, the Greek doctor known as the father of modern medicine, recommended that the bark and leaves of the willow tree could be used to treat headaches, fevers, and pain. The active ingredient in willow is acetylsalicylic acid, better known as Aspirin™. We now know how Aspirin™ works. It inhibits the production of prostaglandins, chemicals that increase the pain sensitivity of the body's nerve endings.

More than 120 prescription and non-prescription drugs, ranging from stimulants to cancer treatments to laxatives, are extracted from plants. In fact, 25 percent of drug prescriptions contain a plant product (Table 13.1).

Table 13.1 Drugs Produced from Plant Products

Plant Species	Drug	Uses
Autumn crocus (bulb and seeds)	Colchicine	Anti-inflammatory, anti-tumour
Cowage (seeds)	L-Dopa	Parkinson's disease
Foxglove (leaves)	Digitalis, digitoxin, digoxin	Heart rhythm regulator
Jimsonweed (seeds)	Scopolamine	Sedative
Pacific yew (bark)	Taxol	Ovarian cancer
Poppy (fruit)	Morphine, codeine	Pain killer
Rosy periwinkle (whole plant)	Vinblastine, vincristine	Hodgkin's disease, leukemia
Wild yam (roots)	Cortisone, diosgenin (estrogen)	Anti-inflammatory, birth control
Willow trees (bark)	Acetylsalicylic acid (Aspirin™)	Pain killer, anti-inflammatory
Yellowbark cinchona (bark)	Quinine	Malaria

Canada's Aboriginal peoples used more than 500 plants for medicinal purposes. Members of Jacques Cartier's 1535 expedition suffered from scurvy, a disease that results from a lack of vitamin C. They were treated by Iroquois healers with a tea made from eastern white cedar and other conifers that are high in vitamin C (Figure 13.4). North American plants continue to be a source of new drugs. Taxol, a potent drug used to treat ovarian and breast cancer, was originally derived from the bark of the Pacific yew tree. The bark of a 15-m tall, 200-year-old tree yielded less than a gram of taxol. Yield is the amount of an agricultural product that is collected and used by humans. Demand for taxol threatened the Pacific yew before methods were developed for making the drug.

There may be many more plant-based drugs that await discovery. Researchers have investigated fewer than 5000 of the 280 000 known plant species as potential sources of new medicines. Human activities threaten many plants before their potential uses can be assessed. The tropical rainforest is losing plant species faster than any of Earth's ecosystems. It could be a "medicine chest" of healing plants that will become extinct before they are even discovered.

Figure 13.4 Tea made from eastern white cedar is high in vitamin C.

Plants as a Source of Fuel

Plants are the main source of fuel for human activities. Humans have used wood and peat fires to cook food and provide heat for over 50 000 years. Fossil fuels such as coal, oil, and natural gas come from the fossilized remains of plants that died 350 million years ago during the Carboniferous period.

The Promise and Peril of Biofuels

The search for alternative energy sources has become increasingly urgent as oil prices rise and fossil fuels run out. There is also concern about greenhouse gases that are produced when fossil fuels are burned. **Biofuels** are energy sources produced from renewable organic materials, including plants and organic waste. Ethanol is the most familiar biofuel. It is a form of alcohol, mostly produced from corn. All cars can run on gas/ethanol blends, while modified engines can run on pure ethanol (Figure 13.5). Biodiesel is produced from plant or animal fats or used cooking oil.

The Canadian government funds programs that encourage the development and production of biofuels. Biofuels are also taxed at a lower rate than fossil fuels. Canadian production of ethanol is expected to reach two billion litres during 2010, while the target for biodiesel production from canola is 500 million litres. Biofuels offer the hope of renewable fuels with lower greenhouse gas emissions. However, using crops for fuel may reduce the availability of agricultural land for food crops and increase the cost of food.

BIOLOGY•SOURCE

Suggested Activity
• E2 Decision-Making Analysis Overview on page 365

Figure 13.5 More and more vehicles are powered by biofuels.

Plants as a Source of Industrial and Building Materials

Plants and plant products play many key roles in building, industry, and the home. Temperate **hardwoods**, such as beech, oak, and maple, and tropical hardwoods, such as mahogany and teak, are dense woods of angiosperms used to make high quality furniture and flooring. **Softwoods** come from gymnosperms, which include conifers, such as pine and spruce trees.

BIOLOGY•SOURCE

Explore More

What is straw-bale housing and how can it support Canadian agriculture and increase the sustainability of other natural resources?

Softwoods are used for furniture and buildings as well, but their long fibres mean that they are also suitable for producing pulp, used for paper and cardboard production. Canada is one of the world's largest producers of softwood lumber and its products. We supply about one-third of the softwood lumber used in the United States. This trade earns Canada $8.5 billion a year. About 280 000 Canadian jobs and 300 communities depend on Canada's softwood lumber industry.

Plants have many industrial uses. Linseed oil is used as a furniture finish. Castor oil is used as motor oil and as a lubricant for hydraulic systems in heavy machinery. A century ago, most industrial products were made from plant products. In fact, plastic was initially made from corn. Although oil-based products currently dominate industry, there is a new interest in industrial products based on plants. New technologies have led to the production of inexpensive plant-based industrial products. Plant-based inks, paints, plastics, and dyes are becoming less expensive and more popular.

Other Uses of Plants

Plants have many other uses. When you use a pencil or pen to jot down a note on a piece of paper, the pencil, the ink, and the paper all come from plants. The money you spend, the violin you play, makeup, a baseball bat: all of these products are made from plants. Many of our clothes are made from cotton, flax, hemp, or sisal fibres (Figure 13.6). Linen is made from flax. Rayon is made from chemically processed cellulose derived from wood, cotton, or bamboo.

Plants also perform important **ecosystem services**. These services are the beneficial processes carried out by living things that are necessary to sustain life on Earth. For example, plants play a key role in nutrient cycles. They are a food source for consumers and they enrich the soil by adding usable nutrients to it. Plant roots bind soil, reducing erosion in terrestrial ecosystems and coastal areas. Plants are also capable of storing or detoxifying toxins and pollutants. Some house plants, such as the spider plant and philodendron, reduce indoor air pollutants.

Plants provide many ecosystem services in urban centres. Trees and other plants in parks and along city streets improve air quality, cool the air, reduce storm water runoff, reduce noise levels, and provide habitat for animals (Figure 13.7). Some studies show a reduction in crime and increase in personal relaxation in urban areas that have more vegetation. Plants also have economic benefits. They increase property values and reduce energy use through shading and wind reduction.

Figure 13.6 These items are all made from plants. The blouse is linen, which is made from flax. The scarf is rayon, which is made from wood pulp. The socks are bamboo rayon, and the T-shirt is cotton.

Figure 13.7 Trees and other plants provide many ecological, economic, and social benefits to cities.

Concept Check

1. List three different ways you used plants today.
2. Distinguish between biofuels and fossil fuels.
3. Provide an example of an ecosystem service performed by plants.

Using Plants Sustainably

It is important to adopt a goal of sustainable development in using plants for agriculture and forestry. **Sustainability** is the capacity to maintain a certain process or state indefinitely. The United Nations has defined **sustainable development** as "development that meets the needs of the present without compromising the ability of future generations to meet their own needs." People practising sustainable development can continue to farm and harvest timber, while still protecting biodiversity. For example, a forest corridor through farmland may be left to connect two areas of parkland, allowing wildlife to move from one area to the other. Trees may be harvested selectively, with only mature individuals taken, instead of cutting down all the vegetation in an area.

Plant Harvest and Horticulture by Aboriginal Peoples

The earliest evidence of crop cultivation in Ontario is found in areas near the Great Lakes around 1250 to 1500 years ago. When Jacques Cartier visited Hochelaga (now Montréal) in 1535, he said, "[The Iroquois] have good and large fields of corn." The Aboriginal peoples of Ontario were skilled farmers who grew several varieties of maize (corn) as well as beans and squash.

Maize, beans, and squash were grown in small fields beside the villages (Figure 13.8). Each field was used for a time and then allowed to lie uncultivated, or fallow, for a number of years. Kernels of maize and dried beans could be stored for several years, providing a stable food supply when game, fish, or wild rice were unavailable. The cultivation of maize, beans, and squash in Ontario probably led to significant increases in population size.

These three crops all benefit from the presence of the others. The broad leaves of the squash plants shade the soil, maintaining soil moisture and preventing weeds from establishing and competing with the crops. The corn stalks support the climbing stems of the bean plants, while the beans house nitrogen-fixing bacteria in root nodules. In a process called **nitrogen fixation**, these nodules "fix" the nitrogen that is in the air pockets in the soil, changing it into a form that plants can use (Figure 13.9). The wisdom of this form of cultivation has been rediscovered in the modern world. On some Mexican farms, fields planted only with maize have been replaced with fields planted with maize, squash, and beans. The result has been a substantial increase in yield.

Worldwide Sustainable Agricultural Initiatives

Many farmers around the world are adopting innovative agricultural techniques — or returning to traditional methods — to increase yield. A 2001 study described over 200 sustainable-agriculture projects carried out in 52 developing countries. These sustainable initiatives increased crop yields by an average of 73 percent.

There are many examples of sustainable initiatives. In Kenya, farmers are planting weeds in their maize fields to act as "trap plants" for stem borer larvae. Previously, stem borer larvae ate about a third of the maize produced in the region. However, the larvae prefer to attack napier grass, a local plant often considered a weed. Napier grass secretes a sticky material that glues down and kills the larvae. By planting napier grass among their maize plants, farmers increased maize yield by nearly 70 percent.

Figure 13.8 Growing maize, beans, and squash together is a form of sustainable agriculture.

Figure 13.9 Bacteria living in the nodules of many legumes are able to transform atmospheric nitrogen into a form that is usable by plants.

Figure 13.10 In Bangladesh, farmers can raise rice and fish in the same paddies.

Figure 13.11 Cashew trees have many uses.

Explore More

Are there ways that we can eat to support sustainable agriculture and economic self-sufficiency in developing countries?

In Bangladesh, farmers are raising fish in the flooded rice paddies, turning one harvest into two (Figure 13.10). In Madagascar, a local researcher developed a method to quadruple rice yield. He transplanted the rice seedlings at an earlier stage, delayed flooding of the rice fields, and used locally available compost instead of costly chemical fertilizers. This method has been so successful that it has now been adopted in China, Indonesia, and Cambodia.

One-third of Argentina's farmers no longer till, or plough, the soil before planting their crops. Tilling puts air into the soil. This increases bacterial decomposition of organic material in soil and releases carbon dioxide from bacterial respiration. Instead of tilling, the farmers plant winter crops or spray biodegradable herbicides to prepare their fields. Untilled fields serve as major carbon sinks because organic material in the soil does not degrade and release atmospheric carbon dioxide, a major greenhouse gas. A one-hectare field that is not tilled before planting can absorb one tonne of carbon each year.

In Thailand, small fields are cultivated for several years and then left fallow for a decade. This method is similar to that used by Ontario's Aboriginal people. The result is productive land with high biodiversity. When fallow, the agricultural fields contain 223 plant species, nearly as many as the 319 plant species found in virgin forests in the same area.

In Cameroon, farmers plant cacao, orange, mango, avocado, and cherry trees among the natural trees of the rainforest. The result is high agriculture yield and high biodiversity. The farmed forest contains more than half the number of species found in natural forests.

In South America, farmers harvest Brazil nuts, cashews, and palm hearts from undamaged rainforests. Some crops, such as Brazil nut trees, will grow only in a rainforest where the overhead tree canopy is not disturbed. Some plants, such as the cashew tree, have many uses (Figure 13.11). The fleshy part is used for juice and in jams and chutney. The cashew nut is roasted and eaten. The liquid in the nut shell has industrial uses. The bark, leaves, and juice from the fruit have medicinal properties. Resins and gums can be extracted from the stems and bark.

Concept Check

1. Define sustainable development.

2. What plants were cultivated by Ontario's Aboriginal people?

3. Provide two examples of sustainable agricultural practices.

Sustainable Agriculture in Canada

The two main agricultural practices used by Canadian farmers to increase crop yields are the use of chemical fertilizers and pesticides. The use of chemical fertilizers, however, releases greenhouse gases and may cause excessive growth of algae if fertilizers run off into lakes or oceans. Many farmers also use manure as an inexpensive source of nutrients for crops, but they must also take care to prevent run-off into streams or standing water.

The two main types of pesticides are herbicides, which control unwanted plants, and insecticides, which control unwanted insects. About 80 percent of Ontario farms use at least one pesticide annually. There are about 5700 chemical pesticides registered for use in Canada, and Canadian farmers spend over a billion dollars on them each year. The risks associated with these chemicals vary with the amount used, how long they last before breaking down, where they are carried by wind and water, and whether they kill beneficial organisms, such as earthworms and insect pollinators. The more pesticides are applied, the higher the environmental risks. Insects and weeds reproduce quickly, evolving to become resistant to pesticides.

Tilling land is also done to prepare the soil for crops and to control weeds, but it increases soil erosion and the loss of soil nutrients. In addition, tilling disrupts wild bees. Bees are important pollinators that nest in holes in soft dirt, tangled grasses, and abandoned rodent burrows. If bees did not pollinate flowers on fruit trees, we would not have fruits, such as cherries (Figure 13.12).

Figure 13.12 Without bees, we would not have cherries or many other fruits.

Integrated Pest Management

Many Canadian farmers have adopted a variety of pest-management strategies designed to increase crop yields while reducing harmful health and environmental effects. This is called **integrated pest management**. Table 13.2 outlines several strategies used in integrated pest management. Of course, each of these strategies has its own risks. For example, selecting insects for biological control must be done carefully so that populations of these introduced insects do not expand uncontrollably.

Table 13.2 Strategies for Integrated Pest Management

Strategy	Explanation
Crop rotation	Changing the crop grown on a plot of land each year means that each crop is less vulnerable to specialized pests and diseases.
Green manure	Growing plants and then tilling them back into the soil increases soil nutrients and improves crop health so they are more resistant to pests.
Planting nitrogen-fixing crops	Growing nitrogen-fixing crops, such as soybean, increases the nitrogen content in the soil, improving crop health.
Biological control	Natural predators, such as birds, ladybird beetles, and spiders, can control some insect pests (Figure 13.13).
Genetically modified crops	Crops can be genetically engineered so they possess desirable traits. For example, Bt corn produces a bacterial toxin that kills the larvae of the corn borer when it feeds on corn.
Pheromones	Pheromones are chemicals used by insects to communicate with one another. Releasing synthetic pheromones may prevent insects from mating or lure them into traps, while not affecting other species.

Figure 13.13 Natural predators, such as this ladybird beetle, eat pest insects, such as these aphids.

Water Management

Canada has an abundance of fresh water. However, this precious resource is not unlimited. Canadian farmers use about 9 percent of available water for irrigating crops (Figure 13.14). Irrigation reduces soil erosion because it prevents rich topsoil from drying out and blowing away.

Figure 13.14 Irrigation of farm fields uses about 9 percent of Canada's water.

Irrigating farmland also carries costs. It may increase the salt content of soil, harming plants. The added water may carry pesticides and fertilizers into ground water, streams, and lakes. If water for irrigation is pumped from underground sources, these sources may not refill. Farmers must manage water use very carefully, using as little water as possible, at the times when their crops need it the most.

Most Ontario farmers maintain vegetation on the edges of streams or ponds. This vegetation is important because it prevents soil erosion and reduces water run-off from the farm. Therefore, it prevents valuable soil, polluting nutrients, and toxic pesticides from being washed into streams and ponds. Most farmers prevent livestock from grazing near water bodies to reduce damage to vegetation and keep manure out of streams and ponds.

Sustainable Forestry in Canada

Canada has over 400 million hectares of forest, representing 10 percent of the world's forests. Large expanses of boreal forest stretch from the Atlantic to Pacific Oceans and make up 75 percent of Canada's forested land (Figure 13.15). Boreal forest is composed mostly of coniferous trees, such as spruce, balsam fir, tamarack, and jack pine. Most of our forests are still intact. Only 6 percent of Canada's forests have been removed and the land converted to cities, farms, mines, or roads. Canadians value their forests: 13 million person-visits are recorded annually in our national parks.

Canada is the world's largest exporter of timber and other forest products. Canada's National Forest Strategy pledges a commitment to **sustainable forest management**. Under this policy, forest products are harvested sustainably, preserving the forest's health and biodiversity. Forest managers plan forest use in consultation with Aboriginal people, forest owners, environmental groups, academics, recreational forest users, and community groups. At present, 146 million hectares of Canada's forests are classified as sustainably managed.

Each year, less than 1 percent of Canada's forests are harvested. Half of the harvested area is replanted with seeds or nursery-raised seedlings, while the other half is left to reseed naturally. However, the growth of much of this regenerating forest is limited due to climate, topography, and other factors. In addition, extensive areas of forests are lost due to fires and other natural disturbances. Therefore, we must be careful to manage Canada's forests wisely.

Figure 13.15 Canada has about one-third of the world's boreal forests.

Figure 13.16 Canada's National Tree Seed Centre collects seeds from all Canadian tree species.

Preserving Genetic Variation of Canada's Forests

Trees are an important natural resource in Canada. Canada's National Tree Seed Centre (NTSC) in Fredericton, New Brunswick, conserves the genetic diversity of our forests. The Centre collects and stores seeds from across the natural ranges of all Canadian tree species. The goal of the Centre is to obtain a diverse collection of genetic material. Therefore, seeds are collected from many individual trees in each population, not just from the "best" or tallest trees (Figure 13.16). Some tree populations are adapted to the unique environmental conditions in which they live. Other populations may be endangered or threatened. When trees are harvested, the cleared areas are planted with genetically improved seedlings grown in seed orchards. The NTSC collection is an increasingly important storehouse of genetic information.

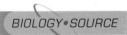

The Plants Around Us

Purpose

To appreciate the many functions of plants in your surroundings

Activity Overview

In this activity, you will work in a group to identify the many plants and plant products that you use in everyday life.

Your teacher will give you a copy of the full activity.

Prelab Questions

Consider the questions below before beginning this activity.

1. How many different kinds of plants and plant products do you eat each day?

2. How many items in Figure 13.17 can you identify that are made of plants?

3. Which textiles are made from plant products?

Figure 13.17 Many of the products in this photo are made from plants.

REQUIRED SKILLS
- Gathering information
- Stating a conclusion

D1 Key Activity

Assessing the Impact of Biofuels

Issue

The use of biofuels rather than fossil fuels is becoming increasingly popular. Many believe that switching to biofuels will reduce greenhouse gas emissions. However, there are possible costs associated with biofuel use. Some believe that their use will cause food prices to rise as land is diverted from food production to fuel production.

Activity Overview

In this activity, you will select a biofuel and assess its total environmental impact, including the greenhouse gas output that results from its production and use and its effect on land use. You will also consider how growing crops for biofuels will affect food availability and the price of food (Figure 13.18). Students will then debate whether or not the government should require all fuel used in Canada to include a substantial percentage of biofuel.

Your teacher will give you a copy of the full activity.

Prelab Questions

Consider the questions below before beginning this activity.

1. What is a biofuel?

2. Name two Canadian plants that are used to produce biofuel.

3. Why do governments encourage the development and production of biofuels?

Figure 13.18 Corn can be grown for food or for biofuel.

Key Concept Review

1. Why is canola described as a "made in Canada" plant?

2. List the top two economically important crops in Canada and describe their uses.

3. Name one crop harvested from each plant part: seeds, fruits, leaves, stems, flowers, roots.

4. List three drugs that are produced from plant products. For each drug, state its use(s) and the plant it is obtained from.

5. Why is the destruction of tropical rainforests a threat to human health?

6. Explain why fossil fuels, such as coal, oil, and natural gas, are plant products.

7. What are biofuels and how do they differ from fossil fuels?

8. What is softwood lumber? Name two products made from softwood lumber.

9. Define the term "ecosystem services."

10. Explain what is meant by the term "sustainability."

11. What are the benefits and risks of the use of chemical fertilizers?

12. Explain the term "trap plant" and describe an example of how such a plant can increase agricultural yield.

13. Describe three sustainable strategies that a farmer might adopt for combating pest weeds and insects.

Connect Your Understanding

14. Some Aboriginal people of Ontario grew three crops in small fields, which were used for a time and then left fallow.
    (a) Use a concept map or another graphic organizer to explain how these crops benefit from being grown together.
    (b) Explain the significance of these agricultural practices to soil fertility and local biodiversity.

15. Use a table to compare the costs and benefits of tilling an agricultural field.

16. Ontario farmers try to maintain vegetation on the banks of ponds and streams on their farms.
    (a) Explain the benefits of this practice.
    (b) Describe two costs associated with this practice.

17. Name three services performed by the ecosystem in the following photo.

Question 17

18. Why does the National Tree Seed Centre collect seeds from a variety of trees in each population?

19. Decisions about the use of biofuels touch on many different issues: food availability, energy independence, use of renewable resources, reduction of greenhouse gas emissions, and the total environmental impact of resource use. How would you weigh all these different issues in deciding whether to use biofuels or another source of energy?

20. Should the Government of Canada encourage the growing of corn and canola for production of biofuels? Justify your answer.

Reflection

21. Have your perceptions about where our food comes from changed as a result of reading this section? Explain your answer.

22. When you buy plant products, do you consider whether they were grown sustainably? Why or why not?

For more questions, go to

Disturbance and Recovery

Section Summary

- Healthy communities experience periodic disturbances.

- Following disturbance, plant communities change over time. This is called ecological succession.

- Primary succession occurs in disturbed areas lacking soil. Secondary succession follows a disturbance that damages a community but leaves the soil intact.

- Succession promotes biodiversity because it allows different types of plant communities to exist in an area.

In 1980, 400 m of the cone blew off Mount St. Helens in Washington (Figure 13.19). In the blast zone, burnt trees lay "toppled like toothpicks." Mud flowed and pumice stone and volcanic ash were flung from the volcano, destroying plants and animals up to 30 km from the new crater. Thirty years later, plants now cover about 75 percent of the ground around the crater. A stable plant community has not yet established, and it may not develop. Mount St. Helens is an active volcano that will likely erupt sometime in the next 200 years. When Mount St. Helens erupted in 1980, plant communities on the mountain slopes had not recovered from a previous eruption in the 1800s.

Figure 13.19 Mount St. Helens erupted on May 18, 1980.

Disturbances Influence Community Structure

Although they may seem stable and unchanging, most healthy plant communities are subject to periodic disturbance. Natural disturbances include fire, flood, frost, drought, or the fall of a single tree in the forest (Figure 13.20). Less frequent natural disturbances include dramatic natural disasters such as hurricanes, volcanic eruptions, and earthquakes. Disturbances can also be caused by human activities, such as mining, deforestation, agriculture, or urbanization.

Disturbances affect communities directly, by killing organisms. They also alter communities indirectly, by changing the availability of abiotic resources such as shelter, nutrients, light, or water. Changes in the abiotic environment mean that the habitat may become suited to a different set of plant and animal species.

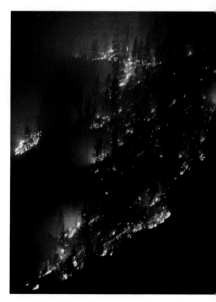

Figure 13.20 Fire is typically a large-scale natural disturbance.

The Benefits of Disturbance

The effects of a disturbance are not always negative. Despite the plant and animal deaths caused by the disturbance, some organisms thrive in the wake of the destruction. Moose and deer benefit from fire because it creates habitats where there is lots of new vegetation to browse. Seeds of some species require exposure to the extremely high temperature of a forest fire before they can germinate, or begin to grow. For example, cones of jack pines are sealed shut by a gummy substance called resin (Figure 13.21). The cones cannot open to release seeds until the resin is scorched by fire.

Figure 13.21 Most jack pine cones open only after they are heated to about 50°C.

The Impact of Disturbance

The type, severity, and frequency of a disturbance will determine its impact. The type of disturbance is important because disturbances change ecosystems in unique ways. Fires, floods, and windstorms alter communities quite differently. The severity of a disturbance determines the extent and intensity of destruction. A hurricane will have a greater effect on a community than a windstorm.

The frequency of disturbance determines how much recovery time there is for the ecosystem. A community that has already been altered by a disturbance may recover more slowly from a second event. Some disturbances happen with predictable frequency, allowing communities to adapt to and even benefit from disturbance. For example, the Canadian Prairies are maintained by fire because trees are destroyed by fire (Figure 13.22). Smaller-scale disturbances tend to occur more frequently. Strong winds may bring down a few trees in a forest each year, while a hurricane will affect forests much less frequently.

Figure 13.22 Fires maintain the Prairie habitat.

Concept Check

1. Provide an example of an ecological disturbance and describe its effects on a plant community.

2. Explain why disturbances can have positive effects on a community.

3. List three factors that determine the impact of a disturbance on a community.

©P

Ecological Succession

Major disturbances such as clearcut logging, volcanic eruptions, or major storms may remove or greatly alter the plant community in an area. Some plant species are well adapted to colonize disturbed areas. Early establishing species are called **pioneer species**. Pioneer species are often adapted to high light or low nutrient environments. Alder trees, for example, are often pioneer species. Alders do well in disturbed areas that have low-nutrient soils because nodules on their roots fix nitrogen, converting it into a form usable by plants.

As the pioneer plant species grow, they change the biotic and abiotic conditions in the disturbed area. The roots of these early plant colonizers bind soil, allowing it to retain more moisture. Many pioneer species fix nitrogen, adding nitrogen to the soil that other species can use. As the leaves shed by pioneer plants decompose, more nutrients accumulate in the soil. Above ground, shoots of pioneer species create shade, moderating temperatures.

Over time, pioneer species are replaced or out-competed by other plants that need richer, moister soils, but are more tolerant of low light levels. As the plant species change, so do the animal species that inhabit the community. This process of replacement of the plants and other organisms that make up a community is called **ecological succession**.

Primary Succession

When a community arises in a lifeless area that has no soil, the change is called **primary succession**. Examples of such areas are new islands and landscapes created by erupting volcanoes or the bare rock left behind by a retreating glacier.

Micro-organisms are generally the first organisms to appear during primary succession. Then lichens and mosses, which grow from windblown spores, colonize the barren ground. Soil gradually develops from the decomposed remains of the early colonizers. Once soil is present, the lichens and mosses may be overgrown by grasses and other herbaceous plants. The seeds of these plants may have blown in from other areas or been carried in by animals. Eventually, shrubs and trees become established. Primary succession from barren ground to a forest community can take hundreds or even thousands of years.

Another type of primary succession, dune succession, occurs along the shores of the Great Lakes. Here, grasses with long horizontal roots, called rhizomes, are usually the first species to colonize the unstable sand (Figure 13.23). These grasses stabilize the sand dune, eventually allowing other species, such as sand cherry and dune willows, to colonize. A mature forest community may eventually develop but this will take thousands of years.

Figure 13.23 (a) These dunes along Lake Huron are undergoing primary succession. (b) Grasses with rhizomes are often the pioneer species.

Primary Succession on Mount St. Helens

When the cone blew off Mount St. Helens in 1980, the eruption affected a large area. Volcanic gases, ash, and pumice covered a fan-shaped area to the north of the crater. Mud flowed in other directions, forming a 30-km desolate landscape covered with ash and strewn with rocks the size of large buildings (Figure 13.24(a)). The new landscape was dry and low in nutrients, without any soil.

Figure 13.24 (a) The eruption of Mount St. Helens provided an excellent opportunity for researchers to study primary succession. (b) Lupines were often the first colonizers on mudflows at Mount St. Helens.

The Mount St. Helens eruption allowed biologists to study the sequence of events during primary succession. They expected that the first organisms to arrive would be photosynthetic bacteria, followed by mosses and lichens. These organisms did move in as early colonizers on the edges of the mudflow, but chance survivors also played an important role in primary succession. A few young saplings buried in snow managed to survive. Some lupines and fireweeds survived as their roots and bulbs tumbled on top of the mudflows, instead of being buried underneath them. The roots of lupines house bacteria that fix nitrogen (Figure 13.24(b)). This helped to enrich the nutrient-poor mudflows formed by the eruption, allowing other seeds to germinate and grow.

Over the course of succession, species diversity generally increases. Biologists monitoring a small mudflow near the crater noted that there were no plants after the 1980 eruption, but by 1984, one species of lupine had started to grow, and by 1990, eight species were present. After 30 years, 20 plant species had established and these covered about 75 percent of the ground. It will take over 100 years for plant communities on Mount St. Helens to stabilize. That may not happen, as this active volcano may erupt again before long.

Often, studying natural processes such as succession can help ecologists manage natural landscapes. Because of the new understanding gained from the study of Mount St. Helens and other ecosystems, foresters now leave 15 percent of the trees and other plants behind when they clear-cut forest. This biological legacy accelerates the process of ecological succession, increasing the rate at which a new forest grows.

Secondary Succession

BIOLOGY•SOURCE

Suggested Activity
• E3 Inquiry Activity Overview on page 376

When a disturbance damages an existing community but leaves soil and plants behind, the change in plant communities that follows is called **secondary succession**. The remaining soil is important, because it contains nutrients that support plant growth as well as a large number of living organisms. Soil is not just dirt: it is a living bank of plant seeds, fungal spores, and insect larvae that can speed the growth of a new community.

Forest areas that have been clear-cut, burned by a forest fire, or cleared for farming and then abandoned recover by secondary succession. Light-loving and fast-growing annual species, which grow, reproduce and die within a year, are usually the pioneer species in the newly cleared area (Figure 13.25). Within a few years, grasses and non-woody perennial plants, which live for more than one year, become established. Shrubs that are shade-tolerant and require richer, moister soil may replace these first plants. Eventually, trees may replace the shrubs.

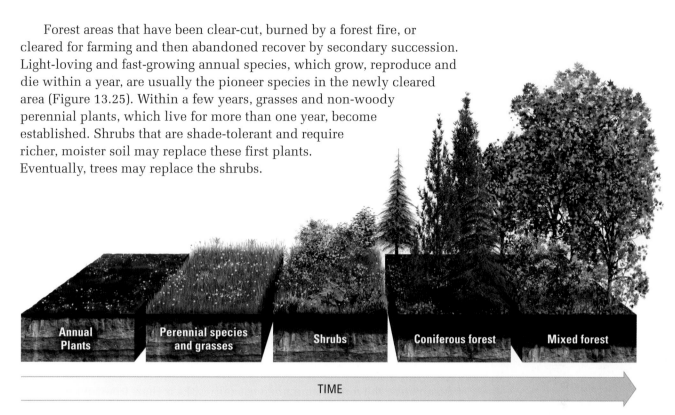

Annual Plants

Perennial species and grasses

Shrubs

Coniferous forest

Mixed forest

TIME

Figure 13.25 Secondary succession occurs following a disturbance that leaves some soil and plant fragments behind.

Secondary Succession in Algonquin Park

Parts of Algonquin Park, in northern Ontario, were logged around 1900. After the forest was cut down, piles of woody debris called slash were left behind. The slash caught fire, and the resulting fires spread through areas of the park. A century later, the herbaceous plants and shrubs that established in burned areas have been replaced by a forest of poplar and white birch (Figure 13.26). Poplar and birch seedlings grow best in bright light and are tolerant of low-nutrient soils. Birch trees shed leaves that decompose rapidly, releasing nutrients.

Young saplings of oak and white pine trees, both shade-tolerant species, are now growing up under the poplar and white birch canopy. Eventually, sugar maple and beech forests will replace the oak and white pine, and finally hemlock, the most shade-tolerant species, will replace the maple and beech trees. Each successional stage is defined by the dominant tree species, but it also has its own species of birds, insects, fungi, ferns, and shrubs.

As the forest fills in during succession and forms an overhead canopy, the interior of the forest changes. Soil moisture increases, light intensity on the forest floor decreases, and air and soil temperatures stabilize. With these changes, the animals in the forest also change. Birds, such as white-throated sparrow and ruffed grouse, that prefer open forest are replaced by birds of the intact forest, such as brown creepers and ovenbirds. On the forest floor, seed abundance and diversity increase leading to higher numbers and diversity of small mammals and soil insects.

Figure 13.26 Areas of Algonquin Park alternate between forests of poplar and white birch, as shown here.

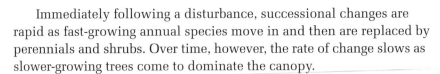

Immediately following a disturbance, successional changes are rapid as fast-growing annual species move in and then are replaced by perennials and shrubs. Over time, however, the rate of change slows as slower-growing trees come to dominate the canopy.

Figure 13.27 Spectacular wildflower displays followed the Yellowstone National Park fires of 1988.

Secondary Succession After the Yellowstone National Park Fires

In 1988, huge fires scorched 400 000 ha of Yellowstone National Park in the United States, burning over a third of the park. In the years after the fires, spectacular wildflower displays filled the burned areas and young conifers sprouted among the wildflowers to begin a new cycle of forest growth (Figure 13.27).

Many of the plant species in Yellowstone National Park are adapted to periodic fires. Before the area was designated as a park in 1872, Yellowstone's grasslands burned every 20 to 25 years, while major forest fires occurred every 300 years or so. After Yellowstone was designated as a park, forest fires were controlled. As a result, the 1988 fire was quite extensive because dead trees and other woody material had accumulated.

Despite the severity and extent of the 1988 fires, few animals died. About 200 of the 50 000 elk in the park, 36 deer, 6 black bears, and 9 bison were the only mammalian casualties. Less than 1 percent of the park's soils heated up enough to kill underground roots and seeds. Fire tends to burn the above-ground parts of plants, leaving the below-ground root systems unharmed. Spectacular regeneration of the grasslands and forests followed the fires. Ash from the fires brought new nutrients to the park's soil, and wildflowers bloomed throughout the park.

Lodgepole pine, the dominant tree species in the park, produces cones that are sealed with gummy resin. Fire is needed to burn the resin away before the cones can open and release their seeds. Scorched lodgepole pine cones released their seeds, producing seed densities of 400 000 seeds per hectare. Healthy lodgepole pine seedlings grew under the blackened canopy of burned trees, forming a new forest (Figure 13.28).

One surprise from the regrowth of Yellowstone National Park was the patchy distribution of the new pine forests. Lodgepole pine trees produce two types of cones. One type of cone opens as soon as it matures. The other type must be burned before it can open and shed its seeds. The distribution of the two types of cones was uneven in the park, leading to a patchy distribution of new pine trees.

Figure 13.28 Lodgepole pine seedlings sprouted following the 1988 fires in Yellowstone National Park

Secondary Succession After Human-Caused Disturbances

Of all species, humans have had the greatest impact on the natural environment (Figure 13.29). Currently, humans use 60 percent of Earth's land, mostly for cities, farms, or rangeland. Unfortunately, human disturbances usually have a negative effect on species diversity. When a forest or grassland is converted to farmland, a diverse community is replaced with crops of a single plant species, such as canola, wheat, or corn.

Figure 13.29 A clearcut hillside is an example of human disturbance to a community.

A large-scale example of human disturbance occurred in the Greater Sudbury area. Since the late 1800s, the centre of Greater Sudbury has been degraded by many human activities, including forestry, mining, and nickel smelting. The original vegetation was killed off by a combination of logging, acid deposition, and acidic soils with high levels of certain metals. The resulting Barrens around Sudbury were bleak, desolate, and lifeless areas totalling 18 500 ha around the three smelters. Only stunted birches and red maples survived in the surrounding areas (Figure 13.30(a)).

Figure 13.30 (a) Prior to 1972, the Sudbury Barrens were lifeless areas surrounding Sudbury's three primary nickel smelters. (b) Young stands of deciduous and coniferous trees now grow on many areas of the former Barrens.

Since 1972, air emission improvements of Sudbury's smelting complexes have reduced sulphur dioxide and metal particle emissions by 90 percent. Reduced sulphur dioxide levels in the air allowed plants to grow, but the acidic soils with high metal concentrations were still a problem.

The first step in restoration was to spread lime on the affected area. Spreading lime reduced the soil acidity, which in turn reduced the toxic effects of the soil metals and permitted plants to grow normally. Grass and legume seeds were added next. The successful grass species were tolerant of heavy metal pollution. The roots of legumes fix nitrogen. These early steps mimicked the natural events of secondary succession, increasing the nutrient availability and moisture of the soil. These changes allowed the survival of trees. Some tree seedlings were planted, while the seeds of other trees blew into the area on their own. Today, Sudbury is a city of parks and trees. The former Barrens are filled with deciduous woods of white birch, trembling aspen, and willow (Figure 13.30(b)).

Not all human-disturbed habitats can be remediated using secondary succession. Many human-caused disturbances are too vast or repeated too frequently to allow succession to proceed. For example, land in the tropical rainforest that is cleared for forestry or agriculture will often not return to its natural state because the nutrients have been lost from the ecosystem.

BIOLOGY•SOURCE

Explore More

How are scientists using plants to clean contaminated soil?

Climax Communities

Ecologists used to think that ecological succession in a region would always proceed through a set of predictable stages to form a climax community. A **climax community** was considered to be a stable, self-perpetuating community that existed in equilibrium with the area's biotic and abiotic environment. This view held that climate was the only factor determining the nature of the climax community, and that the same stable plant community would form in an area regardless of the disturbances that began the process of succession.

We now understand that many factors, not just climate, determine which community will be stable in a particular region and whether a climax community will form at all. Local differences in topography, soil composition, rainfall, and temperature influence plant community development. The other living things found in a region, including animals, fungi, and bacteria, may also alter plant succession and influence the nature of the plant community. Succession is not as predictable as we once thought. In fact, ecologists now believe that the process of succession is often directed by random events, such as the season of the disturbance or local rainfall patterns.

Concept Check

1. What is the main difference between primary and secondary succession?

2. Describe the sequence of successional plant communities that are expected to form in Algonquin Park after it was logged in 1900.

3. Define the term "climax community" and explain how our understanding of this concept has changed.

Succession Promotes Biodiversity

As a plant community changes following a disturbance, each successional stage is defined by the dominant plants found in the ecosystem. The animals change, too, as the tree canopy fills in and as light and soil conditions change. Within a given successional stage, small-scale interactions and disturbances produce patches of different habitat types. This patchiness is important to maintaining biodiversity. Different plants and animals will be adapted to the different patch types. Thus, an ecosystem is often made up of habitat patches, each with a different set of species.

Even the fall of a single tree in a windstorm or ice storm opens up a gap in the canopy and produces a patchy habitat. This was dramatically illustrated when a severe ice storm struck eastern Ontario and western Quebec in January 1998 (Figure 13.31, next page). Some trees had accumulations of up to 10 cm of ice, causing branches and even trunks to break. Many trees were killed outright, and others died over the next few years due to the damage they sustained during the storm. The damage to the tree canopy allowed light to reach the forest floor. As a result, light-loving pioneer species established in a late-successional stage forest.

Figure 13.31 The 1998 ice storm in Ontario and Quebec was a disturbance that initiated secondary succession.

Even within old-growth forest, changing habitat patches help maintain biodiversity. Hooded warblers and Acadian flycatchers are Ontario birds at risk of extinction (Figure 13.32). Acadian flycatchers do best in old-growth forests, under a permanent canopy cover. However, the gap created by the fall of a single large tree allows hooded warblers to persist because light-loving understory plants, such as raspberries, provide nesting habitat. Both birds can survive in an old-growth forest with scattered gaps in the canopy.

(a) (b)

Figure 13.32 (a) The Acadian flycatcher and (b) hooded warbler are both at risk of extinction.

In some of Ontario's boreal forests, biodiversity is maintained because spruce and birch replace each other in a 300-year cycle (Figure 13.33, next page). This cycle occurs because each species creates conditions that favour the other. Some forest animals, such as pine marten and woodland caribou, do well under a spruce forest canopy. On the forest floor, spruce needles decompose slowly, releasing very few nutrients to the soil. The soil becomes nutrient-poor and spruce seedlings cannot grow. Instead, birch seedlings invade spruce stands, changing the forests and the animals that live there.

Many birch trees have root nodules full of bacteria that fix soil nitrogen. In addition, birch leaves decompose rapidly, releasing nutrients to the forest soils. Spruce seedlings grow well in the nutrient-rich soils created by the birch. As a result, the spruce reinvades among the birch trees. These patches of forest types increase the diversity of the forest as a whole.

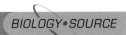

Take It Further

Ecological restoration is often based on the changes that take place during secondary succession. What ecological restoration activities are planned or ongoing in your community? How do these activities accelerate the processes of secondary succession?

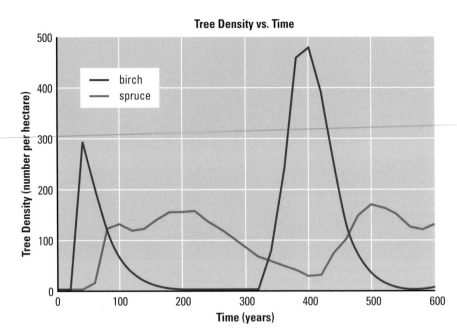

Figure 13.33 Ontario's spruce and birch forests alternate on the basis of nitrogen availability in decomposing leaves and soil.

E3 Inquiry Activity   BIOLOGY·SOURCE

REQUIRED SKILLS
- Recording and organizing data
- Analyzing patterns

Seeing Succession

Question

What evidence of succession do you see in the plant communities around you?

Figure 13.34 There is evidence of succession, even on this school field.

Activity Overview

In this lab, you will compare the plant communities in a relatively undisturbed area with those in an area that has been recently disturbed by human activities or natural events (Figure 13.34).

Your teacher will give you a copy of the full activity.

Prelab Questions

Consider the questions below before beginning this activity.

1. How would you expect light availability and soil moisture to vary between a relatively undisturbed area and a recently disturbed areas?

2. List three characteristics of plant species that would do well in relatively undisturbed areas.

3. List three characteristics of plant species that would do well in recently disturbed areas.

Key Concept Review

1. Explain how type, frequency, and severity of disturbance determine the impact of disturbance on a community.

2. Describe an adaptation that reduces a plant species' vulnerability to fire.

3. Define the term "ecological succession."

4. Describe how pioneer species change their environment and improve the survival of later-successional stage plants.

5. What factors, other than climate, determine the plant community in a particular region?

6. Explain how patchy habitats may increase biodiversity.

Connect Your Understanding

7. Explain why each of the following statements is *true* or *false*.
   (a) A healthy community is in a state of balance, with little change over time.
   (b) Moderate levels of disturbance generally act to reduce species diversity within a community.
   (c) Small-scale disturbances can create patches of different habitats in a community.

8. Using a table, similar to the one below, distinguish between primary and secondary succession. Come up with two other categories for comparison.

Primary and Secondary Succession

	Primary Succession	Secondary Succession
Type of initial disturbance		
Frequency of initial disturbance		
Severity of initial disturbance		
Examples		

9. Describe the role of surviving plants in primary succession on Mount St. Helens.

10. Is the following photo an example of primary or secondary succession? Explain how you came to this decision.

Question 10

11. Does a healthy community maintain a stable and constant composition of species despite disturbance? Explain.

12. Are human-caused disturbances more likely to be damaging to communities than natural disturbances? Explain.

13. (a) What were the Sudbury Barrens?
    (b) What types of pollution led to the formation of the Barrens?
    (c) How were the Barrens remediated?

14. Use a flow chart to explain why birch and spruce forests may alternate in Ontario woodlands.

15. Should ecologists in Algonquin Park allow natural fires to burn within its borders? Justify your decision.

16. Do you see any evidence of succession in your neighbourhood? Explain your answer.

Reflection

17. What part of this section did you find the most interesting? Why?

For more questions, go to *BIOLOGY•SOURCE*

Key Concept Review

1. Describe three ways in which canola plants or products are used. ⓚ

2. (a) Distinguish between cereal grains and legumes. ⓚ
   (b) Name one example of each that can be grown in Canada. ⓚ

3. Is Canada self-sufficient in food production? Explain why or why not. ⓚ

4. What are biofuels and how do they differ from fossil fuels? ⓚ

5. Distinguish between hardwoods and softwoods. ⓚ

6. Explain why plants are important to cities, giving three examples. ⓚ

7. Describe one sustainable forestry practice and one sustainable agricultural practice. ⓚ

8. Use a table to compare the risks and benefits associated with each of the following farming practices.
   (a) fertilizer use ⓚ
   (b) pesticide use ⓚ
   (c) tilling of land ⓚ
   (d) irrigation ⓚ

9. (a) What is Integrated Pest Management (IPM)? ⓚ
   (b) Describe two management strategies that might be used in IPM. ⓚ

10. Why does the National Tree Seed Centre collect seeds from many individuals of each species, rather than collecting seed only from the tallest or healthiest trees? ⓚ

11. Distinguish between primary and secondary succession. ⓚ

12. With reference to the events of primary succession on Mount St. Helens, explain how plants forming a biological legacy accelerated the succession process. ⓚ

13. Your text says, "Soil is not just dirt."
    (a) What else does soil contain? ⓚ
    (b) What role does soil play in secondary succession? ⓚ

14. "Many of the plant species in Yellowstone National Park are adapted to periodic fires." Describe two examples that illustrate this statement. ⓚ

15. One of the early steps in the restoration of the Sudbury Barrens was the seeding of the affected area with legume seeds. Explain how legumes helped to facilitate the process of secondary succession. ⓚ

16. Describe one biotic and one abiotic factor, other than climate, that may help to determine which plant community will develop in a particular region. ⓚ

17. Explain how the severe ice storm that struck Ontario and Quebec in 1998 and killed many trees may have increased biodiversity in affected forests. ⓚ

18. How does succession promote biodiversity? ⓚ

19. Describe a forest that could support populations of both hooded warblers and Acadian flycatchers. ⓚ

Connect Your Understanding

20. Name two ecosystem services provided by the wetland below. ⓐ

Question 20

21. Roots of some plants form associations with nitrogen-fixing bacteria.
    (a) What is nitrogen fixation? ⓚ
    (b) Explain the significance of this association in agriculture. ⓐ
    (c) Explain the importance of this association in succession. ⓐ

22. A farmer has grown the clover, shown in this photo, and will plow it into the soil. Explain how this improves the sustainability of her farm. **a**

Question 22

23. (a) How do Canada's forests contribute to the national economy? **a**
    (b) How do they contribute to our understanding of being Canadian? **a**

24. (a) How are natural and human-caused disturbances similar? **a**
    (b) How do they differ? **a**

25. Forest fires sweep through two forest communities. The fires are identical in size and intensity. Ten years later, you return to the communities and find that one has largely recovered while the other has not. Suggest one or more differences between the two forest communities that could explain this situation. **a**

26. Use a table, such as the one below, to compare pioneer and late-successional stage plants with respect to their need for soil moisture, soil nutrients, and light intensity. **a**

Primary vs. Secondary Succession

	Primary Succession	Secondary Succession
Soil moisture		
Soil nutrients		
Light intensity		

27. (a) Describe the process of dune succession. **k**
    (b) Explain why this is an example of primary succession. **a**

28. Your text states that the plant communities of Mount St. Helens had not reached a stable community when the volcano erupted and may not reach a stable community in the future. Explain why this is so. **a**

29. Explain how secondary succession can be used to remediate a human-disturbed ecosystem. **a**

30. Explain why spruce seedlings cannot thrive under a spruce forest canopy. **a**

Reflection

31. "The most important thing in ecology is to preserve the balance of nature."
    (a) Do you agree with this statement? Why or why not? **c**
    (b) How has your understanding of the "balance of nature" changed as a result of reading about disturbance and succession? **c**

Unit Task Link

Borrow a field guide from the library and head out to a local park or forest. Select and identify a plant that is reasonably abundant and interesting to you. Make sure your plant has green leaves. If it is winter, select an evergreen plant. Look carefully at the distribution of your plant and think about why this plant is found where it is. Consider the following questions.

- What successional stage is the plant community where your plant is found?
- Is your plant growing in bright light, moderate shade, or deep shade?
- Does it grow adjacent to a trail or deep in the woods?
- How moist is the soil at the base of your plant?
- Is it found in association with other plants?

For more questions, go to *BIOLOGY•SOURCE*

Specialized plant structures support plant functions.

Plants and animals live very different lives. While animals move from place to place and eat other organisms for food, plants are rooted in soil and use sunlight to make their food. However, do not be fooled: plants engage much more actively with their environment than you may realize. While animals can search for food, plants may co-operate with fungi, giving their fungal partners sugar in exchange for nutrients from the soil. Plants can elongate their stems or reposition their leaves to capture sunlight. They can modify the growth of their roots to reach a source of water and minerals. Plants change their growth based on the interaction of external factors, such as light, nutrients, temperature, or gravity, and internal factors, such as plant hormones.

When attacked by a predator, an animal can flee or fight. Plants cannot flee, but they can fight back. Thorns, spines, and leaf hairs protect plant stems and leaves from attack by herbivores. Many of our medicines are plant products, used by plants to defend themselves. Some plants can even call in allies to help them defend themselves. Acacia trees, for example, have hollow thorns where ants live and they provide specialized structures to feed the ants (Figure 14.1). In return, the ants attack herbivores that try to feed on the acacia and kill vines that grow around the base of the acacia. If the ants are removed from an acacia, it quickly falls victim to herbivore attack or is overgrown by surrounding vegetation.

(a)

(b)

Figure 14.1 Ants and acacia trees have a mutualistic relationship where both the ant and the tree benefit. (a) There are feeding structures for the ants on the ends of young leaves, and (b) the ants live in hollowed thorns.

©P

Section Summary

- Plant organs include roots, shoots, leaves, and flowers. The structure of monocot and dicot organs differs.

- Flowering plants reproduce sexually, producing seeds. In addition, many plants reproduce asexually.

- The three main tissue systems of plants are dermal, vascular, and ground tissue systems.

Most animals have a characteristic adult form. You were a newborn, a baby, a child, an adolescent, and you will be an adult. At each stage of life, a human has two arms, two legs, two eyes, one nose, and one mouth. A fly was a maggot, a pupa, and then an adult. As an adult, a fly has six legs and one pair of wings. Plants are different from animals. Their adult appearance can vary a lot. A rose bush may have one stem or fifty. Each stem is able to produce flower buds, and two rose bushes may be very different in the number and arrangement of flowers in bloom. However, like animals, the specialized organs of plants have specific functions. These structural adaptations enhance the survival and reproductive success of plants in the environments in which they live.

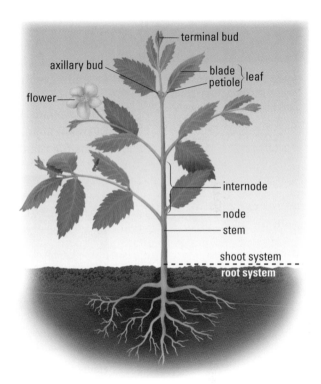

Figure 14.2 A plant has a root system below the ground and a shoot system above. A shoot consists of stems, leaves, and flowers. New shoots grow from buds throughout a plant's life.

Plant Organs

The primary organ systems of a plant are the roots, shoots, leaves, and flowers (Figure 14.2). These organ systems differ between the two groups of angiosperms: dicotyledons and monocotyledons. **Dicotyledons**, or dicots, are the larger group, containing broad-leaf species such as dandelions, canola, and maple trees. **Monocotyledons**, or monocots, contain species with long, thin leaves such as grasses, orchids, and lilies.

Root and Shoot Systems

Roots are structures that anchor a plant in the soil, absorbing minerals and water and providing structural support. Monocots have fibrous root systems. A fibrous root system consists of a mat of thin roots spread out below the soil surface, providing increased exposure to soil nutrients and water (Figure 14.3). In contrast, most dicots have a taproot system that is characterized by one large vertical root with many smaller branches. Carrots, turnips, and beets are examples of dicots with very large, starch-storing taproots.

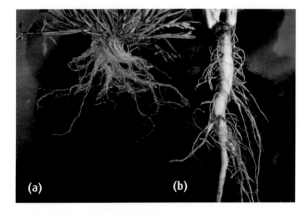

Figure 14.3 (a) Monocots have a fibrous root system consisting of a mat of thin roots. (b) Dicots have a taproot system consisting of one thick central root with thin branches.

Figure 14.4 Many trees in the tropical rainforest have buttress roots because the soils are shallow.

While most roots are below ground, some roots have interesting structures that are adaptations to the plant's environment. For example, buttress roots form on some tall or shallowly rooted tree species to help support them (Figure 14.4). Mangrove trees have above-ground roots that help bring oxygen into the roots.

Shoots are usually above-ground structures consisting of stems, leaves, and flowers. **Stems** are the parts of a plant that support leaves and flowers. **Nodes** are the points on the stem at which leaves are attached, and **internodes** are the portions of the stem between nodes. Stems play an important role in transporting materials in a plant. Vascular tissue runs vertically in the stem. It transports water and minerals from the roots up to the leaves, and food from the leaves to other parts of the plant, such as growing buds, flowers, and roots.

Shoots have modified roles and may vary considerably in their appearance (Figure 14.5). The stems of cacti are specialized to store water. Tubers, such as potatoes, are swollen shoots that store starch. The thorns that protect a hawthorn bush are actually modified branches. An onion is an underground shoot, modified for food storage.

Undeveloped shoots are called **buds**. A terminal bud is found at the tip of a stem. Axillary buds are found in the angles formed by a leaf and the main stem. These angles are called axils. Growth from axillary buds forms the plant's branches.

Figure 14.5 Many plant shoots have modified roles.

(a)　　　　　**(b)**

Figure 14.6 Leaf venation differs between monocots and dicots. (a) Monocot leaves have parallel veins; (b) dicot leaves have a branching veins.

The Leaf

Leaves are the primary food-manufacturing sites of a plant, capturing sunlight and converting light energy to chemical energy during photosynthesis. Most plant leaves are flattened and thin, allowing them to intercept and capture sunlight effectively. The main part of the leaf is the **blade**. A stalk, called a **petiole**, connects the leaf to the stem.

The vein that runs through the petiole and into the blade consists of vascular tissue and support tissue. These veins carry water and nutrients into the leaf and transport sugars from the leaf to other parts of the plant. The **venation**, or arrangement of veins, differs in the leaves of monocots and dicots. In a monocot leaf, several major veins run parallel along the length of the leaf blade. A dicot leaf has a branching network of veins (Figure 14.6).

　　　　　　　　　　　©P

Some plants have highly modified leaves. Leaves, such as the spines on a cactus, are modified so much that you may not recognize them as leaves. The tendrils on a pea plant or a grapevine are modified leaves that allow a plant to attach to and climb along a surface. Because an onion bulb is a modified shoot, the layers of an onion are actually leaves (Figure 14.7). The long leaves of grasses lack petioles altogether. Celery, on the other hand, has enormous petioles — the "stalks" that you eat.

Flowers and Sexual Reproduction

Next time you see a flower, look at it carefully. Many familiar flowers are known for their pretty petals, but there is much more to a flower than petals. In fact, the centre stage for the plant's reproductive action is tucked inside the flower.

While flowers come in many shapes, colours, and sizes, most share the same basic pattern. A flower is a specialized shoot, unique to angiosperms, that usually consists of four different rings of modified leaves: sepals, petals, stamens, and pistils (Figure 14.8). The outermost ring, the **sepals**, covers and protects the flower bud before the blossom opens. An example is a rosebud. The next ring into the flower is composed of **petals**. Petals are often strikingly colourful — they are probably the structures you think of when you picture a flower. Some flower petals have "runway" markings that help guide insect pollinators toward the flower's reproductive parts.

(a)

(b)

Figure 14.7 (a) The red "petals" of a poinsettia are actually leaves. (b) An onion is a modified underground shoot, and the layers of the onion are modified leaves.

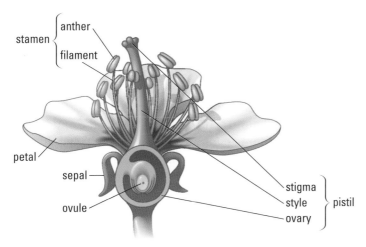

Figure 14.8 A typical flower consists of sepals, petals, pistils, and stamens.

In the centre of the flower are the **stamens**, the male reproductive structures, and the **pistils**, the female reproductive structures. Most flowers have multiple stamens surrounding one or more pistils. Some species, however, have stamens and pistils on separate flowers or even separate plants.

Each stamen consists of a long stalk topped by a sac called an **anther**. Within the anthers, meiosis produces spores that develop into pollen grains. Each pollen grain is a male gametophyte, consisting of two cells surrounded by a thick protective wall. When smelling a flower, you may have dusted your nose with some of these tiny pollen grains.

At the base of each female pistil is an **ovary**. Inside the ovary are structures called **ovules**. Ovules contain the female gametophyte. When fertilized, ovules develop into seeds. Leading to the ovary is a narrow structure called the **style**, which has a sticky tip called the **stigma** (plural, stigmata). A pistil may contain one or more carpels, with each carpel containing one ovule.

Figure 14.9 Pollen has landed on the stigma of this gorse flower. (magnification 250×)

During pollination, pollen grains released from anthers land on the stigmata of flowers (Figure 14.9). Typically, this is after the pollen has been carried by wind or an animal to another flower. Once on a stigma, a pollen grain absorbs water and extends a structure called a pollen tube. The pollen tube, which contains two sperm nuclei, grows toward the ovary through the style. When the pollen tube reaches the ovule in the ovary, a sperm cell fertilizes the egg cell in the ovule and forms a zygote, which develops into the plant embryo. The other sperm cell contributes to the development of a nutrient-rich tissue, called **endosperm**, that nourishes the growing embryo. Several pollen tubes may grow down a style at once, competing with one another to fertilize one ovule.

Monocot flowers tend to have sepals, petals, and reproductive parts in multiples of three. For example, a lily flower has six petals and six stamens. Dicot flowers tend to have parts in multiples of four or five. However, there are exceptions to this general rule. For example, the flowers of mustard, a dicot, have four petals and six stamens.

Concept Check

1. Compare and contrast the functions of roots and shoots.

2. Compare the arrangement of veins in monocot and dicot leaves.

3. Draw the reproductive structures of a flower. For each structure, include a label stating a brief description of its function.

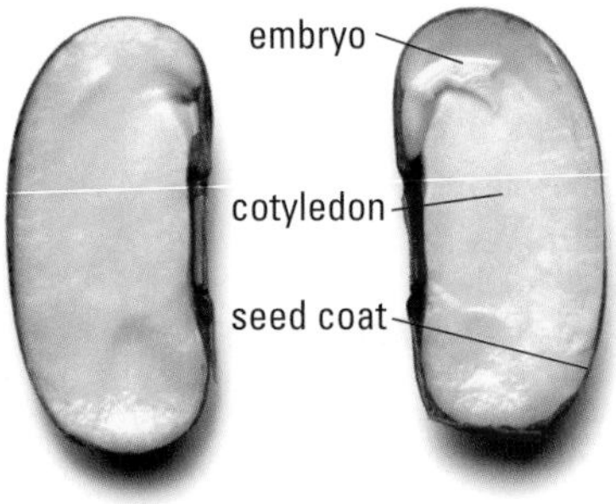

Figure 14.10 Slicing a string bean seed in half reveals the embryo and cotyledons. A tough seed coat surrounds the seed.

embryo

cotyledon

seed coat

Seed Development and Dispersal

After fertilization takes place, the ovule develops into a seed. Seeds have a tough outer layer called a **seed coat** that helps to protect the tiny embryo and endosperm inside (Figure 14.10). In many seeds, the endosperm is the food source for the developing embryo and may contain starch, proteins, and oils. Many plant products, such as wheat flour and popcorn, are made from endosperm. In the embryo, a miniature root and shoot take form. An embryonic leaf, called the **cotyledon**, also develops (Figure 14.11). The cotyledon functions in the storage and transfer of nutrients to the embryo and is especially important in seeds without endosperm. In dicots there are two (*di*) cotyledons. In monocots, there is one (*mono*) cotyledon.

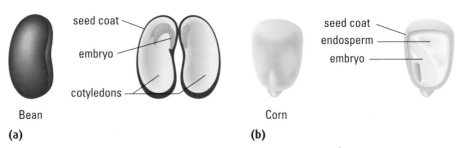

Figure 14.11 Internal structures of (a) dicot and (b) monocot seeds.

Bean (a)   Corn (b)

seed coat, embryo, cotyledons

seed coat, endosperm, embryo

After several cycles of mitosis, the growth and development of the plant embryo within the seed is temporarily suspended. This is the stage when the seed is usually dispersed from the parent plant. In many flowering plants, a fruit develops from the ovary of an angiosperm. Fruits protect seeds and help disperse seeds from the parent plant. You may think of fruits as being sweet and juicy, but there are many types of fruits. Green peppers, walnuts, cucumbers, maple tree keys, coconuts, and corn are all types of fruits.

Seed dispersal can occur in many ways (Figure 14.12). Some seeds travel by sticking onto a passing animal's fur, as burrs. (A burr is actually a fruit, just not a tasty one!) Other seeds are tucked inside fleshy, edible fruits that are attractive to animals as food. The flesh of the fruit gets digested, but the indigestible seed coat protects the embryo. The seed passes through the animal's digestive tract and is eventually deposited as part of the animal's feces, sometimes many kilometres from the original plant. In fact, seeds of some species benefit from being passed through an animal's digestive system, as the digestive enzymes weaken the seed coat, allowing the roots and shoots to emerge.

Some seeds, such as coconuts, travel on water (again, encased in the fruit). Others are so tiny and lightweight that they can be carried by the wind. A dandelion is one example of a plant whose seeds are dispersed by the wind. Some seeds, such as the touch-me-not, are ballistically propelled several metres from the plant. One species of tree in Africa can throw its seeds over 60 m.

Seed Germination

When conditions are favourable, the plant embryo within a seed begins to grow. This process is called **germination**. Most seeds must soak up water in order to germinate. By taking up water, the seed expands and splits its seed coat. The water also triggers metabolic changes in the embryo that enable it to grow.

If you have ever tried to grow garden vegetables, you may have noticed that simply exposing the seeds to a warm, moist environment was often enough. But the conditions for germination vary among plant species. Some plants have more particular requirements. For example, some desert plants germinate only after a heavy rainfall. This allows the seedling to push more easily through the moistened soil, and ensures at least a temporary water supply that can be used by its growing tissues. In climates with harsh winters, some seeds will germinate only after being exposed to a long period of cold. This prevents them from germinating during a warm spell in the middle of winter. Some seeds require exposure to the intense heat of a brush fire before germinating. The fire clears dense shrubs and other growth that would otherwise shade and compete with the seedling.

After breaking out of the seed coat, the journey of a plant shoot through the soil to the surface is a difficult one. Sand and other hard particles in soil are abrasive to new plant tissues sliding past them. Plants have adaptations that protect the developing shoot as it grows toward the surface. For example, some dicots have a hooked shoot tip (Figure 14.13(a), next page). This protects the delicate shoot tip by holding it downward as the shoot moves through the soil. As the shoot breaks through the soil surface, its tip is lifted gently out of the soil and straightens out.

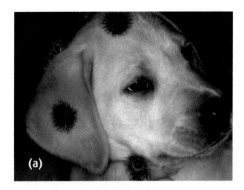

Figure 14.12 Seeds are dispersed in different ways. Seeds may be (a) inside spiny fruit that hitch a ride on animals, (b) inside tasty fruit and dispersed after passing through an animal's body, (c) dispersed by the wind, or (d) ballistically propelled by the fruit.

In most monocots, a sheath surrounding the shoot pushes straight upward, breaking through the soil (Figure 14.13(b)). The delicate shoot then grows upward through this protective tunnel. After emerging into the light, the first leaves expand from the shoot and begin making food by photosynthesis. At this stage, the young plant is called a seedling.

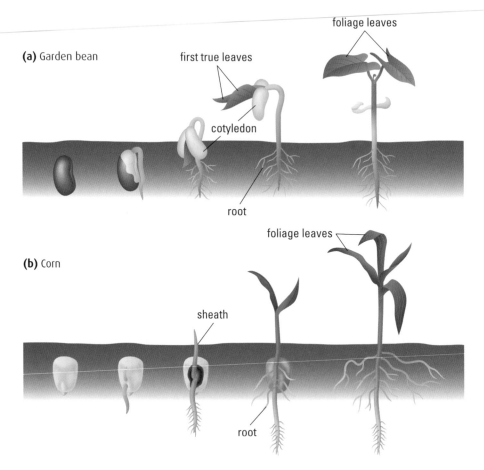

(a) Garden bean

foliage leaves

first true leaves

cotyledon

root

(b) Corn

foliage leaves

sheath

root

Figure 14.13 A range of adaptations protects plants during germination. (a) In some dicots, such as beans, the shoot tip avoids travelling "face-first" by being hooked downwards as it moves through the soil. (b) In some monocots, such as corn, a protective sheath penetrates the soil ahead of the shoot.

Figure 14.14 Strawberry plants reproduce vegetatively via runners.

BIOLOGY•SOURCE

Suggested Activity
• E4 Inquiry Activity Overview on page 391

Vegetative Reproduction

In addition to sexual reproduction, many plants are also capable of asexual reproduction. Asexual reproduction in plants is called **vegetative reproduction**. The offspring, or clones, produced during vegetative reproduction are genetically identical to the original plant.

Vegetative reproduction can occur naturally or with human help. Some plants, such as cacti, drop stems or other shoots that establish new roots and become clones. Other plants, such as strawberry plants and many grasses, send out runners (Figure 14.14). Some trees and shrubs send out shoots from the base of their trunks or from underground stems. These clones may persist long after the original plant dies.

The simplest way to clone a plant is to cut off a leaf or stem and place the cut end in water or soil. In many plants, the cells at the cut end of the petiole or stem become undifferentiated and then form new plant tissues and organs. The result is the formation of a new plant, genetically identical to the original one.

Biologists have been growing plants from single cells in the laboratory for over 50 years. Unlike animal cells, many plant cells, grown under the right conditions, are capable of forming all the tissues and organs of the adult plant. The first plants to be cloned in this way were carrots.

Individual cells taken from a carrot root and grown in culture medium developed into new carrot plants, all genetically identical to the original plant. Vegetative reproduction gives us a way to propagate useful crops or decorative plants, without needing to wait for seeds produced by the desired plant to develop. It also ensures that plants will be genetically identical with the desired traits.

In many woody species, a branch from one plant can be grafted onto the stem of another plant belonging to the same or a closely related species. **Grafting** is widely used by fruit growers, allowing them to combine a high-quality fruit-bearing stem with a tough and hardy root or to put several varieties of a fruit on one plant (Figure 14.15).

Figure 14.15 (a) Shoots of several varieties of apples can be grafted onto a trunk, resulting in (b) a plant with several varieties of fruit.

Concept Check

1. Describe three methods of seed dispersal.

2. Explain how two different adaptations of seed germination in dicots and monocots protect the developing shoot.

3. Give two examples of vegetative reproduction in plants.

A Plant's Main Tissue Systems

Plants have three main tissue systems: dermal, vascular, and ground tissue systems. Figure 14.16 shows the three tissue systems as they occur in a young, non-woody plant.

Dermal Tissue

The **dermal tissue** is the outer covering or "skin" of the plant. The **epidermis**, the dermal tissue of non-woody organs, such as young roots, consists of one or more layers of cells. The epidermis covers and protects all the young parts of the plant. Some epidermis is specialized. For example, the epidermis of leaves and stems secretes a waxy cuticle, an adaptation that helps plants retain water. Many plant species have epidermal hairs that trap or poison insects, protecting the plant from insect herbivores.

Located in the epidermis of leaves and some other tissues are pores called **stomata** (plural, stoma). Gas and water exchange between the environment and the interior of the plant occurs through stoma.

Vascular Tissue

Vascular tissue transports water, mineral nutrients, and organic molecules between roots and shoots. Vascular tissue also contributes to the structural support of the plant. There are two types of vascular tissue. **Xylem** transports water and dissolved minerals upward from roots into shoots. **Phloem** transports food made in mature leaves to the roots and the parts of the shoot system that don't carry out photosynthesis, such as developing leaves, flowers, and fruits.

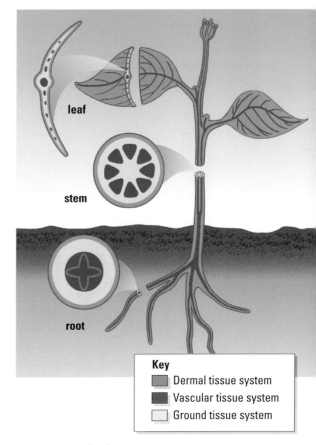

Key
- ■ Dermal tissue system
- ■ Vascular tissue system
- □ Ground tissue system

Figure 14.16 The three main tissue systems are present throughout a plant.

Vascular tissue is located in the centres of roots, but in the stems it is arranged in many separate strands called vascular bundles. A monocot stem has vascular bundles scattered throughout its tissue. The vascular bundles of a dicot stem are arranged in a ring (Figure 14.17).

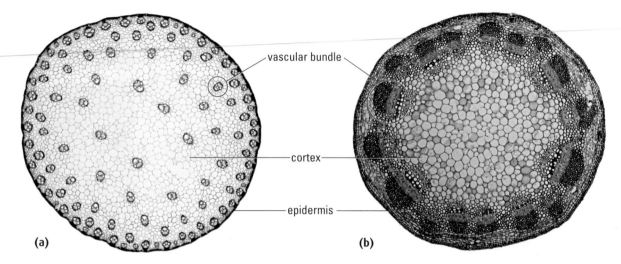

(a)

(b)

Figure 14.17 As viewed in cross section, (a) the vascular bundles of a monocot stem are scattered throughout the ground tissue. (magnification 5×) (b) In contrast, the vascular tissues of a dicot stem are organized in a ring. (magnification 10×)

Ground Tissue

Filling the spaces between the dermal and vascular tissues is **ground tissue.** It makes up most of a young, non-woody plant and functions in photosynthesis in the shoot and in storage and support throughout the plant. The ground tissue of the root consists primarily of a mass of cells called the **cortex.**

Types of Plant Cells

The plant tissues you have been reading about are made up of three basic cell types: parenchyma, collenchyma, and sclerenchyma (Figure 14.18). The most abundant type of cell, the **parenchyma** cell, has thin cell walls and, typically, large central vacuoles. These cells perform a variety of functions in the plant, including food storage, photosynthesis, and cellular respiration. Fruits are made up mostly of parenchyma cells. The food-conducting cells of phloem are also parenchyma cells.

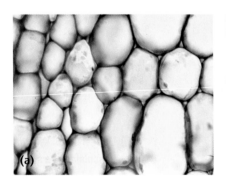
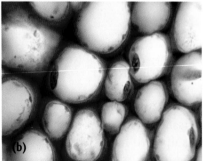
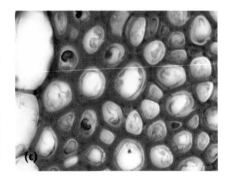

Figure 14.18 Plant tissues consist of three basic cell types. (a) Parenchyma cells have thin cell walls. (magnification 150×) (b) Collenchyma cells have unevenly thickened cell walls. (magnification 250×) (c) Sclerenchyma cells have lignin-rich cell walls. (magnification 275×)

Collenchyma cells have unevenly thickened cell walls. Grouped in strands or cylinders, collenchyma cells provide support in parts of the plant that are still growing. Young stems and petioles often have collenchyma just below their surface. The "strings" of a celery stalk, for example, are collenchyma. These living cells elongate with the stems and leaves they support as these regions grow.

Sclerenchyma cells are specialized for support. Sclerenchyma cells grow and then die within a mature part of a plant. But that does not mean they become useless to the plant after dying. Their lignin-rich cell walls are left behind, creating a "skeleton" that supports the plant. For example, the water-conducting cells of xylem are specialized sclerenchyma cells.

It is important to note that a particular type of plant tissue is not made up of just one type of plant cell. For example, a celery stalk is mostly parenchyma, but collenchyma forms the long strands. Sclerenchyma makes the gritty texture you feel when you bite into the mostly parenchyma fruit of a pear.

The Cellular Structure of a Leaf

Leaves are designed to capture sunlight and allow gas exchange between the surrounding air and the cells inside the leaf that carry out photosynthesis. The upper and lower surfaces of the leaf are covered by tightly packed epidermal cells (Figure 14.19). These cells are covered by a waxy cuticle, reducing the amount of water that is lost by the leaf. The epidermal layer on the lower surface of the leaf contains stomata flanked by guard cells. The **guard cells** regulate the opening and closing of the stomata, controlling the diffusion of gases into the leaf and the loss of water vapour from the leaf.

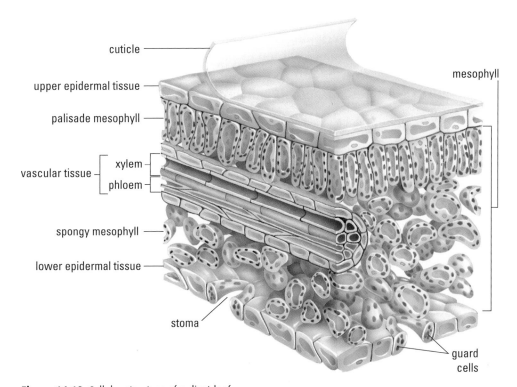

Figure 14.19 Cellular structure of a dicot leaf

The ground tissue of the leaf is made of mesophyll, a type of parenchyma cell that is specialized for gas exchange. Dicots have two layers of mesophyll cells. Under the upper epidermis is a layer of elongated **palisade mesophyll** cells that are specialized for capturing light energy and carrying out photosynthesis. Next to the lower epidermis is a layer of loosely packed **spongy mesophyll** cells, also called **aerenchyma**. Air spaces within the spongy mesophyll allow carbon dioxide and oxygen to circulate within the leaf. These spaces are particularly large in the region above the stomata, to allow gas exchange with the air outside the leaf.

Concept Check

1. List the functions of dermal, ground, and vascular tissues.
2. Describe characteristics of the three main plant cell types.
3. Which cell types provide structural support to the plant body?

Comparing Monocots and Dicots

The oldest angiosperm fossils are 125 million years old, dating from the Cretaceous period, when dinosaurs roamed Earth. Angiosperms are a very successful group of plants, making up about 90 percent of known plant species. Several evolutionary lines of flowering plants arose from the first angiosperms, but two groups have been extremely successful: the monocots and the dicots. The evolutionary lines leading to monocots and dicots separated soon after the origin of the angiosperms. Together, these two groups represent the great majority (97 percent) of modern flowering plants.

The terms monocot and dicot refer to the presence of one or two cotyledons, in the developing embryo. Table 14.1 summarizes the differences between monocots and dicots, as discussed in this section.

Table 14.1 Features of Monocots and Dicots

Feature	Monocots	Dicots
Cotyledons	One	Two
Roots	Fibrous root system	Taproot system
Leaf venation	Parallel veins	Netted veins
Leaf mesophyll	One type of mesophyll	Palisade and spongy mesophyll
Flower parts	Multiples of 3	Multiples of 4 or 5
Developing shoot	Protected by sheath	Hooked
Vascular bundles in stem	Scattered	Arranged in a ring
Secondary growth	Absent	Often present

©P

Plant Propagation

Question

What part of a plant — leaf, stem, or root — regenerates most readily into a new plant?

Activity Overview

In this activity, you will cut leaves, stems, and roots from several plants and place the cuttings in water and in various commercial rooting solutions. You will determine which cuttings are able to form new plant organs.

Your teacher will give you a copy of the full activity.

Prelab Questions

Consider the questions below before beginning this activity.

1. How does a plant benefit from the ability to propagate from a cutting?

2. Do you expect plant propagation to be more successful from leaves, stems, or roots?

3. What ingredients do you think are put in commercial rooting solutions?

Making Hand Sections of Plants

Activity Overview

In this activity, you will learn how to make cross sections of plant structures by hand.

Your teacher will give you a copy of the full activity.

DI Key Activity

E6 Inquiry Activity

BIOLOGY•SOURCE

REQUIRED SKILLS
- Drawing conclusions
- Reporting results

The Structure of Plant Roots, Stems, and Leaves

Question

How is structure related to function in the cells and tissues of plant roots, stems, and leaves?

Activity Overview

In this activity, you will cut and stain a thin cross section of a young celery petiole and view cross section slides of a buttercup (*Ranunculus*) root and a lilac (*Syringa*) leaf. You will identify the cells and tissues that make up each organ (Figure 14.20).

Your teacher will give you a copy of the full activity.

Prelab Questions

Consider the questions below before beginning this activity.

1. Look at the leaves on a celery petiole and determine whether it is a monocot or a dicot. What arrangement of vascular tissue do you expect to see in this cross section?

2. Name three tissues that you will find in both celery and buttercup cross sections.

3. What tissues do you expect to see in the dicot leaf?

Figure 14.20 Cross section of a celery petiole (magnification 10×)

Key Concept Review

1. Set up a table, similar to the one below, listing plant organs and their functions. For each plant organ, describe one structural feature that supports one of its functions.

Plant Structure and Function

Plant Organ	Function	Structural Feature

2. Give an example of
(a) a modified leaf
(b) a modified shoot

3. Name the four rings of modified leaves that make up a flower. State the function of each ring.

4. Name the male and female gametophytes of an angiosperm.

5. List four ways that seeds can be dispersed, and give an example of each.

6. Explain why each of the following statements is incomplete or incorrect.
(a) Within the ovaries of a flower, meiosis produces spores that develop into pollen grains.
(b) Putting a seed in a warm, moist environment will cause it to germinate.

7. Explain the role of endosperm and cotyledon(s) in nourishing a young plant embryo.

8. Young seedlings are adapted to grow through soil without damage to the young shoot. Describe one such adaptation in
(a) monocots
(b) dicots

9. Prepare a table listing the three major tissue systems of plants and stating their structural features and basic functions.

10. In your notebook, set up a table like the one below to show the differences between monocot and dicot structures.

Monocot and Dicot Structures

	Monocot	Dicot
Roots		
Stems		
Leaves		
Flowers		
Seeds		

Connect Your Understanding

11. Describe how plant cloning and grafting are used in agriculture and horticulture.

12. Biologists generally define animal tissue as a unit of many similar cells that perform a specific function. How does this definition of a tissue contrast with what biologists call a "tissue system" in plants?

13. For each photograph below, identify the plant as a monocot or dicot. Give as many reasons as you can for each answer.

(a)   (b)   (c)   (d)

Question 13 ((c) magnification 20×)

Reflection

14. How has your understanding of plant reproduction changed after reading this section?

For more questions, go to BIOLOGY•SOURCE

14.2 Primary and Secondary Growth in Plants

Section Summary

- Primary growth increases the length of plant roots and shoots.
- Secondary growth increases the thickness of woody plants.
- Meristems generate new dermal, vascular, and ground tissue.

The timing of growth and development of parts of a plant is highly dependent on the environment. A whole plant can die, but sometimes only part of the plant dies. If you place your house plant in a shady part of the living room, it may lose half of its leaves. But it can grow more leaves when you put it in the sunny spot near the window.

While you will reach your adult size and stop growing sometime within the next few years, most plants continue to grow their entire lives. This lifelong growth allows plants to modify the growth of their roots and shoots to increase their access to water, soil minerals, and sunlight.

Meristems and Growth

Plants, grow in two ways: in length and in girth, or thickness (Figure 14.21). **Primary growth** accounts for a plant's lengthwise growth from root and shoot tips. Stems and roots of many plants also increase in girth. Growth in girth is called **secondary growth**. While all plants undergo primary growth, only woody dicots undergo secondary growth.

Figure 14.21 Plants undergo primary growth in length and secondary growth in width.

Tissues called **meristems** generate new dermal, vascular, and ground tissue in plants throughout their lives. A meristem consists of groups of cells that divide by mitosis, generating new cells that will later differentiate into one of the three main cell types: parenchyma, collenchyma, and sclerenchyma.

Meristems have roles in both primary and secondary growth. In primary growth, meristems located in the tips of roots and buds of shoots are called **apical meristems**. Apical meristems produce the new cells that enable a plant to grow in length, both above and below ground, as well as to branch.

Figure 14.22 Grasses can be mown without damaging their meristems.

The shoots of some monocots, such as grasses, have **intercalary meristems** at the base of each internode, causing continual elongation of the grass plant. Intercalary meristems cause blades of grass to grow from their base rather than their tips, which is why lawns need regular mowing (Figure 14.22). In secondary growth, two types of meristems, vascular cambium and cork cambium, produce tissue that increases the girth of trees and other woody plants.

Primary growth

Primary growth allows roots to grow toward soil nutrients and water, and allows shoots to gain access to sunlight. Perennial herbs regrow each spring by primary growth, after the shoot system dies back in the winter.

Primary Growth of Roots

The very tip of the root is the **root cap**, a cone of cells that protects the delicate, actively dividing cells of the apical meristem. The root's apical meristem has two roles: it replaces the cells of the root cap that are scraped away by the soil, and it produces the cells for primary growth.

Cells produced during primary growth form three concentric cylinders of developing tissue (Figure 14.23). The outermost cylinder develops into the epidermis (dermal tissue) of the root. The middle cylinder is the bulk of the root tip. It develops into the root's cortex (ground tissue). The innermost cylinder becomes the vascular tissue.

Primary growth depends not only on the addition of new cells by the apical meristem, but on those new cells getting longer. The new cells become longer mainly by taking up water. This process of elongation is what actually forces the root tip through the soil.

BIOLOGY•SOURCE

Explore More

What is inside a root and how does it grow?

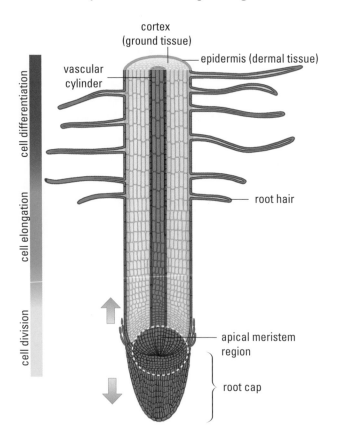

Figure 14.23 New root cells are generated in the apical meristem. Those cells produced toward the bottom of the meristem replenish root cap cells. Those toward the top differentiate into cells of the dermal, ground, and vascular tissue, lengthening the root.

Primary Growth of Shoots

A shoot's apical meristem is a dome-shaped mass of dividing cells at the very tip of the terminal bud (Figure 14.24). Elongation occurs just below this meristem. The elongating cells push the apical meristem upward, instead of downward as in the root.

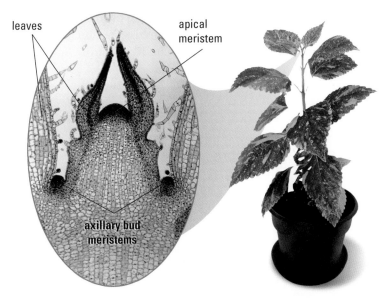

leaves

apical meristem

axillary bud meristems

Figure 14.24 The micrograph of the tip of a *Coleus* plant shows the tightly packed cells characteristic of a meristem. (magnification 30×)

As the apical meristem advances upward, some of its cells are left behind. These pockets of meristematic cells form axillary buds at the bases of new leaves. Axillary buds give rise to branches, which also show primary growth as they grow outward from the main stem. As in the root, the apical meristem forms three concentric cylinders of developing tissue. Similarly, each cylinder in the shoot develops into one of the shoot's three main tissue systems — dermal, ground, or vascular tissues.

Concept Check

1. Draw a simple non-woody plant and label the locations of its meristems.

2. Compare and contrast primary growth in a root and a shoot.

3. Describe the function of the root cap.

Secondary Growth

Secondary growth occurs only in woody dicots such as vines, shrubs, and trees. Monocots do not undergo secondary growth. Thousands of useful products are made from wood — from construction lumber to fine furniture and musical instruments. Wood is the result of secondary growth. Therefore, much of Canada's economy is dependent on secondary growth. Secondary growth involves cell division in two meristematic tissues, called vascular cambium and cork cambium.

BIOLOGY•SOURCE

Suggested Activity

• E7 Inquiry Activity Overview on page 398

Vascular Cambium

The **vascular cambium** is a cylinder of actively dividing cells located between the xylem and phloem. The vascular cambium adds cells on both sides, producing **secondary xylem** toward the inside of the stem and **secondary phloem** toward the outside of the stem (Figure 14.25). This secondary vascular tissue is added to the primary xylem and primary phloem produced by the apical meristem during primary growth. The secondary xylem that is laid down in the growing season of each year accumulates as wood. In a temperate climate like that of Ontario, the vascular cambium is dormant during winter.

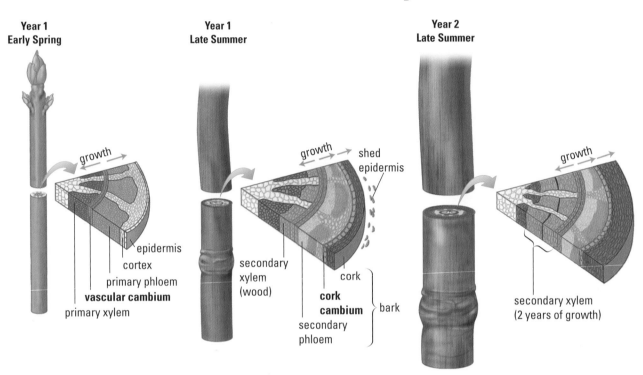

Figure 14.25 Cell division in the vascular cambium and cork cambium contributes to secondary growth.

Figure 14.26 The tree bark has grown around this sign.

With each added layer of xylem, the stem or the root thickens. Remember that secondary growth makes a tree thicker, but not taller. Over time, any object sitting beside a tree or nailed to it will get incorporated into it (Figure 14.26). Woody plants continue to grow in height via apical meristems.

People first became aware of the role of phloem in moving sugar within trees by examining trees that had been girdled. Girdling occurs when a complete ring of bark is removed from the trunk circumference. When an actively growing and photosynthesizing tree is girdled, the bark above the cut area swells as phloem sap accumulates. The trunk and roots of the tree below the cut area are deprived of food, and the tree dies. Girdling is caused by gnawing animals, such as rabbits and rodents, or by humans when a wire or rope is tied too tightly around the tree trunk.

Cork Cambium

As secondary growth begins and the stem or root thickens, the original soft dermal tissue and cortex cells of the young stem are shed. A meristem called **cork cambium** develops from parenchyma cells in the remaining cortex (Figure 14.27). It produces a tough outer layer of **cork**. As these cork cells die, they leave behind thick, waxy walls that help prevent water loss from the stem. Cork also functions as a barrier that helps protect the internal tissues from physical damage and pathogens.

Figure 14.27 A cross section through a tree trunk reveals different layers of tissues. (Note that in the drawing, colours are used to distinguish the different layers.) Sapwood is new xylem that is still actively transporting water. Heartwood is old xylem that no longer transports water.

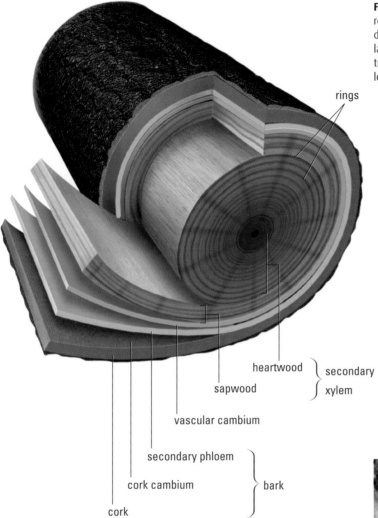

- rings
- heartwood } secondary xylem
- sapwood
- vascular cambium
- secondary phloem } bark
- cork cambium
- cork

BIOLOGY•SOURCE

Explore More

What is cork, and how can it be grown and harvested sustainably?

Everything outside of the vascular cambium is called **bark**: the phloem, cork cambium, and cork. The older phloem dies as it is pushed outward. Along with the cork, this dead phloem helps protect the stem until the bark is shed. This dead tissue is harvested from the cork oak to make corks for bottles, cork flooring, and other cork products (Figure 14.28).

The cork cambium produces a steady supply of new cork, keeping pace with growth from the vascular cambium. Because cork cambium is shed with the rest of the bark, new cork cambium continuously regenerates from parenchyma cells in the still-living phloem left behind.

Figure 14.28 Cork is sustainably harvested from the cork oak by removing the outer layer of bark.

Using Xylem to Determine the Age of Trees

Examining an old tree trunk in cross section enables you to "read" the history of the plant. You can estimate the tree's age by counting its annual growth rings. These rings result from the yearly activity of the vascular cambium. Environmental conditions during the growing season affect xylem growth. The vascular cambium produces xylem cells that can carry a lot of water — cells that are large and thin-walled — when temperatures are cool and water is plentiful, as in the typical spring. In contrast, the vascular cambium produces narrow, thick-walled cells under hot, dry conditions, as in the typical summer. Each tree ring represents a year's growth. It consists of a cylinder of spring wood surrounded by a cylinder of denser summer wood. Differences in ring width reveal the variation in weather patterns from year to year, such as a particularly wet or dry spring.

Concept Check

1. What two tissues does the meristematic vascular cambium tissue produce?

2. Describe how the cork cambium protects a woody plant.

3. In which tissue of a tree trunk are tree rings formed? Describe how tree rings can be used to determine a tree's age.

REQUIRED SKILLS
- Drawing conclusions
- Reporting results

The Secondary Tissues of a Woody Stem

Question

What secondary tissues are present in a woody stem of *Tilia*, the basswood tree?

Activity Overview

You will use a compound microscope to examine prepared slides of a basswood (*Tilia*) stem, drawing and labelling the cells and tissues of the woody stem (Figure 14.29).

Your teacher will give you a copy of the full activity.

Prelab Questions

Consider the questions below before beginning this activity.

1. What is the difference between primary and secondary xylem and phloem?

2. Which tissue provides structural support for a woody plant?

3. What tissues make up bark?

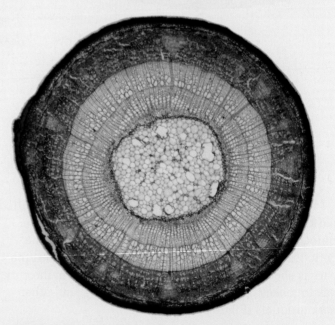

Figure 14.29 Cross section of the stem of a young basswood tree.

Key Concept Review

1. Name and describe the structure that protects the tip of a growing root.

2. Describe how elongation occurs during the primary growth of roots and shoots.

3. Describe the two roles of the root's apical meristem in primary growth.

4. Identify and describe the two types of tissue generated by the vascular cambium that contribute to secondary growth.

5. Distinguish between the location and function of apical meristems, vascular cambium, and cork cambium.

6. Examine the photo below of a root cross section and identify tissues A–C.

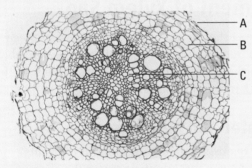

Question 6 (magnification 30×)

Connect Your Understanding

7. Explain why meristems are important to:
   (a) plant growth
   (b) Canada's economy

8. Describe how mitosis and cell elongation combine to produce primary growth.

9. Explain why each of the following statements is incomplete or incorrect.
   (a) Tree trunks are made of dead cells.
   (b) Once cork cambium is shed with the rest of the bark, new cork cannot be formed.

10. Secondary growth occurs only in woody dicots.
    (a) Compare the arrangement of vascular bundles in monocot and dicot stems.
    (b) Using this information explain why secondary growth does not occur in monocot stems.

11. Examine the cross section of a tree trunk below.

Question 11

(a) Approximately how old was this tree when it was cut down?
(b) Match the letters on the photograph with the descriptions below, and explain each choice.
   i) In this year, there was probably a drought.
   ii) In this year, spring was long and wet, and summer was short and hot.

12. Suppose two trees were damaged by two different bark-eating animals. The first animal ate a ring of bark all the way around the tree. The second animal ate the same amount of bark as the first, but peeled it off as a vertical strip. Did the two animals do the same amount of damage to the trees? Explain your answer. **Question 12**

13. Use a Venn diagram to compare the growth of plants and animals.

Reflection

14. After reading this section, how has your understanding of how plants grow changed?

For more questions, go to   *BIOLOGY•SOURCE*

Section Summary

- Root hairs and mycorrhizae increase the surface area of roots, helping them to absorb water and inorganic ions from soil.
- Root pressure and transpiration-pull are responsible for the upward movement of xylem sap within a plant.
- Leaf stomata open and close to regulate leaf transpiration and the movement of gases into and out of the leaf.
- Phloem sap moves through sieve-tube members from sugar sources to sugar sinks by the pressure-flow mechanism.

From the outside, a tree trunk appears silent and unmoving, hardly even alive. But there is lots of activity inside. If you placed a stethoscope on a tree trunk in the early spring just before leaves appeared, you would hear the whoosh of sap running through the tree.

The Upward Movement of Xylem Sap

The tallest trees in Ontario are eastern white pines. The tallest of these trees stretch 50 m from soil to treetop. It is quite a feat that trees are able to carry water and nutrients, against the pull of gravity, from the soil, into their roots, and up their trunks into their leaves.

How Roots Absorb Water and Minerals

One function of plant roots is to absorb water and mineral nutrients from the soil. **Root hairs** are one way that plants increase the absorption of water and minerals. Root hairs are the tiny outgrowths of the root's epidermal cells (Figure 14.30). They increase the root's surface area, growing into the spaces between soil particles and greatly increasing absorption. In addition, the roots of most vascular plants form a symbiotic association with fungi called mycorrhizae. This association increases the ability of the root to absorb water and inorganic ions, especially phosphate. As much as 3 m of fungal hyphae (filaments) can extend from each centimetre along a root.

Once the water gets inside the root, two main forces operate in moving water upward from the roots and throughout the plant. They usually operate at different times of the day.

Root Pressure Push

The first force, called **root pressure**, helps push water up the xylem and usually operates at night. Cells in the root's epidermis and ground tissue use energy from a chemical called adenosine triphosphate (ATP) to accumulate certain minerals. The minerals then move from cell to cell through specialized channels and eventually enter the xylem. Surrounding the vascular tissue is a layer of cells called the **endodermis**.

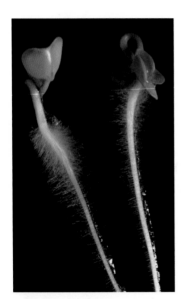

Figure 14.30 Tiny root hairs give each of these radish roots a white, fuzzy appearance. The root hairs increase the root's ability to absorb water and mineral nutrients.

Epidermal cells have waxy cell walls that prevent water and minerals from leaking back out of the xylem. As minerals accumulate in the xylem, water follows by osmosis. **Osmosis** is the diffusion of water across a cell membrane. The osmotic movement of water builds up a positive root pressure. This pressure forces water and minerals up the xylem, pushing xylem sap upward.

Transpiration Pull

Root pressure accounts for only a small part of the sap's upward movement. To get water to the top of the plant, another stronger force is involved. Rather than push water up the plant from the bottom, this force pulls it from the top. Drinking water with a straw is a useful analogy: the suction you create at the top is a pulling force somewhat like the pulling force in plants. In plants, transpiration generates the pull. It is the loss of water through leaves due to evaporation. This force, called **transpiration-pull**, is greatest during the day when transpiration rates are higher (Figure 14.31). Transpiration can pull xylem sap up a tree because of two properties of water: cohesion and adhesion.

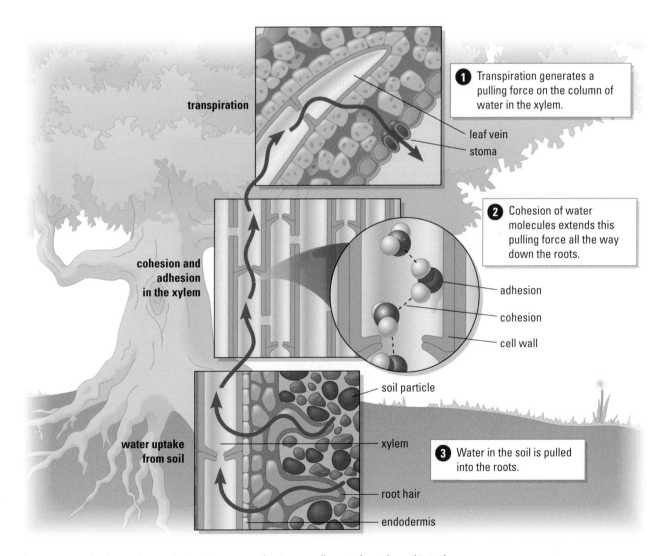

transpiration

1 Transpiration generates a pulling force on the column of water in the xylem.

leaf vein

stoma

cohesion and adhesion in the xylem

2 Cohesion of water molecules extends this pulling force all the way down the roots.

adhesion

cohesion

cell wall

soil particle

water uptake from soil

xylem

3 Water in the soil is pulled into the roots.

root hair

endodermis

Figure 14.31 The force of transpiration is so strong that it can pull water from the soil into the roots and all the way up the tree.

Cohesion and Adhesion

Cohesion is the tendency of molecules of the same kind to stick to one another. Water is a highly cohesive molecule, because areas of slight negative charge near the oxygen atom on one water molecule are attracted to areas of slight positive charge near the hydrogen atoms on other water molecules. These attractions are called hydrogen bonds. In water, hydrogen bonds make the water molecules stick to one another. The water molecules in the xylem tubes form continuous chains, extending all the way from the leaves down to the roots.

Adhesion is the attraction between unlike molecules. Water molecules adhere, or stick to, cellulose molecules in the xylem walls. This assists the upward movement of xylem sap by counteracting the downward pull of gravity. Adhesion also prevents water from falling back down to the roots at night when transpiration rates are lower.

Xylem Cells

Water travels through the plant in two types of xylem cells. **Tracheids** are long cells with tapered ends. **Vessel elements** are wider, shorter cells with less tapered ends. The ends of tracheids or vessel elements overlap, forming tubes (Figure 14.32). The tubes are hollow because the cells have died. Only their cell walls, strengthened and stiffened by lignin, remain to form the walls of the tubes. Water passes from cell to cell through holes, called pits, in these cell walls and through openings in the end walls of vessel elements.

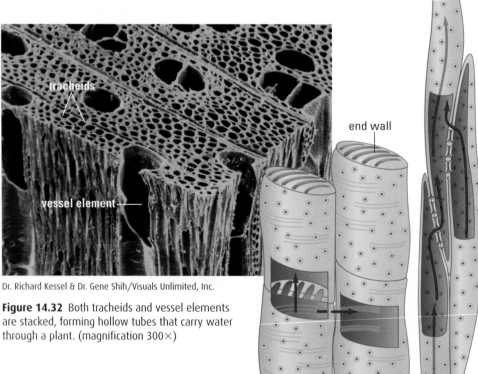

Dr. Richard Kessel & Dr. Gene Shih/Visuals Unlimited, Inc.

Figure 14.32 Both tracheids and vessel elements are stacked, forming hollow tubes that carry water through a plant. (magnification 300×)

©P

In Ontario and Quebec, we take advantage of the movement of xylem sap when we collect maple sap. In the early spring, sugary sap moves into the xylem as it is transported to leaf buds. Taps are placed in the tree xylem to collect sap, which is then boiled into syrup (Figure 14.33). Spring is the only time of the year when xylem transports sugars, and it occurs only in maples and a few other species.

Figure 14.33 Sap is collected from sugar maple trees and boiled into maple syrup.

Regulating Water Loss

Transpiration is required for the upward movement of water and minerals from the roots to the leaves. It also results in evaporative cooling. Cooling prevents leaves from reaching temperatures that could break down the enzymes important to photosynthesis. Transpiration, however, causes a tremendous loss of water from the plant. An average-sized maple tree, for instance, loses more than 220 L of water per hour during the summer. As long as water moves up from the soil fast enough to replace the water that is lost, this amount of transpiration presents no problem. But if transpiration exceeds the rate of water delivery to the leaves, the leaves will wilt. You have probably observed this result if you have ever forgotten to water a house plant. A plant can withstand wilting for a short time, but eventually, without a sufficient supply of water to the roots, the plant will die.

Most transpirational water loss takes place from leaf stomata, which are pores located in the epidermis of leaves. Stomata are adaptations that help plants regulate their transpiration and adjust to changing environmental conditions. The stomata can open and close, affecting the movement of gases in and out of the leaf. A pair of guard cells around each stoma open and close the stoma by changing shape.

During the day, the stomata of most plants are open, allowing carbon dioxide required for photosynthesis to enter. Sunlight and low carbon dioxide levels within the leaf cue the guard cells to actively accumulate potassium ions (K^+) from surrounding cells (Figure 14.34). Due to osmosis, water follows the potassium ions into the guard cells. As water moves into the guard cells, the guard cells swell. The swollen guard cells buckle away from their centres in such a way that a gap called the stoma opens between them.

stoma opening

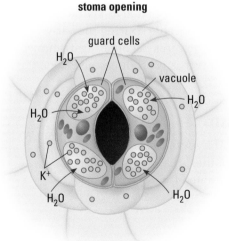

stoma closing

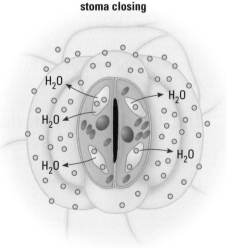

Figure 14.34 Water follows potassium ions from surrounding cells into guard cells, causing them to bulge and push apart at their centres. This forms a gap, opening the stoma. The flow of potassium ions and water out of the guard cells causes them to sag together, closing the stoma.

Stomata typically close at night or when the plant is losing water from transpiration at a faster rate than it is gaining water from the soil. Potassium ions are lost from the guard cells, and water follows. The guard cells sag together as they lose water pressure, closing the stoma.

Concept Check

1. Explain why root pressure is a pushing force.
2. Explain why transpiration is a pulling force.
3. How do stomata open and close?

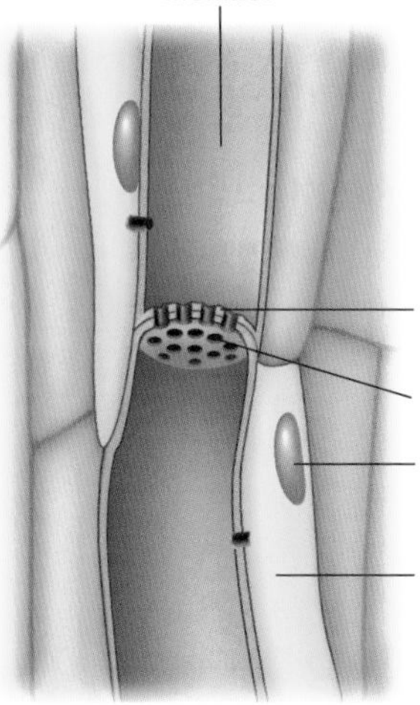

sieve-tube member

sieve plate

pore

nucleus

companion cell

Figure 14.35 Sieve tubes carry phloem sap from sugar sources to sugar sinks.

The Flow of Phloem Sap

The phloem of vascular tissue transports sugar and other organic compounds along with water in a process called **translocation**. The stream of phloem sap moves by bulk flow through chains of cells called **sieve-tube members**. The end walls of these cells are like sieves, allowing the flow of fluid through pores (Figure 14.35). The chain of end-to-end cells forms a sieve tube. In contrast to the xylem cells, sieve-tube members remain alive. However, as they mature, sieve-tube members lose their nuclei and some other organelles. This means they lose the ability to perform some of their necessary cellular functions. **Companion cells** alongside sieve-tube members provide proteins and other resources to the sieve-tube members.

From Source to Sink

Phloem moves sugars from where they are made or stored to where they are used. Sugar sources are sites where sugar is either produced through photosynthesis or where it is released from storage. Mature leaves and root tubers are sugar sources. Phloem moves sugar from a sugar source to a part of the plant where the sugar will be used or stored, called a sugar sink. Roots, developing shoot tips, and fruits are examples of sugar sinks.

Within a plant, the location of sugar sources and sinks can change with the seasons. For example, some storage structures such as beet taproots or potato tubers are sugar sinks during the summer. These plants stockpile sugars, stored in complex carbohydrates such as starch, in these structures when growing conditions are favourable. During the early spring of the following year, these same structures become sugar sources. The plant consumes its stored carbohydrates as it produces new stems and leaves.

The Pressure-Flow Mechanism

Plant biologists have tested a number of hypotheses to explain the movement of phloem sap. The hypothesis called the **pressure-flow mechanism** is widely accepted today.

When sugar is produced in a source such as a mature leaf, ATP energy is used to transport materials across the cell membrane into a sieve-tube member of the phloem (Figure 14.36). This generates a high concentration of sugar at the source end of the phloem. Water follows the sugar into the phloem by osmosis. This generates higher water pressure at the source end than at the sink end of the phloem.

The reverse happens at the sink end. Sugars leave the sieve-tube members, water follows, and pressure is reduced. Water, like any fluid, flows from where its pressure is higher to where it is lower. This process is called the pressure-flow mechanism. The water is returned to the source via the xylem. In summary, the pressure-flow mechanism explains how sap flows through the phloem from areas of high sugar concentration and high water pressure to areas of low sugar concentration and low water pressure — from source to sink.

BIOLOGY·SOURCE

Take It Further

There are two types of wood: hardwoods are angiosperms, while softwoods are conifers. How does the structure of hardwood and softwood differ? Do the terms *hardwood* and *softwood* provide a suitable description of the differences between the two types of wood? Select a wood-based product, such as a rocking chair or paper, and explain why it is made with either softwood or hardwood (or both).

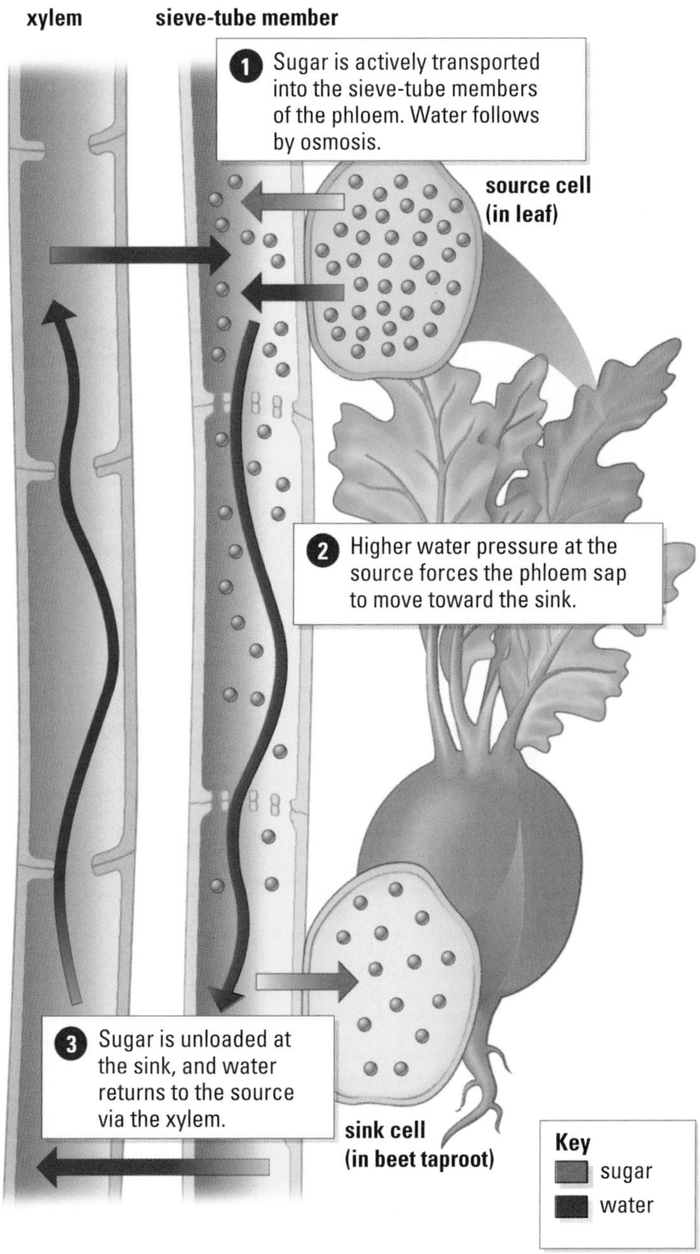

xylem   sieve-tube member

1 Sugar is actively transported into the sieve-tube members of the phloem. Water follows by osmosis.

source cell (in leaf)

2 Higher water pressure at the source forces the phloem sap to move toward the sink.

3 Sugar is unloaded at the sink, and water returns to the source via the xylem.

sink cell (in beet taproot)

Key
sugar
water

Figure 14.36 The pressure-flow mechanism explains how sugar moves from source (the leaf) to sink (the beet taproot).

Measuring Transpiration Rates

Question

Does the transpiration rate change in response to environmental variables such as light, wind, and humidity?

Activity Overview

In this investigation, you will perform an experiment to measure and compare the transpiration rates of leaves under varying environmental conditions, such as intense light, wind, or humidity.

Your teacher will give you a copy of the full activity.

Prelab Questions

Consider the questions below before beginning this activity.

1. What is transpiration?

2. What factors reduce the transpiration rate of leaves?

3. What factors increase the transpiration rate of leaves?

Observing Stoma and Guard Cells

Question

Under what environmental conditions do leaf stomata open or close?

Activity Overview

In this activity, you will make imprints of the bottom surfaces of leaves to observe stomata and guard cells.

Your teacher will give you a copy of the full activity.

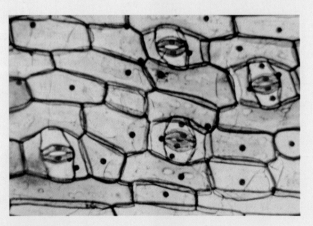

Figure 14.37 Stomata of a spiderwort plant (magnification 50×)

Prelab Questions

Consider the questions below before beginning this activity.

1. What is the function of a stoma?

2. Describe the mechanism that opens and closes stomata.

3. (a) How many stomata are shown in Figure 14.37?
   (b) Are they open or closed?

Key Concept Review

1. Describe two adaptations that increase the surface area available for plant roots to absorb water and minerals from the soil.

2. Explain the role of the following in the ascent of xylem sap within a plant.
   (a) cohesion and adhesion
   (b) tracheids and vessel elements

3. Describe how the guard cells around each stoma change shape to open and close the stomata.

4. Explain how the pressure-flow mechanism drives the flow of phloem sap from sugar source to sugar sink.

Connect Your Understanding

5. Compare and contrast the effects of root pressure and the pressure-flow mechanism.

6. Explain why each of the following statements is incomplete or incorrect.
   (a) Plants absorb proteins from the soil.
   (b) Mycorrhizae are parasitic fungal growths on plant roots.
   (c) Transpiration prevents a plant from wilting.

7. The table below shows temperature and rates of transpiration at different times of day.

Transpiration Rates

Time of Day	Temperature (°C)	Transpiration Rate (g/m²/h)
8 a.m.	14	57
10 a.m.	21	83
12 p.m.	27	161
2 p.m.	31	186
4 p.m.	29	137
6 p.m.	18	78

(a) Graph transpiration rate against temperature.
(b) Describe in words the apparent relationship between transpiration rate and temperature.
(c) Propose a hypothesis to explain why temperature affects transpiration rate in this way.

8. Examine the photo of a leaf and answer the questions below.
   (a) What kinds of sap do you expect to find in the veins of this leaf?
   (b) What direction do you expect each kind of sap will travel? Explain your predictions.

Question 8

9. Water loss by transpiration has been called a "necessary evil."
   (a) How does transpiration benefit a plant?
   (b) How can it harm a plant?

10. If a plant root is deprived of oxygen, will root pressure cease? Explain your answer.

11. The tracheids and vessel elements of xylem are dead at maturity, unlike the sieve-tube members of phloem.
    (a) Explain why tracheids and vessel elements can carry water and minerals up the stem of a plant, despite the fact that they are dead at maturity.
    (b) Would the pressure-flow mechanism of phloem sap movement be possible if sieve-tube members were dead at maturity? Explain your answer.

Reflection

12. It is easy to consider trees as being composed mostly of useless, dead wood. Explain how your view on the importance of wood has changed after reading this section.

For more questions, go to BIOLOGY•SOURCE

Key Concept Review

1. Name a specialized form of each of the following plant organs. Describe the function of each specialized organ.
   (a) root *k*
   (b) stem *k*
   (c) leaf *k*

2. Distinguish between each of the following pairs of terms.
   (a) node and internode *k*
   (b) axillary and terminal bud *k*
   (c) apical and intercalary meristem *k*

3. Name three functions of plant roots. Describe one structural feature of roots that enables them to perform each function. *k*

4. In your notebook, identify structures A–E shown on the flower drawing. State the function of each structure. *k*

Question 4

5. Describe the role of the stigma and the pollen tube in plant fertilization. *k*

6. Both palisade and spongy mesophyll are ground tissues in a plant leaf, but they differ in the arrangement of their cells. Describe these differences and explain their significance. *k*

7. Describe two adaptations of plant leaves that reduce water loss. *k*

8. Describe four methods of seed dispersal, giving one example of each.

9. In your notebook, identify the structures indicated in the monocot and dicot seeds. *k*

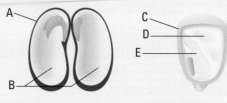

Question 9

10. List and briefly describe the three main tissue systems of plants. *k*

11. Describe three methods of vegetative reproduction in plants. *k*

12. Set up a table to compare the arrangement of vascular tissue in monocot and dicot leaves and stems. *k*

13. Why does girdling kill a tree? *k*

14. Explain the role of the following in stomatal opening and closing.
    (a) environmental factors *k*
    (b) K+ movements into and out of guard cells *k*

15. (a) List the raw materials that plants obtain from soil. *k*
    (b) Describe associations with soil organisms that assist plants in obtaining necessary raw materials. *k*

16. How do sieve-tube members function despite the loss of their nuclei at maturity? *k*

17. Is a beet root a sugar source or a sugar sink? Explain your answer. *k*

Connect Your Understanding

18. (a) How do plants and animals differ in their response to the environment? *k*
    (b) How does this influence the way plants grow? *a*

19. What is the role of each of the following structures in plant development?
    (a) endosperm *k*
    (b) cotyledon *k*
    (c) sheath covering monocot shoot *k*
    (d) seed coat *k*

20.

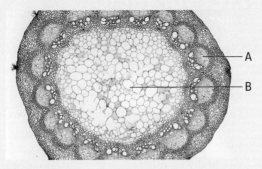

Question 20 (magnification 20×)

(a) In your notebook, identify the type of tissue shown at A and B. ⓚ

(b) Name the plant organ shown in the micrograph. What feature(s) of the cross section allowed you to identify this organ? ⓚ

(c) Is this plant a monocot or dicot? What feature(s) of the cross section allowed you to identify this plant? ⓚ

21. Some seeds germinate readily when they are placed in warm, moist soils. Other seeds require specific conditions such as scorching or a period of exposure to cold temperatures. Under what environmental conditions would plants benefit from having seeds

(a) that germinate readily? ⓐ

(b) germinate only after scorching? ⓐ

(c) germinate after cold temperatures? ⓐ

22. Explain what has happened to the tree in the photograph to the right. ⓚ

23. Identify the cells shown below. For each cell, explain how its structure is adaptive for its function. ⓚ

Question 22

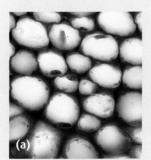
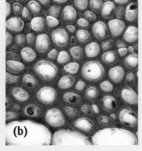

Question 23 (magnification 250× and 275×)

24. Explain why each of the following statements is incomplete or incorrect.

(a) Plant stomata are closed during the day to reduce transpirational water loss. ⓚ

(b) A stoma opens when the guard cells surrounding it lose water. ⓚ

25. Individuals, agriculture, and industry all complete for access to water, which is in short supply in some regions of Canada. An enormous amount of water can be lost by transpiration in a field of plants. One hectare of corn may transpire about three million litres of water over about a single growing season. The beautifully tended grass on a golf course loses equally large amounts of water by transpiration. Should golf courses be banned in all areas where water is in short supply? ⓐ

Reflection

26. Plants are made of different tissues with specialized functions. Has your view on the complexity of plants changed after reading this chapter? Explain your answer. ⓒ

Unit Task Link

Sketch your plant, labelling the stem, leaves, branches, nodes, internodes, axillary buds, and terminal buds. Consider the following questions:

• Is your species an angiosperm? If not, is it a conifer? a fern?

• If your plant is an angiosperm, is it a monocot or a dicot? How can you tell?

• What reproductive structures does your plant produce? Does it produce flowers? pollen grains? seeds?

• If your plant isn't an angiosperm, research how your plant reproduces.

• Does your plant show evidence of secondary growth? How can you tell?

For more questions, go to **BIOLOGY·SOURCE**

Plant growth is regulated by internal and external factors.

Learning Expectations

By the end of this chapter, you will:

Relating Science to Technology, Society, and the Environment

- evaluate, on the basis of research, ways in which different societies or cultures have used plants to sustain human populations while supporting environmental sustainability

Developing Skills of Investigation and Communication

- use appropriate terminology related to plants

- design and conduct an inquiry to determine the factors that affect plant growth

Understanding Basic Concepts

- describe the various factors that affect plant growth

Plants are surprisingly responsive to the world around them and to information from within their bodies. Consider the following three examples.

How does a tree shed its leaves if they are damaged by herbivores or as summer turns to fall? The leaf shedding mechanism is the same in both cases. A changing balance of hormones within the leaf and its petiole causes the leaf to drop. If a leaf is chewed by a deer or exposed to long nights and cool temperatures, the ratio between two hormones changes. This change sends a message to the leaf petiole that causes the leaf to detach from the branch and fall to the ground.

How does an apple tree always produce stalks just strong enough to support the apples that hang from its branches (Figure 15.1)? As the fruit develops, its increasing weight sends a message to the developing stalk. The heavier the apple, the more collenchyma and sclerenchyma cells develop in the stalk. These cells, with their thickened cell walls, are specialized for support. They ensure the fruit does not fall until it is ripe.

Why do plant stems always grow up and plant roots always grow down? The cells in plant roots contain organelles with dense starch grains. Gravity pulls these organelles down to the bottom of the cells and the root responds by producing hormones that direct growth in the right direction. In this chapter, we will consider how plant growth is regulated by internal and external factors.

Figure 15.1 Sturdy stalks support plump apples.

Section Summary

- Plant hormones regulate many functions in plants.
- Auxins, cytokinins, and gibberellins regulate plant growth.
- Abscisic acid (ABA) regulates dormancy in plants.
- Ethene regulates fruit ripening and leaf drop.
- Plant hormones are often used in agriculture.

If you have ever looked at indoor house plants, you may have noticed that the plants are bushier and have more leaves on the side next to the window (Figure 15.2). Maybe you regularly turn them around, so that you can see the attractive side. Plants change their growth in response to light by bending their stems and developing more leaves on the bright side. This response is regulated throught the production of plant hormones. Many aspects of plant growth are controlled by hormones.

Figure 15.2 House plants always grow toward the light.

The Discovery of Auxin

Charles Darwin is famous for his theory of natural selection, but he also studied many other topics in biology. In the late 1800s, Charles Darwin and his son Francis reported on some experiments they conducted to answer the question of how plants grow toward light. They observed that grass seedlings would bend toward light while they were growing. But when the Darwins cut off the tips of the seedlings, the shoots grew straight up, without bending (Figure 15.3). Next, they placed dark caps on the tips of the seedlings, shielding them from light. Again, the seedlings grew straight up rather than bending toward the light source. However, when the Darwins placed clear caps over the tips of the seedlings, or shielded only the lower part of the seedlings, they observed the normal bending response to light.

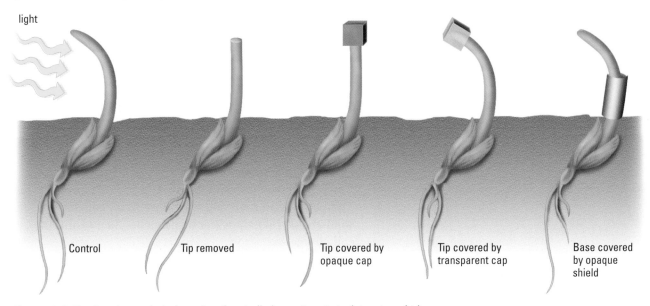

light

Control   Tip removed   Tip covered by opaque cap   Tip covered by transparent cap   Base covered by opaque shield

Figure 15.3 The Darwins conducted a series of controlled experiments to determine which region of a seedling detects light.

The results of these experiments suggested that something in the tip of a shoot senses light. However, the response, which is the bending of the shoot, occurs below the tip. The Darwins hypothesized that a shoot tip detects light and transmits a signal down to the growing region of the shoot. In *The Power of Movement in Plants* (1881), the Darwins suggested, "[When the seedlings are exposed to light], some influence is transmitted from the upper part to the lower part, causing the latter to bend."

It was not until the 1920s that plant physiologists finally succeeded in extracting and identifying the "influence" the Darwins had predicted in the 1800s. This signalling chemical, **auxin**, is a chemical messenger produced in the shoot tip. This chemical messenger was the first plant hormone to be discovered. Plant hormones are chemical signals produced in tiny amounts in one part of the plant that have a specific effect on another part of the plant.

Plant hormones control many key functions in a plant's life. For example, hormones control growth, flowering, fruit production, and the germination of a plant from a seed. Like animals, plants produce hormones in very small amounts, but even tiny amounts can have large effects. Just a few molecules of hormone can cause a cell to respond by turning genes on or off, by inhibiting enzymes, or by changing the properties of the cell membrane.

Five Major Plant Hormones

Plant biologists have identified five major types of plant hormones: auxins, cytokinins, gibberellins, abscisic acid, and ethene. No single hormone acts alone. Instead, a balance of the various hormones controls the life of a plant.

Auxins

The plant hormone whose effects the Darwins observed is one of a class of hormones called auxins. The chief function of auxin is to promote plant growth. The name is from the Greek *auxein*, meaning "to increase."

Auxins are produced in the apical meristems at the tips of shoots. They promote cell elongation, which causes lengthening of the stem. When a seedling is exposed to light from one direction, auxin builds up on the shaded side and stimulates growth beneath the tip. Because the cells on the shaded side are exposed to more auxin, they elongate, or lengthen, more than the cells on the lighted side (Figure 15.4). The uneven growth rate of cells on the two sides of the plant causes the shoot to bend toward the light.

How do auxins make cells elongate? One hypothesis is that auxins trigger mechanisms that loosen the bonds holding the components of the cell walls together. Cells generally have more solutes than their surroundings. Therefore, with their cell walls less rigid, cells on the shaded side take up water by osmosis. As a result, the cell elongates.

Auxins have other functions in a plant. For example, they can stimulate secondary growth of a plant stem by promoting cell division in the vascular cambium. They can also trigger the formation of roots and leaves.

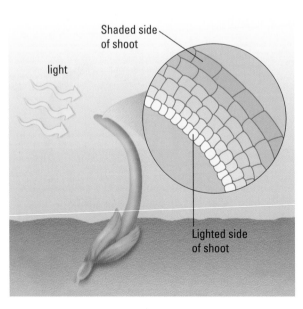

light

Shaded side of shoot

Lighted side of shoot

Figure 15.4 Cells on the shaded side of a plant grow faster than cells on the lighted side, causing the plant to bend toward the light.

Seeds secrete auxins that stimulate the development of the surrounding ovary into fruit. Exposing some kinds of plants to auxins can cause fruit to develop without any need for pollination and seed development. Farmers use this technology to produce seedless tomatoes, cucumbers, and other fruits by spraying the flowering plants with auxins.

Farmers sometimes use synthetic auxins, such as 2,4-D, as herbicides. Because these compounds are more readily absorbed by the broad leaves of dicots than the narrow leaves of monocots, they can be used to kill dicot weeds, such as dandelions. Dicot weeds absorb more herbicide than monocots, leaving cereal grasses, which are monocots, unharmed (Figure 15.5). Of course, there are risks associated with the use of herbicides, as you learned in chapter 13.

Explore More
How does auxin cause a plant to bend toward light?

Figure 15.5 The dicot weeds in the foreground were killed by auxin herbicides, whereas the corn, a monocot, in the background is healthy.

Cytokinins

Cytokinins were first identified from coconut milk, which was known to contain a very effective plant growth factor. **Cytokinins** increase plant growth by stimulating cell division. These hormones are produced in actively growing tissues, particularly in embryos, roots, seeds, and fruits. Cytokinins made in the roots reach target cells in stems by moving upward in xylem sap. Another effect of cytokinins is to slow the aging of flowers and fruits.

Plant hormones rarely work alone, and the effects of cytokinins are affected by the concentration of auxins present. For example, cytokinins entering the shoot system from the roots promote cell division in axillary buds. This encourages branching of the plant. At the same time, auxin travelling down the plant from the terminal bud inhibits branching. The result is fewer and shorter branches near the tip of the plant, where auxin levels are higher than cytokinin levels.

This knowledge can be used in horticulture to make plants bushier. Gardeners, for example, often "pinch back" the terminal buds at the growing tips of the plant (Figure 15.6). This reduces auxin levels compared to cytokinin levels, causing the plant to branch more. Gardeners also add cytokinins to leaf, stem, or root cuttings to stimulate shoot formation.

(a)

(b)

Figure 15.6 (a) This basil plant has been pinched back causing it to become bushier than (b), which has not been pinched back.

Gibberellins

Japanese researchers studying "foolish seedling" disease in rice a century ago were the first to discover gibberellins. The sickly rice seedlings were tall and spindly, and fell over as they grew (Figure 15.7). The cause of their problems was gibberellin. The seedlings were infected with a fungus that produced gibberellin causing the rice to grow excessively. Since the hormone was isolated and identified in 1934, gibberellins have been found to play key roles in plant growth and development.

Produced at the tips of both stems and roots, **gibberellins** cause a wide variety of effects. One of their main roles is to stimulate growth of stems by promoting both cell division and cell elongation. This effect is similar to the effect of auxins. Researchers do not yet fully understand how the actions of these two classes of hormones are related. Also in combination with auxins, gibberellins can influence fruit development.

One use of gibberellins is in growing the Thompson variety of seedless grapes. Applying gibberellins makes the grapes grow larger, and the clusters expand so that there is more space between the individual grapes (Figure 15.8). Some strains of wheat and rice developed during the Green Revolution of the 1970s are dwarf mutants producing less gibberellin than normal plants. These plants have short, stiff stems and fewer leaves, with relatively large heads of grain. Because they are so short, these dwarf varieties are less vulnerable to damage from rain and wind.

Gibberellins are also important in promoting seed germination. For example, with exposure to water, the embryos in some cereal grains, such as barley, release gibberellins that stimulate the breakdown of stored nutrients in the endosperm, making them available to the embryo.

Figure 15.7 In "foolish seedling" disease, gibberellins produced by a fungus cause rice plants to grow tall and fall over.

Figure 15.8 Spraying grapes with gibberellin makes the grapes larger and expands the clusters so air can circulate around the grapes.

Concept Check

1. Explain why the Darwins did not observe any bending of the seedlings when they covered the tips of the seedlings with dark caps.
2. Describe the agricultural use of one plant hormone.
3. Explain how auxins and cytokinins interact in a plant.

Abscisic Acid

When plants face a harsh environment, they may benefit from halting their growth and delaying reproduction. With the onset of winter, during a severe drought, or when exposed to salty soils, a plant is more likely to survive if it becomes dormant. During dormancy, the plant stops growing. At such times, the hormone **abscisic acid**, abbreviated as ABA, is synthesized and transported through the xylem to shoots and leaves. There, it inhibits cell division in buds and in the vascular cambium. In other words, ABA halts primary and secondary growth.

ABA also promotes dormancy in seeds — the opposite effect of gibberellins. Some seeds remain dormant until a downpour washes ABA out of the seeds. Gibberellins do not wash out as easily. Therefore, without the inhibitory effect of ABA, the stimulating effect of gibberellins signals the seeds to germinate.

BIOLOGY·SOURCE

Suggested Activity
- E10 Quick Lab Overview on page 415

©P

ABA also acts as a "stress hormone" in growing plants. For instance, when a plant is dehydrated, ABA builds up in leaves and causes stomata to close. Closing stomata reduces transpiration and prevents further water loss from plants. Gardeners may spray ornamental plants with ABA to increase their tolerance to drought stress during dry periods.

Ethene

In the early 1900s, oranges and grapefruits were ripened for market in sheds. Farmers would heat the sheds with kerosene stoves, believing that the heat ripened the fruit. Plant biologists later learned that the ripening was actually due to **ethene**, a gas released when kerosene is burned. Ethene, also called ethylene, is a naturally occurring plant hormone that stimulates fruit ripening. Farmers use ethene to help in transporting delicate fruits, such as bananas and tomatoes. These fruits are picked, stored, and transported while green and then exposed to ethene for ripening just before they are sold. Using ethene to control fruit ripening means we can eat tropical fruit in the winter, but it also increases our carbon footprint because we are transporting our food longer distances.

Another effect of ethene is to promote leaf drop, the loss of leaves from deciduous trees every autumn (Figure 15.9). Leaf drop is caused by a shift in the amounts of ethene and auxin in leaf petioles. Ethene concentration increases and auxin concentration decreases in response to autumn's shorter days and cooler temperatures. Leaf drop is an adaptation that helps keep trees from drying out in winter. Because their roots cannot take up water from the frozen ground during winter, trees cannot afford to lose water by transpiration from leaves. Coniferous trees do not lose their leaves in winter. Their leaves, which are often shaped like needles, have thick cuticles to minimize water loss.

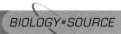

Figure 15.9 Ethene and auxin are two hormones responsible for leaf drop.

E10 **Quick Lab**   *BIOLOGY • SOURCE*

Ripening a Green Tomato

Purpose

To investigate the role of ethene in ripening fruit

Activity Overview

In this activity, you will examine whether the presence of an apple influences the rate of ripening of a green tomato (Figure 15.10).

Prelab Questions

Consider the questions below before beginning this activity.

1. Why would an apple release ethene?

2. What effects does ethene have, other than promoting ripening of fruits?

3. How do farmers take advantage of the role of ethene in ripening green fruits?

Figure 15.10 Some types of fruit release ethene as they ripen.

Key Concept Review

1. Describe the experiments that eventually led to the discovery of auxin, the first plant hormone to be indentified.

2. Explain how auxins cause bending of stems in response to light, as shown below.

Question 2

3. Describe the mechanism by which auxins cause cell elongation.

4. How are cytokinins and abscisic acid transported in plant stems?

5. During winter, which plant hormone inhibits new growth?

6. Describe three agricultural uses of plant hormones.

7. Describe the role of gibberellins in seed germination.

8. Explain why fruits ripen when placed in sheds heated with kerosene stoves.

9. Use a table to summarize the effects of the five main plant hormones.

10. The text says, "No single hormone acts alone." Describe an example of two plant hormones acting in concert to regulate plant functions.

Connect Your Understanding

11. Explain why each of the following statements is incomplete or incorrect.
    (a) House plants bend towards windows because light causes them to grow more on that side.
    (b) The action of two different hormones together doubles the plant's response.

12. How do synthetic auxins, such as the herbicide 2,4-D, kill dicot weeds while leaving monocot crops unharmed?

13. Buds and sprouts often form on tree stumps. Which group of hormones would you expect to stimulate their formation? Explain your answer.

14. (a) If you want your house plants to be bushy and thick instead of tall and spindly, what should you do?
    (b) What hormone is responsible for the effect you describe?

15. Gibberellins were discovered by Japanese researchers studying "foolish seedling" disease in rice. Sickly rice seedlings grew tall and spindly before falling over and dying. A fungus produced the gibberellin, which was found to be an important plant hormone.
    (a) What benefit do you think the fungus derives from producing gibberellins?
    (b) How would you test your hypothesis?

16. As described in your text, some strains of wheat and rice developed during the Green Revolution of the 1970s are dwarf mutants producing less gibberellin than normal plants. These grain plants have short, stiff stems and fewer leaves, with relatively large heads of grain. Would such plants do well in non-agricultural settings, such as in the wild? Why or why not?

17. Plant hormones are widely used in agriculture and horticulture to delay fruit ripening, increase drought tolerance, and produce seedless fruits.
    (a) Do you think there should be any restrictions on the use of hormones by farmers and gardeners? Why or why not?
    (b) If so, what limitations would you like to see, and what is your justification for suggesting them?

Reflection

18. What did you find most difficult to understand in this section? Why?

For more questions, go to **BIOLOGY•SOURCE**

A vine grows round and round the trunk of a tree. A Venus's-flytrap leaf snaps shut to trap an unwary fly. A seed in the dark ground begins to grow toward the surface. A house plant bends toward a brightly lit window. Although plants lack a nervous system, they sense and respond to information about their environment. Plants may not be able to move, but they can and do modify their growth toward or away from features of the world around them.

All plants are sensitive to their surroundings. They respond to such stimuli as light, temperature, gravity, and touch. Most plant responses are too slow to see, as parts of the plant grow in response to stimuli. In a few plant species, however, the response is very rapid indeed.

Rapid Plant Movements

The leaves of the tropical plant *Mimosa pudica* quickly fold up when touched, giving the plant a wilted appearance (Figure 15.11). After a while, the leaves return to their normal position. This response is an example of a rapid plant movement. Touch triggers responses that cause cells at the base of each leaflet to lose ions. Due to osmosis, water follows the ions out of the cells. The cells shrink, causing the leaflet to droop.

Figure 15.11 The leaves of the mimosa plant will close after being touched.

A number of scientists have hypothesized about the function of this leaf-folding behaviour. Some scientists hypothesize that leaf folding in a heavy wind is an adaptation that reduces surface area and saves water. Another hypothesis states that the folding response makes the plant less attractive to animals trying to eat the plant. For example, the rapid movement may bump off or scare away insects, or it may expose spiny projections on the underside of the leaf.

Venus's-flytraps also have very rapid leaf movements. Specialized leaves secrete nectar to attract insects, which walk down the leaf and bump into the three sensitive hairs on the leaf surface (Figure 15.12(a)). As soon as a trigger hair is touched twice, or two hairs are touched in quick succession, the two halves of the leaf close like a trap door. The insect becomes trapped within spines on the edge of the leaf (Figure 15.12(b)). The closing mechanisms is not triggered when the trigger hairs are touched only once. This prevents the leaf from closing on a falling leaf or piece of dust.

The time from when the insect touches a trigger hair until it is trapped within the leaf is only half a second. The closing of the trap may be caused by increased turgor pressure in the leaf's mesophyll cells or by loss of water from the cells that form the trap's hinge. The pressure from the closed leaf pushes the insect against digestive glands on the leaf's surface. The glands secrete enzymes that digest the insect. The Venus's-flytrap is considered to be carnivorous because it "eats" insects.

 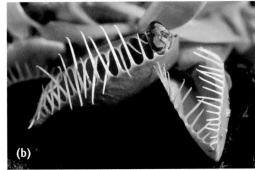

Figure 15.12 When a fly or other insect (a) brushes against the tiny trigger hairs on the surface of a leaf of a Venus's-flytrap, (b) the leaf swings closed to trap the insect. Digestive glands on the leaf surface then secrete enzymes to kill and digest the insect.

Tropisms

Animals can move away from harmful stimuli or undesirable conditions or toward an area with needed resources, but plants are rooted in place. As a result, plants respond to their external environment by changing their patterns of growth. **Tropisms** are slow growth responses that cause parts of a plant to bend or grow toward or away from a stimulus. Growth or bending toward a stimulus is a positive tropism. Growth or bending away from a stimulus is a negative tropism. Tropisms are typically regulated by plant hormones, especially auxins. Unlike rapid plant movements, tropisms are not rapidly reversible.

Responses to Touch

A change in plant growth due to touch is called **thigmotropism**. Most climbing plants have tendrils that respond by coiling and grasping when they touch rigid objects. Thigmotropism enables climbing plants to use objects for support while growing toward sunlight. A tendril responds when it contacts a support, winding completely around it in under an hour (Figure 15.13). This response is due to changes in cell shape within the tendril, as the cells in contact with the support shorten and the cells on the other side of the tendril lengthen.

Another example of thigmotropism is a seedling's response to mechanical stress. For example, a growing seedling may press against a rock in the soil. It is advantageous for the seedling to bend, avoiding the obstacle, instead of damaging itself by growing straight into it and failing to reach the soil surface. Researchers have shown that ethene plays a role in this response.

Figure 15.13 Coiling of tendrils due to thigmotropism allows pea plants to climb toward light.

Responses to Light

Light is a critically important environmental factor in the life of a plant. Plants can detect and respond to variation in light intensity, direction, and wavelength. During photosynthesis, plants convert the energy of visible wavelengths of light into chemical energy in the bonds of glucose and sucrose molecules. Red and blue wavelengths are the most effective wavelengths of visible light for driving photosynthesis, while green wavelengths are the least effective.

The growth of a plant part toward or away from light is an example of **phototropism**. You have already learned how auxins regulate this response in seedlings. Shining light on one side of a shoot tip causes an uneven distribution of auxins, with more on the shaded side than on the lighted side. The shoot tips contain a protein with an attached light-absorbing molecule. When activated by light, this protein signals molecules that affect auxin transport down from the shoot tip.

Light functions as a stimulus for many plant activities, as plants keep track of the seasons by detecting changes in day length. Many events in the lives of plants, from budding to flowering to the shedding of leaves, are triggered by changes in day length.

Responses to Gravity

No matter how a seed lands on the soil, the roots will always grow down into the soil and the shoots will always grow up. Similarly, if you put a potted plant on its side, the shoots will grow up and the roots will grow down (Figure 15.14). A plant's growth response to gravity is called **gravitropism**. Roots have positive gravitropism because they grow in the same direction as the force of gravity. Shoots have negative gravitropism because they grow in the opposite direction to gravity. In space, where there is no gravity, plant roots grow in a straight line, no matter which way is up.

Gravitropism has opposite effects in shoots and roots, and therefore different explanations and hormones may be responsible. Plant biologists do not fully understand gravitropism, although they have located the cells responsible for sensing gravity in the centre of the root cap. One hypothesis for the mechanism for gravitropism is that gravity pulls organelles containing dense starch grains to the low points of cells. The uneven distribution of these organelles may in turn signal the cells to move auxins or cytokinins within the shoot or root, thus affecting the cell's growth.

Coping with Stressful Environments

Plants are often exposed to stressful environmental conditions because, unlike animals, they cannot move to a more suitable habitat. Changes in levels of soil water, salt, and temperature can affect a plant's growth, as well as its ability to reproduce or even to survive. Drought, flooding, or salty soil can devastate natural plant populations as well as agricultural crops. Many plants are adapted to withstand temporary stress, often by going dormant.

Some plants are adapted to live under conditions that are too stressful for other plants. Purple saxifrage, a plant that grows in Canada's arctic, is extremely hardy (Figure 15.15). It grows in a dry rocky environment that is frozen and dark for most of the year. Purple saxifrage survives by forming low dense mats that protect it from the drying wind. Once the snow melts it is able to flower quickly, producing seeds within two months.

Explore More

How does a seedling respond to different wavelengths of light and to gravity?

Suggested Activity

• E11 Inquiry Activity Overview on page 422

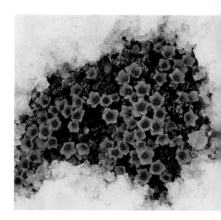

Figure 15.14 The roots and shoots of mature plants respond to gravity by growth.

Figure 15.15 Purple saxifrage is one of Canada's hardiest plants.

Drought

A drought is a prolonged period of inadequate rainfall. When plants adapted to more moderate climates are exposed to drought, they can become stressed and weakened. In a drought, a plant may lose more water through transpiration than it takes up from the soil. This shortage of water inhibits the growth of young leaves, causes existing leaves to wilt, and reduces photosynthesis. Plants respond to drought by conserving water. Plants can conserve water by closing their stomata, thereby slowing down the rate of transpiration. You read earlier in this chapter that the hormone ABA initiates this response.

Some plants have adaptations that enable them to withstand a very dry climate. Cacti and similar plants, called succulents, store water in their fleshy stems and thrive in the desert. Cacti often have spines that are modified leaves instead of broad flat leaves that would lose a lot of water through transpiration. The green, fleshy stems are the main photosynthetic organs. Many succulents, such as jade plants and *Aloe vera*, have thick fleshy leaves (Figure 15.16). The stems and leaves of succulents have a thick cuticle. Some plants adapted to dry conditions have waxy cuticles, while others have an epidermis that is several cell layers thick. The stomata of many desert plants form within epidermal pits, protected by epidermal "hairs." These adaptations all reduce transpirational water loss from the plants' leaves.

Plants adapted to cold, dry arctic regions tend to have very small needle-shaped leaves and grow very low to the ground. These adaptations help reduce transpiration during the short growing season by minimizing exposure to the harsh, dry winds that blow over the landscape.

Figure 15.16 Desert succulents have thick, water-retaining leaves.

Flooding

Waterlogged soil lacks the air spaces that provide oxygen for cellular respiration in the roots. In addition, oxygen moves more slowly through water than through air. Some plants are adapted to live in very wet habitats. Mangrove trees, for example, grow in coastal marshes but have roots that are partly above ground (Figure 15.17). These above-ground roots provide oxygen for the underwater parts of roots. Unlike other roots, mangrove roots show negative gravitropism.

Plants that are not adapted to aquatic environments must often withstand periods of waterlogged soil. The main problem faced by plants in waterlogged soils is the lack of oxygen, which is normally present in soil air pockets. This is why, if you overwater a house plant, its roots will suffocate and die. In some plants, cells that are deprived of oxygen release the hormone ethene. The ethene causes some of the cells in the submerged roots to die. Killing these cells creates air tubes that carry oxygen to the submerged roots.

Figure 15.17 Mangroves have roots that grow above the water.

Concept Check

1. Describe the role of osmosis in controlling the rapid plant movements of *Mimosa pudica*.

2. Distinguish among thigmotropism, phototropism, and gravitropism.

3. Contrast a desert plant's adaptations with the adaptations of a house plant experiencing a temporary drought.

Salt Stress

Too much salt can also threaten the health of plants. When excess salt builds up in the soil, root cells lose water to the soil through osmosis. Most plants cannot survive salt stress for long. The exceptions are the halophytes, salt-tolerant plants with adaptations to remove salt from the plant. In some species, salt glands pump salt out of the plant across the leaf epidermis, and rain washes the salt away. There are other adaptations, too. One salt marsh plant called pickleweed pumps excess salt to stems at the tips of the plant. Then the pickleweed sheds these stems, getting rid of the salt (Figure 15.18).

Figure 15.18 Pickleweed sheds its stem tips where salt has been concentrated.

Defending Against Disease and Herbivory

Plants do not live in isolation in their communities. They interact with many other species. Some of these interactions, such as those with mycorrhizal fungi and nitrogen-fixing bacteria within plant root nodules, benefit both species. Many other interactions are not beneficial to the plant. Plants are subject to infection by viruses, bacteria, and fungi. Each of these pathogens may damage tissues or even kill the plant. Powdery mildew, for example, is a fungal disease that affects many plant species (Figure 15.19). While it rarely kills plants, infected leaves may fall off and photosynthesis will be reduced.

Figure 15.19 Powdery mildew reduces a plant's photosynthetic ability.

Plants have adaptations that defend against infection. A plant's first line of defence against infection is the physical barrier of the plant's epidermis and the waxy cuticle that covers it. However, pathogens can cross this barrier through wounds or openings in the plant, such as the stomata. Once infected, the plant uses chemicals as a second line of defense. Some of the chemicals are antimicrobial. For example, some chemical defences attack molecules in the cell wall of a bacterium. Other chemicals signal lignin production. This hardens the cell walls around the infected area and seals off the invading pathogen from the rest of the plant.

A plant also inherits the ability to recognize and attack certain pathogens. In fact, plant breeders often select for this ability of plants to resist specific diseases. One of the goals of making genetically modified plants is to introduce disease-resistance genes from different plant species into crop plants.

Figure 15.20 Insects, such as this grasshopper, consume plants.

Many insects, mammals, and other animals eat plants (Figure 15.20). As protection from herbivores, plants may have physical defenses such as thorns or chemical defences such as poisons. When exposed to light, potato tubers produce a bitter chemical called solanine, which is a fungicide and insecticide. Solanine is a natural defence that protects tubers from being eaten if they are unearthed. While some people associate the green colour of potatoes with solanine, the green is actually harmless chlorophyll. Nevertheless, the chlorophyll may be a signal that the tuber has been exposed to light and that it therefore contains solanine.

E11 **Inquiry Activity**   *BIOLOGY·SOURCE*

REQUIRED SKILLS
■ Designing an experimental procedure
■ Using appropriate equipment and tools

How Do Plants Grow Up? Exploring Gravitropism

Question

How do plant seedlings respond to gravity?

Activity Overview

In this investigation, you will explore how plants respond to gravity, and discover how plant hormones produced in response to gravity cause a change in growth. You will develop and test your own hypotheses about the effects of gravity on young plant stems. Then you will perform an experiment of your own design.

Your teacher will give you a copy of the full activity.

Prelab Questions

Consider the questions below before beginning this activity.

1. What is positive gravitropism? Which part(s) of the plant do you expect to show this response?

2. What is negative gravitropism? Which part(s) of the plant do you expect to show this response?

3. What plant hormone(s) is (are) responsible for gravitropism?

Regulating Natural Health Products: A Case Study of *Aloe vera*

Issue

Aloe vera is a common house plant but it has been used as a herbal medicine for thousands of years. A number of claims have been made about the medicinal uses of this plant. You will consider whether these claims are supported by modern medicine.

Activity Overview

In this Case Study, you will consider how *Aloe vera* is grown sustainably and whether the medical claims made for aloe products are accurate and supported by modern medical science.

Your teacher will give you a copy of the full activity.

Prelab Questions

Consider the questions below before beginning this activity.

1. Consider Figure 15.21. What drought-tolerant characteristics does *Aloe vera* have?

2. Have you ever used *Aloe vera* to treat an ailment? If so, what ailment were you treating? Was the treatment successful?

3. Should traditional medicines be regulated in the same way as pharmaceutical drugs?

Figure 15.21 Aloe vera is grown around the world.

Key Concept Review

1. Give an example of rapid plant movement. Explain how these movements are controlled at a cellular level.

2. Define the term "tropism." Distinguish between positive and negative tropisms.

3. Set up a table listing plant tropisms, the environmental factors they respond to, and the plant hormone(s) involved in the response.

4. Explain one short-term and one long-term adaptation of plants to drought.

5. How do mangrove trees survive despite the flooding of their roots?

6. Describe the effects of underwatering and overwatering your house plants.

7. Describe two interactions between plants and other organisms, one that benefits the plant and the other that harms the plant.

8. Describe how plants defend themselves against disease.

Connect Your Understanding

9. Use a Venn diagram to show how tropisms are similar to and different from rapid plant movements.

10. (a) Explain what plant response is occurring in this photo below.
    (b) How might this response benefit a plant?

Question 10

11. Explain why each of the following statements is incomplete or incorrect.
    (a) Plants show positive gravitropism.
    (b) Plant growth increases with increasing soil moisture.

12. (a) Describe an environment that you would consider to be stressful to plants.
    (b) Why is this environment stressful?
    (c) Propose some plant adaptations that would increase a plant's survival in this environment.

13. (a) In terms of tropisms, explain what has happened to the tree in the photo below.
    (b) Is the primary or secondary tissue responding? How do you know this?
    (c) How does this adaptation benefit plants?

Question 13

Reflection

14. What do you now know about plant responses to their environment that you did not know previously?

For more questions, go to BIOLOGY•SOURCE

A video called *Lessons from Thin Air* shows Harvard graduates being questioned as they leave the stage in their caps and gowns. Each graduate is shown a tiny tree seedling and a large log and is asked, "Where does the mass in a tree come from?" Most of the Harvard grads answer that trees are made from the water and soil nutrients that trees suck up from their roots. Are they correct? What do trees and other plants obtain from the soil in which they grow? Does the mass in a plant or tree come only from materials in soil? The answer is no.

Figure 15.22 This tree obtained most of its biomass from the air.

The Source of a Plant's "Substance"

In the 4th century B.C.E., the philosopher and scientist Aristotle proposed that soil provides all the substance necessary for plant growth. Almost 2000 years passed before his hypothesis was tested and rejected. The process of science often advances knowledge by rejecting old hypotheses and proposing new ones in their place.

Aristotle's idea was accepted as fact until the 1600s, when a Belgian physician named Jan Baptista van Helmont actually tested the hypothesis. Van Helmont grew a small willow tree in a pot containing 90 kg of soil. As the tree grew, he added nothing to the soil except water. Five years later, van Helmont found that the tree had gained nearly 75 kg while the soil had lost less than 0.1 kg. Since the tree gained far more mass than the soil lost, his data contradicted Aristotle's hypothesis that a plant gains its substance, or mass, from soil.

After conducting this experiment, van Helmont proposed a new hypothesis: Growing plants gain substance from water added to the soil. A century after van Helmont's experiment, Stephen Hales, an English botanist, proposed a third hypothesis: Plants gain their substance from the air (Figure 15.22).

More recent research has indicated that there is some truth in all these early ideas about plant nutrition. Air supplies the plant with carbon dioxide (Figure 15.23). The carbon and oxygen of carbon dioxide are used in photosynthesis, generating sugar molecules. These sugars are the building blocks for the other organic molecules, such as cellulose, that make up the plant's tissues.

Water absorbed by the plant from the soil supplies the hydrogen used in photosynthesis, serves as the solvent for the transport of other molecules through the plant, and makes up about 80–85 percent of the mass of a non-woody plant. Soil is the source of inorganic nutrients called minerals that are dissolved in water and absorbed by the plant's roots.

Mineral Requirements of Plants

While many animals require a complex diet of large organic molecules, plants have simpler needs. In addition to air and water, plants require only simple ions from the soil to survive and grow. Combining these with the products of their photosynthesis, plants can make all the proteins, carbohydrates, and other molecules they need.

Most plants need 17 chemical elements to complete their life cycles — that is, to grow from a seed and produce another generation of seeds. Only three of these chemical elements are not obtained as minerals from the soil. Carbon and oxygen come from CO_2 in the air, and hydrogen comes mainly from water in the soil. Together, these three elements make up about 96 percent of the weight of a plant. The other elements are mineral nutrients absorbed in ionic form from the soil. Table 15.1 lists six of the mineral nutrients plants require in greatest abundance, along with their functions in the plant.

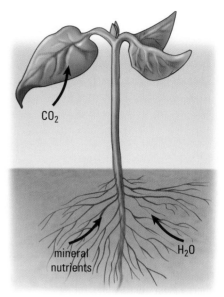

Figure 15.23 A plant obtains nutrients from both the air and the soil. Carbon dioxide and water are used to make sugar in photosynthesis.

Table 15.1 Some Essential Plant Mineral Nutrients

Mineral Nutrient	Function in Plant	Deficiency Symptoms
Nitrogen (N)	· Leaf growth · Protein and DNA synthesis	· Older leaves turn yellow and younger leaves are paler green and smaller · Stunted growth
Phosphorus (P)	· Root, stem, flower, seed development · Important to mitosis and cell division · Nucleic acid and ATP synthesis	· Difficult to identify · Stunted growth · Leaf tips look burnt · Small leaves, purplish colour · Poor flowering
Potassium (K)	· Water balance · Protein synthesis · Regulation of osmosis	· Leaf tips and edges look burnt · Weak stems · Chlorosis (loss of chlorophyll) between veins · Poor fruit development
Calcium (Ca)	· Cell wall formation · Enzyme activity	· New leaves are irregularly shaped · Leaf edges curl down · Poor fruit development
Magnesium (Mg)	· Chlorophyll synthesis · Enzyme activity	· Older leaves are yellow at the edges or between veins · Newer leaves are often yellow with dark spots · Poor fruit development
Sulphur (S)	· Protein synthesis	· Similar to nitrogen deficiency · Younger leaves lighten first, followed by older leaves

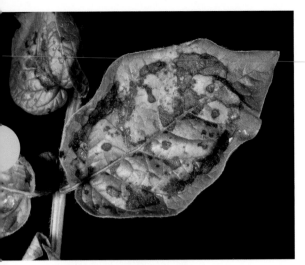

Like animals, plants can suffer from nutritional deficiencies. Without proper nutrition, plant growth may be stunted or the plant may fail to flower. Stems, roots, and leaves may also die. A plant that is magnesium-deficient, for example, is unable to synthesize chlorophyll, and shows a yellowing of its young leaves (Figure 15.24).

A Closer Look at Nitrogen

Nitrogen is a particularly important plant nutrient because it is often in limited supply in a plant's environment. A plant uses nitrogen to produce proteins, nucleic acids, and hormones. Even though nitrogen makes up nearly 80 percent of the atmosphere, many plants suffer from nitrogen deficiency.

Figure 15.24 Nutrient deficiencies affect a plant's functioning. For example, this potato plant is magnesium-deficient.

The problem is that atmospheric nitrogen (N_2) is a gaseous form of nitrogen that plants cannot use. Plants must absorb nitrogen from the soil in the form of mineral ions.

For plants to absorb nitrogen from the soil, the nitrogen must first be converted to ammonium ions (NH_4^+) or nitrate ions (NO_3^-) (Figure 15.25). Certain species of soil bacteria convert atmospheric nitrogen (N_2) to ammonia (NH_3) in a process called nitrogen fixation. Each NH_3 molecule picks up another hydrogen ion from the soil, becoming NH_4^+. Other bacteria called ammonifying bacteria also contribute ammonia to the soil by breaking down organic material such as feces and dead leaves. A third group of bacteria called nitrifying bacteria convert NH_4^+ ions to NO_3^-.

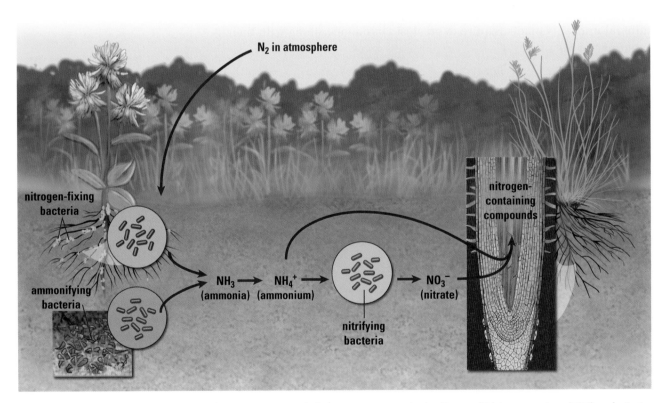

Figure 15.25 Bacteria help convert atmospheric nitrogen (N_2) to ammonium (NH_4^+) and nitrate ions (NO_3^-).

©P

Many nitrogen-fixing bacteria live freely in the soil. However, you can see that a plant adaptation that concentrates this nitrogen-fixing power close to the roots would be beneficial. In fact, some plants, including legumes such as peas, peanuts, alfalfa, and beans, house their own nitrogen-fixing bacteria. The bacteria are found in structures on the legumes' roots called root nodules. The relationship between the legume and the nitrogen-fixing bacteria usually benefits both organisms. The bacteria fix nitrogen for the plant, while the plant provides carbohydrates and other organic nutrients to the bacteria.

Farmers use this adaptation of legumes to improve their fields in the practice of crop rotation. When a field is planted with a non-legume crop, such as corn, its soil gets depleted of nitrogen. But if the farmer plants a legume the following year, the soil's nitrogen supply will be replenished. Farmers usually rotate their crops each year, maximizing the quality of the soil and the crops. In Ontario, farmers often grow soybeans, a legume, in rotation with corn and wheat (Figure 15.26).

BIOLOGY•SOURCE

Suggested Activity
• E13 Inquiry Activity Overview on page 429

Figure 15.26 Soybeans are often planted in a crop rotation with corn and wheat.

Concept Check

1. Did van Helmont's experiment support or disprove Aristotle's hypothesis? Explain.

2. List at least three mineral nutrients required by plants, and describe their contributions to plant function.

3. Nitrogen comprises 80 percent of our atmosphere. Why is it difficult for plants to take up?

Fertilizers

Most farmers in industrialized countries use commercially produced fertilizers containing minerals. These fertilizers are usually enriched in nitrogen (N), phosphorus (P), and potassium (K), the three mineral nutrients most commonly deficient in farm and garden soils. The next time you are in a garden shop, take a minute to examine the sacks of various fertilizers. You will see that each one has a three-number code. A fertilizer marked "10-12-8," for instance, is 10 percent nitrogen, 12 percent phosphorus, and 8 percent potassium (Figure 15.27). These three nutrients are always listed in the same order, and generally written as N-P-K.

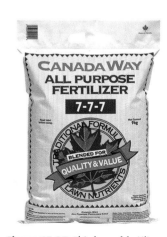

Figure 15.27 This bag of fertilizer contains seven percent nitrogen, seven percent phosphorus, and seven percent potassium.

Figure 15.28 This tomato plant produced no fruit because too much nitrogen fertilizer was applied to the soil.

It is important to use the correct N-P-K ratio for growing specific plants or for fertilizing nutrient-deficient soil. If you are growing tomatoes, for instance, fertilizers marked 5-10-10 or 10-10-10 will provide a healthy balance for your plants. However, if you fertilize your tomatoes with 20-5-5, your plants will get too much nitrogen. The result will be tall, leafy tomato plants, but very few tomatoes (Figure 15.28)!

Unfortunately, any minerals from commercial fertilizers in excess of what crops need are not stored in the soil for later use. They are usually wasted because they are leached from the soil by rainwater or irrigation and often end up polluting ground water, streams, and lakes. Rotating crops is one way to reduce nitrogen fertilizer use. There are also some advantages in using mulch or manure instead of industrial fertilizers, because they release the minerals more gradually. Some farmers plant nitrogen-fixing crops, such as clover, and then plough them into the soil to replenish soil nitrogen. This is called green manure.

Soil pH

The pH scale is a measure of acidity. Most plants grow best in soils with neutral pH, close to 7. Canada's huge boreal forests of conifers are adapted to grow on relatively acidic soils that result from the slow decomposition of organic material in a cold climate (Figure 15.29). Other plants do well in the alkaline soils found in areas with abundant limestone ($CaCO_3$). Plants adapted to low- or high-pH soils have specialized enzymes that function well in acidic or alkaline soils.

Figure 15.29 Soils in the boreal forest are acidic.

Soil pH plays an important role in plant nutrition because it affects the availability of the ions necessary for plant growth. Acidic, low pH soils increase the rate at which phosphorus ions are released by weathering rocks. Acidity in soils may also increase the availability of positively charged ions such as magnesium or calcium. These positive ions bind to negative charges on soil particles, and may be released at low pH when protons are abundant and displace them from their binding sites on soil. Positively or negatively charged ions that are not bound to soil particles are present in soil water. There, they may be taken up by plant roots, but may also be washed out of soil by rainfall before they can be taken up and used by plants.

Diagnosing a Sick Plant

Question

How do nutrient deficiencies and soil conditions affect the health of plants?

Activity Overview

In this activity, each pair of students will be given a description of a sick plant. You will ask questions as you diagnose and treat your plant.

Your teacher will give you a copy of the full activity.

Figure 15.30 This plant is wilted due to a lack of water.

Prelab Questions

Consider the questions below before beginning this activity.

1. What are the main soil nutrients that plants need to grow and flourish?

2. What molecules do plants obtain from the air around them?

3. What soil conditions may negatively affect the health of plants?

E14 **Design a Lab**   *BIOLOGY•SOURCE*

REQUIRED SKILLS
- Designing an experimental procedure
- Using appropriate equipment and tools

01 Key Activity

Factors Affecting Plant Growth

Question

How do various abiotic factors influence plant growth?

Activity Overview

In this activity, you will design a lab to examine the effect of one abiotic factor on plant growth.

Your teacher will give you a copy of the full activity.

Prelab Questions

Consider the questions below before beginning this activity.

1. List four abiotic factors that influence plant growth.

2. What are the three most important plant nutrients?

3. What problems do plants face when they have too much water?

Figure 15.31 Canola plant showing symptoms of nitrogen deficiency

Key Concept Review

1. (a) Describe the three original hypotheses of where plants get their "substance."
   (b) Which one(s) is (are) true?

2. Trace the path of nitrogen from the atmosphere to a plant's roots. Include all nitrogen-containing molecules and ions found in this path and all organisms that are responsible for converting nitrogen from one form to another.

3. Describe the role of three different kinds of bacteria in making nitrogen available to plants.

4. Explain the benefits of crop rotation.

5. List the typical contents of fertilizers.

6. What problems may result from adding fertilizers to agricultural soil?

7. How does soil pH affect the availability of positively charged mineral ions to plant roots?

Connect Your Understanding

8. Compare the tiny tree seedling to the huge tree. Where does the mass in a tree come from?

Question 8

9. Draw a simple diagram of a plant. Which parts will be affected by deficiencies of the six mineral nutrients? Indicate this by circling them on your diagram and briefly describing the symptoms you might see in that plant part.

10. Explain why this statement is incomplete or incorrect: Some plants are able to fix molecular nitrogen (N_2) to ammonia (NH_3).

11. Describe three ways in which knowledge of the importance of soil resources for plant growth and survival might be applied in agriculture or horticulture.

12. Nitrogen is the most abundant molecule in the air you breathe and yet plants have a hard time obtaining enough nitrogen from the soil. Explain why this is so.

13. What alternative methods can farmers use to increase soil fertility, instead of using chemical fertilizers?

14. You are purchasing fertilizer for plants that are suffering nitrogen deficiency. Is this fertilizer suitable? Explain why or why not.

Question 14

15. How does soil pH influence a plant's nutritional status?

Reflection

16. What learning technique did you use to remember which bacteria are responsible for converting atmospheric nitrogen to nitrate?

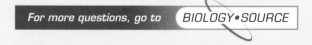

For more questions, go to BIOLOGY•SOURCE

University of British Columbia's Diane Srivastava is a community ecologist. She tackles big questions, studying how the loss of biodiversity impacts the availability of ecosystem services. She finds answers to these big questions in small communities (Figure 15.32).

Up to 60 species of small insects and insect larvae form an aquatic community in a tiny pond called a leaf well. Leaf wells are formed by the overlapping leaves of bromeliads living in the rain forests of Costa Rica.

Bromeliads are epiphytes: plants that grow on the trunks of trees. These plants are not rooted in soil. Instead, they take up nutrients from the decomposition of organisms and leaves that fall into their leaf wells. Dr. Srivastava found that bromeliads grew best when both predatory damselflies and their prey, small insects feeding on the leaf litter, were present in the wells.

Dr. Srivastava says, "as we lose species in an ecosystem, the system doesn't function as well as it should. Rates of biomass and oxygen production slow down. Rates of decomposition slow down, and energy passes more slowly between trophic levels."

Figure 15.32 Dr. Srivastava investigates the community of insects living in the leaf wells of a bromeliad in a Costa Rica rainforest. These white structures are designed to keep spiders away from bromeliads.

Biology CAREERS   Organic Farmer

Organic farmers grow crops and raise animals in a sustainable manner that is harmonious with and not destructive to the environment (Figure 15.33). They grow their crops without the use of synthetic pesticides or chemical fertilizers. They do not use hormones or food additives to increase production of animal products. Organic farmers emphasize animal health and welfare. To be "certified organic," a farm must be inspected by an organic farming inspector, who determines that the farm's products are grown according to a set of guidelines developed by an organic certification body.

The 2006 Census of Canadian Agriculture reported that Canada had 3555 certified organic farms, representing 2 percent of Canadian farms. Another 12 000 farms produced some organic products, but were not certified as organic.

In 2004, the University of Guelph became the first North American institution to offer a BSc in agriculture with a major in organic agriculture. Guelph's Organic Program remains unique in Canada, offering academic and applied learning about organic farming with the theme of "eating sustainably."

Figure 15.33 This organic farmer grows crops without the use of synthetic pesticides.

To find out more, visit BIOLOGY•SOURCE

Key Concept Review

1. What is a plant hormone? 🅚

2. Create a table to show the site of production and the major effects of the five major types of plant hormone: auxin, cytokinin, gibberellin, abscisic acid, and ethene. 🅚

3. (a) Which hormones are responsible for cell elongation? 🅚
   (b) Which hormones are responsible for cell division? 🅚

4. Explain how farmers can stimulate fruit formation in tomatoes that have not been pollinated and are not developing viable seeds. 🅚

5. Which plant tissues produce high levels of cytokinins? 🅚

6. How do cytokinins synthesized in the roots of a plant reach target cells in the plant's stem? 🅚

7. These grapes are large and plump because they have been treated with a hormone.
   (a) Which plant hormone was used to treat these grapes? 🅚
   (b) Describe the effect of the hormone on these grapes. 🅚

Question 7

8. No plant hormone acts alone and a balance of various plant hormones controls the life of a plant. Illustrate this statement by describing the factors that lead to
   (a) germination of a seed following a heavy downpour of rain. 🅚
   (b) leaf drop by deciduous trees in autumn. 🅚

9. Describe why and how a Venus's-flytrap leaf closes rapidly. 🅚

10. Explain the role of osmosis in the rapid plant movements that cause the leaves of *Mimosa pudica* to fold up when touched. 🅚

11. Your text states, "Light functions as a stimulus for many plant activities." Explain why the following provide vital information to plants.
    (a) variation in light intensity 🅚
    (b) changes in day length 🅚

12. Many plants are adapted to survive and reproduce in stressful environmental conditions. Describe the adaptations that allow the following four plants to survive their stressful environment.
    (a) The purple saxifrage grows in Canada's arctic. 🅚
    (b) *Aloe vera* lives in dry or desert conditions. 🅚
    (c) Mangrove trees grow in coastal marshes. 🅚
    (d) Pickleweed grows in salt marshes. 🅚

Question 12

13. Explain how a potato tuber placed on the ground surface can protect itself against attack by fungi or herbivores. 🅚

14. Use a flow chart to show how soil organisms convert nitrogen from one form to another. Which of these nitrogenous compounds can be used by plants? 🅚

15. Why do some Ontario farmers grow soybeans in rotation with corn and wheat? 🅚

16. Why would a gardener use a fertilizer with a code 10-30-10? Explain your answer. 🅚

17. Explain how the conifers of Canada's boreal forests are adapted to grow on low pH soils. 🅚

18. Describe how soil pH affects the availability of ionized nutrients in the soil. 🅚

Connect Your Understanding

19. In the late 1800s, Charles Darwin and his son carried out a series of experiments to determine which region of a seedling detects light. In 1881, Darwin wrote, "[When the seedlings are exposed to light], some influence is transmitted from the upper part to the lower part, causing the latter to bend." Rewrite this statement to reflect how a modern plant physiologist would explain the results from the Darwins' experiments. *a*

20. In 1913, biologist Peter Boyce-Jensen further tested the Darwins' hypothesis that a chemical signal is responsible for phototropism. Examine the results shown below of two treatments he applied to grass seedlings. (Note that chemicals can diffuse through gelatin but not through mica, a rock mineral.)

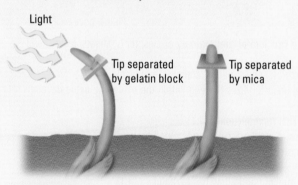

Light

Tip separated by gelatin block

Tip separated by mica

Question 20

(a) How did the seedlings react to each treatment? *a*

(b) Why do you think the seedling with its tip separated by mica grew straight? *a*

21. Your text states that, "Plant hormones control many key functions in a plant's life." Illustrate this statement with three examples, each relating to a different plant hormone. *a*

22. Explain how the use of ethene allows us to eat tropical fruits in winter, while increasing our overall carbon footprint. *a*

23. Explain how plant responses to touch, light, and gravity are regulated by hormones. *a*

24. A young seedling is exposed to light from one direction.

light

Question 24

(a) Describe how auxin levels would differ between the shaded and unshaded side of the shoot. *a*

(b) Describe the effect this difference in auxin levels would have on cells on the shaded and unshaded side of the shoot. *a*

(c) Explain how the young seedling benefits from the effect you have described in (b). *a*

25. Imagine that astronauts on the International Space Station are trying to grow plants to supplement their diet. What problems might they face growing plants in space in terms of providing an ideal environment for plant growth? *a*

Reflection

26. What strategies did you use to remember the functions of the five main plant hormones? *c*

Unit Task Link

Plan and carry out an investigation of how the leaves of your plant respond to reduced light. Build a cardboard structure and place it over some leaves so that they can continue to grow or position themselves to regain access to light. Sketch the position of your leaves in relationship to the obstacle and then return in two days and then seven days later to see if the position of the leaves has changed. Also sketch the position of leaves whose access to light has *not* been blocked and note if the position of these leaves has changed.

In addition, consider the following questions about the species you have chosen:

- Do the leaves of your plant show any damage from insect or mammalian herbivores?

- Does your plant have any defensive structures (e.g., thorns, spines)?

- Does it have any features that protect it against drying out (e.g., waxy cuticle, epidermal hairs on the underside of the leaves)?

For more questions, go to BIOLOGY•SOURCE

KEY CONCEPTS	CHAPTER SUMMARY

13 Plants play key roles in nature and society.

- Plant uses
- Ecosystem services
- Sustainable development
- Disturbance
- Ecological succession
- Plant community

- Plants provide people with food, medicine, fuel, and building and industrial materials. (13.1)
- Plants perform important ecosystem services. (13.1)
- The world's farmers practice a variety of sustainable agricultural and forestry practices. (13.1)
- Healthy plant communities are subject to periodic disturbance. (13.2)
- The type, frequency, and severity of a disturbance determine its impact. (13.2)
- Primary succession occurs in lifeless areas without soil. (13.2)
- Secondary succession occurs when a plant community is damaged or removed from an area, but soil is left behind. (13.2)
- Climate, topography, and soil composition are among the factors determining the nature of a region's plant community. (13.2)

14 Specialized plant structures support plant functions.

- Plant organs: roots, shoots, leaves, flowers
- Seed development
- Sexual reproduction
- Vegetative reproduction
- Plant tissue systems: dermal, vascular, ground tissue
- Plant cell types: parenchyma, collenchyma, sclerenchyma
- Primary and secondary growth
- Meristem
- Root pressure
- Transpiration-pull
- Pressure-flow

- Monocot and dicot plants differ in the structure of their primary organs: roots, shoots, leaves, and flowers. (14.1)
- A flower consists of four sets of structures: sepals, petals, stamens, and pistils. (14.1)
- After the sperm nucleus in the pollen grain fertilizes the egg within the ovule, the ovule develops into a seed. (14.1)
- Plants are capable of sexual and asexual reproduction. (14.1)
- Plants have three main tissue systems: dermal, vascular, and ground tissue. (14.1)
- Plant tissues are made up of three basic cell types: parenchyma, collenchyma, and sclerenchyma. (14.1)
- Plant leaves are designed to capture sunlight and allow gas exchange. (14.1)
- Plants may grow in length, which is primary growth, and in width, which is secondary growth. (14.2)
- Plant roots absorb water and mineral nutrients from soil. (14.3)
- Forces of root pressure and transpiration-pull move water and minerals upward from the roots of a plant. (14.3)
- A pressure-flow mechanism is responsible for the translocation of sugar and other organic compounds from sugar source to sugar sink regions within a plant. (14.3)

15 Plant growth is regulated by internal and external factors.

- Plant hormones: auxins, cytokinins, gibberellins, abscisic acid, ethene
- Growth responses of plants: thigmotropism, phototropism, gravitropism
- Plant defenses
- Soil fertility
- Soil pH
- Plant nutrition

- Plant hormones regulate many aspects of plant growth and development. (15.1)
- Plants may grow in response to touch (thigmotropism), light (phototropism), and gravity (gravitropism). (15.2)
- Some plants are adapted to live in conditions of drought, flooding, and salty soil. (15.2)
- Plants have adaptations that protect them against infection and herbivore attack. (15.2)
- Plants obtain water and minerals from soil. (15.3)
- Soil pH plays an important role in plant nutrition. (15.3)

©P

Key Terms Review

1. Create a concept map that links all of the terms in the list below. Give examples, where applicable, of the various terms. You may add additional terms from the unit that you find helpful. ⓒ

   - ecosystem services
   - sustainable development
   - nitrogen fixation
   - disturbance
   - pioneer species
   - ecological succession
   - stamen
   - pistil
   - vegetative reproduction
   - xylem
   - phloem
   - stomata
   - meristem
   - root pressure
   - transpiration-pull
   - pressure-flow mechanism
   - auxins
   - cytokinins
   - phototropism
   - gravitropism

Key Concept Review

CHAPTER 13

2. List two food items obtained from each of the following categories.
   (a) monocot ⓚ
   (b) dicot ⓚ
   (c) herbaceous plant ⓚ
   (d) woody plant ⓚ
   (e) bark (1 example) ⓚ
   (f) root ⓚ

3. Explain this statement: "Many of the foods we eat contain hidden processed plant products." ⓚ

4. Name a plant-derived pharmaceutical product. Specify the active ingredient of the drug and how it works. ⓚ

5. Explain why the tropical rain forest has been described as a potential medicine chest. ⓚ

6. Distinguish between the source and uses of hardwoods and softwoods. ⓚ

7. Describe two ecosystem services that are performed by the following groups.
   (a) trees along urban streets ⓚ
   (b) house plants ⓚ
   (c) grasses along a stream bank ⓚ

8. Explain why bean plants and birch trees increase soil nutrient levels. ⓚ

9. Create a cost/benefit chart to summarize the negative and positive effects of the following agricultural practices.
   (a) soil tilling ⓚ
   (b) chemical fertilizers ⓚ
   (c) pesticides ⓚ
   (d) crop irrigation ⓚ

10. Briefly describe each of the following strategies for Integrated Pest Management.
    (a) crop rotation ⓚ
    (b) green manure ⓚ
    (c) biological control ⓚ
    (d) pheromones ⓚ

11. Distinguish between the direct and indirect effects of disturbance to a plant community. ⓚ

12. Explain how pioneer plant species change the abiotic environment in a disturbed area. ⓚ

13. How do plants that remain following a disturbance influence the process of ecological succession? ⓚ

14. (a) What events might lead to patchiness within a forest community? ⓚ
    (b) How does patchiness promote plant and animal biodiversity in the forest? ⓚ

CHAPTER 14

15. (a) Describe the structure of an angiosperm pollen grain. ⓚ
    (b) What flower structure produces pollen grains? ⓚ

16. Describe the structure and function of the following.
(a) endosperm tissue Ⓚ
(b) cotyledons Ⓚ

17. "Not all fruits are sweet and juicy."
(a) Describe two fruits that illustrate this statement. Ⓚ
(b) Describe possible dispersal mechanisms for these fruits. Ⓚ

18. Explain why fruit growers may graft a branch from one plant onto the stem of another plant. Ⓚ

19. Name each of the labelled structures and give their function. Ⓚ

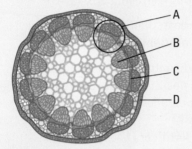

Question 19

20. Use a comparison matrix to compare the two types of vascular tissue. Use at least four characteristics. Ⓚ

21. Explain why this statement is incomplete: "Phloem transports sugars from the leaves to the roots of a plant." Ⓚ

22. Contrast the structure and function of parenchyma, collenchyma, and sclerenchyma cells. Ⓚ

23. Using a table, name each of the labelled parts of the leaf cross section and give the structure's function. Ⓚ

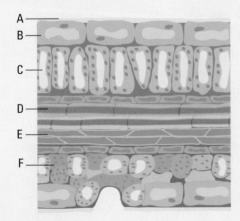

Question 23

24. Using a table similar to the one below, compare the structure of monocots and dicots. Ⓚ

Structures of Monocots and Dicots

	Monocots	Dicots
Flowers		
Leaves		
Roots		
Seeds		
Vascular structure		

25. (a) What is a meristem? Ⓚ
(b) State the name and function of the four types of meristems. Ⓚ

26. (a) List the three concentric cylinders that make up the developing tissues of a root and shoot. Ⓚ
(b) Describe the function of each cylinder. Ⓚ

27. Describe how the following assist plant roots in taking up water and minerals from soil.
(a) root hairs Ⓚ
(b) mycorrhizae Ⓚ

28. Describe the two forces that combine to move water and minerals up the stem of a plant. Ⓚ

29. Describe how leaves regulate transpirational water loss. Ⓚ

30. As a sieve-tube member matures, it loses its nucleus. How does a sieve-tube member obtain necessary enzymes and other proteins when it lacks a nucleus? Ⓚ

31. "The location of sugar sources and sinks changes with the seasons."
(a) Define "sugar source" and "sugar sink." Ⓚ
(b) Provide an example to illustrate this statement. Ⓚ

32. Describe the role of ATP and osmosis in the pressure-flow mechanism for sap flow through the phloem of a plant. Ⓚ

CHAPTER 15

33. Using diagrams, explain how auxins cause cell elongation. Ⓚ

34. Refer to the role of plant hormones as you explain why pinching off the terminal bud at the growing tip of a plant makes the plant bushier. Ⓚ

©P

35. How are seedless cucumbers produced? **k**

Question 35

36. Using a Venn diagram, compare how plants and animals respond to environmental stimuli. **k**

37. Distinguish between rapid plant movements and plant tropisms. **k**

38. Which plant hormone is responsible for
(a) thigmotropism? **k**
(b) phototropism? **k**

39. What plant tissue protects a plant from drought. How does it do this? **k**

40. Describe the defenses that protect a plant against infection. **k**

41. Name six mineral nutrients that plants must obtain in ionic form from soil. For each mineral, state one of its functions in plants. **k**

Connect Your Understanding

42. Imagine a taco salad, such as the one below. In your notebook, draw a sketch of this photo. Label all the types of food used to make this meal. For each food, list the plants that this food is derived from. For example, mustard is made from ground mustard seeds, vinegar, which is fermented from plants such as barley or apples, and sugar, which comes from plants such as cane or beets. **a**

Question 42

43. Write a paragraph explaining why nitrogen-fixing crops are important to agriculture and how their use can improve ecosystem sustainability. **a**

44. The transition from fossil fuels to biofuels is contentious.
(a) Explain why the issue is contentious. Use a cost/benefit chart to summarize your ideas. **a**
(b) Are you for or against the use of biofuels? Explain why. **a**

45. Use a flow diagram to explain how the rotation of farmed and fallow fields influences biodiversity in agricultural areas. **a**

46. How can tilled soils contribute to climate change? **a**

47. (a) Explain the basis of sustainable forest management. **a**
(b) Why is sustainable forest management important to Canada's economy? **a**

48. A disturbance is usually thought of as a negative event. Explain why disturbance is beneficial to ecological communities and to biodiversity. **a**

49. Make a table to compare the root systems of monocots and dicots. Use at least three categories of comparison. **a**

50. Describe each of the following structures and explain why it is adaptive for the plant.
(a) above-ground root **a**
(b) modified shoot **a**
(c) modified leaf **a**

51. How do angiosperms benefit from having sticky stigmas? **a**

52. Consider the following photo.

Question 52

(a) Does this species undergo primary growth? Explain why or why not. **a**
(b) Does this species undergo secondary growth? Explain why or why not. **a**
(c) What adaptations does this species have to reduce transpirational water loss? **a**

53. Plants move water, carbon dioxide, and sugar molecules. Pretend you are one of these molecules and describe your journey within the plant, making sure you mention your various locations and the types of cells you encounter. **a**

54. Seeds have many adaptations that improve their dispersal. Describe two such adaptations for plants you are familiar with. ⓐ

55. Some seeds will germinate only after exposure to a period of cold weather or the intense heat of a fire. Explain why these limitations may be adaptive. ⓐ

56. Ground tissue has different functions in different plant organs. Contrast the functions of ground tissue in a plant root, stem, and leaf. ⓐ

57. Your friend brings you a dozen roses for your birthday, and reminds you to cut their stems under the tap before you place them in water. With reference to cohesion and adhesion of water molecules, explain why this good advice will keep your roses from wilting. ⓐ

58. "Plant leaves are designed to capture sunlight and allow gas exchange." Describe two adaptations of a dicot leaf that illustrate this statement. ⓐ

59. Explain how the synthesis and transport of auxin accounts for each of the Darwins' experimental results, illustrated in Figure 15.3 on page 411. ⓐ

60. Explain why a few molecules of a plant hormone can have such a large effect on growth or development in a plant. ⓐ

61. Explain how abscisic acid can help a plant survive harsh conditions. ⓐ

62. When dandelion stems and leaves break, they exude a sticky, bitter, white substance called latex.
    (a) What function do you think this latex serves? ⓐ
    (b) How would you test this hypothesis? ⓣ

Question 62

63. Your friend scoffs when you tell him that most of the mass of a giant oak tree comes from the air around the tree's leaves. Explain how you will convince your friend that you are correct. ⓐ

64. How does the use of green manure reduce water pollution? ⓐ

Skills Practice

65. The following graph shows how Ontario's spruce and birch forests alternate over hundreds of years. Redraw this graph in your notebook. Using the scale on the right hand side of the graph, add a line to your graph to show how the availability of soil nitrogen varied over time. ⓣ

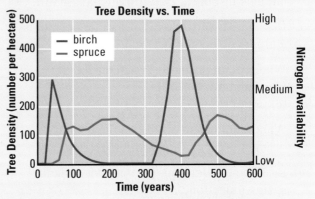

Question 65

66. The table below summarizes the results of an experiment that examined the effects of three treatments on the growth of a normal seedling and two mutant seedlings.

Question 66

(a) Propose a hypothesis to explain why rubbing the normal seedling had the same effect as adding artificial ethene. ⓣ
(b) Which mutant is insensitive to ethene? Explain. ⓣ
(c) What can you infer about the other mutant's production of ethene? ⓣ
(d) How might each mutant be at a disadvantage in nature compared to a normal seedling? ⓣ

©P

Revisit the Big Ideas and Fundamental Concepts

67. Create a concept map that shows the relationships among the following terms: secondary succession, disturbance, pioneer species, soil conditions, light availability, nutrient availability. **ⓒ**

68. Explain the general principles of integrated pest management. **ⓐ**

69. Describe three associations that plants form with other organisms where both partners benefit. **ⓚ**

70. Explain what is meant by this statement: "A balance of various hormones controls the life of a plant." Give specific examples. **ⓔ**

Science, Technology, Society, and the Environment

71. (a) Why is it important to harvest crops and forests sustainably? **ⓐ**
(b) Explain how these practices benefit society. **ⓣ**

72. Growing and harvesting crops sustainable is good for the environment and may benefit the cultures that grow them. However, some crops grown using sustainable methods may be more expensive to consumers. How do you convince the general public to pay more for their food? **ⓐ**

73. In 2002, the Pew Research Center carried out a major survey of global attitudes towards genetically modified plants. Consider the following results.
- 63 percent of Canadians said, "Scientifically altered fruits and vegetables are bad," 31 percent said, "Scientifically altered fruits and vegetables are good," and 6 percent said they did not know.
- 55 percent of Americans, 81 percent of Germans, and 89 percent of French respondents said that scientifically altered fruits and vegetables are bad because "they could hurt human health and the environment."

(a) How seriously should governments consider such survey findings? **ⓣ**
(b) What government response, if any, is appropriate? **ⓣ**

Reflection

74. List three uses of plants that you were unfamiliar with before reading this unit. **ⓒ**

75. "A society grows great when old people plant trees whose shade they know they will never sit in." What do you think this ancient Greek proverb means? Do you agree with it? Explain why or why not. **ⓒ**

76. "Plants are boring."
(a) Do you agree or disagree with this statement? Why or why not?
(b) Has your opinion of plants changed after reading this unit? Explain why or why not. **ⓒ**

E15 Unit Task

Adopt a Plant

Question

How is your selected plant species important in nature and to human society? How do its structures and growth support this role?

Task Overview

You will select a plant species that is growing in your neighbourhood. It can be a small annual herb, a shrub, or a tree. You will then research this species and conduct experiments about the importance of light to its growth.

You will write a case study on your plant species. The case study will include information on the species' location, overall structure, mode of reproduction, defensive structures, and response to reduced light.

Figure 15.34 The trillium is Ontario's provincial flower. It is a shade-tolerant, perennial species that flowers in the spring.

For some questions, answers may vary slightly depending on the method or data chosen for the solution.

page 103, B1 Quick Lab

2. 2 m

page 104, 4.1 Check and Reflect

13. TCAGCC

16. six

page 113, 4.2 Concept Check

2. two

page 115, 4.2 Check and Reflect

16. 4

page 123, 4.3 Check and Reflect

14. 4

page 124, Chapter 4 Review

10. 44; 22

13. 23; 46

14. 1

23. (a) 11
    (b) 20
    (c) 208

page 125, Chapter 4 Review

30. 12

31. (a) 156
    (b) 78

34. TACGTAGTCCGGCGG

page 134, 5.1 Concept Check

2. 50% *A*, 50% *a*

page 138, 5.1 Check and Reflect

14. *AB, Ab, aB, ab*

17. 25%

18. 50%; 25%

19. $\frac{1}{2}$ black (*Bb*), $\frac{1}{2}$ chocolate (*bb*)

20. *BBAA, BBAa, BBaa, BbAA, BbAa, Bbaa, bbAa, bbAA, bbaa*; 9 black and Agouti : 3 black and coloured belly : 3 chocolate and Agouti : 1 chocolate and coloured belly

page 141, 5.2 Concept Check

2. six

3. O or B

page 145, 5.2 Check and Reflect

5. O

8. pink and white

12. I^AI^A, I^AI^B, I^BI^B

page 151, 5.3 Check and Reflect

7. X

8. (a) X^hY
   (b) 100%
   (d) 50%
   (e) 100%

9. $X^DX^D, X^DXd, X^DY, X^dY$; 50% unaffected females, 25% unaffected males, 25% affected males

11. (c) X^RY and X^RX^r
    (d) no; X^RX^R or X^RX^r
    (e) red-eyed males are X^RY, ruby-eyed males are X^rY

page 152, Chapter 5 Review

4. (a) tall
   (b) tall
   (c) yellow
   (d) axial flowers and round seeds

page 153, Chapter 5 Review

25. (b) *TtGg*, tall with green seeds
    (c) 100% tall with green seeds

26. (b) roan (*RW*) and white (*WW*)

27. *ABC, aBC*

29. X^HY and X^HX^h or X^hX^h

33. (a) 3.4 : 1
    (c) *Gg*

page 161, 6.1 Check and Reflect

5. 1.5–2%

9. (a) mustard plant
   (b) rice plant

17. (a) A and C

page 165, B14 Quick lab

2. CTATGT

page 173, B15 Quick lab

1. one

page 179, Unit B Review

16. (a) *BB*
    (b) *Tt*
    (c) *ll*

page 180, Unit B Review

45. (b) 23

page 181, Unit B Review

52. (b) *DaB, dAb*

63. *PW, Pw, pW, Pw*

64. (b) $\frac{3}{4}$

page 182, Unit B Review

70. (a) GGCCCGAATTCTT

GLOSSARY

Note: The numbers in parentheses at the end of each definition indicate the page number in this book where the term is defined.

A

abscisic acid a plant hormone that inhibits cell division in buds and in the vascular cambium (414)

adaptation an inherited characteristic that improves an organism's ability to survive and reproduce in a particular environment (189)

adaptive radiation evolution from a common ancestor that results in diverse species adapted to different environments; also called divergent evolution (228)

aerenchyma loosely-packed parenchyma cells with air spaces (390)

aerobic the ability to function in the presence of oxygen (243)

algae (singular, *alga*) protists that have a lifestyle similar to plants (41)

alimentary canal a digestive tract with two openings, a mouth and an anus (288)

allele alternative version of a gene (129)

alternation of generations life cycle of plants that alternates between diploid and haploid forms of the plant (58)

alveoli (singular, *alveolus*) air sacs in the lungs that provide a very large surface area for gas exchange (330)

amino acids twenty different kinds of building blocks of protein (278)

amniotes evolutionary branch of the phylogenetic tree of animals made up of reptiles, mammals, and birds (72)

amniotic egg waterproof egg with a shell (72)

analogous structures structures in distantly related species that are anatomically different but perform the same function (203)

anaphase third stage of mitosis, when the sister chromatids separate to become individual chromosomes, which move to opposite poles of the cell (107)

anaphase I third stage of meiosis I, when homologous chromosomes separate from the tetrad and move to opposite poles of the spindle (110)

anaphase II third stage of meiosis II, when the sister chromatids separate and the individual chromosomes move to opposite poles of the cell (111)

aneurysm a bulge in the wall of an artery (320)

angiosperms plants that have flowers as reproductive structures (61)

anther part of the stamen that produces pollen (383)

aorta artery that supplies oxygen-rich blood to all the systems of the body (312)

aortic valve valve between the left ventricle and the aorta (311)

apical meristems meristems located in the tips of roots and buds of shoots (393)

arrhythmia a condition in which the heart beats irregularly, too quickly, or too slowly (320)

arteries large blood vessels that carry blood from the heart to the tissues (305)

arteriosclerosis an advanced stage of plaque build-up, which occurs when the deposits on the artery wall harden (319)

artificial selection the selective breeding of domesticated plants and animals to produce offspring with genetic traits that humans value (205)

asexual reproduction process that produces offspring that inherit all their genetic material from just one parent (105)

asthma a chronic and potentially life-threatening disorder of the respiratory system in which airways become narrowed, making breathing very difficult (337)

asymmetrical having no symmetry (66)

atherosclerosis a narrowing of the arteries resulting from plaque building up inside the artery wall (319)

atria (singular, *atrium*) the two upper chambers of the heart, which receive blood returning to the heart (311)

atrioventricular valves valves that are located between the atria and ventricles (32)

autosomes chromosomes other than the sex chromosomes (29)

auxins plant hormones that promote cell elongation (397)

B

bacilli (singular, *bacillus*) rod-shaped bacteria (32)

bacteriophages viruses that attack and infect specific bacterial cells (29)

bark plant tissue composed of phloem, cork cambium, and cork (397)

bilateral symmetry arrangement having mirror-image right and left sides (67)

bile a yellow or greenish alkaline fluid produced the liver and stored in the gallbladder that separates small fat droplets, which enables digestive enzymes to break down the fats more efficiently (292)

binary fission reproductive process in which bacteria divide, producing two identical cells (34)

binomial two-part Latin name of a species (17)

binomial nomenclature system of naming specific species developed by Swedish botanist Carolus Linnaeus (17)

biodiversity variety of life in the world or a particular habitat or ecosystem (6)

bioinformatics science of handling and analyzing biological data (157)

biological species concept idea that defines a species as a population or group of populations whose members have the ability to breed with one another in nature and produce fertile offspring (224)

biopsy cutting procedure to obtain a sample of tissue (294)

biosphere zone on Earth where all life exists, including the atmosphere, continents, and oceans (4)

biotechnology use of organisms to make useful products (162)

bipedalism the ability to walk on two feet (256)

blade main, usually flattened part of the leaf (382)

blastopore first opening that forms in an animal's digestive tract during embryological development and becomes a mouth or an anus (67)

blastula hollow ball of cells that forms during an animal's embryological development (66)

blood pressure the force that blood exerts against artery walls; measured in millimetres of mercury (mm Hg), a standard unit of liquid pressure (306)

body plan body structure unique to a species (66)

bolus chewed clump of food (290)

breathing the process of moving air into and out of the lungs; also called ventilation (331)

bronchi (singular, *bronchus*) air tubes that connect the trachea to the lungs (330)

bronchioles finer tubes branching from each bronchus (330)

bronchitis a condition in which the trachea become irritated or infected and produce excess mucus; may become chronic when individuals are exposed to cigarette smoke or other harmful air pollutants (337)

bronchodilator a drug that causes the narrowed airways, such as in asthma, to expand (337)

bryophytes seedless plants, such as mosses and their relatives, that do not have any rigid support structures, such as lignin-reinforced cell walls (60)

buds undeveloped shoots (382)

C

calorie the amount of energy required to raise the temperature of 1 g of water by 1°C; one dietary Calorie is equal to 1000 calories (281)

capillaries microscopic blood vessels with a high surface area resembling a network of tiny tubes (305)

carbohydrates compounds made of carbon, hydrogen, and oxygen atoms; a major source of energy for your body (278)

cardiovascular disease disease that affects the heart and blood vessels (300)

cardiovascular system the circulatory system in humans and other vertebrates (302)

carrier testing genetic testing to determine if an individual carries a copy of a mutation that his or her children could inherit (120)

cell cycle orderly sequence of events in a eukaryotic cell's life (100)

cellular slime mould a protist that has a lifestyle similar to fungi (44)

centromere region where two chromatids are joined tightly together (102)

cephalization development of a distinct head with sense organs (67)

chemical digestion the chemical breakdown of food into smaller pieces, such as breaking down the large molecules of carbohydrates, fats, and proteins to produce smaller molecules during hydrolysis (287)

chemoautotrophs organisms that synthesize their own organic molecules from simple inorganic materials without using light energy (243)

cholesterol a fat manufactured by the liver that is part of cell membranes and used to synthesize hormones, bile, and vitamin D (321)

chromatin mass of very long fibres consisting of DNA and protein (98)

chromosome one long, condensed DNA molecule containing hundreds or thousands of genes (98)

chromosome theory of inheritance theory that states that genes are located at specific positions on chromosomes, and the segregation and assortment of these chromosomes during meiosis is responsible for inheritance patterns (146)

chronic obstructive pulmonary disease (COPD) a serious condition that occurs when chronic bronchitis and emphysema are found together and can lead to respiratory failure (337)

chyme acidic, nutrient-rich liquid formed from the bolus by the churning action of the stomach (291)

cilia short, hair-like structures protruding from a cell that move fluid and particles over the cell's surface; sometimes used for movement and food gathering (41, 330)

ciliates protists with cilia (41)

clade an evolutionary branch on a phylogenetic tree (253)

cladistics method used to determine the sequence of branches in a phylogenetic tree based on shared homologous structures (253)

cladogram a phylogenetic diagram that specifies the derived characters of clades (253)

classes taxonomic groups of similar orders (17)

climax community a self-perpetuating plant community (374)

cocci (singular, *coccus*) spherical-shaped bacteria (32)

codominance inheritance pattern in which both alleles are completely expressed at the same time, and so a heterozygous individual has a mixture of the two parental phenotypes (139)

co-evolution the process in which one species evolves in response to the evolutionary changes in another species (233)

collenchyma plant cells that have unevenly thickened cell walls (389)

colonoscopy procedure in which a thin, lighted tube with an attached camera is inserted through the rectum to diagnose intestinal disorders (294)

companion cells cells alongside sieve tubes that provide resources to the sieve-tube members (402)

complete dominance inheritance pattern in which one allele is expressed and the other is not (139)

conjugation reproductive process in which two bacterial cells temporarily join and directly exchange genetic material (34)

conservation biology application of biology to counter the loss of biodiversity (81)

continental drift the movement of Earth's landmasses relative to each other (247)

convergent evolution distantly related species that live in similar environments and develop similar adaptations (229)

cork dead cells with thick, waxy walls that protect the stem of woody plants (397)

cork cambium meristematic tissue that produces cork (396)

coronary arteries arteries that cover the surface of the heart and supply the heart muscle with the necessary nutrients (313)

cortex ground tissue of the root consisting primarily of parenchyma cells (388)

cotyledon embryonic leaf of the plant embryo (384)

cross-fertilization fertilization that occurs when sperm from the pollen of one plant fertilize the eggs in the flower of a different plant (128)

crossing over exchange of genetic material between homologous chromosomes in prophase I (112)

cumulative selection the evolution of a simple structure into a complex structure through a series of small adaptations (235)

cystic fibrosis a fatal genetic disease in which abnormally thick mucus blocks the airways and leads to infection that damages the lung tissue (338)

cytokinesis process by which the cytoplasm is divided in two (100)

cytokinins plant hormones that increase plant growth by stimulating cell division (413)

D

dead zones aquatic areas with low levels of oxygen that cannot support life (76)

deletion chromosomal change that occurs when a fragment of a chromosome is lost (119)

deoxyribonucleic acid (DNA) molecule that composes the genetic material (97)

derived characters homologous structures that are common to all the organisms in a clade (253)

dermal tissue outer covering of the plant (387)

descent with modification theory that descendants of the earliest organisms spread into various habitats over millions of years and accumulated different adaptations to diverse ways of life; also called evolution (196)

deuterostome animal in which the blastopore develops into an anus during embryological development

developmental disability lifelong disability due to mental or physical impairments (67)

diabetes a group of diseases in which high levels of blood glucose result from a problem with insulin secretion, insulin action, or both (341)

diagnostic genetic testing testing used to confirm a diagnosis when symptoms for a particular condition are present (120)

diaphragm a large dome-shaped sheet of muscle that forms the bottom wall of the chest cavity (331)

diastolic pressure the lowest recorded pressure in an artery during the relaxation phase of the heartbeat; in the measurement 120/70, 70 is the diastolic pressure (314)

dichotomous key a tool used by scientists and non-scientists to identify organisms with which they are unfamiliar (14)

dicotyledons group of angiosperms that contains broad-leaved species, such as dandelions, canola, and maple trees; also called dicots (381)

diffusion the process by which molecules move across a membrane from an area of higher concentration to an area of lower concentration (306)

diffusion gradient the gradual change in the concentration of solutes in a solution as a function of the distance through a solution (300)

dihybrid offspring of parents that differs in two traits (134)

dihybrid cross genetic cross between hybrids that differ in two traits (134)

dikaryotic having two nuclei per cell (50)

dinoflagellates unicellular, photosynthetic protists with a cell wall made of cellulose and two flagella (44)

diploid (2n) having two sets of chromosomes, one set from each parent (50, 109)

directional selection individuals at one end of the phenotype range that have a higher fitness than individuals in the middle or at the other end of the range (217)

disruptive selection individuals at the upper and lower ends of the range of phenotypes that have higher fitness than individuals near the middle; also called diversifying selection (217)

DNA chip small glass wafer or slide spotted with an array of single-stranded DNA fragments (160)

DNA sequencing methods of determining the order of nucleotides in DNA (157)

domain broadest taxonomic group (21)

dominant allele that determines the trait that a heterozygous individual expresses (129)

Down syndrome condition in which the individual carries an extra copy of chromosome 21 (116)

duodenum the first section of the small intestine (292)

duplication chromosomal change that occurs when part of a chromosome is repeated (119)

E

ecological niche the sum total of a species' use of the biotic and abiotic factors in its environment (198)

ecological succession the process of replacement of the plants and other organisms that make up a community (369)

ecosystem diversity a diverse range of habitats, the various organisms that live in the habitats, and the relationships that connect them (9)

ecosystem services the beneficial processes carried out by living things that are necessary to sustain life on Earth (360)

embryo reproductive structure that develops into a plant (58)

emphysema a condition that occurs when the cilia lining the airways are damaged, such as by environmental pollutants, and no longer filter and channel particles (337)

endodermis a layer of cells surrounding the vascular tissue in plants that prevents water and minerals from leaking out of the xylem (400)

endoscopy procedure in which a narrow tube with an attached camera is inserted into the throat and passed into the esophagus, stomach, and upper intestine (294)

endosperm nutrient-rich tissue that nourishes the growing seed embryo (384)

endospore dormant stage of bacteria in which the outer cell has disintegrated, leaving a highly resistant, thick internal wall that circles the DNA and a small amount of cytoplasm (35)

enzymes proteins that speed up specific chemical reactions without being consumed in the reactions (279)

epidermis dermal tissue of nonwoody plants (387)

epiglottis a cartilage flap that prevents food from moving into the air passageway as the food passes through the pharynx and into the esophagus (290)

eras blocks of time in the geologic time scale; the boundaries between eras are marked by a major change (or turnover) in the forms of life (245)

esophagus a long, muscle-encased tube that connects the pharynx to the stomach (290)

ethene a gaseous plant hormone important in fruit ripening and leaf drop; also called ethylene (415)

eukaryotes organisms that contain membrane-bound organelles, such as nuclei and mitochondria (21, 244)

evolution the theory that all species are descendants of ancient species that were different from modern-day species (118)

ex-situ conservation protecting species by removing them from their natural habitat (81)

extinct no longer existing because the last member of the species has died (77)

F

family taxonomic group of similar genera (17)

fats molecules formed from fatty acids and glycerol that store energy in your body and help your body absorb fat-soluble vitamins; can be divided into saturated, unsaturated, and trans fats; also called lipids (279)

feathers modified scales that grow on birds' skin (72)

feces undigested food and other waste products (294)

fibre a complex carbohydrate; also called cellulose (278)

fibrin a strand-like protein that traps red blood cells and platelets to form a clot over a break in a blood vessel (304)

fitness the ability of an individual to survive and reproduce in its specific environment (199)

flagella (singular, *flagellum*) long, whip-like structures that some cells use for movement (33)

flowers reproductive structures of plants that attract animals to help spread the plants' seeds (58)

fossil preserved remains or markings left by organisms (186)

fossil record the chronological collection of life's remains in the rock layers, recorded during the passage of time (200)

founder effect a type of genetic drift that happens when a few individuals, whose allele frequencies do not represent gene pool of their original population, colonize a new habitat (221)

fruit the ripened ovary of a flower (61)

fruiting body reproductive structure of fungi that appears above the ground (49)

functional food a food that has health benefits, including disease prevention, that are beyond the normal nutritional benefit of the food (282)

G

gametes sex cells; eggs and sperm (109)

gametophyte haploid generation of a plant that produces gametes (58)

gastric juice a mixture of hydrochloric acid, enzymes, and mucus secreted by glands in the stomach lining (291)

gene unit of inherited information that carry a code for a specific trait or function (6, 97)

gene flow the exchange of genes of one population with another population; occurs when fertile individuals or their gametes (sex cells) migrate between populations (221)

gene locus (plural, *gene loci*) site on a chromosome that a specific gene occupies (146)

gene map diagram that shows the relative locations and distances of genes on a chromosome (147)

gene pool all the alleles in all the individuals that make up a population (214)

gene therapy process of supplementing or replacing a gene in order to treat a medical condition (172)

genetic diversity the sum of all the different forms of genes present in a particular species (6)

genetic drift a change in the gene pool of a population due to chance (219)

genetic engineering intentional production of new genes and alteration of genomes by the substitution or introduction of new genetic material (162)

genetic linkage tendency for alleles for different genes on the same chromosome to be inherited together (147)

genetic recombination exchange of DNA segments (110)

genetically modified organism (GMO) an organism with genetic material that has been altered through genetic engineering (167)

genome full DNA sequence of an organism (155)

genomics study of genomes (158)

genotype genetic makeup or combination of alleles for an individual (130)

genus (plural, *genera*) taxonomic group of closely related species (17)

geologic time scale Earth's geological history organized into distinct blocks of time called eras (245)

germination process of early seed growth into a seedling (385)

gibberellins plant hormones that stimulate growth of stems by promoting cell division and cell elongation (414)

gills folds in the body surface of fish that are specialized for gas exchange (328)

glucose a type of sugar that provides fuel for work done by the body's cells (278)

glycogen a chain of many glucose molecules (278)

gradualism the evolution of a species by gradual accumulation of small genetic changes over a long period of time (229)

grafting transfering of a branch from one plant onto the stem of another plant belonging to a closely related species (389)

gravitropism a plant's growth in response to gravity (419)

ground tissue tissue filling the spaces between the dermal and vascular tissues (385)

guard cells cells that regulate the opening and closing of the stomata (389)

gymnosperms plants that bear seeds that are not protected and enclosed in an ovary (61)

H

habitat fragmentation splitting a habitat into fragments, which may prevent species from using resources in all parts of the habitat (77)

haploid (*n*) having a single set of chromosomes that contain genetic material (50, 109)

hardwoods dense wood produced by angiosperms (359)

Hardy-Weinberg equilibrium a condition when populations do not undergo any change to their gene pools and therefore are not currently evolving (215)

heart attack an event that occurs when the blood supply to heart tissue is slowed or stopped (319)

heart failure a condition in which the heart cannot pump blood efficiently because it cannot fill with enough blood or cannot send the blood to the rest of body with enough force (320)

hemoglobin a protein that binds oxygen in the lungs and releases it throughout the body (302)

hereditary inherited (127)

heritable can be inherited; can pass from one generation to the next (130, 197)

heterozygous having two alleles that are different from each other (129)

histones proteins that DNA coils around (98)

homeostasis the state of internal stability maintained by the body (333)

hominids humans and all their ancestral species that occurred after the split from ancestral chimpanzees (256)

hominoids a group of primates that have relatively large brains, lack tails, and have swinging arms (255)

homologous chromosomes two chromosomes of a matching pair, each carrying the same series of genes (109)

homologous structures similar structures in species that share a common ancestor (202)

homozygous having two alleles identical to each other (129)

hormones chemicals made by the endocrine system and secreted into the blood (314)

hybrid an offspring that results from crossing two true-breeding varieties of the same species, or offspring that results from the mating of individuals from two different species (128, 224)

hydrolysis a process that breaks chemical bonds in food molecules by adding water to them in the presence of specific enzymes (287)

hypertension a condition where a person's blood pressure is 140/90 or higher for an extended period; also called high blood pressure (320)

hyphae (singular, *hypha*) tiny threads of cytoplasm in fungi that are surrounded by a plasma membrane and covered by a cell wall (49)

hypothesis a suggested explanation of observations, which can be tested by further research or experiments (189)

I

in vitro fertilization process of fertilizing an egg in a test tube or laboratory dish and transferring the embryo to the uterus (169)

incomplete dominance inheritance pattern in which the phenotype of a heterozygous individual falls between the two parental phenotypes (139)

inferior vena cava vein entering the heart from the lower body (313)

influenza a common viral infection of the upper respiratory system spread by airborne droplets and contact with contaminated objects; also called the flu (336)

inheritance patterns predictable patterns seen in the transmission of traits from one generation to the next (127)

in-situ conservation protecting species in their natural habitats (81)

insulin a chemical produced by the pancreas and that controls the level of blood glucose (341)

integrated pest management farming using a variety of pest management strategies to increase crop yields while reducing health and environmental effects (363)

intercalary meristem meristem located at the base of each internode in some monocots, such as grasses (391)

internodes the portions of a plant stem between nodes (382)

interphase the growing stage of the cell cycle (100)

invasive species non-native species that harm ecosystems where they are introduced (78)

inversion chromosomal change that occurs when a fragment of the original chromosome is reversed (119)

invertebrates animals that do not have a backbone (69)

K

karyotype display of all the chromosomes in a cell or individual (108)

keystone species species that have a disproportionately large effect on the ecosystems in which they live (10)

kingdoms taxonomic groups of similar phyla (17)

L

larynx an organ in the neck that contains vocal cords which vibrate, producing sounds; also called the voice box (330)

law of independent assortment Mendel's second law, which states that genes that segregate independently in meiosis do not influence each other's inheritance (134)

law of segregation Mendel's first law, which states that two alleles for a trait or gene separate during meiosis (130)

leaves the primary food-manufacturing sites of a plant (382)

lignin a chemical that hardens cell walls of plants allowing them to stand upright (58)

lungs internal, thin-walled sacs with a high surface area for gas exchange; found in reptiles, birds, mammals, and some amphibians (329)

lymph clear, watery fluid made of protein molecules, salt, glucose, and other substances (307)

lymph vessels structures that transport fluid away from cells (293)

lymphatic system a network of vessels, nodes (connecting points), and organs that collects the fluid that leaves capillaries, "screens" it for micro-organisms, and returns it to the circulatory system (307)

M

mass extinctions brief episodes of great species loss (248)

mechanical digestion the physical breakdown of food into smaller pieces, such as by chewing, chopping, and grinding (287)

meiosis form of cell division that produces four cells, each containing half the number of chromosomes as the parent cell (108)

meristem tissue that generates new dermal, vascular, and ground tissue in plants (393)

metaphase second stage of mitosis, when the spindle fibres move the sister chromatids so that they line up in middle of the cell (107)

metaphase I second stage of meiosis I, when the tetrads move to the middle of the cell and line up (110)

metaphase II second stage of meiosis II, when the spindle fibres move the sister chromatids so that they line up in the middle of the cell (111)

microevolution a generation-to-generation change in the frequencies of alleles within a population (215)

mimicry one species, the mimic, resembles another species, the model, in order to gain survival advantage (234)

minerals inorganic nutrients, such as calcium, iron, phosphorus, copper, sodium, and zinc (280)

mitosis reproductive process in which a cell makes a copy of its genetic material and divides into two genetically identical cells (100)

monocotyledons group of angiosperms containing species with thin leaves, such as grasses, orchids, and lilies; also called monocots (381)

monohybrid offspring of parents that differs in just one trait (128)

monohybrid cross genetic cross between hybrids that differ in one trait (129)

morphology study of form and structure of organisms (18)

mucus a sticky substance that coats, lubricates, and protects membranes (290)

multicellular made of many cells (23)

mutation any change to the DNA of a cell (119)

mycelium (plural, *mycelia*) branching, interwoven mat of hyphae of a fungus (49)

mycorrhizae fungus that forms a mutualistic association with roots of a plant (49)

N

natural selection the process by which individuals with inherited characteristics well-suited to their environment leave more offspring on average than do individuals with adaptations less suited to the environment (197)

newborn screening detection of genetic disorders at birth through simple tests performed in hospitals (121)

nitrogenous base single or double ring of carbon and nitrogen atoms in DNA (99)

nodes the points on the stem at which leaves are attached (382)

non-disjunction failure of homologous chromosomes to separate during anaphase I or II of meiosis resulting in gametes with atypical numbers of chromosomes (117)

non-vascular plants plants that lack vascular tissue for conducting water and nutrients, such as mosses and their relatives (60)

nucleosomes DNA and histone structures resembling beads (98)

nucleotides subunits in DNA (99)

nutraceutical a substance that is purified from foods and taken like a medicine to provide health benefits including disease prevention (282)

nutrients chemicals in food that help your body perform all its functions (277)

O

orders taxonomic groups of similar families (17)

organic molecules molecules that contain the element carbon; organic compounds include carbohydrates, lipids, proteins, and nucleic acids (242)

osmosis diffusion of water across the cell membrane (403)

ovary plant female reproductive structure containing ovules (384)

overexploitation unsustainable use of resources, such as harvesting organisms faster than the organisms can reproduce (79)

ovules plant reproductive structures that develop into seeds when fertilized (384)

P

pacemaker a region of the heart muscle that sets the rate of contraction for the heart (313)

paired limbs pairs of external appendages, such as legs and antennae, that extend from animals' bodies (68)

palisade mesophyll elongated cells that are specialized for capturing light (390)

pancreatic juice a clear, alkaline liquid produced by the pancreas and that neutralizes the acidic chyme and contains enzymes that further break down carbohydrates, proteins, and fats (292)

parenchyma thin-walled cells with large central vacuoles (388)

periods time spans in the geologic time scale that are shorter than eras (245)

peristalsis a series of wave-like muscle contractions that forces the bolus of food along the digestive system (290)

petals usually colourful, modified leaves that are part of a flower (383)

petiole stalk that connects the leaf blade to the stem (382)

pharynx a short tube in the upper portion of the throat that is shared by the digestive system and respiratory system (290)

phenotype an organism's expressed physical, physiological, and behavioural traits (130, 214)

phloem plant vascular tissue that transports food made in leaves to other parts of the plant (388)

phototropism a change in plant growth due to light (419)

phyla (singular, *phylum*) taxonomic group of similar classes (17)

phylogenetic tree a branching diagram that represents the evolutionary relationships among species or groups (18, 251)

phylogeny the evolutionary development and history of a species or group of organisms (18, 251)

phytoplankton photosynthetic organisms in plankton that form the base of food chains for most aquatic organisms (44)

pioneer species early establishing species (369)

pistil female reproductive structure in plants (383)

plankton communities of mostly microscopic organisms that drift or swim near the surface of ponds, lakes, and oceans (44)

plaque a patchwork of cholesterol, calcium, and fat deposits that sticks to the interior walls of arteries (318)

plasma a straw-coloured solution that makes up fifty-five percent of the volume of blood and that is made of water, proteins, dissolved nutrients, and wastes, such as carbon dioxide (302)

plasmid small, circular DNA molecule found in bacteria (163)

plasmodial slime mould a large, branching protist that has a lifestyle similar to fungi (44)

plasmodium a single mass of cytoplasm that is undivided by membranes or cell walls and contains many nuclei (44)

platelets cell fragments made when the cytoplasm of certain bone marrow cells divides (304)

pneumonia a serious infection of the lungs in which the alveoli fill with fluid, preventing oxygen from reaching the blood; can be caused by a variety of viruses, bacteria, fungi, and parasites (336)

pollen grains small male gametophytes that contain cells that develop into sperm (61)

polygenic trait that has a range of phenotypes due to the additive affects of multiple genes (142)

prenatal testing medical testing used to detect gene mutations or chromosomal alterations in a fetus (120)

pressure-flow mechanism mechanism that explains the movement of food through the phloem (404)

presymptomatic testing (predictive testing) genetic testing for disorders that appear after birth or later in life (120)

primary abiogenesis the theory that the first living things on Earth arose from non-living material (242)

primary growth growth that increases plant length (393)

primary succession succession that occurs following a disturbance that leaves a habitat without soil (369)

primates a group of mammals that have grasping hands and feet with opposable first digits (255)

probability likelihood that a particular event will occur (131)

probiotics foods that contain substances that support health and that may help to strengthen the body's natural defence against disease (282)

prokaryotes unicellular organisms that lack nuclei, and any other organelles bound by a membrane (21, 241)

prophase first stage of mitosis, when the sister chromatids become visible and attach to the spindle, and the nuclear envelope breaks down (106)

prophase I first stage of meiosis I, when each duplicated chromosome pairs with its corresponding homologous chromosome, forming a tetrad (110)

prophase II first stage of meiosis II, when a spindle forms and attaches to the centromeres of the sister chromatids in each haploid daughter cell (111)

protein a complex molecule constructed from amino acids (278)

protists eukaryotic organisms that do not fit into the animal, plant, or fungi kingdoms (38)

protostome animal in which the blastopore develops into a mouth during embryological development (67)

pseudopodia (singular, *pseudopodium*) cellular extensions of streaming cytoplasm that enable a cell to move in the direction of the extensions (41)

pulmonary circuit circuit in which blood travels from the right side of the heart through the pulmonary arteries to the lungs to pick up oxygen and release carbon dioxide, and then travels to the left side of the heart through the pulmonary veins (312)

pulmonary valve valve between the right ventricle and the pulmonary artery (311)

punctuated equilibrium the theory that long periods of little evolutionary change (equilibrium) in a species are broken, or punctuated, by shorter periods of rapid speciation (230)

Punnett square diagram that shows the expected proportions of all possible outcomes of a genetic cross. (131)

purines double-ring nitrogenous bases adenine (A) and guanine (G) (99)

pyrimidines single-ring nitrogenous bases thymine (T) and cytosine (C) (99)

R

radial symmetry arrangement having body parts like pieces of a pie around an imaginary central axis (66)

recessive allele that is not expressed in a heterozygous individual (129)

recombinant DNA technology technology that combines genes from different sources into a single DNA molecule (163)

rectum final portion of the colon (294)

red blood cells cells that carry oxygen from the lungs to all the tissues of the body, making up about 45 percent of blood volume (302)

refugia any local environments that have escaped regional ecological change; in agriculture, refugia are blocks of land in fields that are not sprayed with pesticides (261)

reproductive isolation the inability of two organisms to reproduce due to some kind of physical or behavioural barrier (225)

respiratory surface gas exchange membrane in most multicellular organisms (327)

restriction enzymes bacterial proteins that cut DNA wherever a particular nucleotide sequence occurs (156)

restriction fragments pieces of DNA made by cutting it with restriction enzymes (156)

root cap thimble-like cone of cells that protects the actively dividing cells of the root apical meristem (394)

root hairs tiny outgrowths of the root's epidermal cells that increase the root's surface area (400)

root pressure force that helps push water up the xylem (400)

S

saliva watery liquid that contains digestive enzymes, mucus, and other chemicals to help chemically digest food (289)

scientific name two-part Latin name of a species, in which the first part is the genus to which the species belongs and the second part is the species name (17)

sclerenchyma plant cells specialized for support that grow and then die in mature plant tissue (389)

secondary growth growth that increases plant width (393)

secondary phloem phloem cells produced by the inside of vascular cambium (396)

secondary succession succession that occurs following a disturbance that damages an existing community but leaves soil and plants behind (370)

secondary xylem xylem cells produced by the outside of vascular cambium (396)

seed coat the tough outer layer of a seed (384)

seeds plant embryos encased in a protective covering along with a food supply (68)

segments repeating parts (68)

sepals structures that cover and protect the flower bud and are usually green (383)

severe acute respiratory syndrome (SARS) a serious pneumonia-like respiratory disease that is caused by a coronavirus and spread through coughing or sneezing (338)

sex chromosomes set of chromosomes that determine an individual's sex (109)

sex-linked gene any gene located on a sex chromosome (148)

sexual reproduction process in which two parents provide genetic material in order to produce offspring (108)

sexual selection a form of natural selection in which individuals with certain inherited traits are more likely to obtain mates than other individuals (218)

sieve-tube members phloem cells with end walls like sieves (404)

sinusitis a condition caused by viruses or bacteria in which the sinuses become swollen and irritated (336)

sister chromatids two identical joined copies of a chromosome (102)

softwoods wood produced by gymnosperms that is softer than hardwood (359)

somatic cells cells of the body (105)

speciation the origin of new species (224)

species population whose members can breed freely in nature and produce fertile offspring (6)

species diversity the variety of species and relative abundance in a given area (8)

sphincter muscular valve, such as between the stomach and esophagus (290)

sphygmomanometer a pressure cuff used for measuring blood pressure (314)

spirochetes spiral-shaped bacteria (32)

spongy mesophyll loosely-packed cells in the lower mesophyll, also called aerenchyma (390)

spores reproductive cells released by organisms (41)

sporophyte diploid generation of a plant that produces spores (58)

stabilizing selection individuals near the centre of the phenotype range that have a higher fitness than individuals at either end of the range (217)

stamen male reproductive structure (383)

stems parts of a plant that support leaves and flowers (382)

stigma (plural, *stigmata*) sticky tip of the pistil where the pollen lands (384)

stoma (plural, *stomata*) pores in the epidermis that control gas and water exchange in plants (387)

stroke an event that occurs if a blood clot forms in an artery going to the brain, resulting in lack of oxygen for the tissue downstream from the blockage (320)

stromatolites layered rocks that form when certain prokaryotes bind thin layers of sediment together (241)

structural diversity differences in structure among organisms (33)

style plant female reproductive structure that supports the stigma (384)

sudden cardiac arrest an event that occurs when a heart suddenly stops functioning, such as from drowning, electrocution, trauma, or choking (319)

superior vena cava vein entering the heart from the upper body (313)

survival of the fittest the results of differences in rates of survival and reproduction; also called natural selection (199)

sustainability the ability to be maintained at a consistent level (361)

sustainable development development where the needs of the present are met without compromising the needs of future generations (361)

sustainable forest management preserving the forest's health and biodiversity by harvesting forest products sustainably (364)

synapsis the close association between homologous chromosomes in early meiosis (112)

synergistic effects impacts of several human activities that combine, resulting in greater environmental damage than any of the activities on its own (80)

systemic circuit circuit in which oxygen-rich blood from the lungs gathers in the left atrium and is then pumped to the left ventricle and through the aorta to all of the systems of the body (312)

systolic pressure the highest recorded pressure in an artery when the ventricles contract; in the measurement 120/70, 120 is the systolic pressure (314)

T

taxon (plural, *taxa*) level in a classification hierarchy, such as species, genus, family, order, class, phylum, kingdom (18)

taxonomy science of naming, identifying, and classifying species (16)

telomeres protective end caps of chromosomes (102)

telophase final stage of mitosis, when chromosomes begin to uncoil, the spindle fibres disappear and nuclear envelopes re-form (107)

telophase I fourth stage of meiosis I, when the nuclear membrane re-forms around each cluster of chromosomes (110)

telophase II fourth stage of meiosis II, when separate nuclei begin to form around each group of chromosomes, resulting in four haploid nuclei (111)

test cross genetic cross to determine genotype by breeding an individual of unknown genotype with a homozygous recessive individual (133)

theory a set of statements that explains a group of facts or phenomena, have been tested repeatedly, and are supported by evidence; can be used to make predictions about natural phenomena (187)

thigmotropism a change in plant growth due to touch (418)

tissue groups of cells that performs a particular function (66)

trachea airway held open by C-shaped rings of cartilage; also called the windpipe (330)

tracheal system a system of tubes that extend through an insect's body for the purpose of gas exchange (329)

tracheids long, tapered secondary xylem cells (402)

trait characteristic of an organism, such as hair colour or the sound of a person's voice (97)

transduction reproductive process in which bacteria receive new genetic material as viruses that infect them carry genes from one cell and inject them into another (34)

transformation reproductive process in which bacteria take up pieces of DNA from the environment (34)

transgenic genetically modified organism that has acquired one or more genes from a different type of organism (167)

translocation in a chromosome, change that occurs when a fragment of one chromosome attaches to a nonhomologous chromosome; in a plant, movement of water, sucrose, and other organic compounds in phloem (119, 404)

transpiration process in which plants release water vapour into the atmosphere (62)

transpiration-pull   force that pulls water up a woody stem (401)

trisomy   condition in which an individual has three copies of a particular chromosome (116)

tropisms   growth responses that cause parts of a plant to bend or grow slowly toward or away from a stimulus (418)

true-breeding plant   plant that produces offspring identical in appearance to itself generation after generation, when self-fertilized (128)

tumours   groups of cancer cells (338)

U

unicellular   consisting of a single cell (21)

uniformitarianism   the theory that Earth was formed entirely by slow-moving processes, such as erosion and sedimentation, and that these slow forces continue to shape the landscape (188)

V

variation   differences among members of the same species (197)

vascular cambium   cylinder of actively dividing cells located between the xylem and phloem in woody dicots (396)

vascular plants   plants that have vascular tissues for transporting water and nutrients, such as ferns, club mosses, and horsetails (58)

vascular tissue   plant tissue that transports water, mineral nutrients, and organic molecules between roots and shoots (58)

vascularization   the formation of tubes to carry fluid throughout an organism (60)

vegetative reproduction   asexual reproduction in plants (386)

veins   blood vessels that transport blood from the capillaries to the heart (306)

venation   arrangement of veins on a leaf (382)

ventricles   the two lower chambers of the heart, which pump blood out of the heart to the body (311)

vertebrae (singular, *vertebra*) series of skeletal segments that enclose the nerve cord (72)

vertebrates   animals that have a backbone (69)

vessel elements   wide, short secondary xylem cells (402)

vestigial structures   remnants of structures that may have had important functions in an ancestral species but have no clear function in some of the modern descendants of that species (202)

villi (singular, *villus*)   small, finger-like projections on the wall of the small intestine that contain blood vessels and lymph vessels for absorbing nutrients (292)

vitamins   organic nutrients that regulate your body processes and perform chemical reactions (279)

W

water mould   a protist that has a lifestyle similar to fungi (44)

white blood cells   cells that guard against infection, fight parasites, and attack bacteria (304)

X

xylem   plant vascular tissue that transports water and dissolved minerals upward from roots into shoots (388)

Z

zooflagellates   protists with flagella (41)

zygote   diploid cell that forms when gametes fuse and eventually develops into a distinct individual (58, 109)

Mammals, 61, 72, 73, 201, 247, 248
Marine habitats, 78, 328, 329
Marsupials, 201, 247
Mass extinctions, **248**
Medulla oblongata, 333
Meiosis, **108**, 108–115, 117, 118, 130, 146, 383
Mendel, Gregor, 127–131, 139, 146, 214
Meristems, **393**
Mesophyll, 390
Metaphase, **107**
Metaphase I, **110**, 112
Metaphase II, **111**
Mice, 154, 159, 171
Microclimates, 62
Microevolution, **215**, 216–217, 218–219, 259
Miller, Stanley, 242
Mimicry, **234**
Minerals, **280**
    plants and, 425–428
    roots and, 400
Mitochondria, 244
Mitosis, **42**, 96, **100**, 101, 106–108, 113, 384
Molecular biology, 204, 252
Molluscs, 235
Monocots, 381, 382, 383, 384, 386, 390, 393, 413
Monoculture(s), 7, 262, 361, 372
Monohybrid crosses, 128–129, **129**, 130
Monohybrids, **128**
Morgan, Thomas Hunt, 136, 148
Morphology, **18**
Morphs, 127
Mosquitoes, 13, 41
Mosses, 58, 59, 60, 369
Mouth, 288, 289–290
Mucus, **290**, 330, 337, 338
Multicellular organisms, **23**, 245
Mushrooms, 47–48
Mutations, **119**, 120, 215, 254, 259
Mycelium, **49**
Mycorrhizae, **49**, **400**

N

Nanaloricus mysticus, 4
Nanoparticles, 342
Natural selection, 196–200, **197**, 203
    artificial selection and, 205, 218–219
    and disease, 213–214, 260
    evidence for, 205–207
    and genetic variation, 245
    and microevolution, 216–217
    and punctuated equilibrium, 230
    and sexual selection, 218
Nervous system, 314
Newborn screening, **121**
Newton, Isaac, 286
Nitrogen, 425, 426–427, 427–428
Nitrogen fixation, **361**, 373, 375, 426
Nitrogenous base, **99**

Nodes, **382**
Non-disjunction, **117**, 117–118
Non-vascular plants, **60**
Nuclear transplantation, 170
Nucleic acids, 29, 30
Nucleosomes, **98**
Nucleotides, **99**, 99–100, 155
Nutraceuticals, **282**
Nutrients, **277**, 278–280
    for cells, 301
    exchanges between blood and cells, 306–307
Nutrition
    bacteria and, 33
    labels, 282

O

Oceans, 78, 243
Oparin, Alexander, 242
Orders, **17**
Organelles, 244
Organic farmers, 431
Organic molecules, **242**, 242–243
Organisms, identification of, 14–15
Osmosis, **403**, 405, 417
Ovaries, **384**
Overexploitation, **79**
Ovules, **384**
Oxygen, 243
    in aquatic animals, 328
    blood and, 306, 312
    and cells, 301, 327
    and human life, 327
    in respiratory system, 332

P

Pacemaker, **313**, 313–314
    artificial, 320
Paired limbs, **68**
Paleontologists, 200, 265
Palisade mesophyll cells, **390**
Palm oil, 56
Pancreas, 342
Pancreatic juice, **292**
Pandemics, 259
Pangaea, 247
Paramecia/*Paramecium*, 42, 43, 105
Parasites, 48
Parenchyma cells, **388**, 389, 390, 397
Parkinson's disease, 159
Penguins, 236
Peptidoglycan, 245
Pericardium, 311
Periods, **245**
Peristalsis, **290**, 292, 294
Pesticides, 5, 6, 10, **79**, 217, 261, 362–363
Petals, **383**
Petioles, **382**, 383, 387, 389, 415
PH levels, 44, 65, 79, 428
Pharmaceuticals, 169, 171, 358–359
Pharynx, **290**, 330

Phenotypes, **130**, 133, 140–141, **214**, 214–215
Phenylalanine, 121
Phenylketonuria (PKU), 121
Phloem, **388**, 396, 397, 404–405
Phosphorus, 425, 427–428
Photoautotrophs, 33
Photoheterotrophs, 33
Photosynthesis
    carbon dioxide and, 403, 425
    fungi and, 48
    green algae and, 60
    leaves and, 382, 389
    light and, 419
    monocots and, 386
    oxygen and, 243, 357
    phloem and, 388
    prokaryotes and, 241–242, 243, 245
    sugars and, 404, 425
Phototropism, **419**
Phyla, **17**
Phylogenetic trees, **19**, 19–20, 72–73, 252–255
Phylogeny, **18**, **251**, 251–252
Physical activity. *See* Exercise
Phytoplankton, 44, **44**
Pioneer species, **369**
Pistils, **383**
Plankton, **44**
Plants
    animals compared to, 380
    as building materials, 359
    cells, 101, 388–389
    characteristics of, 57
    climate change and, 62
    cloning of, 386–387
    diseases, 48
    diversity of, 57–64
    ecosystem services by, 360
    evolution of, 58
    food from, 278
    as foundation of ecosystems, 57
    as fuel, 359
    fungi and, 51, 380
    genetically modified, 168–169, 170–171
    gravity and, 419
    and herbivorous insects, 234
    hormones, 411–416
    industrial uses of, 360
    and light, 411–412, 419
    major groups of, 59–62
    movements by, 417–418
    organs, 381–385
    as pharmaceuticals, 358–359
    primary growth in, 394–395
    propagation of, 385–387
    reproduction of, 58–59, 60–62, 383–384
    responsiveness of, 410
    secondary growth of, 395–398
    soil and, 424–430
    stressful environments and, 419–421

©P

CREDITS

COVER: Manfred Kage/Science Photo Library. **CONTENTS**: p. v George Grall/National Geographic/Getty Images; p. vi © Laurent/BSIP/Maxx Images; p. vii © David Hall/Seaphotos.com; p. viii Andreas Rentz/Getty Images; p. ix © Juan Carlos López/Age Fotostock/Maxx Images. **THEMES IN BIOLOGY**: p. xiv (top left) © Purestock/Jupiter Images, (inset) AJ Photo/Science Photo Library, (bottom) © iStockphoto; p. xvi (a) © iStockphoto, (b) Steve Gschmeissner/Science Photo Library, (c) Astrid & Hanns-Frieder Michler/Science Photo Library; p. xvii (top) © Dorling Kindersley, (bottom) David Aubrey/Science Photo Library; p. xviii Andrew Wong/Stringer/Getty Images; p. xix (top right) James Zipp/Photo Researchers/First Light, (middle, left to right) Ray Coleman/Photo Researchers/First Light, William Ervin/Science Photo Library, Francesco Tomasinelli/Photo Researchers, Inc.; p. xxi (top left) Pascal Goetgheluck/Science Photo Library, (top right) Maximilian Stock Ltd./Science Photo Library, (middle) © Don Johnston/All Canada Photos, (bottom) Craig Greenhill/Newspix/Getty Images.

UNIT A: Pages 2-3 George Grall/National Geographic/Getty Images; p. 4 Photo by R. M. Kristensen, Zoological Museum of Copenhagen. © 1983 R. M. Kristensen; p. 5 © Kochergin/Shutterstock; p. 6 (left) Agricultural Research Service/ US Dept. of Agriculture/Photo by Scott Bauer, (right) © Scott Camazine; p. 7 © Nigel Cattlin/Alamy/Getstock.com; p. 8 (top, left to right) Eye Of Science/Science Photo Library, Christian Darkin/Science Photo Library, Npologuy/Dreamstime.com/Getstock.com, (middle, left to right) © Alexander Chelmodeev/Shutterstock, Norbert Wu/Minden Pictures/National Geographic Stock, (bottom, left to right) © Gavriel Jecan/Age Fotostock/Maxx Images, © Animals Animals/Maxx Images, © Carl Reader/Age Fotostock/Maxx Images; p. 10 (top) Genlady/Dreamstime.com/Getstock.com, (middle) E. Gueho/Science Photo Library, (right) Xinhua /Landov; p. 11 Ray Boudreau; p. 13 (left) © Kletr/Shutterstock, (right) © Michael Pettigrew/Shutterstock; p. 14 © Ronald Wittek/Age Fotostock/Maxx Images; p. 15 (top to bottom) Selena/Dreamstime.com/Getstock.com, Matthew Ward © Dorling Kindersley, Matthew Ward © Dorling Kindersley, Neil Fletcher and Matthew Ward © Dorling Kindersley, Richard Bloom/Gap Photo/Visuals Unlimited, Inc., © Don Johnston/Age Fotostock/Maxx Images, © SuperStock/Maxx Images, Treephoto/Dreamstime.com/Getstock.com, Matthew Ward © Dorling Kindersley; p. 16 (top, left to right) Cheryl Casey/Dreamstime.com/Getstock.com, © Georgie Holland/Age Fotostock/Maxx Images, Stevengibson/Dreamstime.com/Getstock.com, (middle) © Ipatov/Shutterstock; p. 17 (top) © blickwinkel/Laule/Alamy/Getstock.com, (middle) © pmphoto/Shutterstock; p. 18 (top) David Aubrey/Science Photo Library, (middle) © Shutterstock; p. 19 (left to right) Huan/Dreamstime.com/Getstock.com, © Iourii Tcheka/Shutterstock, © Jonathan Larsen/Shutterstock, © Lana Langlois/Shutterstock; p. 23 (left to right) NIAID/CDC/Science Photo Library, NASA/Science Photo Library, Astrid & Hanns-Frieder Michler/Science Photo Library, © Christopher Meder - Photography/Shutterstock, Smr78/Dreamstime.com/Getstock.com, © Digital Vision/Jupiter Images; p. 24 Dave Starrett; p. 27 (top) © Thomas Sbampato/Imagebroker/Maxx Images, (bottom) Phil A. Dotson/ Photo Researchers/First Light; p. 28 CDC/Photo Researchers/First Light, (inset) Juergen Berger/Science Photo Library; p. 29 (top to bottom) Biozentrum, Universtiy of Basel/Science Photo Library, Dr. Timothy Baker/Visuals Unlimited, Inc., James Cavallini/ Photo Researchers/First Light; p. 30 © Mediscan/Alamy/Getstock.com; p. 31 (top) Cloudia/Dreamstime.com/Getstock.com, (bottom) Thierry Berrod, Mona Lisa Production/Science Photo Library; p. 32 (top) CNRI/Science Photo Library, (bottom, left to right) © Mediscan/Alamy/Getstock.com, Dennis Kunkel Microscopy, Inc./Visuals Unlimited, Inc., Dennis Kunkel Microscopy, Inc./Visuals Unlimited, Inc.; p. 33 (top to bottom) Dennis Kunkel Microscopy, Inc./Phototake/Getstock.com, Tom Adams/Visuals Unlimited, Inc., A.B. Dowsett/Science Photo Library, B. Boonyaratanakornkit & D.S. Clark, G. Vrdoljak/EM Lab, U of C Berkeley/Visuals Unlimited, Inc.; p. 35 (top) Kenneth Garrett/National Geographic Stock, (inset) A. Barry Dowsett/Photo Researchers, Inc., (bottom) © FLPA/Bob Gibbons/Maxx Images; p. 36 (top) Scott Camazine/Photo Researchers/First Light, (bottom) Dr. Jack Bostrack/Visuals Unlimited, Inc.; p. 38 © Alaska Stock/Maxx Images, (inset) Dr. David Phillips/Visuals Unlimited, Inc.; p. 39 (top) Daniel

Cox/Photolibrary/Getty Images, (middle, left to right) Steve Gschmeissner/Science Photo Library, Steve Gschmeissner/Science Photo Library, Eye of Science/Science Photo Library; p. 41 (top) Michael Abbey/Visuals Unlimited, Inc., (middle, a-d) Eye of Science/Science Photo Library, Dr. David J. Patterson/Science Photo Library, Eric Grave/Science Photo Library, Michael Abbey/Visuals Unlimited, Inc.; p. 43 (right, top to bottom) Michael Abbey/Visuals Unlimited, Inc., (left) Michael Abbey/Visuals Unlimited, Inc.; p. 44 (top) Biophoto Associates/Photo Researchers/First Light, (left) Dr. Robert Calentine/Visuals Unlimited, Inc.; p. 45 (top) © Warren Kovach/Alamy/Getstock.com, (bottom) Richard Haynes; p. 46 Michael Abbey/Visuals Unlimited, Inc., p. 47 © Stephen Dorey - Commercial/Alamy; p. 48 (top, left to right) Michael P. Gadomski/ Photo Researchers/First Light, Aleksander/Dreamstime.com/Getstock.com, © John Lennie, (middle, left to right) Dr. Nick Kurzenko/Science Photo Library, David M. Phillips/Visuals Unlimited, Inc., David Cavagnaro/Visuals Unlimited, Inc., (bottom) © Inga Spence/Alamy/Getstock.com; p. 50 © Arco Images GmbH/Alamy, (inset) Microfield Scientific Ltd./Science Photo Library; p. 52 (top) © Dorling Kindersley, (bottom) K. Bartlett/School of Environmental Health/UBC; p. 53 Wally Eberhart/Visuals Unlimited, Inc.; p. 55 © Sergey Toronto/Alamy; p. 56 Mattias Klum/National Geographic Stock, (inset) Art Wolfe/Photo Researchers/First Light; p. 60 (top to bottom) Sherman Thomson/Visuals Unlimited, Inc., © blickwinkel/Koenig/Alamy/Getstock.com, © Regina Müller/Maxx Images, © Shari L. Morris/age fotostock/Maxx Images; p. 61 (top) Glen Oliver/Visuals Unlimited, Inc., (inset) Larry Mellichamp/Visuals Unlimited, Inc., (bottom left) Peter Chadwick© Dorling Kindersley, (bottom right) © Bill Draker/Rolfnp/Alamy/Getstock.com; p. 63 (top to bottom) Dave King © Dorling Kindersley, Tolimir/Dreamstime.com/Getstock.com, © allOver - Collection 163/Alamy/Getstock.com; p. 65 (centre) © Kelvin Aitken/Age Fotostock/Maxx Images, (bottom right) Georgette Douwma/Science Photo Library; p. 66 (top) George Grall/National Geographic Stock, (middle) Dave Roberts/Science Photo Library; p. 68 Ribe/Dreamstime.com/Getstock.com; p. 69 Doug Sokell/Visuals Unlimited, Inc.; p. 74 (top to bottom) Cbpix/Dreamstime.com/Getstock.com, Dave King © Dorling Kindersley, © Daryl H/Shutterstock, Michael Fogden/OSF/Photolibrary/First Light; p. 76 © PixMenStudio/Alamy; p. 77 (top to bottom) © Dale Wilson/Alamy, © Robert Shantz/Alamy/Getstock.com, Jack Milchanowski/Visuals Unlimited, Inc.; p. 78 (top two) Fisheries and Oceans Canada/Peches et Oceans Canada, (middle, left to right) Melissa Farlow/National Geographic Stock, David Cappaert, (bottom) © David M. Dennis/Animals Animals/Maxx Images; p. 79 Melissa Farlow/National Geographic Stock; p. 80 © Oleksiy Maksymenko 2/Alamy/Getstock.com, © blickwinkel/McPhotos/JOS/Alamy/Getstock.com, © Author's Image Ltd./Alamy; p. 81 (top to bottom) Mari Tefre/Svalbard Global Seed Vault, © Redmond Durrell/Alamy/Getstock.com, Ross Frid/Visuals Unlimited, Inc.; p. 83 (top) Maria Stenzel/National Geographic Stock, (bottom) © D. Allen Photography/Animals Animals/Maxx Images; p. 85 (top) David Kilper/WUSTL Photo, (bottom) The Canadian Press (Kingston Whig-Standard/Michael Lea); p. 86 Sinclair Stammers/Science Photo Library; p. 90 (left to right) Thomas & Pat Leeson/Photo Researchers/First Light, © Robert Shantz/Alamy/Getstock.com; p. 91 (top, left to right) Matt Meadows/Science Photo Library, Michael Abbey/Visuals Unlimited, Inc., Biophoto Associates/Photo Researchers/First Light, (middle) © blickwinkel/Alamy/Getstock.com; p. 92 (bottom, left to right) Juan Carlos Calvin/ A.G.E. Foto Stock/First Light, Dave King © Dorling Kindersley, © Rubberball/First Light; p. 93 © 1989 Matthew Gilligan, Savannah State College, Savannah, GA. **UNIT B**: Pages 94–95 © Laurent/BSIP/Maxx Images; p. 96 Dr. Y. Nikas/Phototake/Getstock.com; p. 97 (top) Bob Thomas/Photographers Choice/Getty Images, (bottom) Science & Society Picture Library/Getty Images; p. 98 Jennifer Waters/Photo Researchers/First Light; p. 99 A. Barrington Brown/Science Photo Library; p. 101 (left) Dr. David Phillips/Visuals Unlimited, Inc., (right) Dr. Robert Calentine/Visuals Unlimited, Inc.; p. 102 Power and Syred/Science Photo Library; p. 103 Biophoto Associates/Science Photo Library; p. 105 (top) Jennifer C. Waters/Photo Researchers, Inc./First Light, (bottom) Dr. Richard Kessel & Dr. Gene Shih/Visuals Unlimited, Inc.; pp. 106–107 Photographs by Dr. Conly L. Rieder, East Greenbush, New York, USA; p. 108 Dept. of Clinical Cytogenetics, Addenbrookes Hospital/Science Photo Library; p. 109 (left to right) Eye of Science/Science Photo Library, Dr. Y. Nikas/Phototake/Getstock.com, Biophoto Associates/Photo Researchers, Inc.; pp. 110–111 © Clare A. Hasenkampf/Biological Photo Service. All rights reserved; p. 112 © B. John/Visuals Unlimited, Inc.; p. 114 © Bob Daemmrich/Photo Edit Inc., (inset) Dr. Bruce Heming/University of Alberta/Bio-DiTRL;